MECHAN

[For B.Sc. Students of Mathematics, Physics and Engineering Courses of All Indian Universities]

P. DURAIPANDIAN
M.A., M. Phil.
Formerly Professor of Mathematics
Tamil Nadu Educational Services

LAXMI DURAIPANDIAN
B.Sc. (Hons.), M. Phil.
Formerly Professor of Mathematics
Tamil Nadu Educational Services

MUTHAMIZH JAYAPRAGASAM
M.Sc.

S Chand And Company Limited

(ISO 9001 Certified Company)

S Chand And Company Limited

(ISO 9001 Certified Company)

Head Office: Block B-1, House No. D-1, Ground Floor, Mohan Co-operative Industrial Estate, New Delhi – 110 044 | Phone: 011-66672000

Registered Office: A-27, 2nd Floor, Mohan Co-operative Industrial Estate, New Delhi – 110 044 Phone: 011-49731800

www.**schandpublishing.com**; e-mail: **info@schandpublishing.com**

Branches

Chennai	:	Ph: 23632120; chennai@schandpublishing.com
Guwahati	:	Ph: 2738811, 2735640; guwahati@schandpublishing.com
Hyderabad	:	Ph: 40186018; hyderabad@schandpublishing.com
Jalandhar	:	Ph: 4645630; jalandhar@schandpublishing.com
Kolkata	:	Ph: 23357458, 23353914; kolkata@schandpublishing.com
Lucknow	:	Ph: 4003633; lucknow@schandpublishing.com
Mumbai	:	Ph: 25000297; mumbai@schandpublishing.com
Patna	:	Ph: 2260011; patna@schandpublishing.com

First Edition 1979

Subsequent Editions and Reprints 1981, 82, 83, 85, 87, 88, 90, 91, 93, 94, 95, 97, 99, 2001, 2003, 2005, 2006, 2007, 2008, 2009, 2010, 2011, 2012, 2013, 2014, 2015, 2016, 2018, 2020 (Twice)

Reprint 2022 (Twice)

ISBN: 978-81-219-0272-4 **Product Code:** H6MEN68MENS10ENAF0XO

PRINTED IN INDIA

By Vikas Publishing House Private Limited, Plot 20/4, Site-IV, Industrial Area Sahibabad, Ghaziabad – 201 010 and Published by S Chand And Company Limited, A-27, 2nd Floor, Mohan Co-operative Industrial Estate, New Delhi – 110 044.

PREFACE TO THE SIXTH REVISED EDITION

The work has been revised completely without changing its inherent character that was received well by the students and professors so long. A special feature of revision is an elaboration of solutions of the illustrative examples to make the book for self-study.

Constructive criticism is most welcome.

P. DURAIPANDIAN

PREFACE TO THE FIRST EDITION

The book treats the subject systematically, using vectors in accordance with the present requirement. It is essential that the reader should have a proper knowledge of the fundamentals of vector algebra. The book caters to the needs of undergraduates of Mathematics, Physics and Engineering courses of all Indian Universities.

A particular feature of the book is that the important results of the subject are pulled out and presented as independent pieces under the caption BOOK WORKS. The REMARKS appended to them play an essential role in that they provide incidental additional facts aiming at a near perfection. The book includes an abundance of examples and pictures, as well as a good selection of exercises most of which are provided with hints.

Lack of proper understanding of the fundamental concepts of Mechanics, makes many students dislike Mechanics. Bearing this in mind, the fundamental concepts are presented, comparatively with more possible details, in such a manner that even of first reading of them will give the reader sufficient mastery over them. This feature will commend the book to the students.

P. DURAIPANDIAN
LAXMI DURAIPANDIAN
MUTHAMIZH JAYAPRAGASAM

CONTENTS

INTRODUCTION

1. MECHANICS

Mechanics is the science which deals with the effects of forces on material bodies. Under the influence of forces, a body may be in motion or in rest.

Dynamics. Dynamics is the science which deals with the motion of particles or bodies under the influence of forces. *Kinematics* is that aspect of dynamics which deals with the motion without reference to the forces producing it.

Statics. Statics is the science which deals with the conditions for lack of motion under given forces.

The way in which statics and dynamics coalesce into mechanics, it suggests one to learn mechanics in the coalesced form. However, some universities prescribe statics and dynamics separately for studies under semester system. For such syllabi, the following classification will meet with their requirement.

STATICS

Chapter 2	:	Forces
Chapter 3	:	Equilibrium of a particle
Chapter 4	:	Forces on a rigid body
Chapter 5	:	Reduction of forces on a rigid body
Chapter 6	:	Centre of mass
Chapter 7	:	Stability of equilibrium
Chapter 8	:	Virtual work
Chapter 9	:	Hanging strings

DYNAMICS

Chapter 1	:	Kinematics
Chapter 2	:	Forces (sections 2.1, 2.1.1, 2.2)
Chapter 10	:	Rectilinear motion under constant forces
Chapter 11	:	Work, energy and power
Chapter 12	:	Rectilinear motion under varying forces
Chapter 13	:	Projectiles
Chapter 14	:	Impact
Chapter 15	:	Circular motion
Chapter 16	:	Central orbits
Chapter 17	:	Moment of inertia
Chapter 18	:	Two dimensional motion of a rigid body
Chapter 19	:	Theory of dimensions

2. VECTORTREATMENT

The physical quantities in Mechanics are vectors. So Mechanics has to be treated using vector theory. However, some books use scalar methods which are, in general, laborious.

Some of the vector results used in the book are listed below.

Vector Addition

Notation. $|\bar{a}| = a, \quad |\overline{AB}| = AB.$

1. $\overline{AB} + \overline{BC} + \overline{CA} = \bar{0}, \ \overline{AB} + \overline{BC} + \overline{CD} + \overline{DA} = \bar{0}$, etc.

2. If $\bar{c}$ lies in the plane formed by $\bar{a}, \ \bar{b}$, then $\bar{c}$ can be expressed as

$$\bar{c} = l\bar{a} + m\bar{b}.$$

3. If $\bar{a}$ and $\bar{b}$ are nonparallel vectors and if $l\bar{a} + m\bar{b} = \bar{0}$, then

$$l = 0, \quad m = 0.$$

4. $\bar{a} = a\,\hat{a}, \ \overline{AB} = AB\ \widehat{AB}, \ \hat{a} = \dfrac{\bar{a}}{|\bar{a}|} = \dfrac{\bar{a}}{a}.$

5. Unit vector corresponding to $a\bar{i} + b\bar{j}$ is

$$\frac{a\bar{i} + b\bar{j}}{|a\bar{i} + b\bar{j}|} = \frac{a\bar{i} + b\bar{j}}{\sqrt{a^2 + b^2}}.$$

6. Unit vector making angles α, $90^\circ - \alpha$ with $\bar{i}$, $\bar{j}$ directions is

$$\cos\alpha\,\bar{i} + \cos(90^\circ - \alpha)\,\bar{j} \ \text{ or } \ \cos\alpha\,\bar{i} + \sin\alpha\,\bar{j}.$$

7. The P.V. of the point which divides AB in the ratio $m : n$ is

$$\frac{n\bar{a} + m\bar{b}}{m + n},$$

where $\bar{a}$, $\bar{b}$ are the P.V.'s of A, B. The P.V. of the midpoint of AB is $\frac{1}{2}(\bar{a} + \bar{b})$.

8. If $\bar{e}_1$, $\bar{e}_2$ are vectors of equal magnitude, then $\bar{e}_1 + \bar{e}_2$ lies along the bisector of the angle between them.

9. If the P.V.'s of the vertices of a triangle are $\bar{a}, \bar{b}, \bar{c}$ then the P.V. of the centroid is

$$\frac{\bar{a} + \bar{b} + \bar{c}}{3}.$$

10. If the P.V.'s of the vertices of a triangle are $\bar{a}, \bar{b}, \bar{c}$ then the P.V of the incentre is

$$\frac{a\bar{a} + b\bar{b} + c\bar{c}}{a + b + c}.$$

11. If H, S are the orthocentre and circumcentre of a triangle ABC, then

(*i*) AH is parallel to SM

(*ii*) AH = 2SM,

where M is the midpoint of BC.

Scalar Multiplication

1. (*a*) $a = |\overline{a}| = \sqrt{\overline{a} \cdot \overline{a}}$ because $\overline{a} \cdot \overline{a} = |\overline{a}|^2 = a^2$

   (*b*) $AB = \sqrt{\overline{AB} . \overline{AB}}$.

2. If $\hat{e}_1, \hat{e}_2$ are unit vectors including an angle α, then

$$\hat{e}_1 \cdot \hat{e}_2 = \cos \alpha.$$

3. In a triangle ABC,

$$\overline{AB} \cdot \overline{BC} = AB \cdot BC \cdot \cos(180^\circ - B).$$

4. If $\overline{a} \cdot \overline{F} = 0$, where $\overline{a}$ is not a zero vector and $\overline{a}$, $\overline{F}$ are not perpendicular to each other, then $\overline{F} = \overline{0}$.

5. If $\overline{F}$ is not perpendicular to both $\overline{a}$ and $\overline{b}$ and if $\overline{a} \cdot \overline{F} = 0$, $\overline{b} \cdot \overline{F} = 0$, then $\overline{F} = \overline{0}$.

6. Angle θ between $\overline{a}$ and $\overline{b}$ is given by $\cos \theta = \dfrac{\overline{a} \cdot \overline{b}}{ab}$, $\sin \theta = \dfrac{|\overline{a} \times \overline{b}|}{ab}$, $\tan \theta = \dfrac{|\overline{a} \times \overline{b}|}{\overline{a} \cdot \overline{b}}$.

7. If $\overline{a} = a_1 \overline{i} + a_2 \overline{j} + a_3 \overline{k}$, $\overline{b} = b_1 \overline{i} + b_2 \overline{j} + b_3 \overline{k}$, then

$$\overline{a} \cdot \overline{b} = a_1 b_1 + a_2 b_2 + a_3 b_3.$$

8. $\overline{v} = (\overline{v} \cdot \overline{i})\, \overline{i} + (\overline{v} \cdot \overline{j})\, \overline{j} + (\overline{v} \cdot \overline{k})\, \overline{k}$.

Vector Multiplication

1. If $\hat{n}$ is the unit vector perpendicular to both $\overline{a}, \overline{b}$ such that $\overline{a}, \overline{b}, \hat{n}$ form a right - handed triad, then

$$\overline{a} \times \overline{b} = ab \sin \theta\, \hat{n},$$

   where θ is the angle between $\overline{a}, \overline{b}$.

2. If $\hat{e}_1, \hat{e}_2$ are unit vectors, then

$$\hat{e}_1 \times \hat{e}_2 = \sin \theta\, \hat{n},$$

   where θ is the angle between $\hat{e}_1, \hat{e}_2$.

3. If $\overline{a}$ and $\overline{b}$ are parallel, then

$$\overline{a} \times \overline{b} = \overline{0}$$

4. If $\overline{a} = a_1 \overline{i} + a_2 \overline{j} + a_3 \overline{k}$, $\overline{b} = b_1 \overline{i} + b_2 \overline{j} + b_3 \overline{k}$, then

$$\overline{a} \times \overline{b} = \begin{vmatrix} \overline{i} & \overline{j} & \overline{k} \\ a_1 & a_2 & a_3 \\ b_1 & b_2 & b_3 \end{vmatrix}.$$

KINEMATICS

1.1 BASIC UNITS

The fundamental quantities in mecnanics are length, time and mass. The following three are important systems of units:

(*i*) The metre-kilogram-second system (M.K.S system)

(*ii*) The centimetre-gram-second system (C.G.S system)

(*iii*) The foot-pound-second system (F.P.S system)

Mass and its units. Now we proceed to define mass and its unit. It has been observed that a material body causes different expansions in a spring balance in different places on the earth's surface and that two bodies which cause equal expansions in a place, also cause equal expansions in other places. Two such bodies seem to have something in common. This common property is called the mass of the bodies. In other words, these bodies are said to have the same mass. The units of mass are given below.

Kilogram. The M.K.S. unit of mass is the mass of a piece of metal, arbitrarily chosen and preserved in Paris. This unit is called a kilogram.

Pound. The F.P.S unit of mass is the mass of a piece of metal preserved in London. This unit is called a pound.

UNITS

Quantity	*M.K.S. units*	*C.G.S. units*	*F.P.S. units*
Length	Metre (m.)	cm.	Foot (ft.)
Time	Second (sec.)	sec.	Second (sec.)
Mass	Kilogram (kg.)	gm.	Pound (lb.)

1.2 VELOCITY

When a particle moves from a point to another point, the particle is said to undergo a *displacement.* In other words, displacement is *just a change of position.* When the change of position is from the point P to the point P' the respective displacement is denoted by the vector $\overline{PP'}$.

Definition. Velocity. The rate of displacement, that is, the rate of change of position is called the *velocity* of the particle. Velocity is denoted by $\bar{v}$.

Suppose $\bar{r}$ is the position vector of a moving particle with reference to a fixed point O. Then $\bar{r}$ is a vector function of the scalar variable t, the time. This vector function is written more specifically as $\bar{r}(t)$. It is evident that, in general, both the direction and magnitude of $\bar{r}(t)$ vary as the scalar t varies.

Let P and P' be the positions of the particle at times t and $t + \Delta t$. Then the position vectors of P and P' at these moments are

$$\bar{r}(t),\ \bar{r}(t+\Delta t).$$

Now the displacement of the particle in time Δt is

$$\overline{PP'} = \overline{OP'} - \overline{OP} = \bar{r}(t+\Delta t) - \bar{r}(t).$$

So the time-rate of displacement of the particle is

$$\lim_{\Delta t \to 0} \frac{\overline{PP'}}{\Delta t} = \lim_{\Delta t \to 0} \frac{\bar{r}(t+\Delta t)-\bar{r}(t)}{\Delta t} = \frac{d}{dt}\bar{r}(t).$$

Thus the velocity $\bar{v}$ of the particle is given by

$$\bar{v} = \frac{d\bar{r}}{dt}.$$

Convention. It is customary to denote $\dfrac{d\bar{r}}{dt}$ by $\dot{\bar{r}}$ with the specification that the dot stands for differentiation with respect to time t. So

$$\bar{v} = \dot{\bar{r}}.$$

Direction of $\bar{v}$. Now we shall show that the direction of the velocity at P is the direction of the tangent to the path at P.

Let A be a fixed point on the path. Let the arcual distances of P and P' from A be

$$s,\quad s+\Delta s.$$

Then $\bar{r}$ is a vector function of s and there exists a functional relation between s and t. So

$$\bar{v} = \frac{d\bar{r}}{dt} = \frac{d\bar{r}}{ds}\cdot\frac{ds}{dt}. \qquad ...(1)$$

But we have

$$\frac{d\bar{r}}{ds} = \lim_{\Delta s \to 0} \frac{\bar{r}(s+\Delta s)-\bar{r}(s)}{\Delta s}$$

$$= \lim_{\Delta s \to 0} \frac{\overline{PP'}}{\Delta s} = \lim_{\Delta s \to 0} \left(\frac{PP'}{\Delta s}\right) \widehat{PP'}$$

$$= \lim_{\Delta s \to 0} \left(\frac{PP'}{\Delta s}\right)\left(\lim_{\Delta s \to 0} \widehat{PP'}\right) = (1)\left(\hat{T}\right) = \hat{T},$$

where $\hat{T}$ is the unit vector along the tangent at P to the path, in the sense in which s increases. Hence (1) becomes

$$\bar{v} = \frac{ds}{dt}\ \hat{T} = \dot{s}\hat{T}.$$

So $\bar{v}$ is along the tangent at P and has a magnitude $\dot{s}$.

Speed. The magnitude of velocity, namely $\dot{s}$, is called speed. Speed is a scalar. However, in general, the word velocity is freely used as a vector and also as a scalar.

Units of Velocity

M.K.S.	1 metre / second (1 m./sec.)
C.G.S.	1 centimetre / second (1 cm./sec.)
F.P.S.	1 foot / second (1 ft. /sec.)

v km./h. $= v\times\frac{5}{18}$ m./sec.

v m./sec.$= v\times\frac{18}{5}$ km./h.

1.2.1. Velocity of a particle describing a circle.

Let a particle P describe a circle with centre O and radius a. If A is a fixed point on the circle and angle AOP is θ, then

$$s = \text{arc } AP = a\theta.$$

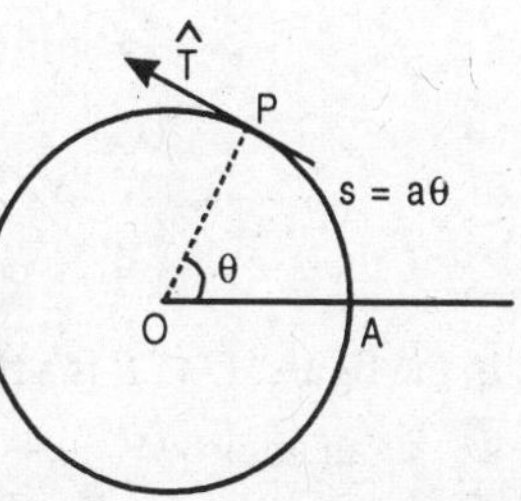

Let $\hat{T}$ be the unit vector along the tangent to the circle at P in the sense in which s increases. Then the velocity of P is

$$\bar{v} = \dot{s}\,\hat{T} = a\dot{\theta}\,\hat{T}.$$

Here the speed of P is $a\dot{\theta}$. ($\dot{\theta}$ is the angular velocity of P about O which will be defined later).

1.2.2 Resultant velocity.

If a particle has two velocities $\bar{v}_1$ and $\bar{v}_2$, then

$$\bar{v}_1+\bar{v}_2$$

is said to be the resultant velocity of the particle.

Bookwork 1.1. To find the magnitude and direction of the resultant of the velocities $\bar{v}_1$ and $\bar{v}_2$.

Now the resultant is $\bar{v}_1+\bar{v}_2$. Let the angle between $\bar{v}_1$ and $\bar{v}_2$ be α. Then the magnitude of $\bar{v}_1+\bar{v}_2$ is

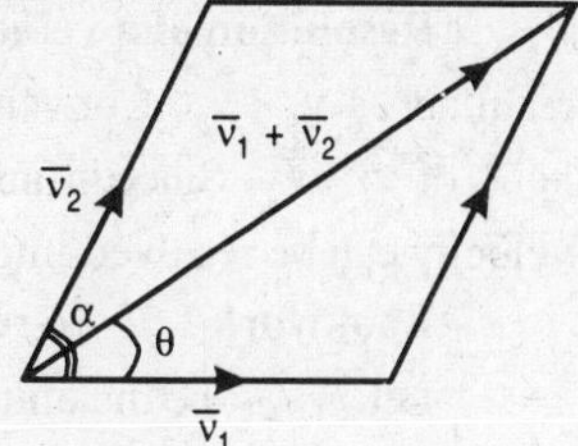

$$\left|\bar{v}_1+\bar{v}_2\right| = \sqrt{\left(\bar{v}_1+\bar{v}_2\right)\cdot\left(\bar{v}_1+\bar{v}_2\right)}$$

$$= \sqrt{\bar{v}_1\cdot\bar{v}_1+\bar{v}_2\cdot\bar{v}_2+2\bar{v}_1\cdot\bar{v}_2}$$

$$= \sqrt{v_1^2+v_2^2+2v_1v_2\cos\alpha},$$

where $\left|\bar{v}_1\right| = v_1$, $\left|\bar{v}_2\right| = v_2$.

Let θ be the angle between $\bar{v}_1$ and the resultant $\bar{v}_1+\bar{v}_2$. Then

$$\tan\theta = \frac{\left|\bar{v}_1\times\left(\bar{v}_1+\bar{v}_2\right)\right|}{\bar{v}_1\cdot\left(\bar{v}_1+\bar{v}_2\right)} = \frac{\left|\bar{0}+\bar{v}_1\times\bar{v}_2\right|}{v_1^2+v_1v_2\cos\alpha}$$

$$= \frac{\left|v_1 v_2 \sin\alpha \hat{n}\right|}{v_1(v_1 + v_2 \cos\alpha)} = \frac{v_1 v_2 \sin\alpha}{v_1(v_1 + v_2 \cos\alpha)}$$

$$= \frac{v_2 \sin\alpha}{v_1 + v_2 \cos\alpha}.$$

$$\therefore \qquad \theta = \tan^{-1} \frac{v_2 \sin\alpha}{v_1 + v_2 \cos\alpha}.$$

Corollary 1. If $\overline{v_1}$ and $\overline{v_2}$ are of equal magnitude, say v, then

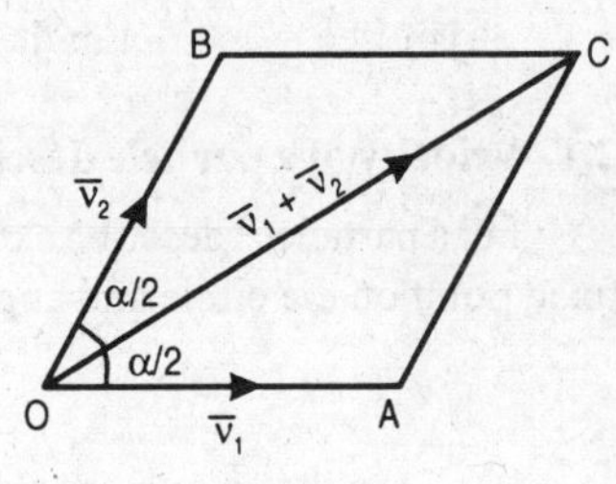

$$\left|\overline{v}_1 + \overline{v}_2\right| = \sqrt{v^2 + v^2 + 2v^2 \cos\alpha}$$

$$= v\sqrt{2(1 + \cos\alpha)}$$

$$= v\sqrt{4\cos^2 \alpha/2}$$

$$= 2v \cos\alpha/2.$$

In the figure, $OACB$ is a rhombus. So OC bisects $\angle AOB$. So the resultant is equally inclined to $\overline{v}_1$ and $\overline{v}_2$ at an angle $\alpha/2$.

Corollary 2. If $\overline{v}_1$ and $\overline{v}_2$ are perpendicular to each other, then choosing $\overline{i}$ and $\overline{j}$ in their directions,

$$\overline{v}_1 = v_1 \overline{i}, \ \overline{v}_2 = v_2 \overline{j}.$$

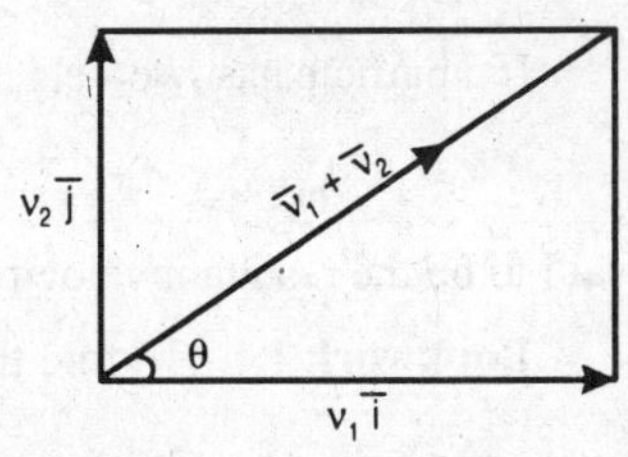

$$\therefore \qquad \left|\overline{v}_1 + \overline{v}_2\right| = \left|v_1 \overline{i} + v_2 \overline{j}\right|$$

$$= \sqrt{v_1^2 + v_2^2}.$$

$$\tan\theta = \frac{v_2}{v_1}$$

$$\text{or} \qquad \theta = \tan^{-1} \frac{v_2}{v_1}.$$

Resolution of a velocity into its components. Given the velocities $\overline{v}_1$ and $\overline{v}_2$, we have the resultant as $\overline{v}_1 + \overline{v}_2$. Conversely, if $\overline{v}_1 + \overline{v}_2$ is given, the quantities $\overline{v}_1$ and $\overline{v}_2$ are said to be components of $\overline{v}_1 + \overline{v}_2$. Since infinite number of parallelograms can be formed with a given diagonal a given velocity can be resolved into two components in infinite number of different ways.

Bookwork 1.2. To resolve a velocity $\overline{v}$ into components in two given directions.

Let $\hat{e}_1, \hat{e}_2$ be the unit vectors in the given directions. Let them make angles α, β with $\overline{v}$. Now $\overline{v}$ may be expressed as a linear combination of $\hat{e}_1, \hat{e}_2$ as

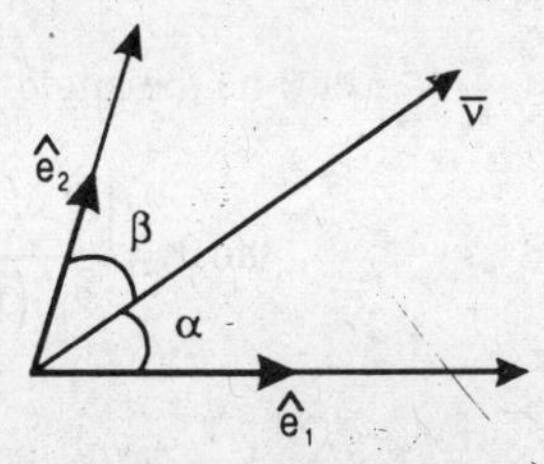

$$\overline{v} = a\hat{e}_1 + b\hat{e}_2.$$

Multiplying this vectorially by $\hat{e}_1$,

$$\hat{e}_1 \times \overline{v} = a(\hat{e}_1 \times \hat{e}_1) + b(\hat{e}_1 \times \hat{e}_2)$$

$$\text{i.e.,} \qquad v \sin\alpha \ \hat{n} = \overline{0} + b \sin(\alpha + \beta)\hat{n},$$

where $\hat{n}$ is the unit vector perpendicular to both $\hat{e}_1, \hat{e}_2$ such that $\hat{e}_1, \hat{e}_2, \hat{n}$ form a right-handed triad.

$$\therefore \qquad b = \frac{v \sin\alpha}{\sin(\alpha+\beta)}.$$

Multiplying vectorially by $\hat{e}_2$,

$$\widehat{e_2} \times \bar{v} = a\, \widehat{e_2} \times \widehat{e_1} + b\, \widehat{e_2} \times \widehat{e_2}$$

i.e.,
$$v \sin\beta\left(-\hat{n}\right) = a \sin(\alpha+\beta)\left(-\hat{n}\right).$$

$$\therefore \qquad a = \frac{v \sin\beta}{\sin(\alpha+\beta)}.$$

$$\therefore \qquad \bar{v} = \frac{v \sin\beta}{\sin(\alpha+\beta)}\, \hat{e}_1 + \frac{v \sin\alpha}{\sin(\alpha+\beta)}\, \hat{e}_2$$

Component of a vector in a given direction. Given a vector $\overline{V}$ and a direction specified by a unit vector $\hat{e}$, the scalar quantity

$$\overline{V} \cdot \hat{e}$$

is called the component of $\overline{V}$ in the direction of $\hat{e}$.

Bookwork 1.3. To express the velocity $\bar{v}$ in terms of its components in two perpendicular directions.

Let $\bar{i}, \bar{j}$ be the unit vectors along the perpendicular directions. Then, from Vector Algebra, we have

$$\bar{v} = (\bar{v}\cdot\bar{i})\bar{i} + (\bar{v}\cdot\bar{j})\bar{j}.$$

If $\bar{v}$ makes angles α, $90° - \alpha$ with $\bar{i}, \bar{j}$, then

$$\bar{v}\cdot\bar{i} = v\cdot 1\cdot\cos\alpha,$$
$$\bar{v}\cdot\bar{j} = v\cdot 1\cdot\cos(90° - \alpha) = v \sin\alpha.$$

$$\therefore \qquad \bar{v} = v\cos\alpha\,\bar{i} + v\sin\alpha\,\bar{j}.$$

Note. $v\cos\alpha$, $v\sin\alpha$ are the components of $\bar{v}$ in the perpendicular directions which make angles α, $90° - \alpha$ with $\bar{v}$.

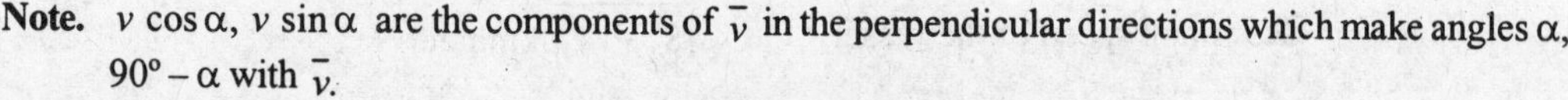

EXAMPLES

Example 1. A particle has two velocities $\bar{v}_1$ and $\bar{v}_2$. Its resultant velocity is equal to $\bar{v}_1$ in magnitude. Show that, when the velocity $\bar{v}_1$ is doubled, the new resultant is perpendicular to $\bar{v}_2$. **(M.U.)**

Since the magnitude of $\overline{v_1} + \overline{v_2}$ is equal to the magnitude of $\overline{v_1}$,

$$\left|\bar{v}_1 + \bar{v}_2\right| = \left|\bar{v}_1\right| \quad \text{or} \quad \left|\bar{v}_1 + \bar{v}_2\right|^2 = \left|\bar{v}_1\right|^2$$

i.e.,
$$(\bar{v}_1 + \bar{v}_2).(\bar{v}_1 + \bar{v}_2) = \bar{v}_1.\bar{v}_1 \text{ or } \bar{v}_1.\bar{v}_1 + 2\bar{v}_1.\bar{v}_2 + \bar{v}_2.\bar{v}_2 = \bar{v}_1 . \bar{v}_1$$

i.e.,
$$(2\bar{v}_1 + \bar{v}_2).\bar{v}_2 = 0.$$

So the resultant of $2\bar{v}_1$ and $\bar{v}_2$ is perpendicular to $\bar{v}_2$.

Example 2. A particle has two velocities of equal magnitudes inclined to each other at an angle θ. If one of them is halved, the angle between the other and the original resultant velocity is bisected by the new resultant. Show that $\theta = 120^\circ$. **(M.U., Bn.U.)**

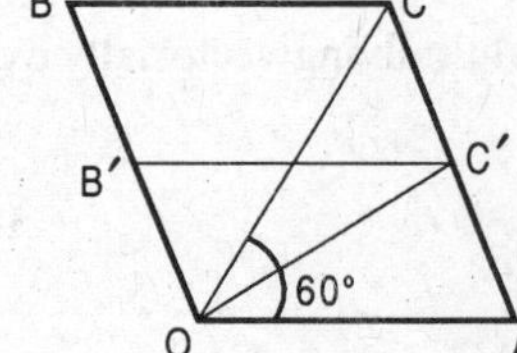

Let $\overline{OA}$, $\overline{OB}$ be the given velocities. Complete the parallelogram $OACB$. Since $OA = OB$, OC bisects $\angle AOB$. Let B' be the midpoint of OB. Complete the parallelogram $OAC'B'$. Now C' is the midpoint of AC. Since OC' is the bisector of $\angle AOC$,

$$\frac{OA}{OC} = \frac{AC'}{C'C} = 1.$$

So $OA = OC$. But $OA = OB$. Hence ΔOCA is an equilateral triangle and

$$\angle AOC = 60^\circ \qquad \therefore \angle AOB = 120^\circ.$$

Example 3. A man seated in a train whose velocity is 80 km.p.h. throws a ball horizontally and perpendicular to the train with a velocity of 60 km. p.h. Find the velocity of the ball immediately after the throw. **(M.U.)**

The ball has two velocities, one is due to the motion of the train and the other is due to the throw. These velocities are perpendicular to each other. So the magnitude of the resultant velocity is

$$\sqrt{80^2 + 60^2} \text{ km. p.h.} = 100 \text{ km. p.h.}$$

The direction is in a horizontal plane and is inclined to the velocity of the train at an angle θ given by

$$\theta = \tan^{-1}\frac{60}{80} = \tan^{-1}\frac{3}{4}.$$

Example 4. A boat which can steam in still water with a velocity of 48 km.p.h. is steaming with its bow pointed due east when it is carried by a current which flows northward with a speed of 14 km.p.h. Find the actual distance it would travel in 12 minutes.

The boat has two velocities, one is due to steaming and the other due to the current.

$$\text{Resultant speed of the vessel} = \sqrt{48^2 + 14^2} \text{ km.p.h.}$$

$$= 50 \text{ km.p.h.}$$

$$\text{Distance travelled in 12 minutes} = \frac{50 \times 12}{60} \text{ km.} = 10 \text{ km.}$$

Example 5. A stream is running at a speed of 4 ml.p.h. Its breadth is one quarter of a mile. A man can row a boat at a speed of 5 ml.p.h. in still water. Find the direction in which he must row in order to go perpendicular to the stream and the time it takes him to cross the stream so. **(M.U.)**

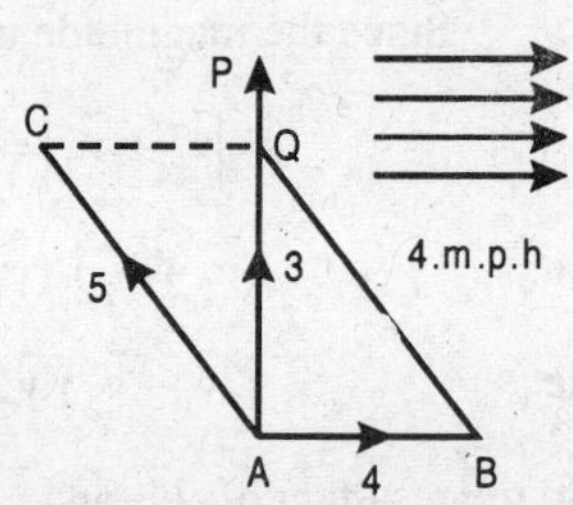

Let AP be the actual path of the boat. Let $\overline{AB}$ denote the velocity of the stream and $\overline{AC}$, denote the velocity of the boat due to rowing. Complete the parallelogram $ABQC$. Then Q will lie on AP and $\overline{AQ}$ will denote the resultant velocity of the boat. Now

$$AQ = \sqrt{BQ^2 - AB^2} = \sqrt{AC^2 - AB^2} = \sqrt{5^2 - 4^2} = 3.$$

So the resultant speed of the boat is 3 ml.p.h. and the time the man takes to cross the stream is

$$\frac{1}{4}\times\frac{1}{3}\text{ hour} = 5\text{ minutes},\quad \angle CAQ = \tan^{-1}\frac{4}{3}.$$

Example 6. A boat capable of moving in still water with a speed of 10 km.p.h., crosses a river, 2 km. broad, flowing with a speed of 6 km.p.h. Find (*i*) the time of crossing by the shortest route and (*ii*) the minimum time of crossing.

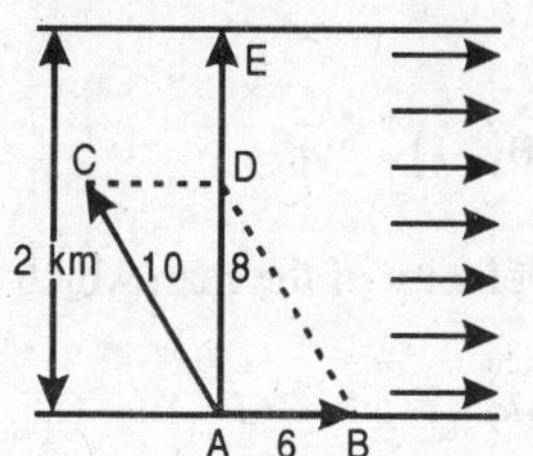

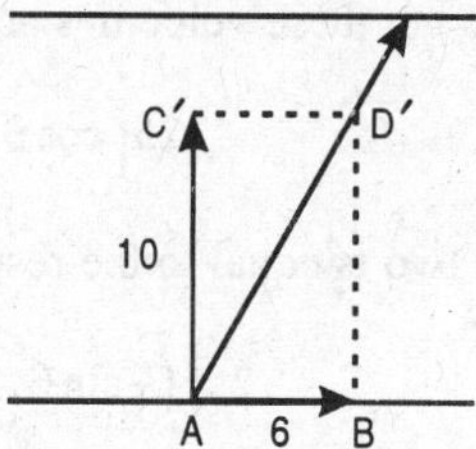

(*i*) The shortest route is the route AE perpendicular to the stream. Let $\overline{AB}$ and $\overline{AC}$ denote respectively the velocity of the current and the velocity of the boat due to rowing so that the resultant velocity $\overline{AD}$ is along AE. Its magnitude AD is

$$AD = \sqrt{10^2 - 6^2} = 8.$$

So, in this case, the resultant speed is 8 km.p.h. and the time taken to cross the stream by the boat is

$$2/8 \text{ hour or 15 minutes.}$$

(*ii*) The time of crossing is minimum when the component of the resultant velocity of the boat in the direction perpendicular to the stream is maximum. This perpendicular component is maximum when the boat is rowed with its bow pointing towards the point opposite to the starting point. It is just the velocity of the boat due to rowing alone and it is denoted by AC' in the figure. Its magnitude is 10. Hence the time taken to cross the stream is

$$\frac{\text{displacement perpendicular to the stream}}{\text{speed in this direction}} = \frac{2}{10}\text{ hour.}$$
$$= 12\text{ minutes.}$$

In this case the actual course of the boat is AD'.

Example 7. A man can swim perpendicularly across a stream of breadth 100 m. in 4 minutes when there is no current and in 5 minutes when there is a downward current. Find the velocity of the current. **(M.U.)**

The velocity of the man in still water is

$$\frac{100}{4} = 25\text{ m./mt.}$$

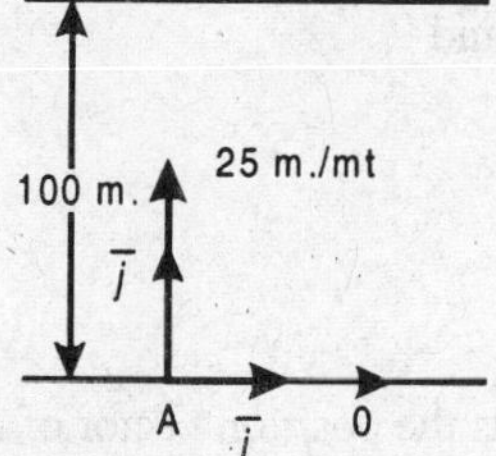

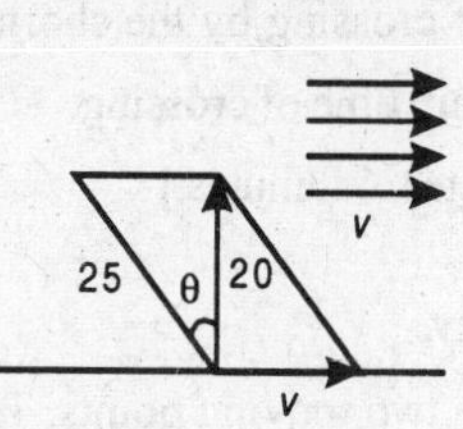

Velocity of the man perpendicular to the bank when there is a current is

$$\frac{100}{5} = 20 \text{ m./mt.}$$

This is the resultant of his own velocity of 25 m./mt. say, inclined to the perpendicular to the bank at an angle θ, and the current's velocity, say *v*. Taking the unit vectors $\bar{i}$ along the bank and $\bar{j}$ perpendicular to the bank we get these velocities as

$$25\left[\cos\theta\,\bar{j}+\sin\theta\left(-\bar{i}\right)\right],\ v\bar{i}.$$

The resultant of these two is equal to the resultant velocity of the man which is $20\bar{j}$. So

$$25\left[\left(-\sin\theta\,\bar{i}+\cos\theta\,\bar{j}\right)+v\bar{i}\right] = 20\bar{j}.$$

$$\therefore \quad \left.\begin{aligned} -25\sin\theta + v &= 0 \\ 25\cos\theta &= 20 \end{aligned}\right\} \text{ or } 25^2 = v^2 + 20^2 \text{ or } v = 15.$$

So the velocity of the current is 15 m./mt.

EXERCISES

1. A point possesses velocities represented by *AB* and *AC*, two sides of a triangle. Show that its resultant velocity is represented by 2 AM, where *M* is the midpoint of *BC*. **(M.U.)**
   [Hint: In the parallelogram *ABDC*, $\overline{AD}$ denotes the resultant velocity. But $\overline{AD} = 2\,\overline{AM}$.**]**

2. A ship is steaming north at $8\sqrt{3}$ km.p.h. and a man walks across its deck in a direction due west at 8 km.p.h. Find his resultant velocity in space. **(M.U.)**
   [Ans. 16 km.p.h., 30° west of north**]**

3. A man keeps his boat at right angles to the current and rows across a stream, $\frac{1}{4}$ km. broad. He finds that he reaches the opposite bank $\frac{1}{8}$ km. below the point opposite to the starting point. Find the speed of the current if the speed of boat due to rowing alone is 6 km.p.h.
   [Ans. 3 km.p.h.**]**

4. A stream is running at 3 km.p.h.and its breadth is 100 metres. If a man can row a boat at 5 km.p.h. in still water, find the direction in which he must row in order to go straight across the stream and show that the time he takes to do so is 90 seconds.
   [Ans. Inclined to the perpendicular to the stream at an angle $\tan^{-1} \frac{4}{3}$**]**

5. A man who can row a boat at 10 km.p.h. in still water wishes to cross a river, 1 km. broad, flowing at 6 km.p.h. Find
   (*i*) the time of crossing by the shortest route and
   (*ii*) the minimum time of crossing. **(C.U.)**
   [Ans. 7.5 minutes, 6 minutes.**]**

1.2.3 Relative velocity.

Let *A* and *P* be two moving points. Then $\overline{AP}$ is the position vector of *P* with reference to *A*. That is, $\overline{AP}$ specifies the position of *P* relative to *A*. So

$$\frac{d}{dt}(\overline{AP})$$

is the *velocity of P relative to A*.

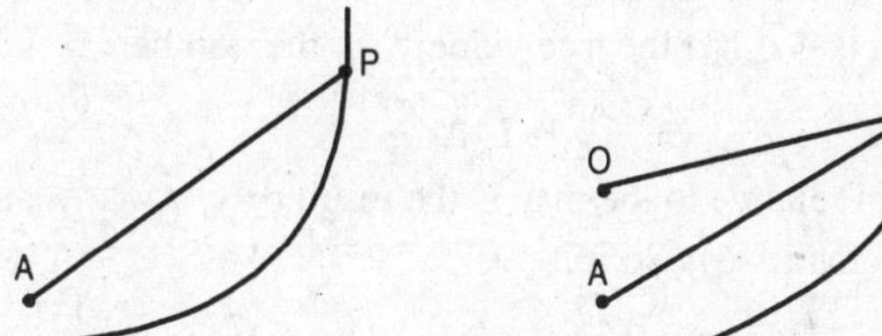

Relative velocity. If A and P are two moving points, then $\frac{d}{dt}(\overline{AP})$ is the velocity of P relative to A.

Remark 1. Now, taking a fixed point O,

$$\frac{d}{dt}\left(\overline{AP}\right) = \frac{d}{dt}\left(\overline{OP} - \overline{OA}\right) = \overline{V}_P - \overline{V}_A,$$

where $\overline{V}_A$ and $\overline{V}_P$ are the velocties of A and P. Thus

the velocity of a point P relative to another point A is the vector sum of the velocity of P and the reversed velocity of A.

Motion of P relative to A. This motion is equivalent to the situation in which A is at rest and P moves with a velocity $\overline{V}_P - \overline{V}_A$. Obtaining this situation is said to reduce A to rest assuming P to move with a velocity which is the resultant of

(*i*) velocity of P and

(*ii*) reversed velocity of A

EXAMPLES

Example 1. A train travels at the rate of 27 km/h. Rain which is falling vertically appears to a man in the train to make an angle of $\tan^{-1} 6/5$ with the vertical. Find the magnitude of the true velocity of the rain. **(A.U.)**

Let $\overline{i}$ be the unit vector in the direction opposite to that of the train. Let $\overline{j}$ be the unit vector vertically downward and v, the magnitude of the true velocity of the rain. Then the true velocity of the rain is $v\overline{j}$. Thus

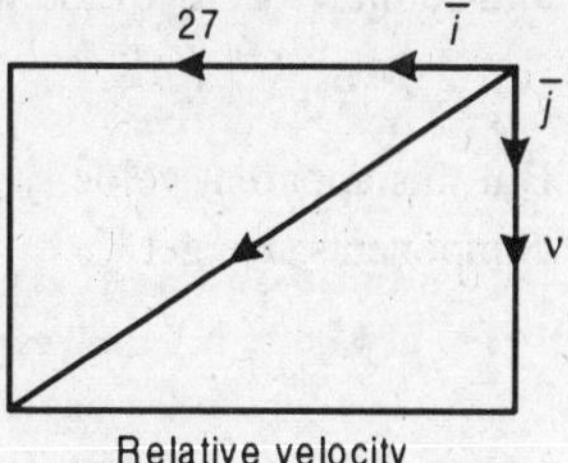

Relative velocity

$$\begin{Bmatrix}\text{Vel. of rain} \\ \text{relative to man}\end{Bmatrix} = \begin{pmatrix}\text{Vel. of} \\ \text{rain}\end{pmatrix} + \begin{pmatrix}\text{Reversed} \\ \text{vel. of man}\end{pmatrix}$$

$$= v\overline{j} + 27\,\overline{i}.$$

This makes an angle of $\tan^{-1} 27/v$ with the vertical. So, using the given angle $\tan^{-1} 6/5$,

$$\frac{27}{v} = \frac{6}{5} \quad \text{or} \quad v = 22\tfrac{1}{2} \text{ km./h.}$$

Example 2. To a man walking along a level road at 5 km./h., the rain appears to beat into his face at 8 km./h. at an angle 60° with the vertical. Find the direction and magnitude of the true velocity of the rain. **(M.U.)**

Let $\bar{i}, \bar{j}$ be the horizontal and vertically downward unit vectors such that the velocity of the man is $5\bar{i}$. Let the true velocity of the rain be

$$v_1\,\bar{i}+v_2\,\bar{j}.$$

Then the velocity of the rain relative to the man is the result of $v_1\,\bar{i}+v_2\,\bar{j}$ and the reversed velocity of the man $-5\bar{i}$. So it is

$$\left(v_1\bar{i}+v_2\bar{j}\right)-5\bar{i} \quad \text{or} \quad \left(v_1-5\right)\bar{i}+v_2\,\bar{j}.$$

This is given to be

$$8\left[\left(\cos 60^\circ\,\bar{j}+\sin 60^\circ\left(-\bar{i}\right)\right)\right] \quad \text{or} \quad 4\bar{j}-4\sqrt{3}\,\bar{i}.$$

Equating the $\bar{i}$ components and also the $\bar{j}$ components,

$$v_1-5=-4\sqrt{3}, \quad v_2=4.$$

Thus the true velocity of the rain is

$$\left(5-4\sqrt{3}\right)\bar{i}+4\bar{j}.$$

Its magnitude is

$$\sqrt{\left(5-4\sqrt{3}\right)^2+4^2}=4\cdot 44\,\text{km/h}.$$

and it is inclined to the vertical at an angle

$$\tan^{-1}\frac{4\sqrt{3}-5}{4}.$$

Example 3. A ship sails north-east at 15 km.p.h. and, to a passenger on board, the wind appears to blow from north with a velocity of $15\sqrt{2}$ km.p.h. Find the true velocity of the wind. **(M.U.)**

Let $\bar{i}$ and $\bar{j}$ be the unit vectors towards east and north and the true velocity of the wind be $v_1\,\bar{i}+v_2\,\bar{j}$. Now the velocity of the ship is

$$15\left(\cos 45^\circ\,\bar{i}+\sin 45^\circ\,\bar{j}\right)$$

and so the velocity of the wind relative to the ship is

$$\left(v_1\,\bar{i}+v_2\,\bar{j}\right)-15\left(\cos 45^\circ\,\bar{i}+\sin 45^\circ\,\bar{j}\right).$$

But this apparent velocity is given to be $15\sqrt{2}\left(-\bar{j}\right)$. Equating the $\bar{i}$ components and also the $\bar{j}$ components, we get

$$v_1=15\cos 45^\circ, \quad v_2-15\sin 45^\circ=-15\sqrt{2}.$$

i.e.,
$$v_1=\frac{15}{\sqrt{2}} \quad \text{and} \quad v_2=-\frac{15}{\sqrt{2}}.$$

So the true velocity of the wind is

$$\frac{15}{\sqrt{2}}\bar{i}-\frac{15}{\sqrt{2}}\bar{j}.$$

Its direction is towards south-east and magnitude is 15.

Example 4. A person travelling eastward finds the wind to blow from north. On doubling his speed he finds it to come from north-east. Show that, if he trebles his speed, the wind would appear to him to come from a direction making an angle $\theta = \tan^{-1} \frac{1}{2}$ north of east. **(M.U., K.U.)**

Method 1. Let the unit vectors towards east and north be $\bar{i}, \bar{j}$ and the true velocity of the wind be $a\bar{i}+b\bar{j}$ and the man's velocity be $u\bar{i}$. Now the relative velocities of the wind in the 3 cases are

$$(a\bar{i}+b\bar{j})-u\bar{i},\ (a\bar{i}+b\bar{j})-2u\bar{i},\ (a\bar{i}+b\bar{j})-3u\bar{i}.$$

From the given conditions they are of the form

$$a\bar{i}+b\bar{j}-u\bar{i} = -\lambda\bar{j} \qquad ...(1)$$

$$a\bar{i}+b\bar{j}-2u\bar{i} = -\mu\left(\frac{1}{\sqrt{2}}\bar{i}+\frac{1}{\sqrt{2}}\bar{j}\right) \qquad ...(2)$$

$$a\bar{i}+b\bar{j}-3u\bar{i} = -\gamma(\cos\theta\,\bar{i}+\sin\theta\,\bar{j}). \qquad ...(3)$$

On the RHS of (1), the $\bar{i}$ – component is 0. So also on the LHS. So

$$a-u=0 \text{ or } a=u.$$

On the RHS of (2), $\bar{i}$ and $\bar{j}$ components are equal. So also on the LHS. Therefore

$$a-2u=b \text{ or } b=-u.$$

From (3), we get

$$-\gamma\cos\theta = a-3u,\ -\gamma\sin\theta = b.$$

$$\therefore \qquad \tan\theta = \frac{b}{a-3u} = \frac{-u}{u-3u} = \frac{1}{2}.$$

Note. The above method is applicable for any general case.

Method 2. Now the velocity of the man is eastward. Its reversed velocity is westward. Let this reversed velocity be $\bar{v}$ denoted by $\overline{AB}$. Let $\overline{BC}$ be the true velocity of the wind. Then, by triangle law of addition, their resultant is $\overline{AC}$ which is given to be towards south.

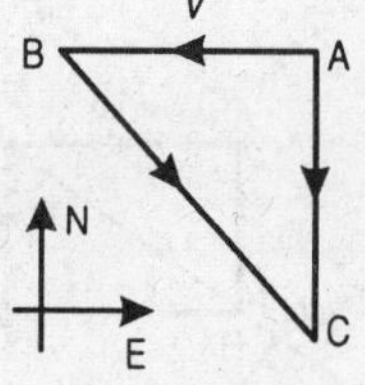

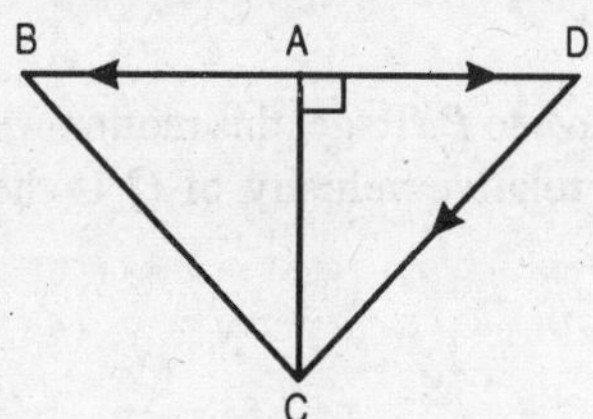

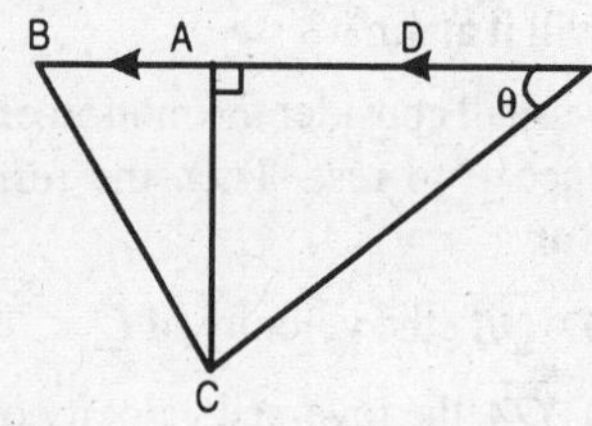

In the second case we shall add one more $\bar{v}$ denoted by $\overline{DA}$ to double the reversed velocity. Now the resultant is $\overline{DC}$ and its direction is given to be from northeast. So

$$\angle ADC = 45^\circ.$$

$$\therefore \qquad AD = AC = v.$$

Again, adding one more $\bar{v}$ denoted by $\overline{ED}$ to treble the reversed velocity, we get the resultant as $\overline{EC}$. Now, it is given that $\overline{CE}$ makes with the eastern direction an angle θ. So $\angle AEC = \theta$ and from the ΔEAC,

$$\tan\theta = \frac{AC}{AE} = \frac{v}{2v} = \frac{1}{2}.$$

Example 5. The cars A and B are moving due east and due north at 60 km.p.h. and 80 km.p.h. respectively. At noon A is west of B at a distance 40 km. When are the cars nearest to each other and what is the distance between them then? **(M.U.)**

In the first figure $\overline{AC}$ and $\overline{BD}$ denote the actual velocities of A and B. In the second figure

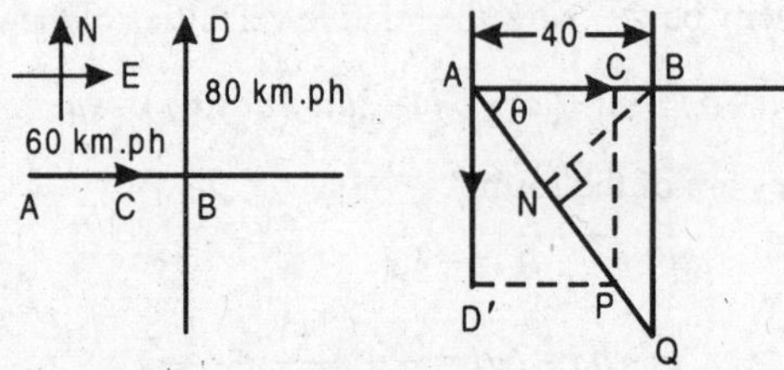

the reversed velocity of B, namely $\overline{AD'}$ is introduced to A to reduce B to rest and to consider the relative motion of A. Now $\overline{AP}$ denotes the velocity of A relative to B and AQ is the path of A in this relative motion. If BN is the perpendicular drawn from B to AQ, then BN is the minimum distance between the cars. Now the relative speed of A is

$$AP = \sqrt{60^2 + 80^2} \text{ km.p.h.} = 100 \text{ km.p.h.}$$

So, if the time taken by A to move from A to N in its relative motion is t hours and if the angle $CAP = \theta$, then

$$t = \frac{AN}{\text{relative speed}} = \frac{AB\cos\theta}{100} = \frac{40}{100} \times \frac{3}{5} = \frac{6}{25} \text{ hr.}$$

The minimum distance between the cars is

$$BN = AB \sin\theta = 40 \times \frac{4}{5} = 32 \text{ km.}$$

Example 6. A ship P is sailing due east at a speed of 16 km./h. when another ship Q which is due north of P at a distance of 10 km. from it, starts at a speed of 12 km./h. and sails southward. Find the velocity of Q relative to P. What is the least distance apart that Q will attain from P and how long after starting will it attain it? **(M.U.)**

We shall consider the motion of Q relative to P. To get this motion we shall reduce P to rest. Then the respective relative velocity of Q is the resultant of

(*i*) $\overline{QB}$, the velocity of Q

(*ii*) $\overline{QA}$, the reversed velocity of P.

This velocity is $\overline{QR}$ and QR' is the path of the relative motion of Q. If N is the foot of the perpendicular drawn from P to QR', the minimum distance between P and Q is PN.

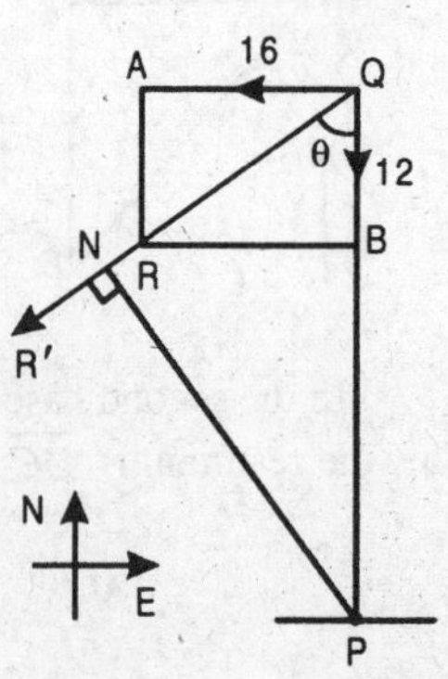

$$\left.\begin{array}{l}\text{The velocity of}\\ Q \text{ relative to } P\end{array}\right\} = \left|\overline{QR}\right| = \sqrt{12^2 + 16^2} = 20.$$

Let $\angle BQR = \theta$. Then, from ΔBQR,

$$\sin\theta = \frac{16}{20} = \frac{4}{5}, \quad \cos\theta = \frac{12}{20} = \frac{3}{5}.$$

Now, from $\Delta\ QNP$.

$$PN = PQ \sin\theta = 10 \times \frac{4}{5} = 8.$$

$$QN = PQ \cos\theta = 10 \times \frac{3}{5} = 6.$$

So the minimum distance between P and Q is

$$PN = 8 \text{ km}.$$

The time to attain this situation is

$$\frac{QN}{\text{Relative velocity}} = \frac{6}{20} = \frac{3}{10}\text{hr}.$$

Example 7. Two cars A, B are travelling with velocities u, v towards O along two perpendicular roads XO and YO. Initially they are at X, Y and $XO = a$, $YO = b$. Show that they will be nearest to each other after a time

$$\frac{au + bv}{u^2 + v^2}.$$ **(Bn.U., M.U.)**

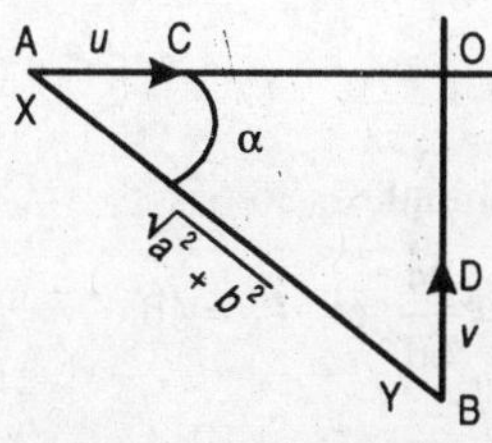

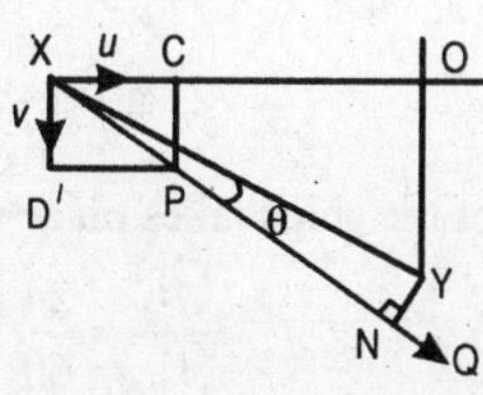

In the first figure $\overline{XC}$ and $\overline{YD}$ are the velocities of A and B. If angle $OXY = \alpha$, then

$$\cos\alpha = \frac{OX}{XY} = \frac{a}{\sqrt{a^2 + b^2}}, \quad \sin\alpha = \frac{OY}{XY} = \frac{b}{\sqrt{a^2 + b^2}}. \qquad \text{...(1)}$$

In the second figure $\overline{XD'}$ is the reversed velocity of B and $\overline{XP}$ is the velocity of A relative to B.

Here $XP = \sqrt{u^2 + v^2}$. The line XPQ is the path of A in its motion relative to B. If N is the foot of the perpendicular drawn from Y to XQ, NY is the minimum distance between the cars A and B. If θ is the angle NXY, then the time T taken by A to move from X to N in its relative motion, is

$$T = \frac{XN}{\text{Relative speed}} = \frac{XY \cos\theta}{\sqrt{u^2 + v^2}} = \frac{\sqrt{a^2 + b^2}\cos(PXC - \alpha)}{\sqrt{u^2 + v^2}}.$$

But we have

$$\cos PXC = \frac{u}{\sqrt{u^2 + v^2}}, \quad \sin PXC = \frac{v}{\sqrt{u^2 + v^2}}. \qquad \text{...(2)}$$

Using (1) and (2) we get T as

$$\frac{au + bv}{u^2 + v^2}.$$

Example 8. A ship A observes another ship B, 20 kilometres due east of A. B is steaming north at 24 km.p.h. After 24 minutes if the ships are found to be nearest to each other at a distance of 12 km.,find the velocity of A. **(M.U.)**

The minimum distance between the ships is given to be 12 km. So the path of the relative motion of A will be a straight line at a perpendicular distance 12 km. from B. That is, the path will touch the circle with centre at B and radius 12. So there are two such paths, say AC and AD, where C and D are the points of contact. Now

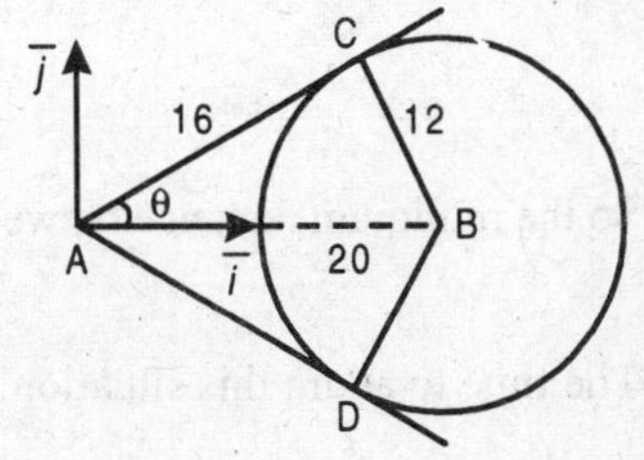

$$AC = AD = \sqrt{20^2 - 12^2} = 16, \cos\theta = 4/5, \sin\theta = 3/5,$$

where θ is the angle BAC.

Case (*i*). *AC* is the relative path of *A*. Let the actual velocity of A be $u_1\bar{i}+v_1\bar{j}$, where $\bar{i}$ and $\bar{j}$ are unit vectors in the eastern and northern directions. The actual velocity of B is $24\bar{j}$. So the velocity of A relative to B is

$$(u_1\bar{i}+v_1\bar{j})-24\bar{j}.$$

If the relative speed is V_1, then

$$u_1\bar{i}+(v_1-24)\bar{j} = V_1\widehat{AC} = V_1(\cos\theta\bar{i}+\sin\theta\bar{j})$$

$$= V_1\left(4/5\,\bar{i}+3/5\,\bar{j}\right). \qquad ...(1)$$

The nearest approach of the ships takes place after 24 minutes. So

$$\frac{AC}{V_1} = \frac{24}{60} \text{ or } \frac{16}{V_1} = \frac{24}{60} \text{ or } V_1 = 40.$$

Substituting in (1), we have

$$u_1\bar{i}+(v_1-24)\bar{j} = 32\bar{i}+24\bar{j}.$$

Hence $u_1 = 32$ and $v_1 - 24 = 24$. Or $u_1 = 32$ and $v_1 = 48$. So the magnitude of the velocity of A is

$$\sqrt{32^2+48^2} = 16\sqrt{13}$$

and the direction is at an angle $\tan^{-1} 48/32$ or $\tan^{-1} 3/2$ north of east.

Case (*ii*). *AD* is the relative path of *A*. If, in this case, the true velocity of A is $u_2\bar{i}+v_2\bar{j}$, then

$$u_2\bar{i}+(v_2-24)\bar{j} = V_2(\cos\theta\bar{i}-\sin\theta\bar{j}) = 40\left(4/5\,\bar{i}-3/5\,\bar{j}\right).$$

That is, $u_2 = 32$ and $v_2 = 0$. So the velocity of A is 32 km.p.h eastward.

Example 9. A ship A steaming in the direction 30° north of east at 30 knots, sees another ship B at 20 nautical miles in the east. Find the minimum speed of B so that it may intercept A. (One knot is the speed of 1 nautical mile per hour). **(M.U.)**

Let $\overline{AC}$, $\overline{BP}$ be the actual velocities of A, B. Now we shall reduce A to rest. Then, for B to meet A, the velocity of B relative to A, should be along BA. Let it be $\overline{BQ}$. If $\overline{BD}$ is the reversed velocity of A, then, from

$$\overline{BD}+\overline{DQ} = \overline{BQ},$$

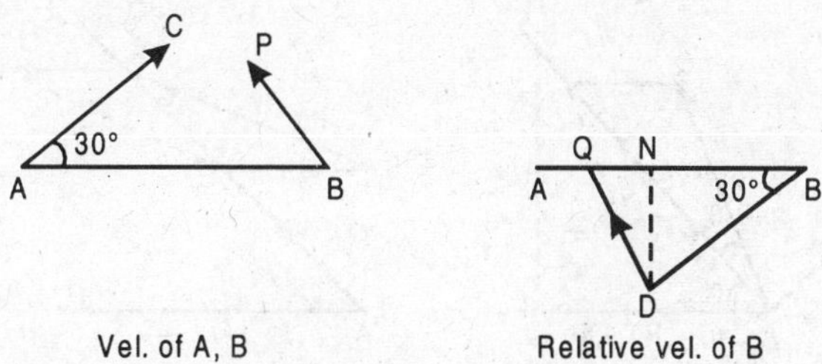

Vel. of A, B Relative vel. of B

we see that $\overline{DQ}$ is the actual velocity of B. Now we require the situation in which DQ is a minimum. DQ is a minimum when DQ is perpendicular to BA. Let DN be perpendicular to BA. Thus the required minimum velocity of B is

$$DN = BD \sin 30^\circ = 30 \times \tfrac{1}{2} = 15 \text{ knots}.$$

Example 10. A cruiser which can steam at 30 knots receives a report that an enemy vessel, steaming due north at 20 knots, is at 29 nautical miles away in a direction 30° N of E. Show that the cruiser can overtake the vessel in almost 2 hrs. **(M.U.)**

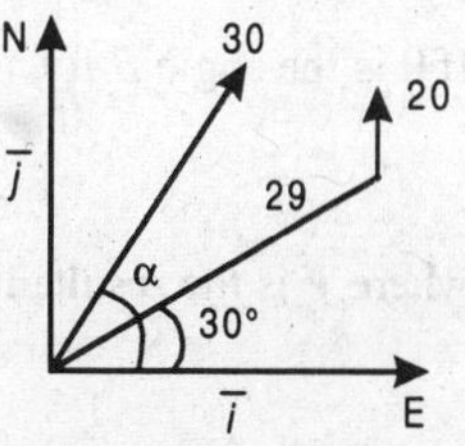

Let $\overline{i}$, $\overline{j}$ be the unit vectors towards east and north. Then the velocity of the enemy vessel is $20\,\overline{j}$. Let the velocity of the cruiser to meet the enemy vessel be

$$30\left(\cos\alpha\,\overline{i} + \sin\alpha\,\overline{j}\right). \qquad ...(1)$$

Then, to reduce the enemy vessel to rest, we shall introduce the reversed velocity of the enemy vessel, $-20\,\overline{j}$, to (1). Thus the velocity of the cruiser relative to the enemy vessel is

$$30\cos\alpha\,\overline{i} + 30\sin\alpha\,\overline{j} - 20\,\overline{j}. \qquad ...(2)$$

Let the time that will be taken by the cruiser to reach the enemy vessel with this velocity be t hours. Then

$$\left[30\cos\alpha\,\overline{i} + (30\sin\alpha - 20)\,\overline{j}\right] t = 29\,(\cos 30^\circ\,\overline{i} + \sin 30^\circ\,\overline{j})$$

$$\therefore \quad (30\cos\alpha)\,t = 29\cos 30^\circ,$$

$$(30\sin\alpha - 20)\,t = 29\sin 30^\circ.$$

Finding 30 (cos α) t and (sin α) t, and squaring and adding, we get

$$500\,t^2 - 580\,t - 841 = 0,$$

whose positive root is nearly 2.

Example 11. The wind is blowing due east with a speed u. An aeroplane which has a constant speed v in still air flies at a constant height to a point at a distance x in the east and a distance y in the north from the starting point in time t and flies back to the starting point in time t'. Show that

$$tt' = \frac{x^2 + y^2}{v^2 - u^2}$$

and that on each journey the plane must be steered in a direction inclined to the line of flight at an angle

$$\sin^{-1} \frac{uy}{v\sqrt{x^2 + y^2}}. \qquad \textbf{(M.U.)}$$

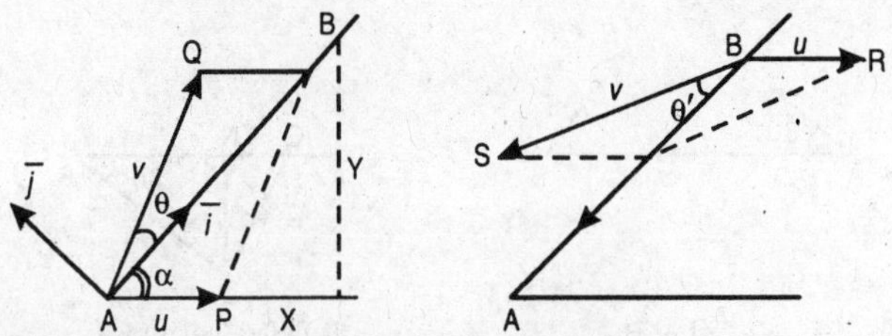

Let A be the starting point and B, the other given point. Then

$$AB^2 = x^2 + y^2.$$

Let AB be inclined to the eastern direction at an angle α. Let $\bar{i}$ be the unit vector in the direction of $\overline{AB}$ and $\bar{j}$ the unit vector in the direction perpendicular to $\bar{i}$. In the journey from A to B, the resultant velocity of the plane is the resultant of

(*i*) u in the direction of $\overline{AP}$,

(*ii*) v in the direction of $\overline{AQ}$.

If θ is the angle BAQ, then this resultant is

$$\{u\cos(-\alpha)\bar{i} + u\sin(-\alpha)\bar{j}\} + \{v\cos\theta\bar{i} + v\sin\theta\bar{j}\} = V\bar{i},$$

where V is the resultant speed of the plane. Thus

$$V = u\cos\alpha + v\cos\theta, \qquad ...(1)$$

$$0 = -u\sin\alpha + v\sin\theta. \qquad ...(2)$$

$$\therefore \qquad v\sin\theta = u\sin\alpha, \quad \theta = \sin^{-1}\frac{u\sin\alpha}{v},$$

where $\sin\alpha = y/\sqrt{x^2+y^2}$. Therefore

$$\theta = \sin^{-1}\frac{uy}{v\sqrt{x^2+y^2}}.$$

In the return journey, from B to A, the resultant velocity of the plane is the resultant of

(*i*) u in the direction of $\overline{BR}$.

(*ii*) v in the direction of $\overline{BS}$.

If θ' is the angle ABS, then the resultant velocity in the return journey is

$$\{u\cos(-\alpha)\bar{i} + u\sin(-\alpha)\bar{j}\} + \{v\cos\theta'(-\bar{i}) + v\sin\theta'\bar{j}\},$$

where V' is the resultant speed.

$$\therefore \qquad V' = -u\cos\alpha + v\cos\theta' \qquad ...(3)$$

$$0 = -u\sin\alpha + v\sin\theta'. \qquad ...(4)$$

From (2) and (4) we see that $\theta = \theta'$. That is, the directions in which the plane should be steered are equally inclined to the line of flight AB. Since V and V' are the resultant speeds

$$AB = Vt, \qquad AB = V't'.$$

$$\therefore \quad AB^2 = VV'tt' = (u\cos\alpha + v\cos\theta)(-u\cos\alpha + v\cos\theta')\,tt'$$

$$= (u\cos\alpha + v\cos\theta)(-u\cos\alpha + v\cos\theta)\,tt'$$

$$= (v^2\cos^2\theta - u^2\cos^2\alpha)\,tt'$$

$$= \left\{v^2(1-\sin^2\theta) - u^2(1-\sin^2\alpha)\right\}tt'$$

$$= \left\{v^2 - u^2 - (v^2\sin^2\theta - u^2\sin^2\alpha)\right\}tt'$$

$$= (v^2 - u^2)\,tt' \text{ by (2).}$$

But $AB^2 = x^2 + y^2$. So the result, as stated.

EXERCISES

1. A steamer is travelling due east at the rate of u km./h. A second steamer is travelling at $2u$ km../h. in a direction θ north of east and appears to be travelling north east to a passenger on the first steamer. Prove that $\theta = \frac{1}{2}\sin^{-1}\frac{3}{4}$.

[Hint: Relative velocity, $2u\,(\cos\theta\,\bar{i} + \sin\theta\,\bar{j}) - u\,\bar{i}$, is north eastward. So the $\bar{i}, \bar{j}$ components are equal. So $2\cos\theta - 1 = 2\sin\theta$. Square $2(\cos\theta - \sin\theta) = 1$**]**

2. To a cyclist riding due west at 10 km.p.h. the wind appears to blow from south. When he doubles his speed, it appears to him to blow from south-west. Show that the speed of the wind is $10\sqrt{2}$ km.p.h. and it is from south-east. **(Bn.U., M.U.)**

[Hint: If $\bar{i}, \bar{j}$ are east and north unit vectors and if the true velocity of the wind is $v_1\bar{i} + v_2\bar{j}$,

then $\left(v_1\bar{i} + v_2\bar{j}\right) - \left(-10\bar{i}\right) = \lambda\bar{j};\ \left(v_1\bar{i} + v_2\bar{j}\right) - \left(-20\bar{i}\right) = \mu\left(\frac{1}{\sqrt{2}}\bar{i} + \frac{1}{\sqrt{2}}\bar{j}\right)$.

$\therefore \quad v_1 + 10 = 0;\ v_1 + 20 = \mu/\sqrt{2},\ v_2 = \mu/\sqrt{2};$ So $v_1 = -10,\ v_2 = 10$**]**

3. To a man travelling towards north-east the wind appears to come from north. But, when he doubles his speed, the wind appears to him to come from a direction inclined at an angle $\theta = \cot^{-1} 2$ east of north. Find the true velocity of the wind. **(Bn.U., M.U., M.K.U.)**

[Hint: See Example 4. $\theta = \tan^{-1}\frac{1}{2} = \cot^{-1}2$**]**

4. To a man walking at 4 km.p.h. along a road running due west, the wind appears to blow from south, while to a cyclist travelling in the same direction at 8 km.p.h. it appears to come from south-west. What is the true direction and speed of the wind? **(M.U., M.K.U.)**

[Ans. $4\sqrt{2}$ km.p.h. from S.E.**]**

5. Two men A and A' walk with velocities 6 km.p.h. and 8 km.p.h., along two straight roads which cross at right angles at O. When A' is at O, A is at a distance 100 m. from O and walking towards O. Show that they will be nearest together when A has walked 36 m. **(M.U., K.U.)**

6. The courses of two ships A and B are towards north and east and their speeds are 12 and 16 knots respectively. At noon A is east of B and 10 nautical miles away. Find the time when they are nearest. (A knot is the speed of a nautical mile per hour.) **(M.U.)**

[Ans. 24 minutes past noon**]**

7. Two cars A and B are moving due north and due east at 40 and 30 km.p.h. At noon B is west of A, at a distance of 20 km. When are the cars closest to each other and what is the distance between them at that time? **(M.K.U.)**

[Ans. $t = 6/25$ h., 16 km.]

8. A destroyer steaming north at the rate of 15 km./h. observes a plane carrier due east of itself at a distance of 10 km. If the latter is steaming due west at the rate of 20 km./h., after what time are they at the least distance from each other and what is the least distance? **(M.U.)**

[Ans. $t = 8/25$ h., 6 km.]

9. Two motor cars A, B are travelling along straight roads at right angles to each other, with velocities of 21 km.p.h. and 28 km.p.h, towards C, the point at which the roads cross. If AC is half a mile when BC is three-quarters of a mile, find the shortest distance between the cars during the subsequent motion. **(M.U.)**

[Ans. 0·05 km.]

10. At a given instant, one steamer is 20 km. west of another. The first travels north-east at 20 km.p.h. and the second north-west at the rate of 16 km.p.h. Find the distance of nearest approach between them.

[Ans. $20/\sqrt{82}$ km.]

11. A ship A observes another ship B, 10 km. due west of A; B is steaming north at 12 km.p.h. After 24 minutes the ships are found to be nearest at a distance 6 km. apart. Find the velocity of A.

[Hint: Let $\bar{i}$ and $\bar{j}$ be the unit vectors respectively towards east and north and A, B the initial positions of the ships. Draw tangents BC and BD to the circle with centre A and radius 6. The relative motion of B can be either along BC or along BD. Now $BC = BD = 8$ and the relative speed of B is $8 \times 60/24$ km.p.h. = 20 km.p.h. Let angle $ABC = \theta$ = angle ABD.

(*i*) If along BC and if the velocity of A is $u_1\bar{i}+u_2\bar{j}$, then $12\bar{j}-(u_1\bar{i}+u_2\bar{j}) = 20(\cos\theta\bar{i}+\sin\theta\bar{j})$ gives $u_1 = 16$, $u_2 = 0$.

(*ii*) If along BD and if the velocity of A is $v_1\bar{i}+v_2\bar{j}$, then $12\bar{j}-(v_1\bar{i}+v_2\bar{j}) = 20(\cos\theta\bar{i}-\sin\theta\bar{j})$ gives $v_1 = -16$, $v_2 = 24$.]

12. At an instant, if the distance between two moving points A and B is a, if V is their relative speed and if u and v are the components of V along and perpendicular to AB, show that their distance when they are nearest to each other, is av/V and that the time that elapses, when they are nearest to each other, is au/V^2. **(M.U.)**

[Hint: Let $\bar{i}$ and $\bar{j}$ be the unit vectors along AB and perpendicular to AB. Let the relative path of A be AP and let it make angles θ and $90° - \theta$ with the $\bar{i}$ and $\bar{j}$ directions. Then

$$u\bar{i}+v\bar{j} = V(\cos\theta\bar{i}+\sin\theta\bar{j}) \text{ or } \cos\theta = u/V,\ \sin\theta = v/V.$$

So $BN = a\sin\theta = av/V$ and $T = AN/V = a\cos\theta = au/V^2$]

1.3 ACCELERATION

Definition. Acceleration. Acceleration of a particle is the time-rate of change of its velocity. That is, if $\bar{v}$ is its velocity at time t, then its acceleration $\bar{a}$ at time t is

$$\frac{d\bar{v}}{dt}.$$

Remark. As in the case of relative velocity, acceleration of a particle P relative to a moving point A is

$$\frac{d}{dt}(\bar{v}_P - \bar{v}_A) = \frac{d\bar{v}_P}{dt} - \frac{d\bar{v}_A}{dt} = \bar{a}_P - \bar{a}_A$$

where $\bar{a}_P$ and $\bar{a}_A$ are the accelerations of P and A.

Units of Acceleration

SYSTEM	UNIT
M.K.S.	1 metre/second^2 or 1 m./sec^2.
C.G.S.	1 cm./second^2 or 1 cm./sec^2.
F.P.S.	1 foot/second^2 or 1 ft./sec^2.

1.3.1 Rectilinear motion.

Rectilinear motion. When a particle moves along a straight line, the motion of the particle is said to be rectilinear.

Scalar method. Let the position vector of the particle at time t with respect to a fixed point O on the straight line be $\bar{r} = x\bar{i}$, where $\bar{i}$ is the unit vector along the straight line. Then $\bar{i}$ is a constant vector and so the velocity and the acceleration of the particle are

$$\bar{v} = \dot{\bar{r}} = \dot{x}\,\bar{i}\ ,\ \bar{a} = \ddot{\bar{r}} = \ddot{x}\,\bar{i}\,.$$

In this case the motion may be studied, considering the scalar velocity and scalar acceleration,

$$\dot{x},\ \ddot{x}.$$

An important result. The acceleration $\ddot{x}$ in the rectilinear motion can be expressed differently as

$$\ddot{x} = \frac{d\dot{x}}{dt} = \frac{d\dot{x}}{dx}\frac{dx}{dt} = \frac{dv}{dx}v \quad \text{or} \quad \ddot{x} = v\frac{dv}{dx}.$$

1.3.2 Rectilinear motion with a constant acceleration.

Bookwork 1.4. Let a particle move along a straight line with a constant acceleration a. Then to show that

$$v = u + at \qquad ...(1)$$

$$s = ut + \tfrac{1}{2}at^2 \qquad ...(2)$$

$$v^2 = u^2 + 2as, \qquad ...(3)$$

where u is the initial velocity of the particle and

(*a*) v is the velocity of the particle at time t.

(*b*) s is the distance of the particle at time t from a chosen fixed point on the line.

(*i*) Now the scalar acceleration is a. So

$$\frac{d^2s}{dt^2} = a.$$

Integrating this w.r.t t,

$$\frac{ds}{dt} = at + A \text{ or } v = at + A.$$

When $t = 0$, $v = u$. This gives that $A = u$. So

$$v = u + at. \qquad ...(1)$$

(*ii*) Rewriting (1) as

$$\frac{ds}{dt} = u + at$$

and integrating w.r.t. t,

$$s = ut + \tfrac{1}{2}at^2 + B.$$

But, when $t = 0$, $s = 0$. This gives that $B = 0$.

$$\therefore \qquad s = ut + \tfrac{1}{2}at^2. \qquad ...(2)$$

(*iii*) We know that acceleration can be written as $v\frac{dv}{ds}$. Therefore

$$v\frac{dv}{ds} = a \text{ or } v\,dv = a\,ds.$$

Thus, on integration,

$$\frac{v^2}{2} = as + C \text{ or } v^2 = 2\,as + C'.$$

But initially, that is, when $v = u$, $s = 0$. This gives

$$u^2 = 2\,a \times 0 + C' \text{ or } C' = u^2.$$

$$\therefore \qquad v^2 = u^2 + 2\,as. \qquad ...(3)$$

Graphical methods. The rectilinear motion of a particle can be graphically represented by curves like

(*i*) Time-speed curve

(*ii*) Time-distance curve

(*iii*) Acceleration-distance curve.

Now we shall consider only time-speed curve. Let the speed v be a function of time t, say $v = v(t)$. Choose Ox as the t-axis and Oy as the v-axis. We know that, for the curve $y = f(x)$,

(*i*) Slope $= \frac{dy}{dx}$

(*ii*) Area under the curve $= \int_a^b y\,dx.$

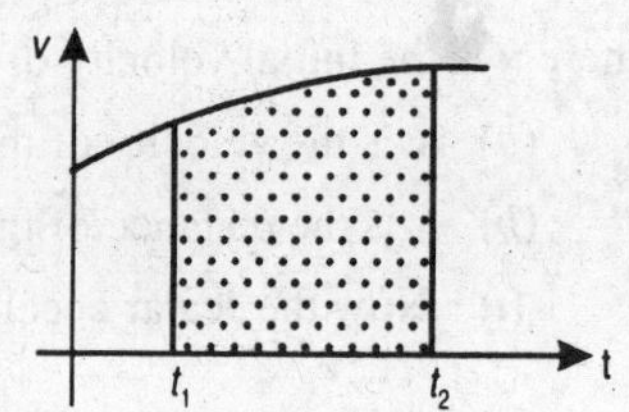

So also, for the time-speed curve, we have

$$\left.\begin{array}{l}\text{Slope of the curve}\\ \text{at any point P}\end{array}\right\} = \frac{dv}{dt} = \text{acceleration at P}$$

$$\left.\begin{array}{l}\text{Area under the curve}\\ \text{from } t = t_1 \text{ to } t = t_2\end{array}\right\} = \int_{t_1}^{t_2} v\,dt = \int_{t_1}^{t_2} \frac{ds}{dt}\,dt$$

$$= \int_{s_1}^{s_2} ds = s_2 - s_1$$

$$= \{\text{Distance described in the interval}$$

When the acceleration is a constant a, the slope of the curve is the same constant and so the curve is a straight line whose slope is a.

EXAMPLES

Example 1. If a point moves in a straight line with uniform acceleration and covers successive equal distances in times t_1, t_2, t_3, then show that

$$\frac{1}{t_1} - \frac{1}{t_2} + \frac{1}{t_3} = \frac{3}{t_1 + t_2 + t_3}. \qquad \textbf{(M.U.)}$$

Let s be the successive equal distances and v_1, v_2, v_3, the initial velocities for the successive distances and v_4, the final velocity in the third distance. Since the acceleration is a constant, the mean velocities in the three intervals and in the total interval are

$$\frac{1}{2}(v_1 + v_2),\ \frac{1}{2}(v_2 + v_3),\ \frac{1}{2}(v_3 + v_4),\ \frac{1}{2}(v_1 + v_4).$$

$$\therefore \quad \frac{s}{t_1} = \frac{1}{2}(v_1 + v_2), \qquad \text{...(1)}$$

$$\frac{s}{t_2} = \frac{1}{2}(v_2 + v_3), \qquad \text{...(2)}$$

$$\frac{s}{t_3} = \frac{1}{2}(v_3 + v_4), \qquad \text{...(3)}$$

$$\frac{3s}{t_1 + t_2 + t_3} = \frac{1}{2}(v_1 + v_4), \qquad \text{...(4)}$$

From (1) – (2) + (3) and from (4), we get the result as stated.

Example 2. A train moving at 30 m./sec. reduces its speed to 10 m./sec. in a distance of 240 m. At what distance will the train come to a stop? If the brake power is increased by 12 ½%, show that the train will stop in a total distance of 240 m. **(M.K.U.)**

In the first and the second cases let the retardations be

$$a \text{ m/sec}^2., \quad a' \text{ m/sec}^2.$$

Now, for the first phase of the first case, we have

$$u = 30, \quad v = 10, \quad s = 240.$$

So, by $v^2 = u^2 - 2as$, we get a from

$$100 = 900 - 2a \times 240 \text{ as } a = 5/3.$$

Let s_1 be the distance travelled by the train in the second phase. In that phase the initial velocity is 10 and the final velocity is 0 and therefore

$$0 = 10^2 - 2as_1 \text{ or } s_1 = \frac{100}{2a} = \frac{100\times 3}{2\times 5} = 30\,\text{m}.$$

In the second case, the retardation is

$$a' = a + a\times\frac{12\tfrac{1}{2}}{100} = \frac{9a}{8} = \frac{9}{8}\times\frac{5}{3} = \frac{15}{8}.$$

If s_2 is the distance in this case

$$0 = 30^2 - 2\left(\frac{15}{8}\right)s_2 \text{ or } s_2 = 240.$$

Example 3. The speed of a train increases at a constant rate α from 0 to v, and then remains constant for an interval and finally decreases to 0 at a constant rate β. If s is the total distance described, prove that the total time T occupied is

$$T = \frac{s}{v} + \frac{v}{2s}\left(\frac{1}{\alpha} + \frac{1}{\beta}\right).$$ **(M.U.,K.U.,Bn.U.)**

Let the durations of the three intervals be t_1, t_2, t_3 and the constant velocity be v. Let us consider the time-speed graph $OABC$. If AP, BQ are perpendicular to the t-axis, then

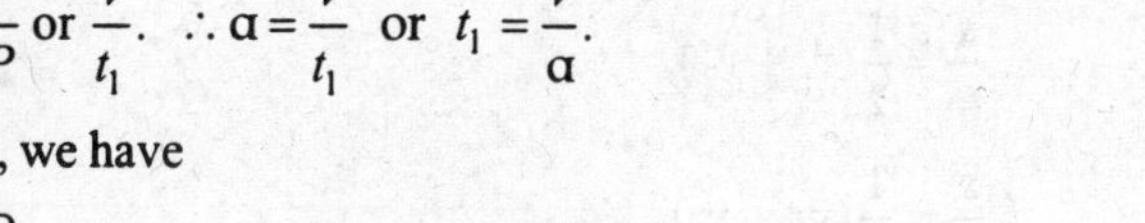

$$OP = t_1, PQ = t_2, QC = t_3.$$

Now the slope denotes the acceleration. But the slope of OA is

$$\frac{AP}{OP} \text{ or } \frac{v}{t_1}. \quad \therefore \alpha = \frac{v}{t_1} \text{ or } t_1 = \frac{v}{\alpha}.$$

On similar lines, for the third interval, we have

$$\frac{BQ}{CQ} \text{ or } \frac{v}{t_3}. \quad \therefore \beta = \frac{v}{t_3} \text{ or } t_3 = \frac{v}{\beta}.$$

$$\therefore \quad T = t_1 + t_2 + t_3 = \frac{v}{\alpha} + t_2 + \frac{v}{\beta}. \qquad ...(1)$$

Now the total area under the graph is equal to the total distance travelled by the train. So

$$s = \Delta\, OPA + \square\, APQB + \Delta\, QCB$$

$$= \frac{1}{2}t_1\, v + t_2 v + \frac{1}{2}t_3\, v = \frac{1}{2}\frac{v}{\alpha}.v + t_2 v + \frac{1}{2}\frac{v}{\beta}.v$$

$$= \frac{1}{2}\frac{v^2}{\alpha} + t_2\, v + \frac{1}{2}\frac{v^2}{\beta}.$$

$$\therefore \quad \frac{s}{v} = \frac{1}{2}\frac{v}{\alpha} + t_2 + \frac{1}{2}\frac{v}{\beta}. \qquad ...(2)$$

Now (1) − (2) gives

$$T - \frac{s}{v} = \frac{1}{2}\frac{v}{\alpha} + \frac{1}{2}\frac{v}{\beta} \text{ or } T = \frac{s}{v} + \frac{v}{2}\left(\frac{1}{\alpha} + \frac{1}{\beta}\right).$$

EXERCISES

1. A body has an initial velocity u and a constant acceleration α. Show that the distance it travelled in the tth second is $u+\frac{1}{2}\alpha(2t-1)$. If a, b, c are the distances described in the pth, q^{th}, r^{th} seconds, show that $a(q-r)+b(r-p)+c(p-q)=0$. **(K.U.)**

[**Hint:** Distance in the tth second $=(ut+\frac{1}{2}at^2)-[u(t-1)+\frac{1}{2}a(t-1)^2]$. Thus

$$a=u+\tfrac{1}{2}\alpha(2p-1),\ b=u+\tfrac{1}{2}\alpha(2q-1),\ c=u+\tfrac{1}{2}\alpha(2r-1).$$

Eliminating u and $\frac{1}{2}\alpha$,

$$\begin{vmatrix} a & 1 & 2p-1 \\ b & 1 & 2q-1 \\ c & 1 & 2r-1 \end{vmatrix}=0 \quad \text{or} \quad \begin{vmatrix} a & 1 & p \\ b & 1 & q \\ c & 1 & r \end{vmatrix}=0]$$

2. A point is moving with uniform acceleration, in the seventh and eleventh seconds from the commencement, it moves through 640 cms. and 920 cms. Find its initial velocity and the acceleration with which it moves. **(Bn.U.)**

[**Hint:** Distance moved in the tth second is $u+at-\frac{a}{2}$. So $u+a(7)-\frac{a}{2}=640$, $u+a(11)-\frac{a}{2}=920$. $\therefore\ u=185,\ a=70$]

3. A point moves with a uniform acceleration and v_1, v_2, v_3 denote its average velocities in three successive intervals of time t_1, t_2, t_3. Prove that $v_1-v_2 : v_2-v_3 = t_1+t_2 : t_2+t_3$. **(M.U., M.K.U., Bn.U)**

[**Hint:**	***Duration***	***Initial velocity***	***Final velocity***
Interval 1	t_1	u *(say)*	$u+\alpha t_1$
Interval 2	t_2	$u+\alpha t_1$	$u+\alpha(t_1+t_2)$
Interval 3	t_3	$u+\alpha(t_1+t_2)$	$u+\alpha(t_1+t_2+t_3)$

Acceleration is a constant. So the mean velocity in an interval is half the sum of the initial and final velocities of that interval. Hence

$$v_1=u+\tfrac{1}{2}\alpha t_1,\ v_2=u+\tfrac{1}{2}\alpha(2t_1+t_2),\ v_3=u+\tfrac{1}{2}\alpha(2t_1+2t_2+t_3).$$

$$\therefore\quad v_2-v_1=\tfrac{1}{2}\alpha(t_1+t_2),\ v_3-v_2=\tfrac{1}{2}\alpha(t_2+t_3).]$$

4. The two ends of a train moving with a constant acceleration pass a certain point with velocities u and v respectively. Show that the velocity with which the middle of the train passes the same point is $\sqrt{\frac{1}{2}(u^2+v^2)}$. **(M.U., M.K.U., Bn.U., C.U)**

[**Hint:** If s is the length of the train, a its acceleration and V the required velocity, $v^2=u^2+2as$, $V^2=u^2+2a\left(\frac{1}{2}s\right)$. Eliminate s]

5. A train moves in a straight line with a uniform acceleration and describes distances a and b in successive intervals of durations t_1 and t_2. Show that its acceleration is

$$\frac{2(bt_1-at_2)}{t_1 t_2 (t_1+t_2)}.$$ **(M.U., Bn.U)**

[**Hint:** $a=ut_1+\frac{1}{2}\alpha t_1^2$, $a+b=u(t_1+t_2)+\frac{1}{2}\alpha(t_1+t_2)^2$, where α is the acceleration. Find α, eliminating u]

6. A train moves in a straight line with a uniform acceleration and describes equal distances s in two successive intervals of durations t_1 and t_2. Show that its acceleration is

$$\frac{2s(t_1-t_2)}{t_1 t_2 (t_1+t_2)}.$$ **(Bn.U)**

7. A body travels a distance s in t seconds. It starts from rest and ends at rest. In the first part of the journey, it moves with a constant acceleration a, and in the second part with a constant retardation a'. Show that $aa' t^2 = 2s(a + a')$. **(M.U., C.U., M.K.U.)**

[Hint: Let the max.vel. be v and the times for the two parts be t_1, t_2. By $v = u + at$,

$$v = at_1, \quad v = a't_2 \quad \therefore\ v\left(\frac{1}{a}+\frac{1}{a'}\right) = t. \qquad ...(1)$$

If s_1, s_2 are the respective distances, by $v^2 = u^2 + 2as$,

$$v^2 = 2as_1, \quad v^2 = 2a's_2 \quad \therefore\ v^2\left(\frac{1}{a}+\frac{1}{a'}\right) = 2s. \qquad ...(2)$$

Eliminate v from (1), (2)]

8. A lift ascends with a constant acceleration a, then with a constant velocity and finally stops with a constant retardation a. If the total distance travelled is s, and the total time occupied is T, show that the time for which the lift was ascending with constant velocity is $\sqrt{T^2 - 4s/a}$. **(M.U., A.U.)**

[Hint: With the notations of the Example sum,

$$s = \frac{v^2}{2\alpha}+vt_2+\frac{v^2}{2\beta}, T = \frac{v}{\alpha}+t_2+\frac{v}{\beta}.$$

So $s = \dfrac{v^2}{a}+vt_2,\ T = \dfrac{2v}{a}+t_2$ since $\alpha = \beta = a$. Eliminating t_2, $v^2 - aTv + as = 0$

or $v = a\,\dfrac{T \pm \sqrt{T^2 - 4s/a}}{2}$. Find t_2]

9. For $1/m$ of the distance between two stations a train is uniformly accelerated and for $1/n$ of the distance it is uniformly retarded. It starts from rest at one station and comes to rest at the other. Prove that its greatest velocity is $1 + 1/m + 1/n$ times its average velocity.

[Hint: Average velocity $= \dfrac{\text{Total distance}}{\text{Total time}} = \dfrac{s}{T}$. To show that

$$v = \left(1+\frac{1}{m}+\frac{1}{n}\right)\frac{s}{T};$$

Consider the 3 areas under the time-speed graph,

$$\frac{1}{2}t_1 v = \frac{s}{m}, \quad t_2 v = s - \frac{s}{m} - \frac{s}{n}, \quad \frac{1}{2}t_3 v = \frac{s}{n}.$$

Multiply the first and the second results by 2 and then add all]

10. A car A can acquire in 1 minute, by a uniform acceleration, a speed of 90 m./sec. When it is halting at a place in a straight narrow road, it sees a car B approaching it from behind with a uniform speed of 60 m./sec. Show that it will just be possible to avoid collision if the car A starts in full force before the car B has approached it within 1200 m. **(C.U.)**

[**Hint:** If a is the acceleration of A, by $v = u + at$,

$$90 = a \times 60 \quad \text{or} \quad a = 3/2.$$

If, at t sec., vel. of A = vel. of B, then

$$(3/2)\, t = 60 \quad \text{or} \quad t = 40.$$

Distances travelled in t by A, B are 1200 m., 2400 m.]

11. A car A can acquire in 1 minute, by a uniform acceleration, a speed of 30 ml.p.h. When it is halting at a place in a straight narrow road, it sees a car B approaching it from behind with a uniform speed of 20 ml.p.h. Show that it will be just possible to avoid collision if A starts in full force before B approaches it within one-nineth of a mile.

12. Two particles start simultaneously from the same point and move along two straight lines, one with a uniform velocity u and the other with a constant acceleration a starting from rest. Show that their relative velocity is least at time $u/a \cos\alpha$ and the least velocity is $u \sin \alpha$, where α is the angle between the straight lines. **(M.U.,M.K.U.,Bn.U.,C.U.)**

[**Hint:** If V is the relative speed at time t, then

$$V^2 = u^2 + (0+at)^2 + 2(u)(at)\cos(180^\circ - \alpha) = u^2 + a^2t^2 - 2uat\cos\alpha$$

Now V^2 is minimum, when $\frac{dV}{dt} = 0$ or when $t = (u \cos\alpha)/a$]

13. Two cars start off to race with velocities u_1, u_2 and travel along straight parallel tracks with constant accelerations f_1, f_2. If the race ends in a dead heat, prove that the length of the track is

$$\frac{2(u_1 - u_2)(u_1 f_2 - u_2 f_1)}{(f_1 - f_2)^2}. \qquad \textbf{(M.U.)}$$

[**Hint:** Now no one is the winner. Let the equal time of travel be t. Then, by $s = ut + \frac{1}{2}at^2$,

$u_1 t + \frac{1}{2} f_1 t^2 = u_2 t + \frac{1}{2} f_2 t^2$ or $t = -\frac{2(u_1 - u_2)}{f_1 - f_2}$ Substitute this in $u_1 t_1 + \frac{1}{2} f_1 t^2$ or $t(u_1 + \frac{1}{2} f_1 t)$]

1.4 COPLANAR MOTION

When a particle moves in a plane, its motion is said to be coplanar.

1.4.1 Velocity and acceleration in a coplanar motion.

In this section we obtain the components of velocity and acceleration of a particle P moving in a plane, along three different pairs of perpendicular directions, namely,

(*i*) two fixed perpendicular directions,

(*ii*) the directions tangential and normal to the path of the particle

(*iii*) the radial and transverse directions.

Bookwork 1.5. To find the components in two fixed perpendicular directions.

Let Ox and Oy be two fixed perpendicular directed lines in the plane of motion. Let $\bar{i}$ and $\bar{j}$ be the unit vectors in these directions. If $P(x, y)$ is the position of the particle, then the position vector of P with respect to O is

$$\bar{r} = \overline{OP} = x\bar{i} + y\bar{j}.$$

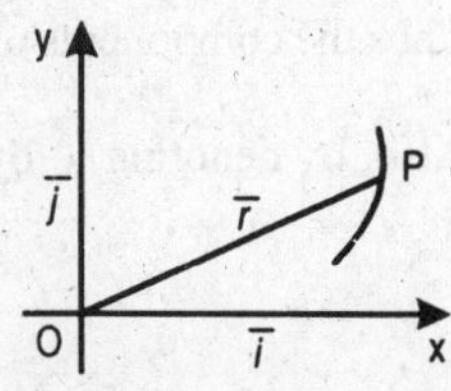

Now we get the velocity and acceleration of the particle to be

$$\bar{v} = \dot{x}\bar{i} + \dot{y}\bar{j} \text{ and } \bar{a} = \ddot{x}\bar{i} + \ddot{y}\bar{j}$$

by differentiating $\bar{r}$ respectively once and twice respect to t. So in the $\bar{i}$ and $\bar{j}$ directions the components of the velocity are

$$\dot{x}, \dot{y}$$

and the components of the acceleration are

$$\ddot{x}, \ddot{y}.$$

Book work 1.6. To find the components of the acceleration of a particle in the tangential and normal directions.

Let PQ be the direction tangential to the path of the particle in the sense in which the arcual distance s of the particle measured from a fixed point A increases. Let PR be the inward-drawn normal. If $\hat{T}$ and $\hat{N}$ are the unit vectors in these directions, then we know that the velocity of the particle is

$$\bar{v} = \dot{s}\,\hat{T}. \qquad ...(1)$$

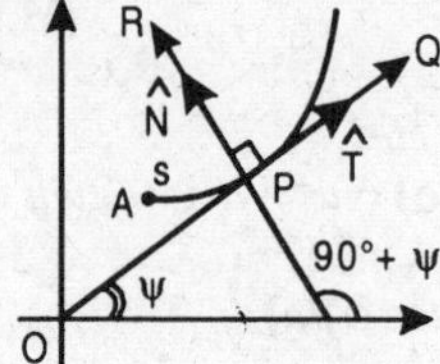

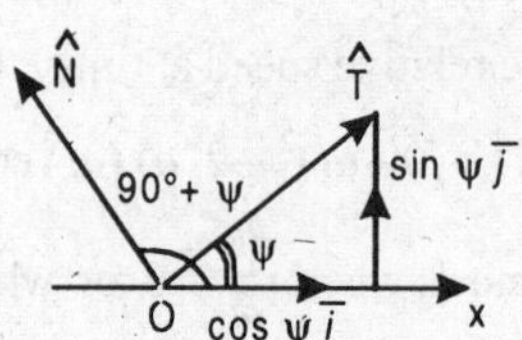

Here the unit vector $\hat{T}$ is not a constant vector since it varies in direction with time t. So the acceleration of the particle is

$$\bar{a} = \frac{d\bar{v}}{dt} = \frac{d}{dt}(\dot{s}\,\hat{T}) = \ddot{s}\,\hat{T} + \dot{s}\frac{d\hat{T}}{dt}.$$

To find the derivative of $\hat{T}$, choose two perpendicular lines as the x and y axes and let $\bar{i}$ and $\bar{j}$ be the unit vectors in the x and y directions. Suppose $\hat{T}$ makes an angle ψ with the x axis. Then

$$\hat{T} = \cos\psi\,\bar{i} + \sin\psi\,\bar{j}.$$

But $\hat{N}$ makes an angle $90^\circ + \psi$ with Ox. Hence

$$\hat{N} = \cos(90^\circ + \psi)\,\bar{i} + \sin(90^\circ + \psi)\,\bar{j} = -\sin\psi\,\bar{i} + \cos\psi\,\bar{j}.$$

$$\therefore \quad \frac{d\hat{T}}{dt} = -\sin\psi\frac{d\psi}{dt}\bar{i} + \cos\psi\frac{d\psi}{dt}\bar{j} = \frac{d\psi}{dt}\hat{N}.$$

$$= \frac{d\psi}{ds}\frac{ds}{dt}\hat{N} = \frac{\dot{s}}{\rho}\hat{N},$$

where ρ is the radius of curvature of the path at P. Hence

$$\bar{a} = \ddot{s}\,\hat{T} + \dot{s}\left(\frac{\dot{s}\hat{N}}{\rho}\right) = \ddot{s}\hat{T} + \frac{\dot{s}^2}{\rho}\hat{N}. \qquad ...(2)$$

Thus the components of acceleration of the particle in tangential and normal directions are $\ddot{s}$ and $\frac{\dot{s}^2}{\rho}$.

Also, by denoting $\dot{s}$ by v, we have

$$\bar{a} = \frac{dv}{dt}\hat{T} + \frac{v^2}{\rho}\hat{N}. \qquad ...(3)$$

Corollary. If the path of the particle is a circle of radius a and centre O and if the angle $AOP = \theta$, then $s = a\theta$. In this case, from (1) and (2),

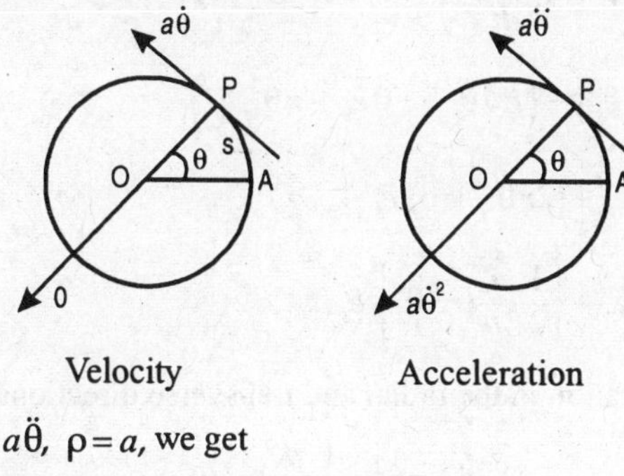

Velocity Acceleration

and since $\dot{s} = a\dot{\theta},\ \ddot{s} = a\ddot{\theta},\ \rho = a$, we get

$$\overline{v} = \dot{s}\,\hat{T} = a\dot{\theta}\,\hat{T},$$

$$\overline{a} = a\ddot{\theta}\,\hat{T} + \frac{(a\dot{\theta})^2}{a}\,\hat{N} = a\ddot{\theta}\,\hat{T} + a\dot{\theta}^2\,\hat{N}.$$

Bookwork 1.7. To find the components of velocity and acceleration of a particle in the radial and transverse directions.

Now we obtain the components in terms of polar coordinates. Let (Oxy) be a fixed rectangular frame and $\overline{i}$ and $\overline{j}$ be unit vectors in the x and y directions. Choose O as the pole and Ox as the initial line and let P be (r, θ). Then the direction of OP in the sense in which r increases is called the *radial direction* and the direction perpendicular to OP in the sense in which θ increases is called the *transverse direction*. Let $\hat{e}_r$ and $\hat{e}_s$ be the unit vectors in these two directions.

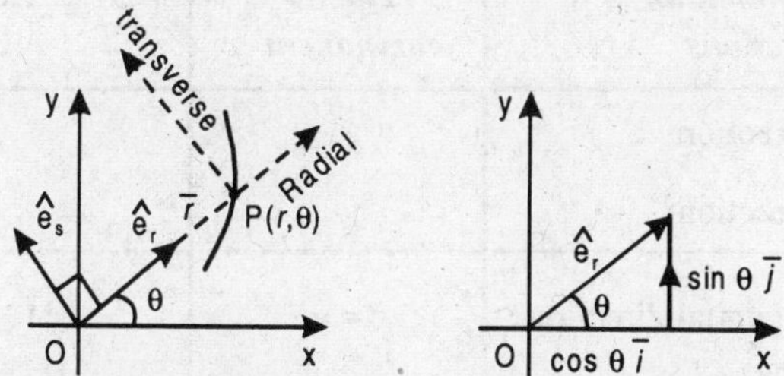

Then the position vector of P with respect to O is $\overline{r} = r\,\hat{e}_r$. So the velocity of P at time t is

$$\overline{v} = \frac{d\overline{r}}{dt} = \frac{d}{dt}(r\,\hat{e}_r) = \dot{r}\,\hat{e}_r + r\frac{d\hat{e}_r}{dt}.$$

But $\hat{e}_r = \cos\theta\,\overline{i} + \sin\theta\,\overline{j}$.

$$\hat{e}_s = \cos(\pi/2 + \theta)\,\overline{i} + \sin(\pi/2 + \theta)\,\overline{j} = -\sin\theta\,\overline{i} + \cos\theta\,\overline{j}$$

$$\therefore\quad \frac{d\hat{e}_r}{dt} = -\sin\theta\dot{\theta}\,\overline{i} + \cos\theta\dot{\theta}\,\overline{j} = \dot{\theta}\hat{e}_s$$

$$\frac{d\hat{e}_s}{dt} = -\cos\theta\dot{\theta}\,\overline{i} - \sin\theta\dot{\theta}\,\overline{j} = -\dot{\theta}\hat{e}_r$$

$$\therefore\quad \overline{v} = \dot{r}\,\hat{e}_r + r(\dot{\theta}\,\hat{e}_s) = \dot{r}\,\hat{e}_r + r\dot{\theta}\,\hat{e}_s. \ldots(1)$$

So the components of the velocity in the radial and transverse directions are $\dot{r}$ and $r\dot{\theta}$.

Further the acceleration of the particle is

$$\bar{a} = \frac{d\bar{v}}{dt} = \left(\ddot{r}\,\hat{e}_r + \dot{r}\frac{d\,\hat{e}_r}{dt}\right) + \left(\dot{r}\dot{\theta}\hat{e}_s + r\ddot{\theta}\hat{e}_s + r\dot{\theta}\,\frac{d\,\hat{e}_s}{dt}\right)$$

$$= \left(\ddot{r}\,\hat{e}_r + \dot{r}\dot{\theta}\,\hat{e}_s\right) + \left(\dot{r}\dot{\theta}\hat{e}_s + r\ddot{\theta}\hat{e}_s - r\dot{\theta}^2\,\hat{e}_r\right)$$

$$= (\ddot{r} - r\dot{\theta}^2)\,\hat{e}_r + (2\dot{r}\dot{\theta} + r\ddot{\theta})\,\hat{e}_s$$

$$= (\ddot{r} - r\dot{\theta}^2)\,\hat{e}_r + \left\{\frac{1}{r}\frac{d}{dt}(r^2\,\dot{\theta})\right\}\hat{e}_s. \qquad ...(2)$$

So the components of acceleration in the radial and transverse directions are

$$\ddot{r} - r\dot{\theta}^2,\ \frac{1}{r}\frac{d}{dt}(r^2\,\dot{\theta}).$$

Corollary. If the path of the particle is a circle whose centre is O and radius is a, then (1) and (2) become

$$\bar{v} = (0)\,\hat{e}_r + a\dot{\theta}\,\hat{e}_s,$$

$$\bar{a} = (-a\dot{\theta}^2)\,\hat{e}_r + (a\ddot{\theta})\,\hat{e}_s$$

because $r = a$, $\dot{r} = 0$ and $\ddot{r} = 0$. It may be noted that these results are the same as the results obtained in the previous bookwork.

Components of Velocity and Acceleration

Perpendicular directions	*Velocity component*	*Acceleration component*
x direction	$\dot{x}$	$\ddot{x}$
y direction	$\dot{y}$	$\ddot{y}$
Tangential direction	$\dot{s} = v$	$\ddot{s} = \frac{dv}{dt} = v\frac{dv}{ds}$
Normal direction	0	$\frac{\dot{s}^2}{\rho} = \frac{v^2}{\rho}$
Radial direction	$\dot{r}$	$\ddot{r} - r\dot{\theta}^2$
Transverse direction	$r\dot{\theta}$	$2\dot{r}\dot{\theta} + r\ddot{\theta} = \frac{1}{r}\frac{d}{dt}(r^2\dot{\theta})$
In circular motion, tangential direction	$a\dot{\theta}\ (= v)$	$a\ddot{\theta} = \frac{dv}{dt}$
In circular motion inward drawn normal direction	0	$a\dot{\theta}^2 = \frac{v^2}{a}$

1.4.2 Angular velocity.

In the general motion of a particle moving in space its *angular velocity* about a point can be defined to be a vector quantity. This general motion is beyond the scope of this book and in this book we confine ourselves to the study of the motion of a particle in a plane.

Definition. Let P be a particle having a coplanar motion. Let O be a fixed point and OA be a fixed line in the plane of motion. Then the time-rate of change of the angle AOP is called the *angular velocity* of the particle about O. That is, if the angle $AOP = \theta$, then

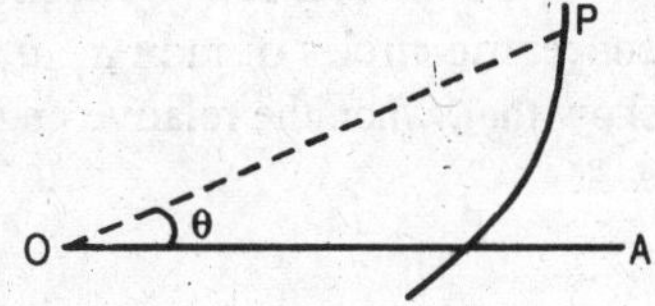

$$\frac{d\theta}{dt} = \dot{\theta}$$

is the angular velocity of the particle about O. The unit of angular velocity is one radian per second.

In the circular motion of a particle we obtained that the linear velocity v and angular velocity $\dot{\theta}$ about the centre are related as

$$v = a\dot{\theta} \text{ or } \dot{\theta} = v/a.$$

In general, we see that $\dot{\theta}$ can be obtained from the transverse component $r\dot{\theta}$ of the velocity by dividing it by r. Thus we obtain the result that the angular velocity of a particle P about a point O, is

$$\frac{\text{the component of velocity of P perpendicular to OP}}{\text{OP}}. \qquad ...(1)$$

Also, if v is the velocity of P and if ϕ is the angle between OP and the tangent at P, then the velocity component in the transverse direcion is $v \sin \phi$. But we know that the transverse component of the velocity is $r\dot{\theta}$. So

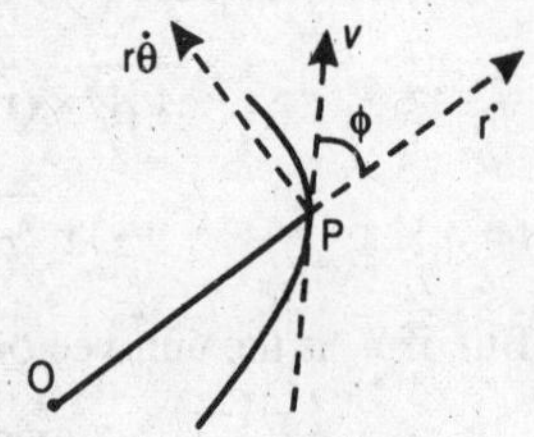

$$r\dot{\theta} = v \sin\phi$$

$$\therefore \qquad \dot{\theta} = \frac{v \sin\phi}{r} = \frac{rv \sin\phi}{r^2} = \frac{|\bar{r} \times \bar{v}|}{r^2}, \qquad ...(2)$$

since $\bar{v} = v\hat{T}$.

1.4.3 Relative angular velocity.

Let A_1 and A_2 be two particles moving in a plane. If their velocities are v_1 and v_2 making angles α_1 and α_2 with A_1A_2, as shown in the figure, then the component, in the direction perpendicular to $A_1 A_2$, of the velocityof A_2 relative to A_1 is $v_2 \sin \alpha_2 - v_1 \sin \alpha_1$ because the velocity components of A_1 and A_2 in this direction are $v_1 \sin \alpha_1$ and $v_2 \sin \alpha_2$. So, from (1) of the previous section, the angular velocity of A_2 relative to A_1 is

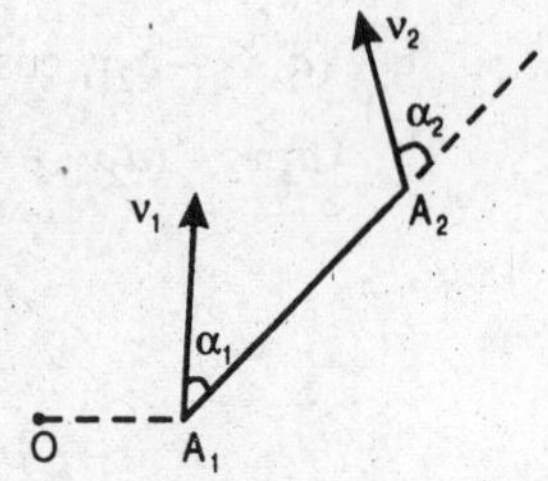

$$\frac{v_2 \sin\alpha_2 - v_1 \sin\alpha_1}{A_1A_2}. \qquad ...(1)$$

Also $\overline{A_1A_2}$ is the position vector of A_2 with reference to A_1. So, if $\bar{v}_1$ and $\bar{v}_2$ are the velocity vectors of A_1 and A_2, then the velocity of A_2 relative to A_1 is $\bar{v}_2 - \bar{v}_1$ and consequently the angular speed of A_2 about A_1 is obtained from (2) of the previous section as

$$\dot{\theta} = \frac{|\overline{A_1A_2} \times (\bar{v}_2 - \bar{v}_1)|}{A_1A_2^{\,2}} = \frac{|\overline{A_1A_2} \times (\bar{v}_1 - \bar{v}_2)|}{A_1A_2^{\,2}}. \qquad ...(2)$$

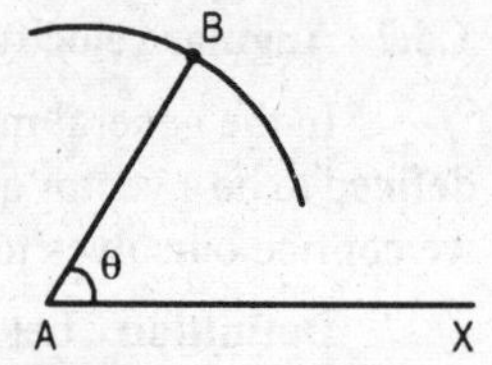

A Particular Case. When AB is a constant, the motion of B relative to A is along the circle whose centre is A and radius is AB. If AB makes an angle θ with a constant direction AX, then $\dot{\theta}$ is the angular velocity of B relative to A.

Bookwork 1.8. (Concentric circles). Two particles A_1, A_2 describe concentric circles of radii a_1, a_2 and centre O with speed v_1, v_2. We shall show that, when the relative angular velocity of one particle about the other vanishes,

$$\cos A_1OA_2 = \frac{a_1 v_1 + a_2 v_2}{a_2 v_1 + a_1 v_2}. \qquad \textbf{(M.U.,S.V.U)}$$

Suppose

$$\overline{OA_1} = a_1 \overline{r_1}, \ \overline{OA_2} = a_2 \overline{r_2},$$

where $\overline{r_1}$ and $\overline{r_2}$ are unit vectors. Let $\overline{s_1}$ and $\overline{s_2}$ be the unit vectors respectively perpendicular to $\overline{r_1}$ and $\overline{r_2}$ as shown in the figure. Then the velocities of A_1 and A_2 are

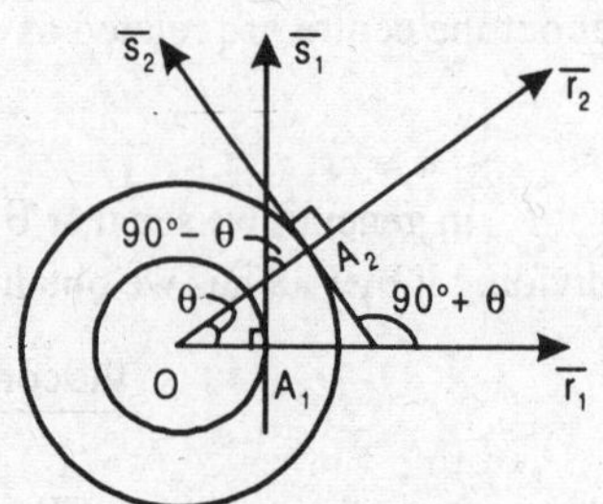

$$\overline{v_1} = v_1 \overline{s_1}, \quad \overline{v_2} = v_2 \overline{s_2}.$$

We know, from (2) of section 1.4.3, that the angular velocity of A_2 about A_1 is

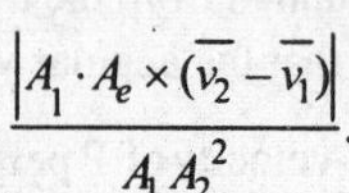

$$\frac{\left|\overline{A_1 \cdot A_e} \times (\overline{v_2} - \overline{v_1})\right|}{A_1 A_2^{\,2}}.$$

When this vanishes , we have

$$\overline{A_1A_2} \times (\overline{v_2} - \overline{v_1}) = \overline{0} \ \text{ or } \ (a_2 \overline{r_2} - a_1 \overline{r_1}) \times (v_2 \overline{s_2} - v_1 \overline{s_1}) = \overline{0}$$

i.e.,

$$a_2 v_2 \ \overline{r_2} \times \overline{s_2} - a_2 v_1 \ \overline{r_2} \times \overline{s_1} - a_1 v_2 \ \overline{r_1} \times \overline{s_2} + a_1 v_1 \ \overline{r_1} \times \overline{s_1} = \overline{0}.$$

But, if $\overline{k}$ is the unit vector, perpendicular to the plane of motion, so that $\overline{r_1} \times \overline{s_1} = \overline{k}$, $\overline{r_2} \times \overline{s_2} = \overline{k}$, then

$$\overline{r_1} \times \overline{s_2} = \sin(90^\circ + \theta)\,\overline{k} = \cos\theta\,\overline{k},$$

$$\overline{r_2} \times \overline{s_1} = \sin(90^\circ - \theta)\,\overline{k} = \cos\theta\,\overline{k}.$$

$$\therefore \quad (a_2 v_2 - a_2 v_1 \cos\theta - a_1 v_2 \cos\theta + a_1 v_1)\,\overline{k} = \overline{0}.$$

$$\therefore \quad a_2 v_2 - (a_2 v_1 + a_1 v_2)\cos\theta + a_1 v_1 = 0.$$

$$\therefore \quad \cos\theta = \frac{a_1 v_1 + a_2 v_2}{a_2 v_1 + a_1 v_2}.$$

EXAMPLES

Example 1. A vertical circular disc of radius a rolls on a ground without slipping along a straight line with a linear velocity u. Find the velocity of any point on its rim. **(M.U.)**

Let A_0 be the initial point of contact of the given line with the disc. Suppose that, after a time t, A is the point of contact and C is the position of the centre. It is given that the linear velocity of the disc is u. So, if $A_0A = s$, then

$$\dot{s} = u.$$

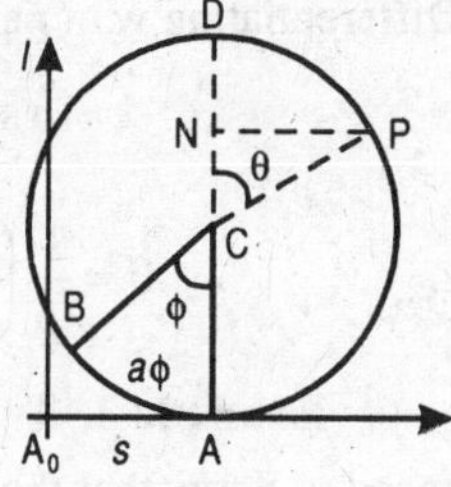

Also, if at time t, B is the position of the point of the disc which was in coincidence with A_0 initially and if angle $ACB = \phi$, then

$$A_0A = \overset{\frown}{BA} \text{ or } s = a\phi.$$

$$\therefore \quad \frac{ds}{dt} = a\frac{d\phi}{dt} \quad \text{or} \quad \frac{d\phi}{dt} = \frac{\dot{s}}{a} = \frac{u}{a}.$$

That is, the angular velocity of B about C is the constant u/a. So the angular velocity of any other point on the rim about C also is u/a. Hence, choosing an arbitrary point P on the rim, we get

$$\dot{\theta} = \frac{u}{a}, \qquad \text{...(3)}$$

where θ is the angle made by CP with the vertical diameter AD as shown in the figure.

Let $\bar{i}$ be the unit vector in the direction of A_0A and $\bar{j}$, the unit vector in the vertically upward direction. Let PN be the perpendicular drawn from P to AD. Then the position vector $\bar{r}$ of the point P with respect to the fixed point A_0, is

$$\bar{r} = \overline{A_0A} + \overline{AN} + \overline{NP} = s\bar{i} + (a + a\cos\theta)\,\bar{j} + a\sin\theta\,\bar{i}$$
$$= (s + a\sin\theta)\,\bar{i} + (a + a\cos\theta)\,\bar{j}$$

Hence the velocity $\bar{v}$ of P is

$$\bar{v} = \dot{\bar{r}} = (\dot{s} + a\cos\theta\,\dot{\theta})\,\bar{i} + (-\,a\sin\theta\,\dot{\theta})\,\bar{j}$$
$$= [u + a\cos\theta\,(u/a)]\bar{i} - [a\sin\theta\,(u/a)]\bar{j}$$
$$= u(1+\cos\theta)\,\bar{i} - u\sin\theta\,\bar{j}.$$

Its magnitude is

$$|\bar{v}| = u\sqrt{(1+\cos\theta)^2 + \sin^2\theta}$$
$$= u\sqrt{2+2\cos\theta} = u\sqrt{4\cos^2\theta/2} = 2u\cos\theta/2.$$

Its direction is perpendicular to AP because

$$\overline{AP}\cdot\bar{V} = (\overline{AN} + \overline{NP})\cdot\bar{V}$$
$$= [a(1+\cos\theta)\,\bar{j} + a\sin\theta\,\bar{i}]\cdot[u(1+\cos\theta)\bar{i} - u\sin\theta\,\bar{j}] = 0.$$

Remark. Velocity of A, the bottommost point of the disc, is zero because its value is $u(1+\cos\pi)\,\bar{i} - u\sin\pi\,\bar{j} = \bar{0}$. So, this point of the disc is instantaneously at rest. As such, this point is the *instantaneous centre of rotation* and, at that instant, the entire disc rotates about this point. The corresponding angular velocity is obtained from the angular velocity of P about A, by using "$v = a\dot{\theta}$" as

$$\frac{|v|}{AP} = \frac{|u(1+\cos\theta)\,\bar{i} - u\sin\theta\,\bar{j}|}{|(a + a\cos\theta)\,\bar{j} + a\sin\theta\,\bar{i}|} = \frac{u}{a}.$$

Example 2. Show that the angular velocity about a fixed point A of a particle P moving uniformly in a straight line, varies inversely as the square of the distance of the line from the fixed point. **(M.U.)**

Let AN be perpendicular to the line and $AN = p$. Then AN is a fixed line and let

$$\angle NAP = \theta.$$

Now $\dot{\theta}$ is the angular velocity of P about A. Let $PN = x$. Then

$$x = p\tan\theta$$

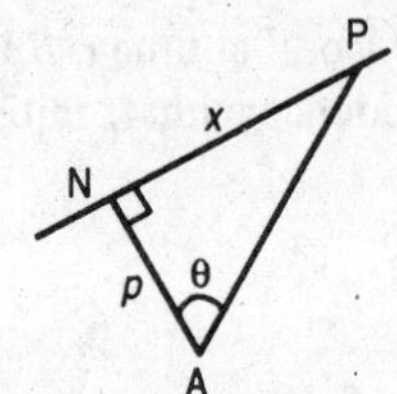

Differentiating w.r.t t and using $\dot{x} = k$, a constant,

$$\dot{x} = p\sec^2\theta\,\dot{\theta} \quad \text{or} \quad \dot{\theta} = {}^k\!/_p \cos^2\theta$$

i.e.,
$$\dot{\theta} = \frac{k}{p}\left(\frac{AN}{AP}\right)^2 = kp\frac{1}{AP^2}.$$

Example 3. Two particles A, B describe a circle of radius a in the same sense and with same speed u. Show that the relative angular velocity of each with respect to the other is ${}^u\!/_a$. **(M.U.)**

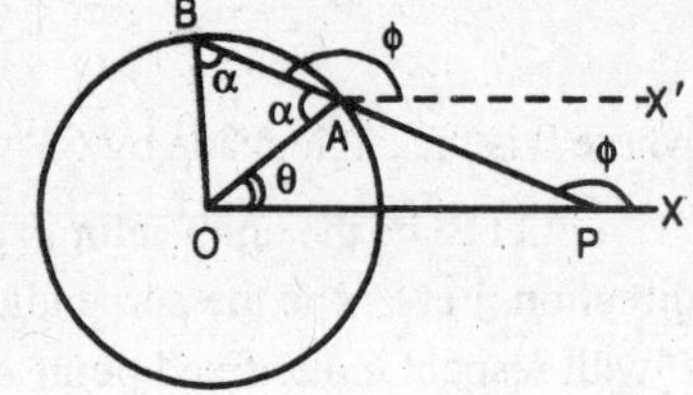

Let O be the centre of the circle and OX, a fixed line. Let BA intersect OX at P. Since A and B have same speed, AB is a constant and ΔOAB is an unchanging isosceles triangle but revolving about O. Let the base angles be α, α. Let $\underline{|XOA} = \theta$. Then $\dot{\theta}$ is the angular velocity of A about O. So from "$v = a\,\dot{\theta}$",

$$a\dot{\theta} = u \quad \text{or} \quad \dot{\theta} = {}^u\!/_a.$$

Let $\underline{|XPB} = \phi$. Then, from ΔPOA.

$$\phi = \theta + \underline{|OAP} = \theta + 180^\circ - \alpha$$

Let AX' be the fixed direction parallel to OX. Then the angle made by AB with this fixed direction is ϕ and the angular velocity of B about A is

$$\frac{d\phi}{dt} = \frac{d}{dt}(\theta + 180^\circ - \alpha) = \frac{d\theta}{dt} = \frac{u}{a}.$$

Example 4. The line joining two points A, B is of constant length a and the velocities of A, B are in directions which make angles α and β respectively with AB. Prove that the angular velocity of AB about A is $\dfrac{u\sin(\beta-\alpha)}{a\cos\beta}$, where u is the velocity of A. **(M.U.)**

Let v be the velocity of B. Then its components along AB and perpendicular to A are

$$v\cos\beta, \quad v\sin\beta.$$

For the velocity of A, the components are

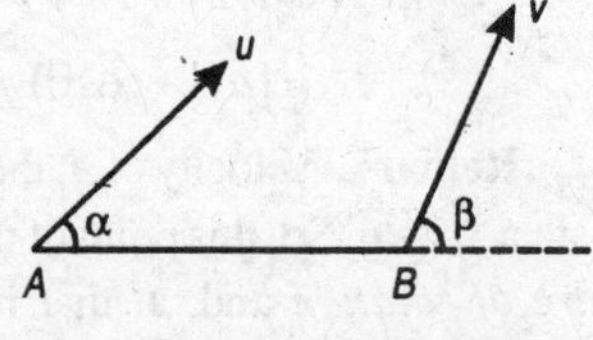

$$u\cos\alpha, \quad u\sin\alpha.$$

Thus the components of the velocity of B relative to A are

$$v\cos\beta - u\cos\alpha,$$
$$v\sin\beta - u\sin\alpha.$$

Since AB is of constant length, the component of the velocity of B relative to A along AB is zero. So

$$v\cos\beta - u\cos\alpha = 0 \text{ or } v = \frac{u\cos\alpha}{\cos\beta}. \qquad ...(1)$$

If the angular velocity of AB about A is ω, then

$$\omega = \frac{\text{Component of relative velocity of B perpendicular to AB}}{\text{Length of AB}}$$

$$= \frac{v\sin\beta - u\sin\alpha}{a} = \frac{\dfrac{u\cos\alpha}{\cos\beta}.\sin\beta - u\sin\alpha}{a} \text{ by (1)}$$

$$= \frac{u \sin(\beta - \alpha)}{a \cos \beta}.$$

Example 5. Two points are describing concentric circles of radii $3a$ and $5a$ in the same sense with angular velocities ω and ω'. Show that the angular velocity of the line joining them when its length is $4a$ is equal to ω'. **(M.U.)**

With the notations of the Bookwork 1.8 (Concentric circles),

$$a_1 = 3a,\ a_2 = 5a,\ v_1 = 3a\,\omega,\ v_2 = 5a\,\omega'$$

Now $OA_1 = 3a$, $OA_2 = 5a$, and when $A_1A_2 = 4a$, ΔA_1OA_2 is a triangle right angled at A_1 so that $\cos\theta = 3/5$. If the angular velocity of A_1A_2 is λ, then

$$\lambda = \frac{a_1v_1 + a_2v_2 - (a_1v_2 + a_2v_1)\cos\theta}{A_1A_2^{\,2}}$$

$$= \frac{3a(3a\omega) + 5a(5a\omega') - [3a(5a\omega') + 5a(3a\omega)]\,3/5}{(4a)^2}$$

$$= \frac{16a^2\omega'}{16a^2} = \omega'.$$

EXERCISES

1. If the angular velocity of a point moving on a plane curve is constant about a fixed origin, show that its transverse acceleration is proportional to its radial velocity.

[Hint: $\dot{\theta} = c$; Transverse acceleration $= 2\dot{r}\dot{\theta} + r\ddot{\theta} = 2c\dot{r} + 0$**]**

2. A particle moves so that the radial and transverse components of its velocity are ar and $b\theta$. Show that the radial and transverse components of its acceleration are

$$a^2r - \frac{b^2\theta^2}{r},\quad ab\theta + \frac{b^2\theta}{r}.$$

[Hint: Now $\dot{r} = ar$ and $r\dot{\theta} = b\theta$. Differentiate them w.r.t. t and obtain $\ddot{r} - r\dot{\theta}^2$ and $2\dot{r}\dot{\theta} + r\ddot{\theta}$ in terms of r and θ**]**

3. A point moves along a circle. Show that at any instant its angular velocity about the centre is twice its angular velocity about any point on the circumference. **(A.U.,M.U.)**

[Hint: Let O Be the centre and AOB be a fixed diameter. If P is the moving point and $\angle AOP = \theta$, $\angle ABP = \phi$, then $\theta = 2\phi$. $\therefore\ \frac{d\theta}{dt} = 2\frac{d\phi}{dt}$**]**

4. If a point moves so that its angular velocities about two fixed points are the same, prove that it describes a circle. **(M.U.,AmU.)**

[Hint: Let A, B be the fixed points, and P, the moving point. Produce AB to C. If angle $CBP = \theta$, angle $CAP = \phi$, then

$$\frac{d\theta}{dt} = \frac{d\phi}{dt} \quad \text{or} \quad \frac{d}{dt}(\theta - \phi) = 0.$$

So $\theta - \phi = k$, a constant. Thus $\angle APB = k$ and AB subtends the angle k at P. Hence the locus of P is a circle**]**

5. Points A_1 and A_2 describe concentric circles of radii a_1 and a_2 with speeds varying inversely as the radii. Show that their relative velocity is parallel to the line $A_1 A_2$ when the angle between the radii through A_1 and A_2 is

$$\cos^{-1} \frac{2a_1a_2}{a_1^2 + a_2^2}. \qquad \text{(M.U.)}$$

[Hint: See Bookwork 1.8. Set $v_1 = \frac{k}{a_1},\ v_2 = \frac{k}{a_2}$]

6. Two planets describe nearly circles of radii a_1 and a_2 round the sum as centre with speeds varying inversely as the square roots of the radii. Show that their relative angular velocity vanishes when the angle between the radii to these planets is

$$\cos^{-1}\left[\frac{\sqrt{a_1a_2}}{a_1 - \sqrt{a_1\, a_2} + a_2}\right] \qquad \text{(M.U.)}$$

[Hint: See Bookwork 1.8. Set $v_1 = \frac{k}{\sqrt{a_1}},\ v_2 = \frac{k}{\sqrt{a_2}}$ and use

$(\sqrt{a_1})^3 + (\sqrt{a_2})^3 = (\sqrt{a_1} + \sqrt{a_2})\ (a_1 - \sqrt{a_1}\sqrt{a_2} + a_2)$]

7. Two points A and B move with speeds v and $2v$ along two concentric circles with centres at O and radii $2r$ and r repectively. If angle $OAB = \alpha$, show that $\cot \alpha = 2$ when their relative motion is along AB. **(M.U.)**

[Hint: See Bookwork 1.8. Set $a_1 = 2r,\ a_2 = r,\ v_1 = v,\ v_2 = 2v$; $\cos\theta = 4/5, \sin\theta = 3/5$. But $\frac{\sin\alpha}{r}$ $= \frac{\sin[180^\circ - (\theta + \alpha)]}{2r}$ which gives $\cot\alpha = 2$]

8. Two particles A_1, A_2 describe concentric circles of radii a_1, a_2 with angular speeds ω_1, ω_2 about the common centre O. Show that, when the relative angular velocity of one particle about the other vanishes,

$$\cos A_1OA_2 = \frac{a_1^2\omega_1 + a_2^2\omega_2}{a_1a_2(\omega_1 + \omega_2)}. \qquad \text{(M.U.)}$$

[Hint: See Bookwork 1.8. Set $v_1 = a_1\omega_1, v_2 = a_2\omega_2$]

9. Two points A_1 and A_2 describe concentric circles of radii a_1 and a_2 with angular velocities ω_1 and ω_2 respectively. Show that the angular velocity of one about the other is

$$\frac{(a^2 + a_1^2 - a_2^2)\omega_1 + (a^2 + a_2^2 - a_1^2)\omega_2}{2a^2}, \qquad \text{(M.U.)}$$

where a is the distance between them.

[Hint: With the notations of Bookwork 1.8, the angular speed is

$$\frac{\left|\overline{A_1A_2} \times (\overline{v}_2 - \overline{v}_1)\right|}{A_1A_2^2} = \frac{\left|(a_2\overline{r}_2 - a_1\overline{r}_1)\times(a_2\omega_2\overline{s}_2 - a_1\omega_1\overline{s}_1)\right|}{a^2}.$$

Use $\cos\theta = \frac{a_1^2 + a_2^2 - a^2}{2a_1a_2}$]

FORCES

2.1 NEWTON'S LAWS OF MOTION

Newton enunciated three laws of motion which are used as axioms for developing the subject. These laws are

N.1. A particle remains at rest or in a state of uniform motion in a straight line unless acted on by an impressed force.

N.2. The rate of change of momentum of a particle is proportional to the impressed force and it is in the direction of the force.

N.3. To every action there is an equal and opposite reaction.

2.1.1 Forces.

The first law, N.1., means that a particle cannot change its uniform motion in a straight line or its state of rest, on its own accord. That is, to effect a change from the uniform motion of a particle in a straight line or from its state of rest, an external agent is necessary and this agent is called *force*.

Linear momentum. If m is the mass of the particle and $\bar{v}$, its velocity, then $m\bar{v}$ is called the *linear momentum* or simply the *momentum* of the particle. If $\bar{r}$ is the position vector of the particle, then its linear momentum is $m\dot{\bar{r}}$.

N.1. establishes the existence of the force. We shall now show that N.2 enables us to measure it.

Measuring a force. Let the position vector of a particle of mass m be $\bar{r}$. Then, by N.2, we get

$$\frac{d(m\dot{\bar{r}})}{dt} = k\bar{F} \quad \text{or} \quad m\ddot{\bar{r}} = k\bar{F},$$

where k is a constant and $\bar{F}$ is the impressed force. Now denoting the acceleration $\ddot{\bar{r}}$ by $\bar{a}$, we may rewrite this equation as

$$m\bar{a} = k\bar{F}.$$

Further, if $\bar{a} = a\hat{e}$ and $\bar{F} = F\hat{e}$, where $\hat{e}$ is the unit vector in the direction of the acceleration, then the equation takes the form

$$ma\hat{e} = kF\hat{e} \quad \text{or} \quad ma = kF.$$

Let us now define the unit force as that force which produces a unit acceleration on a particle of unit mass. By this choice, we get that, when $F = 1$ and $m = 1$, $a = 1$. Consequently k becomes 1 and N.2 results in the equation.

$$m\bar{a} = \bar{F} \quad \text{or} \quad m\ddot{\bar{r}} = \bar{F}$$

which is called *the equation of motion of the particle*. This equation enables us to measure force. Its scalar form is $ma = F$.

Units of force. In the M.K.S., C.G.S, and F.P.S. systems the units of force are respectively a *newton*, a *dyne* and a *poundal*.

Newton. A newton is that force which, acting on a particle of mass 1kg., produces on it an acceleration of 1 m./sec^2.

Dyne. A dyne is that force which, acting on a particle of mass 1 gram, produces on it an acceleration of 1 cm./sec^2.

Poundal. A poundal is that force which, acting on a particle of mass 1lb., produces on it an acceleration of 1 ft./sec^2.

Remark. 1 newton = 10^5 dynes.

2.1.2 Types of forces.

The forces with which we will be concerned in this book are earth's gravitation, tension, reaction and resistance and we will be omitting the forces like electromagnetic and magnetostatic forces.

***(i)* Earth's gravitation.** It is Newton who found that two particles attract each other with a force of attraction whose magnitude is

$$\frac{\gamma m_1 m_2}{r^2}$$

where m_1 and m_2 are the masses of the particles r, the distance between them and γ, a universal constant.

Weight. The force of attraction of the earth on a body is called the *weight* of the body.

This force is towards the centre of the earth, that is, vertically downwards. For different places on the earth's surface or in the same place but at greatly differing altitudes, r varies slightly and the force of attraction on a given particle correspondingly varies. The acceleration due to this force, close to the surface of the earth, has been observed through experiments conducted in vacuum, to be about

$$9{\cdot}8 \text{ metres/sec}^2., \ 980 \text{ cm/sec}^2., \ 32 \text{ feet/sec}^2.,$$

respectively in the M.K.S., C.G.S. and F.P.S. systems. Now, denoting this acceleration by g, we get the weight of a body of mass m to be mg. So the weights of bodies of masses m kilograms, m grams and m pounds are respectively.

$$m \times 9{\cdot}8 \text{ newtons}, \ m \times 980 \text{ dynes}, \ m \times 32 \text{ poundals}.$$

Definition. The weights of a kilogram, a gram, a pound, a tonne (metric ton) and a ton are respectively called a *kilogram weight,* a *gram weight,* a *pound weight,* a *tonne weight* and a *ton weight.*

Note. It is erroneous to say that the weight of a man is 64 kg. Technically his mass is 64 kg. and his weight is 64 kilogram weight.

***(ii)* Tension.** Tension is a force which comes into play when an elastic body is deformed by application of forces.

Hooke's law. It has been found by experiments that tension of an elastic string or a spiral spring varies as the ratio of the extension of the string beyond its natural length, to its natural length. This fact was discovered by Hooke and hence this law is known as *Hooke's law*. The constant of proportionality is called the *coefficient of elasticity* of the string or the *modulus of elasticity* of the string. This coefficient is usually denoted by λ so that

$$\text{tension} = \lambda \frac{\text{extension}}{\text{natural length}}.$$

When a string is taut, the tension on it is the same everywhere. When it lies over a smooth object, then also the tension on it is the same everywhere.

***(iii)* Reaction.** It is observed from experiments that whenever two bodies have contact with each other, each is subject to the action of a force, the forces being equal in magnitude but opposite in direction. This fact was enunciated by Newton as N.3. These forces are called the *reactions* of the bodies.

Normal reaction and friction. We shall now consider the *reaction* acting on one of these bodies. When this force is resolved into two components, one along the direction normal to the surface of the body at the point of contact and the other along the direction opposite to the tangential direction in which the body has a tendency to move, the components are called the *normal*

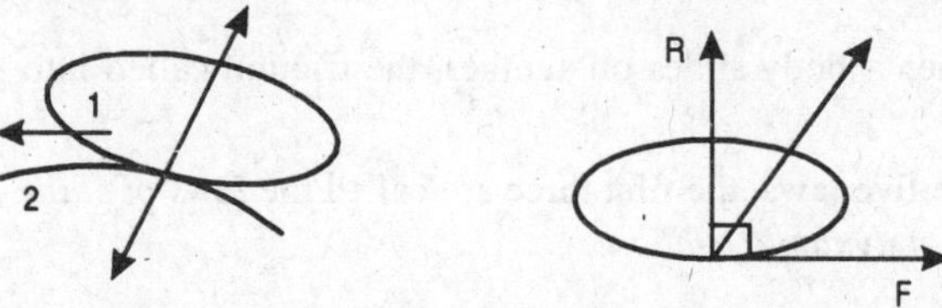

reaction and the *friction* respectively. It is important to note the difference between reaction and the normal reaction. When the bodies are *smooth*, which, of course, is an ideal case, the friction itself vanishes and the reaction is the normal reaction itself.

Limiting friction. It has been observed through experiments that there is a limit to the amount of friction that can be called into play. This maximum limit is called the *limiting friction. When* one body is just on the point of sliding on another body, the equilibrium is said to be *limiting equilibrium* and the friction then exerted is the *limiting friction*. It has also been observed that the limiting friction bears a constant ratio to the normal reaction. This constant is called the *coefficient of friction*. If the *limiting friction* is F and the *normal reaction* is R and if the coefficient of friction is μ, then

$$\frac{F}{R} = \mu \quad \text{or} \quad F = \mu R.$$

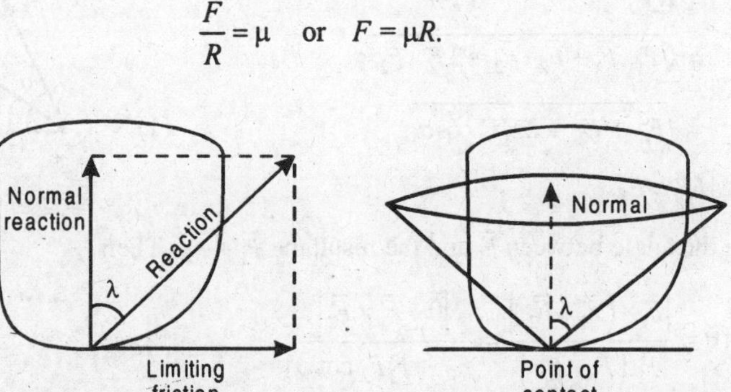

Angle of friction and cone of friction. When the friction is the limiting friction, the angle between the reaction and the normal to the surface is called the *angle of friction*. The right circular cone with its vertex at the point of contact, with its axis along the normal to the surface and with its semi-vertical angle equal to the angle of friction, is called the *cone of friction*. If the angle of friction is λ, then

$$\tan\lambda = \frac{\text{limiting friction}}{\text{normal reaction}} = \mu \quad \text{or} \quad \lambda = \tan^{-1}\mu.$$

Laws of friction. It is observed from experiments that the nature of friction is governed by the following laws of friction :

Law 1. The friction acts opposite to the direction in which the body moves or has a tendency to move (relative to the other body in contact).

Law 2. When the bodies are at rest, the friction called into play is just sufficient to prevent the motion of any of the bodies.

Law 3. There is a limit to the amount of friction that can be called into play. This limit bears a constant ratio to the normal reaction. This constant depends upon the nature and material of the surfaces in contact and not on the measure of the areas in contact.

Law 4. When a body slides on another, the friction called into play is slightly less than the limiting friction.

Law 5. When a body slides on another, the friction called into play is independent of its relative speed.

Of the above five laws, the first three are called the *laws of static friction* and the other two are called the *laws of dynamic friction.*

2.2 RESULTANT OF TWO FORCES ON A PARTICLE

If a particle is acted on by two forces $\bar{F}_1$ and $\bar{F}_2$, then

$$\bar{F}_1 + \bar{F}_2$$

is said to be the resultant force on the particle.

Bookwork 2.1. To find the magnitude and direction of the resultant of $\bar{F}_1$ and $\bar{F}_2$.

Now the resultant is $\bar{F}_1 + \bar{F}_2$. Let the angle between $\bar{F}_1$ and $\bar{F}_2$ be α. Then the magnitude of $\bar{F}_1 + \bar{F}_2$ is

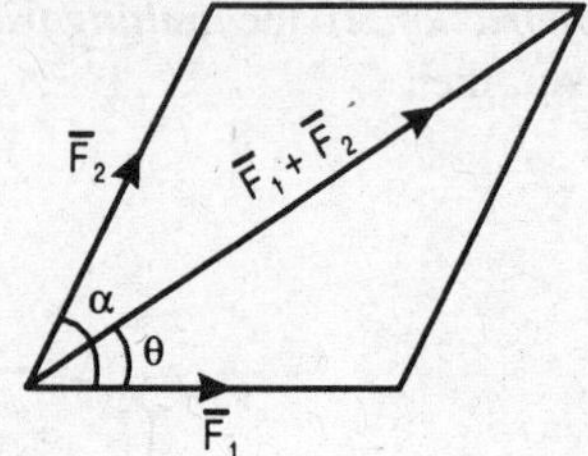

$$\begin{aligned} |\bar{F}_1 + \bar{F}_2| &= \sqrt{(\bar{F}_1 + \bar{F}_2)\cdot(\bar{F}_1 + \bar{F}_2)} \\ &= \sqrt{\bar{F}_1 \cdot \bar{F}_1 + \bar{F}_2 \cdot \bar{F}_2 + 2\bar{F}_1 \cdot \bar{F}_2} \\ &= \sqrt{F_1^2 + F_2^2 + 2F_1F_2 \cos\alpha}, \end{aligned} \qquad \text{...(1)}$$

where $|\bar{F}_1| = F_1, |\bar{F}_2| = F_2$.

Let θ be the angle between $\bar{F}_1$ and the resultant $\bar{F}_1 + \bar{F}_2$. Then

$$\begin{aligned} \tan\theta &= \frac{|\bar{F}_1 \times (\bar{F}_1 + \bar{F}_2)|}{\bar{F}_1 . (\bar{F}_1 + \bar{F}_2)} = \frac{|\bar{0} + \bar{F}_1 \times \bar{F}_2|}{F_1^2 + F_1F_2 \cos\alpha} \\ &= \frac{|F_1F_2 \sin\alpha\, \hat{n}|}{F_1(F_1 + F_2\cos\alpha)} = \frac{F_1F_2 \sin\alpha}{F_1(F_1 + F_2\cos\alpha)} \\ &= \frac{F_2 \sin\alpha}{F_1 + F_2\cos\alpha}. \end{aligned}$$

$$\therefore \qquad \theta = \tan^{-1} \frac{F_2 \sin\alpha}{F_1 + F_2 \cos\alpha} \qquad \text{...(2)}$$

Corollary 1. If $\bar{F}_1$ and $\bar{F}_2$ are of equal magnitude, say F, then

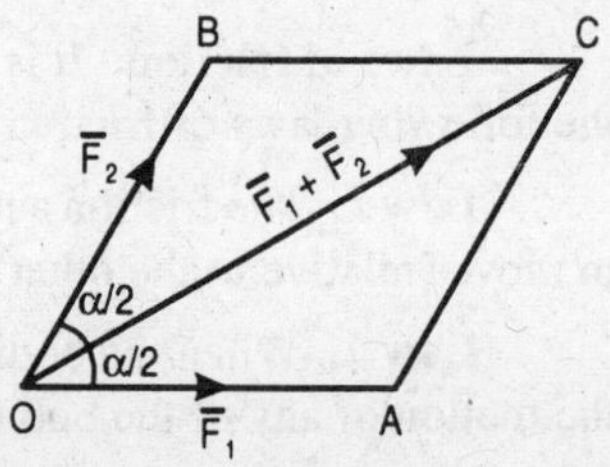

$$\begin{aligned} |\bar{F}_1 + \bar{F}_2| &= \sqrt{F^2 + F^2 + 2F^2 \cos\alpha} \\ &= F\sqrt{2(1 + \cos\alpha)} \\ &= F\sqrt{4\cos^2 \alpha/2} \\ &= 2F\cos \alpha/2. \end{aligned}$$

In the figure, $OACB$ is a rhombus. So OC bisects $\angle AOB$. So the resultant is equally inclined to $\overline{F}_1$ and $\overline{F}_2$ at an angle $\alpha/2$.

Corollary 2. If $\overline{F}_1$ and $\overline{F}_2$ are perpendicular to each other, then choosing $\overline{i}$ and $\overline{j}$ in their directions,

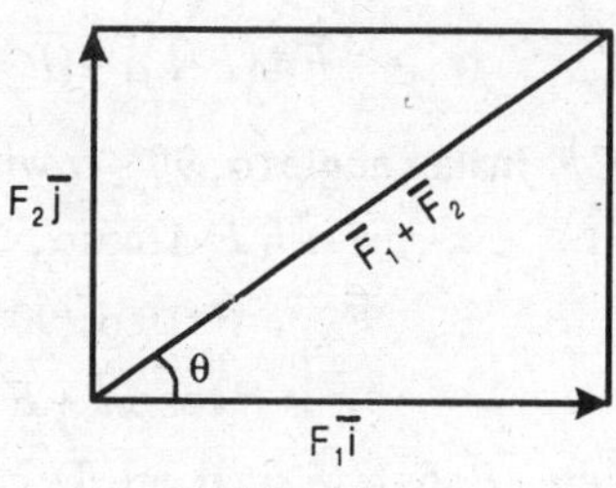

$$\overline{F}_1 = F_1\overline{i}, \qquad \overline{F}_2 = F_2\overline{j}.$$

$$\therefore \quad |\overline{F}_1 + \overline{F}_2| = |F_1\overline{i} + F_2\overline{j}|$$

$$= \sqrt{F_1^2 + F_2^2}.$$

$$\tan\theta = \frac{F_2}{F_1} \quad \text{or} \quad \theta = \tan^{-1}\frac{F_2}{F_1}.$$

Resolution of a Force into its components. Given the forces $\overline{F}_1$ and $\overline{F}_2$, we have the resultant as $\overline{F}_1 + \overline{F}_2$. Conversely, if $\overline{F}_1 + \overline{F}_2$ is given, the quantities $\overline{F}_1$ and $\overline{F}_2$ are said to be components of $\overline{F}_1 + \overline{F}_2$.Since infinite number of parallelograms can be formed with a given diagonal, a given force can be resolved into two components in infinite number of different ways.

Bookwork 2.2. To resolve a force $\overline{F}$ into components in two given directions.

Let $\hat{e}_1, \hat{e}_2$ be the unit vectors in the given directions. Let them make angles α, β with $\overline{F}$. Now $\overline{F}$ may be expressed as a linear combination of $\hat{e}_1$, $\hat{e}_2$ as

$$\overline{F} = a\hat{e}_1 + b\hat{e}_2. \qquad \text{...(1)}$$

Multiplying this vectorially by $\hat{e}_1$,

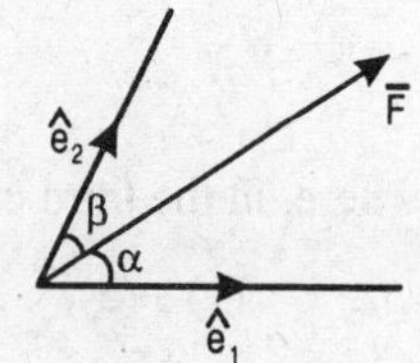

$$\hat{e}_1 \times \overline{F} = a\hat{e}_1 \times \hat{e}_1 + b\hat{e}_1 \times \hat{e}_2$$

i.e., $$F \sin\alpha\,\hat{n} = \overline{0} + b\sin(\alpha+\beta)\,\hat{n},$$

where $\hat{n}$ is the unit vector perpendicular to both $\hat{e}_1$ and $\hat{e}_2$ such that $\hat{e}_1$, $\hat{e}_2$, $\hat{n}$ form a right-handed triad.

$$\therefore \quad b = \frac{F\sin\alpha}{\sin(\alpha+\beta)}.$$

Multiplying (1) vectorially by $\hat{e}_2$,

$$\hat{e}_2 \times \overline{F} = a\,\hat{e}_2 \times \hat{e}_1 + b\,\hat{e}_2 \times \hat{e}_2$$

i.e., $$F\sin\beta(-\hat{n}) = a\sin(\alpha+\beta)(-\hat{n}).$$

$$\therefore \quad a = \frac{F\sin\beta}{\sin(\alpha+\beta)}.$$

$$\therefore \quad \overline{F} = \frac{F\sin\beta}{\sin(\alpha+\beta)}\hat{e}_1 + \frac{F\sin\alpha}{\sin(\alpha+\beta)}\hat{e}_2.$$

Component of a force in a given direction. Given a force $\overline{F}$ and a direction specified by the unit vector $\hat{e}$, the scalar quantity

$$\overline{F}\cdot\hat{e}$$

is the component of $\overline{F}$ in the direction of $\hat{e}$.

Bookwork 2.3. To express the force $\overline{F}$ acting in a plane in terms of its components in two perpendicular directions in the plane.

Let $\overline{i}, \overline{j}$ be the unit vectors along the perpendicular directions. Then, from Vector Algebra, we have

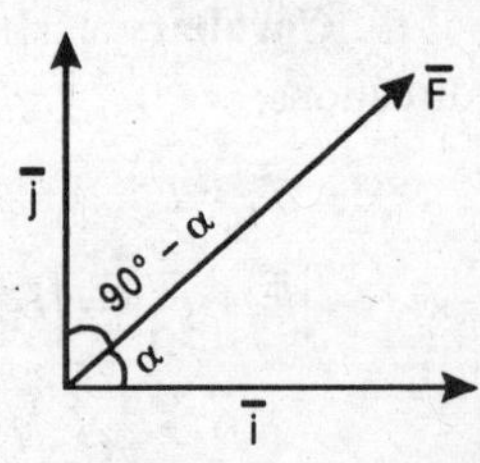

$$\overline{F} = (\overline{F}\cdot\overline{i})\overline{i} + (\overline{F}\cdot\overline{j})\overline{j}.$$

If $\overline{F}$ makes angles α, $90^\circ - \alpha$ with $\overline{i}$, $\overline{j}$, then

$$\overline{F}\cdot\overline{i} = F\cdot 1\cdot\cos\alpha,$$

$$\overline{F}\cdot\overline{j} = F\cdot 1\cdot\cos(90^\circ - \alpha) = F\sin\alpha.$$

$$\therefore \quad \overline{F} = F\cos\alpha\,\overline{i} + F\sin\alpha\,\overline{j}.$$

Note. $F\cos\alpha$, $F\sin\alpha$ are the components of $\overline{F}$ in the perpendicular directions which make angles α, $90^\circ - \alpha$ with $\overline{F}$.

EXAMPLES

Example 1. The magnitude of the resultant of two given forces P, Q is R. If Q is doubled, then R is doubled. If Q is reversed, then also R is doubled. Show that

$$P : Q : R = \sqrt{2} : \sqrt{3} : \sqrt{2}.$$ **(M.U., Bn.U., M.K.U)**

Let α be the angle between P, Q. Then, considering the magnitudes of the resultants in the three cases,

$$P^2 + Q^2 + 2PQ\cos\alpha = R^2, \quad \text{...(1)}$$

$$P^2 + 4Q^2 + 4PQ\cos\alpha = 4R^2, \quad \text{...(2)}$$

$$P^2 + Q^2 - 2PQ\cos\alpha = 4R^2, \quad \text{...(3)}$$

where, in the third case, the angle between the forces is $180^\circ - \alpha$.

$$\left.\begin{array}{l}(1)+(3) : 2P^2 + 2Q^2 = 5R^2 \\ (2)+2(3) : P^2 + 2Q^2 = 4R^2\end{array}\right\} \therefore P^2 = R^2,\ Q^2 = \frac{3}{2}R^2.$$

$$\therefore \quad P^2 : Q^2 : R^2 = R^2 : \tfrac{3}{2}R^2 : R^2 = 2 : 3 : 2.$$

Example 2. The magnitude of the resultant of the forces $\overline{F}_1$ and $\overline{F}_2$ acting on a particle is equal to the magnitude of $\overline{F}_1$. When the first force is doubled, show that the new resultant is perpendicular to $\overline{F}_2$. **(M.U., Bn.U.)**

Since the magnitude of $\overline{F}_1 + \overline{F}_2$ is equal to the magnitude of $\overline{F}_1$,

$$|\overline{F}_1 + \overline{F}_2| = |\overline{F}_1| \quad \text{or} \quad |\overline{F}_1 + \overline{F}_2|^2 = |\overline{F}_1|^2.$$

$$\therefore \quad (\overline{F}_1 + \overline{F}_2)\cdot(\overline{F}_1 + \overline{F}_2) = \overline{F}_1\cdot\overline{F}_1$$

or $$\overline{F}_1\cdot\overline{F}_1 + 2\overline{F}_1\cdot\overline{F}_2 + \overline{F}_2\cdot\overline{F}_2 = \overline{F}_1\cdot\overline{F}_1$$

or $$(2\overline{F}_1 + \overline{F}_2)\cdot\overline{F}_2 = 0.$$

So the resultant of $2\overline{F}_1$ and $\overline{F}_2$ is perpendicular to $\overline{F}_2$.

Example 3. Two forces of equal magnitudes act on a particle and they include an angle θ. If one of them is halved, the angle between the other and the original resultant is bisected by the new resultant. Show that $\theta = 120^\circ$.

Let $\overline{OA}, \overline{OB}$ be the given forces. Complete the parallelogram $OACB$. Since $OA = OB$, OC bisects $\angle AOB$. Let B' be the midpoint of OB. Complete the parallelogram $OAC'B'$. Now C' is the midpoint of AC. Since OC' bisects $\angle AOC$,

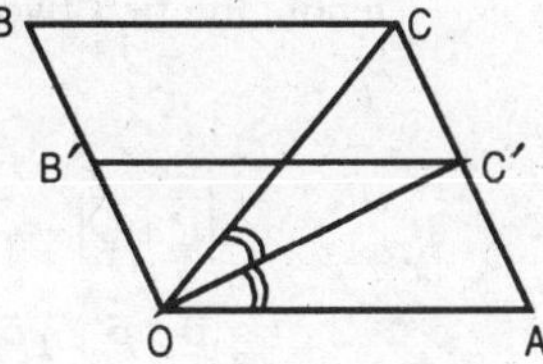

$$\frac{OA}{OC} = \frac{AC'}{C'C} = 1.$$

So $OA = OC$. But $OA = OB$. Hence ΔOCA is an equilateral triangle and

$$\angle AOC = 60^\circ. \quad \therefore \quad \angle AOB = 120^\circ.$$

Example 4. Two forces of magnitudes P and Q act at a point. Their resultant is inclined to the first at an angle α and has a magnitude R. If the magnitude of the first force is increased by R, show that the new resultant will make an angle $\alpha/2$ with the first force. **(M.K.U., C.U)**

Let the given forces be $P\hat{e}_1$, $Q\hat{e}_2$, where $\hat{e}_1, \hat{e}_2$ are the unit vectors in the directions of the forces. Then their resultant is

$$P\hat{e}_1 + Q\hat{e}_2 = R\hat{e}_3, \text{ say,} \qquad \text{...(1)}$$

since the magnitude is R. ($\hat{e}_3$ is the respective unit vector). It is given that the angle between $\hat{e}_1$ and $\hat{e}_3$ is α.

Next, P is increased by R and so the new resultant is

$$\begin{aligned}(P+R)\hat{e}_1 + Q\hat{e}_2 &= R\hat{e}_1 + (P\hat{e}_1 + Q\hat{e}_2) && \text{by rearrangement}\\ &= R\hat{e}_1 + R\hat{e}_3 && \text{by (1)}\\ &= R(\hat{e}_1 + \hat{e}_3).\end{aligned}$$

But the direction of $\hat{e}_1 + \hat{e}_3$ is the direction which bisects the angle between $\hat{e}_1$ and $\hat{e}_3$ which is α. So the angle between the new resultant and the first force $P\hat{e}_1$ is $\alpha/2$.

Geometrical method. In the figure $ABCD$ is a parallelogram, $AB = P$, $AD = Q$, $AC = R$ and

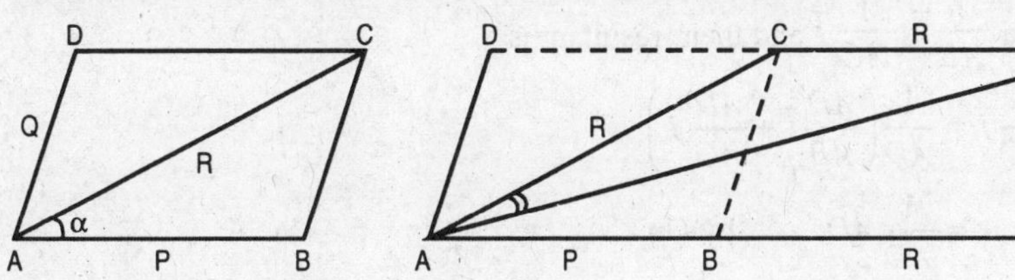

$\angle BAC = \alpha$. Also $AEFD$ is a parallelogram, where

$$R = BE = CF = AC.$$

So ΔAFC is isosceles and

$$\begin{aligned}\angle CAF &= \angle CFA \quad \text{(Base angles are equal)}\\ &= \angle FAE, \text{ Alternate angle.}\end{aligned}$$

Thus AF bisects $\angle CAE$ and so $\angle FAE = \alpha/2$.

Example 5. The resultant of two forces P, Q is of magnitude P. Show that, if P is doubled, the new resultant is perpendicular to the force Q and its magnitude is

$$\sqrt{4P^2 - Q^2}$$

(M.K.U, M.U., Bn. U.)

Denote the first two forces by $\overline{P}, \overline{Q}$. Then their resultant and the new resultant are

$$\overline{P}+\overline{Q}, \quad 2\overline{P}+\overline{Q}.$$

$$\therefore \qquad \left|\overline{P}+\overline{Q}\right|^2 = \left|\overline{P}\right|^2 \text{ or } \left(\overline{P}+\overline{Q}\right)\cdot\left(\overline{P}+\overline{Q}\right) = \overline{P}\cdot\overline{P}$$

$$\therefore \qquad \overline{P}\cdot\overline{P}+2\overline{P}\cdot\overline{Q}+\overline{Q}\cdot\overline{Q} = \overline{P}\cdot\overline{P} \text{ or } (2\overline{P}+\overline{Q})\cdot\overline{Q}=0. \qquad (1)$$

So the new resultant is perpendicular to $\overline{Q}$. Also

$$\begin{aligned}\left|2\overline{P}+\overline{Q}\right|^2 &= \left(2\overline{P}+\overline{Q}\right)\cdot\left(2\overline{P}+\overline{Q}\right)\\ &= \left(2\overline{P}+\overline{Q}\right)\cdot\left(2\overline{P}\right)+\left(2\overline{P}+\overline{Q}\right)\cdot\overline{Q}\\ &= \left(4P^2+2\overline{P}\cdot\overline{Q}\right)+0 \qquad \text{by (1)}\\ &= 4P^2-\overline{Q}\cdot\overline{Q} \qquad \text{by (1)}\end{aligned}$$

$$\therefore \qquad \left|2\overline{P}+\overline{Q}\right| = \sqrt{4P^2-Q^2}.$$

Example 6. ABC is a triangle, right-angled at A and AD is the perpendicular from A to BC. Show that the resultant of the forces acting along AB, AC with magnitudes $1/_{AB}, 1/_{AC}$ acts along AD and its magnitude is $1/_{AD}$. **(M.U., A.U.)**

Let $\overline{i}$, $\overline{j}$ be the unit vectors along AB, AC. Let

$$\angle BAD = \alpha.$$

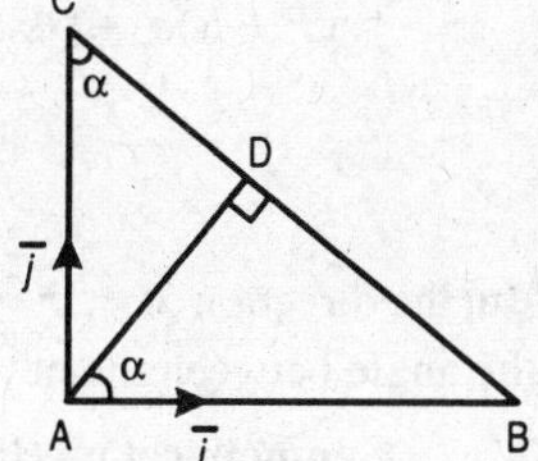

Now the unit vector along AD is

$$\begin{aligned}AD &= \cos\alpha\,\overline{i}+\sin\alpha\,\overline{j}\\ &= \frac{AD}{AB}\overline{i}+\frac{AD}{AC}\overline{j} \qquad \text{...(1)}\end{aligned}$$

Now the forces are $\dfrac{1}{AB}\overline{i}, \dfrac{1}{AC}\overline{j}$ and their resultant is

$$\begin{aligned}\frac{1}{AB}\overline{i}+\frac{1}{AC}\overline{j} &= \frac{1}{AD}\left(\frac{AD}{AB}\overline{i}+\frac{AD}{AC}\overline{j}\right)\\ &= \frac{1}{AD}\widehat{AD} \qquad \text{by (1)}\end{aligned}$$

which is along AD with a magnitude $1/_{AD}$.

Example 7. The resultant of the forces F_1, F_2 acting at O is R. If any transversal meets the lines of action of F_1, F_2, R at A_1, A_2, B, prove that **(M.U., M.K.U., K.U)**

$$\frac{F_1}{OA_1}+\frac{F_2}{OA_2}=\frac{R}{OB}.$$

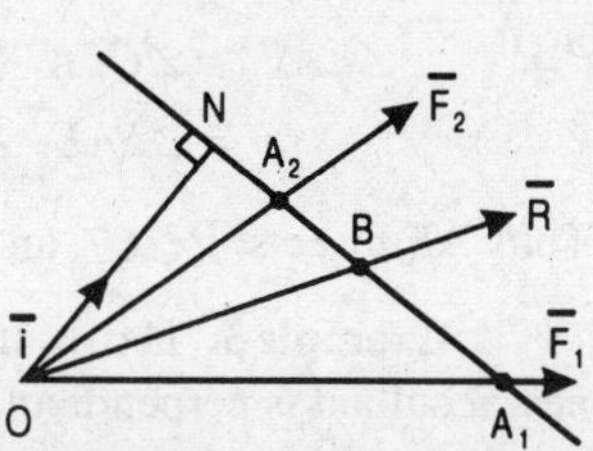

Draw ON, the perpendicular to the transversal. Let $\overline{i}$ be the unit vector along ON. Let the forces and the resultant, in vectors, be

$$\overline{F}_1, \overline{F}_2, \overline{R}.$$

Then

$$\overline{F}_1+\overline{F}_2=\overline{R}. \quad \text{...(1)}$$

The angles between $\bar{i}$ and the forces $\bar{F}_1, \bar{F}_2, \bar{R}$ are

$$\angle A_1ON, \quad \angle A_2ON, \quad \angle BON.$$

Multiplying (1) by $\bar{i}$ scalarly, we get

$$\bar{F}_1 \cdot \bar{i} + \bar{F}_2 \cdot \bar{i} = \bar{R} \cdot \bar{i}.$$

$\therefore$
$$\bar{F}_1 \cdot 1 \cdot \cos A_1ON + F_2 \cdot 1 \cdot \cos A_2ON = R \cdot 1 \cdot \cos BON$$

i.e.,
$$F_1 \frac{ON}{OA_1} + F_2 \frac{ON}{OA_2} = R\frac{ON}{OB} \quad \text{or} \quad \frac{F_1}{OA_1} + \frac{F_2}{OA_2} = \frac{R}{OB}.$$

Remark. This result can be extended to n forces $F_1, F_2, ...F_n$ acting at O. In this case we have

$$\lambda_1 \frac{F_1}{OA_1} + \lambda_2 \frac{F_2}{OA_2} + ... + \lambda_n \frac{F_n}{OA_n} = \frac{R}{OB},$$

where $\lambda_r = 1$ or -1 according as $\cos A_rON$ is +ve or –ve.

Example 8. Show that the resultant of two forces sec B, sec C acting along the sides AB, AC of a triangle ABC is a force

$$\tan B + \tan C$$

acting along AD, where D is the foot of the perpendicular from A on BC. **(M.U., M.K.U)**

Draw $B'AC'$ parallel to BC. Then

$$\angle B'AB = B, \quad \angle C'AC = C.$$

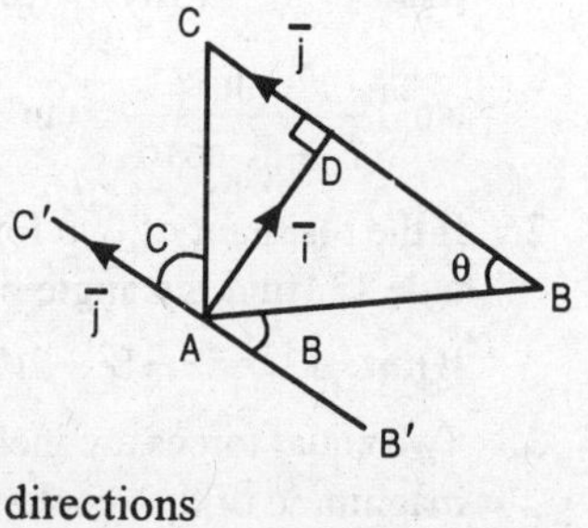

Let the unit vectors along AD, AC′ be $\bar{i}, \bar{j}$. Now the force sec B is along AB. Resolving it into components in the $-\bar{j}$ and $\bar{i}$ directions, it is

$$\sec B \cos B(-\bar{j}) + \sec B \sin B\,\bar{i} \quad \text{or} \quad -\bar{j} + \tan B\,\bar{i}. \qquad ...(1)$$

Resolving sec C which is along AC into components in the $\bar{j}$ and $\bar{i}$ directions

$$\sec C \cos C\,\bar{j} + \sec C \sin C\,\bar{i} \quad \text{or} \quad \bar{j} + \tan C\,\bar{i}. \qquad ...(2)$$

Adding (1) and (2), we get the result as stated.

Example 9. Two forces of magnitudes F_1 and F_2 act at a point. They are inclined at an angle α. If the forces are interchanged, show that their resultant is turned through the angle.

$$2\tan^{-1}\left(\frac{F_1 - F_2}{F_1 + F_2}\tan\frac{\alpha}{2}\right).$$

(M.U., Bn.U.)

Let the forces be $F_1\hat{e}_1$ and $F_2\hat{e}_2$. Then $\hat{e}_1 \cdot \hat{e}_2 = \cos\alpha$. After the interchange, the forces will be represented by the vectors $F_2\hat{e}_1$ and $F_1\hat{e}_2$. So the resultants before and after the interchange are respectively $F_1\hat{e}_1 + F_2\hat{e}_2$ and $F_2\hat{e}_1 + F_1\hat{e}_2$. If θ is the angle between them, then

$$\cos\theta = \frac{(F_1\hat{e}_1 + F_2\hat{e}_2).(F_2\hat{e}_1 + F_1\hat{e}_2)}{|(F_1\hat{e}_1 + F_2\hat{e}_2)|\;|(F_2\hat{e}_1 + F_1\hat{e}_2)|}$$

$$= \frac{F_1F_2 + F_1^2\cos\alpha + F_2^2\cos\alpha + F_1F_2}{\sqrt{F_1^2 + F_2^2 + 2F_1F_2\cos\alpha}\sqrt{F_1^2 + F_2^2 + 2F_1F_2\cos\alpha}}$$

$$\therefore \quad \frac{1 - \tan^2 \theta/_2}{1 + \tan^2 \theta/_2} = \frac{2F_1F_2 + (F_1^2 + F_2^2)\cos\alpha}{(F_1^2 + F_2^2) + 2F_1F_2\cos\alpha}.$$

Thus, by componendo and dividendo,

$$\tan^2 \theta/2 = \frac{(F_1 - F_2)^2 - (F_1 - F_2)^2 \cos\alpha}{(F_1 + F_2)^2 + (F_1 + F_2)^2 \cos\alpha}$$

$$= \left(\frac{F_1 - F_2}{F_1 + F_2}\right)^2 \frac{1 - \cos\alpha}{1 + \cos\alpha} = \left(\frac{F_1 - F_2}{F_1 + F_2}\right)^2 \frac{2\sin^2 \alpha/2}{2\cos^2 \alpha/2}$$

$$= \left(\frac{F_1 - F_2}{F_1 + F_2}\right)^2 \tan^2 \alpha/2$$

from which we get the result as stated.

EXERCISES

1. If the resultant of forces $3P$, $5P$ is equal to $7P$, find

(*i*) the angle between the forces

(*ii*) the angle which the resultant makes with the first force. **(M.K.U.)**

[Hint: $(7P)^2 = (3P)^2 + (5P)^2 + 2(3P)(5P)\cos\alpha$ or $\alpha = 60°$. If θ is the other angle, then θ is

$\tan^{-1} \dfrac{F_2 \sin\alpha}{F_1 + F_2 \cos\alpha} = \tan^{-1} \dfrac{5\sqrt{3}}{11}$.]

2. If the resultant of two forces acting at a point with magnitudes 7 and 8 is a force with magnitude 13, find the angle between the two given forces. **(M.U.)**

[Hint: $13^2 = 7^2 + 8^2 + 2(7)(8)\cos\alpha$; $\alpha = 60°$.]

3. Two equal forces are inclined at an angle 2θ. The magnitude of their resultant is three times the magnitude of the resultant when the forces are inclined at an angle 2ϕ. Show that

$$\cos\theta = 3\cos\phi.$$ **(M.U., M.K.U.)**

[Hint: $\sqrt{P^2 + P^2 + 2.P \cdot P \cdot \cos 2\theta} = 3\sqrt{P^2 + P^2 + 2 \cdot P \cdot P \cdot \cos 2\phi}$.]

4. The resultant of two forces of magnitudes P and Q acting at a point, has magnitudes $(2n + 1)\sqrt{P^2 + Q^2}$ and $(2n - 1)\sqrt{P^2 + Q^2}$ when the forces are inclined at α and $90° - \alpha$ respectively. Show that $\tan\alpha = \dfrac{n-1}{n+1}$. **(M.U., M.K.U., Bn.U., C.U.)**

[Hint: Find $2PQ\sin\alpha$, $2PQ\cos\alpha$ from the following and divide:

$(2n + 1)^2 (P^2 + Q^2) = P^2 + Q^2 + 2PQ\cos\alpha$, $(2n - 1)^2 (P^2 + Q^2) = P^2 + Q^2 + 2PQ\cos(90 - \alpha)$.]

5. The resultant of two forces P, Q is R. If P is doubled, then R is doubled. If Q is doubled and reversed, then also R is doubled. Show that

$$P : Q : R = \sqrt{6} : \sqrt{2} : \sqrt{5}.$$

6. Two forces of magnitudes $k\cos A$, $k\cos B$ act along CA, CB of a ΔABC. Prove that their resultant is $k\sin C$. **(M.K.U, C.U.)**

[Hint: Formula. $\cos^2 A + \cos^2 B + \cos^2 C = 1 - 2\cos A\cos B\cos C$.

$(\text{Resultant})^2 = k^2\cos^2 A + k^2\cos^2 B + 2k^2\cos A\cos B(\cos C)$]

7. The greatest resultant that two forces can have is of magnitude R, and the least is of magnitude S. Show that, when they act at an angle 2α, the magnitude of their resultant is

$$\sqrt{R^2 \cos^2 \alpha + S^2 \sin^2 \alpha}. \qquad \textbf{(M.U., M.K.U., Bn.U.)}$$

[Hint: If the given forces are of magnitudes P and Q $(P > Q)$, then $P + Q = R$, $P - Q = S$. Find $\sqrt{P^2 + Q^2 + 2PQ\cos 2\alpha}$.]

8. Show that the resultant of the forces $\lambda_1 \overline{OA}$, $\lambda_2 \overline{OB}$ is

$$(\lambda_1 + \lambda_2)\overline{OP},$$

where P divides AB in the ratio $\lambda_2 : \lambda_1$. **(M.K.U.)**

[Hint: $\overline{OP} = \dfrac{\lambda_1 \overline{OA} + \lambda_2 \overline{OB}}{\lambda_1 + \lambda_2}$; Resultant $= \lambda_1 \overline{OA} + \lambda_2 \overline{OB}$]

9. Two forces of magnitudes P and Q act at a point. They are such that, if the direction of one is reversed, then the resultant turns through a right angle. Show that $P = Q$. **(M.U., M.K.U)**

[Hint: $(P\hat{e}_1 + Q\hat{e}_2)\cdot(P\hat{e}_1 - Q\hat{e}_2) = 0$. So $P^2 - Q^2 = 0$ or $P = Q$]

10. If two forces $\overline{P}, \overline{Q}$ acting at a point is such that their sum and difference are perpendicular to each other, show that $P = Q$. **(M.U.)**

[Hint: $\left(\overline{P} + \overline{Q}\right) . \left(\overline{P} - \overline{Q}\right) = 0$. So $P^2 - Q^2 = 0$ or $P = Q$]

11. The resultant of two forces of magnitudes P and Q acting at a point is $\overline{F}_1$. If the second force is replaced with a third force of magnitude R, the new resultant is $\overline{F}_2$. Show that the resultant of $\overline{F}_1$ and the reversed of $\overline{F}_2$ has a magnitude $|Q - R|$. **(M.U.)**

[Hint: If $\hat{e}_1$, $\hat{e}_2$ are unit vectors so that $P\hat{e}_1 + Q\hat{e}_2 = \overline{F}_1$, $P\hat{e}_1 + R\hat{e}_2 = \overline{F}_2$, then $|\overline{F}_1 - \overline{F}_2| = |(Q - R)\,\hat{e}_2| = |Q - R|$.]

12. Two forces $\overline{P}$ and $\overline{Q}$ which are inclined at an angle α act on a particle. If the sum of their components in certain two perpendicular directions are X and Y, show that

$$\alpha = \cos^{-1} \frac{X^2 + Y^2 - P^2 - Q^2}{2PQ}.$$

[Hint: If $\overline{i}, \overline{j}$ are the unit vectors in the perpendicular directions, $\overline{P} + \overline{Q} = X\overline{i} + Y\overline{j}$. $(\overline{P} + \overline{Q})\cdot(\overline{P} + \overline{Q}) = (X\overline{i} + Y\overline{j})\cdot(X\overline{i} + Y\overline{j})$ gives $P^2 + Q^2 + 2PQ\cos\alpha = X^2 + Y^2$.]

13. Two forces P, Q acting at a point along two straight lines inclined at an angle α have a resultant R. Two other forces P', Q' acting along the same lines have a resultant R'. Show that the angle between the two resultants is

$$\cos^{-1} \frac{PP' + QQ' + (PQ' + P'Q)\cos\alpha}{RR'}. \qquad \textbf{(M.U.)}$$

[Hint: If $\hat{e}_1$, $\hat{e}_2$ are the unit vectors in the given directions and θ is the angle between R, R', then

$\hat{e}_1.\hat{e}_2 = \cos\alpha,\ \cos\theta = \dfrac{(P\hat{e}_1 + Q\hat{e}_2)\cdot(P'\hat{e}_1 + Q'\hat{e}_2)}{RR'}$]

14. Two forces $\overline{P}$ and $\overline{Q}$ acting at a point have the resultant $\overline{R}$. When the first force is doubled the new resultant bisects the angle between $\overline{R}$ and $\overline{P}$. Show that $|\overline{P}| = |\overline{R}|$.

[**Hint:** $\overline{P} + \overline{Q} = \overline{R}$. The new resultant is

$$2\overline{P} + \overline{Q} = \overline{P} + (\overline{P} + \overline{Q}) = \overline{P} + \overline{R}.$$

Thus it is the resultant of $\overline{P}$ and $\overline{R}$ and bisects the angle between them. So $|\overline{P}| = |\overline{R}|$]

15. Two forces of magnitudes $P+Q, P-Q$ acting at a point include an angle 2α. Show that, if their resultant makes with the bisector of the angle between the forces an angle θ, then

$$P\tan\theta = Q\tan\alpha.$$ **(M.U.)**

[**Hint:** If the forces are $(P+Q)\hat{e}_1, (P-Q)\hat{e}_2$, then

$$\hat{e}_1\cdot\hat{e}_2 = \cos 2\alpha,\ |\hat{e}_1\times\hat{e}_2| = |\sin 2\alpha\hat{n}| = \sin 2\alpha.$$

Now $\hat{e}_1 + \hat{e}_2$ is a vector along the bisector. So

$$\tan\theta = \frac{\left|[(P+Q)\hat{e}_1 + (P-Q)\hat{e}_2]\times(\hat{e}_1+\hat{e}_2)\right|}{[(P+Q)\hat{e}_1 + (P-Q)\hat{e}_2]\cdot(\hat{e}_1+\hat{e}_2)} = \frac{2Q\sin 2\alpha}{2P + 2P\cos 2\alpha} = \frac{Q}{P}\tan\alpha]$$

16. The greatest resultant and the smallest resultant that two given forces can have are of magnitudes R and S. Show that, if the given forces and a third force whose magnitude is $\sqrt{RS}$ keep a particle in equilibrium, then two of these three forces are perpendicular to each other.

(M.U.,T.U.)

[**Hint:** $R = P+Q, S = P-Q$ and so $RS = P^2 - Q^2$. Thus $\left(\sqrt{RS}\right)^2 + Q^2 = P^2$ which shows that, of the forces $P, Q, \sqrt{RS}$, the forces Q and $\sqrt{RS}$ are perpendicular.]

2.2.1 Resultant of three forces related to a triangle acting at a point.

In this section we shall consider, in particular forces pertaining to a triangle and acting at a point. Here the following formulae will be used:

1. $\overline{AB} + \overline{BC} + \overline{CA} = \overline{0}$
2. If M is the midpoint of AB, then $\overline{OM} = \tfrac{1}{2}(\overline{OA} + \overline{OB})$
3. If G is the centroid of the ΔABC, then

$$\overline{OG} = \tfrac{1}{3}(\overline{OA} + \overline{OB} + \overline{OC}); \quad \overline{OA} + \overline{OB} + \overline{OC} = 3\overline{OG}.$$

Equilibrium. When the resultant of the forces acting at a point is zero, then the forces are said to be in equilibrium.

EXAMPLES

Example 1. Forces of magnitudes F_1, F_2, F_3 act on a particle. If their directions are parallel to $\overline{BC}, \overline{CA}, \overline{AB}$, where ABC is a triangle, show that the magnitude of their resultant is

$$\sqrt{F_1^2 + F_2^2 + F_3^2 - 2F_2F_3\cos A - 2F_3F_1\cos B - 2F_1F_2\cos C}.$$ **(M.U., Bn. U.)**

The given forces are

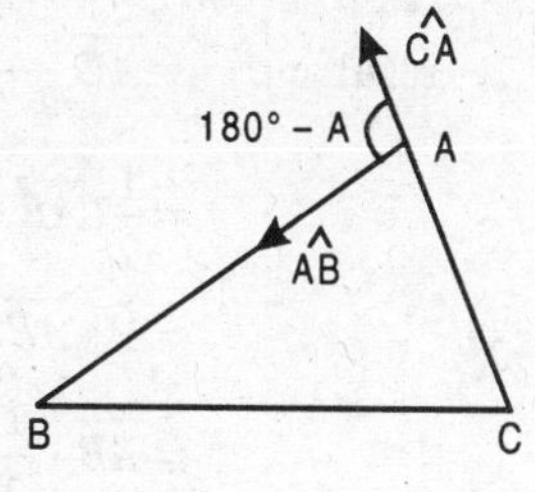

$$F_1\widehat{BC},\ F_2\widehat{CA},\ F_3\widehat{AB},$$

where

$$\widehat{BC}, \widehat{CA}, \widehat{AB}$$

are the unit vectors parallel to $\overline{BC}, \overline{CA}, \overline{AB}$. If the magnitude of their resultant is F, then we have

$$\begin{aligned} F^2 &= (F_1\widehat{BC} + F_2\widehat{CA} + F_3\widehat{AB})\cdot(F_1\widehat{BC} + F_2\widehat{CA} + F_3\widehat{AB}) \\ &= F_1^2 + F_2^2 + F_3^2 + 2F_2F_3\widehat{CA}\cdot\widehat{AB} + 2F_3F_1\widehat{AB}\cdot\widehat{BC} + 2F_1F_2\widehat{BC}\cdot\widehat{CA}) \\ &= F_1^2 + F_2^2 + F_3^2 - 2F_2F_3\cos A - 2F_3F_1\cos B - 2F_1F_2\cos C \end{aligned}$$

because $\widehat{CA}\cdot\widehat{AB} = \cos(180° - A) = -\cos A$ etc.

Example 2. The sides BC, CA, AB of a ΔABC are bisected in D, E, F. Show that the forces represented by DA, EB, FC are in equilibrium. **(M.K.U.)**

The forces act through the centroid, since D is the midpoint of BC,

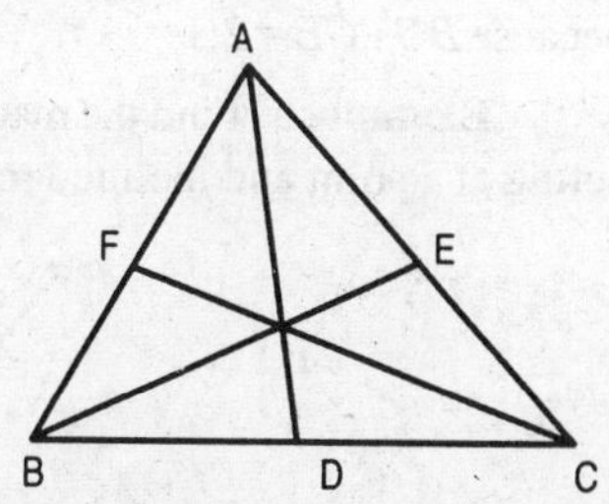

$$\begin{aligned} \overline{AD} &= \tfrac{1}{2}(\overline{AB} + \overline{AC}) \\ &= \tfrac{1}{2}(\overline{AB} - \overline{CA}). \end{aligned}$$

But $\overline{DA} = -\overline{AD}$. Hence

$$\begin{aligned} \overline{DA} &= -\tfrac{1}{2}(\overline{AB} - \overline{CA}), \\ \overline{EB} &= -\tfrac{1}{2}(\overline{BC} - \overline{AB}), \\ \overline{FC} &= -\tfrac{1}{2}(\overline{CA} - \overline{BC}). \end{aligned}$$

Adding these three, we get the resultant as $\overline{0}$. So the forces are in equilibrium.

Example 3. ABC is a triangle. G is its centroid and P is any point in the plane of the triangle. Show that the resultant of forces represented by $\overline{PA}, \overline{PB}, \overline{PC}$ is $3\overline{PG}$ and find the position of P, if the three forces are in equilibrium. **(M.K.U.)**

Let O be any base point. Then it is evident that

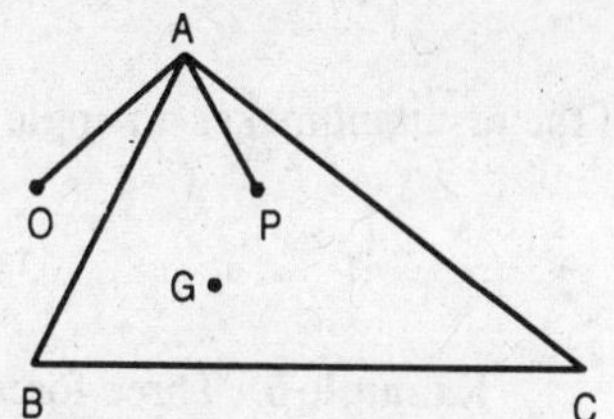

$$\overline{PA} = \overline{PG} + \overline{GO} + \overline{OA}.$$

$$\begin{aligned} \therefore \quad \Sigma\overline{PA} &= 3\overline{PG} + 3\overline{GO} + \left(\overline{OA} + \overline{OB} + \overline{OC}\right) \\ &= 3\overline{PG} - 3\overline{OG} + \left(3\overline{OG}\right) \\ &= 3\overline{PG}. \end{aligned}$$

This becomes zero and the forces are in equilibrium when P coincides with the centroid G.

Example 4. ABC is a triangle and D,E,F are the midpoints of the sides. Forces represented by AD, $\tfrac{2}{3}BE$ and $\tfrac{1}{3}CF$ act on a particle at the point where AD and BE meet. Show that the resultant is represented in magnitude and direction by $\tfrac{1}{2}AC$ and that its line of action divides BC in the ratio 2:1. **(M.U.)**

Since D is the midpoint of BC, $\overline{AD} = \tfrac{1}{2}(\overline{AB} + \overline{AC})$, etc. So

$$\text{resultant} = \overline{AD} + \frac{2}{3}\overline{BE} + \frac{1}{3}\,\overline{CF}$$

$$= \frac{1}{2}(\overline{AB} + \overline{AC}) + \frac{2}{3}.\frac{1}{2}(\overline{BA} + \overline{BC}) + \frac{1}{3}.\frac{1}{2}\,(\overline{CA} + \overline{CB})$$

$$= \tfrac{1}{2}(\overline{AB} - \overline{CA}) + \tfrac{1}{3}(-\overline{AB} + \overline{BC}) + \tfrac{1}{6}\,(\overline{CA} - \overline{BC})$$

$$= \overline{AB}\left(\frac{1}{2} - \frac{1}{3}\right) + \overline{BC}\left(\frac{1}{3} - \frac{1}{6}\right) + \overline{CA}\left(-\frac{1}{2} + \frac{1}{6}\right)$$

$$= \frac{1}{6}\left[\overline{AB} + \overline{BC} + \overline{CA}\right] - \frac{1}{2}\,\overline{CA} = \frac{1}{6}\left[\overline{0}\right] + \frac{1}{2}\,\overline{AC}.$$

Thus the resultant is $\tfrac{1}{2}\overline{AC}$ parallel to the side AC and it passes through the centroid which is the meeting point of the medians AD, BE.

Let the resultant intersect BC at P. Then GP is parallel to AC and

$$\frac{BP}{PC} = \frac{BG}{GE} = \frac{2}{1}.$$

because $BG : GE = 2{:}1$.

Example 5. Find the magnitude and direction of the resultant of three coplanar forces P, $2P$, $3P$ acting at a point and inclined mutually at an equal angle of 120°. **(M.K.U., Bn.U.)**

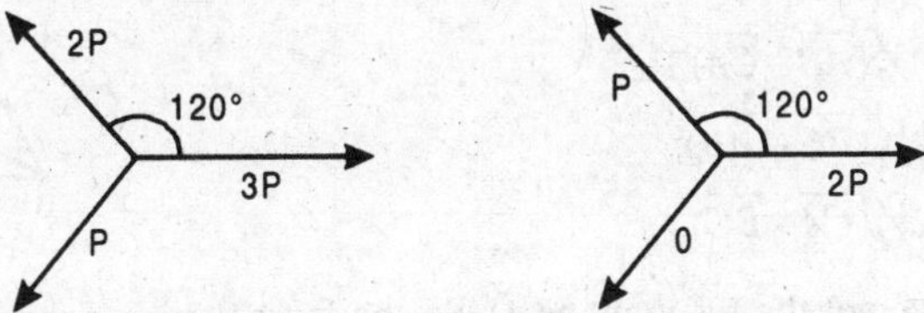

Considering only P, P, P, from the given forces we see that their resultant is zero since they are equally inclined to one another. So the remaining forces are $2P$, P as in the second figure. Their resultant is

$$\sqrt{4P^2 + P^2 - 4P^2 \cos 120^\circ} = \sqrt{3}\,P.$$

If the resultant makes an angle θ with the given force $3P$, then

$$\tan\theta = \frac{P \sin 120^\circ}{2P + P\cos 120^\circ} = \frac{1}{\sqrt{3}} \text{ or } \theta = 30^\circ.$$

Example 6. Three forces proportional to the sides of a triangle act at the vertices towards and perpendicular to the corresponding sides. Prove that the forces are in equilibrium.

Let ABC be the triangle and AD, BE, CF, its altitudes. Then the given forces are of the form

$$\lambda a\,\widehat{AD},\ \lambda b\,\widehat{BE},\ \lambda c\,\widehat{CF},$$

These forces concur at the orthocentre. So their resultant acts through the orthocentre. This resultant is

$$\lambda(a\,\widehat{AD} + b\,\widehat{BE} + c\,\widehat{CF}). \qquad ...(1)$$

Multiplying this scalarly by $\widehat{BC}$, we get

$$\lambda\{a(0)+b\cos(90^\circ - C)+c\cos(90^\circ + B)\}$$

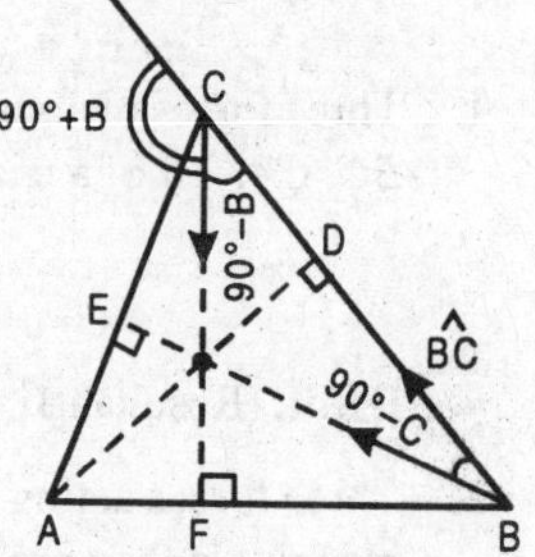

or

$$\lambda(b\sin C - c\sin B).$$

This quantity vanishes because we have

$$\frac{b}{\sin B}=\frac{c}{\sin C}.$$

So the vector (1) either vanishes or is perpendicular to BC. Similarly, it either vanishes or is perpendicular to CA. It cannot be perpendicular to both BC and CA. So it must vanish.

Remark. Three forces proportional to the sides of a triangle acting perpendicular to the sides at their midpoints, are in equilibrium. **(M.U.,M.K.U.)**

In this case the forces meet at the circumcentre S. If D, E, F are the midpoints of the sides, then the resultant is

$$\lambda(a\widehat{DS}+b\widehat{ES}+c\widehat{FS}).$$

Multiply this scalarly by $\widehat{BC}$, etc.

Example 7. S and H are the circumcentre and orthocentre of a triangle ABC. Show that

(*i*) the resultant of the forces $\overline{SA}, \overline{SB}, \overline{SC}$ acting at S is $\overline{SH}$,

(*ii*) the resultant of the forces $\overline{HA}, \overline{HB}, \overline{HC}$ acting at H is $2\overline{HS}$.

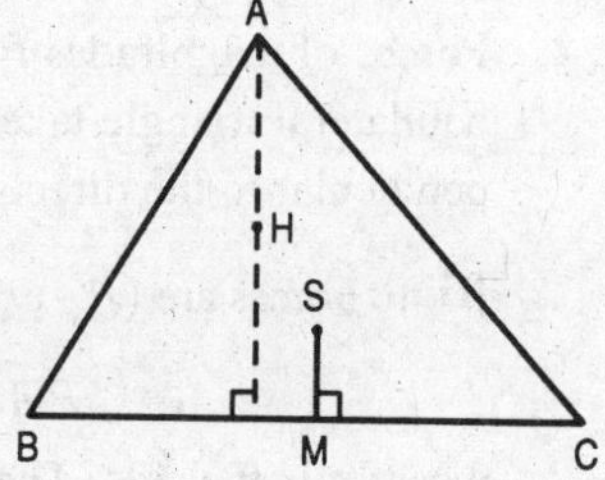

Let M be the midpoint of BC. Then M divides BC in the ratio 1:1. So

$$\overline{SM}=\frac{\overline{SB}+\overline{SC}}{2}$$

or

$$\overline{SB}+\overline{SC}=2\overline{SM}. \qquad ...(1)$$

Similarly, we have

$$\overline{HB}+\overline{HC}=2\overline{HM}. \qquad ...(2)$$

But we know, from geometry, that AH is parallel to SM and $AH = 2\ SM$. So

$$\overline{AH}=2\overline{SM}. \qquad ...(3)$$

(*i*) $\overline{SA}+\overline{SB}+\overline{SC} = \overline{SA}+2\overline{SM}$ by (1)

$= \overline{SA}+\overline{AH}$ by (3)

$= \overline{SH}.$

(*ii*) $\overline{HA}+\overline{HB}+\overline{HC} = \overline{HA}+2\overline{HM}.$ by (2)

$= 2\overline{MS}+2\overline{HM}$ by (3)

$= 2\left(\overline{MS}+\overline{HM}\right)=2\left(\overline{HM}+\overline{MS}\right)=2\overline{HS}.$

EXERCISES

1. Three forces of equal magnitudes P act on a particle. If their directions are parallel to the sides BC, CA, AB of a triangle ABC, show that the magnitude of their resultant is

$$P\sqrt{(3-2\cos A-2\cos B-2\cos C)}.$$

[**Hint:** $(\text{Resultant})^2 = P(\widehat{AB}+\widehat{BC}+\widehat{CA})\cdot P(\widehat{AB}+\widehat{BC}+\widehat{CA})$]

2. Three forces acting at a point are parallel to the sides of a triangle ABC, taken in order, and in magnitude they are proportional to the cosines of the opposite angles. Show that the magnitude of their resultant is proportional to $\sqrt{(1-8\cos A\cos B\cos C)}$. **(M.U.)**

[**Hint:** Forces: $k\cos A\,\widehat{BC}, k\cos B\,\widehat{CA}, k\cos C\,\widehat{AB}$; $(\text{Resultant})^2$ is

$$k^2(\cos A\,\widehat{BC}+\cos B\,\widehat{CA}+\cos C\,\widehat{AB})\cdot(\cos A\,\widehat{BC}+\cos B\,\widehat{CA}+\cos C\,\widehat{AB}).$$

Use $\cos^2 A+\cos^2 B+\cos^2 C = 1-2\cos A\cos B\cos C$.]

3. Three forces of magnitudes P, Q, R act at a point. Another set of three forces P', Q', R' act at another point. If the directions of the forces in both the cases are parallel to the sides BC, CA, AB of a triangle ABC, and if their resultants are parallel to each other, then show that

$$(QR'-Q'R)\sin A+(RP'-R'P)\sin B+(PQ'-P'Q)\sin C = 0.$$

[**Hint:** $(P\widehat{BC}+Q\widehat{CA}+R\widehat{AB})\times(P'\widehat{BC}+Q'\widehat{CA}+R'\widehat{AB}) = \overline{0}$.]

4. Forces of magnitudes $P-Q$, P, $P+Q$ act at a point in directions parallel to the sides of an equilateral triangle taken in order. Show that the resultant is of magnitude $Q\sqrt{3}$ acting perpendicular to the direction of the second force. **(A.U., M.K.U.)**

[**Hint:** Forces are $(P-Q)\widehat{AB}, P\widehat{BC}, (P+Q)\widehat{CA}$. Summing the P-terms only,

$$P\widehat{AB}+P\widehat{BC}+P\widehat{CA} = {}^{P}\!/_{a}(\overline{AB}+\overline{BC}+\overline{CA}) = \overline{0},$$

where a is the side. The left out forces are $-Q\widehat{AB}$, $Q\widehat{CA}$. They are equal in magnitude. So their resultant bisects $\angle A$ and so is perpendicular to BC.]

5. D, E, F, are midpoints of the sides of a triangle ABC. If O is any point in space, show that the forces $\overline{OA}, \overline{OB}, \overline{OC}, \overline{DO}, \overline{EO}, \overline{FO}$ are in equilibrium. **(M.U.)**

[**Hint:** $\Sigma\overline{OA}+\Sigma\overline{DO} = \Sigma\overline{a}+\Sigma\{-\tfrac{1}{2}(\overline{b}+\overline{c})\} = \overline{0}$, where $\overline{OA}=\overline{a}$, $\overline{OB}=\overline{b}$, $\overline{OC}=\overline{c}$]

6. G and G' are the centroids of two triangles ABC and $A'B'C'$ in space. Show that the forces $\overline{GA}, \overline{GB}, \overline{GC}$ are in equilibrium. Also show that the resultant of the forces $\overline{AA'}, \overline{BB'}, \overline{CC'}$ acting at a point is $3\overline{GG'}$.

[**Hint:** $\overline{AG}=\overline{OG}-\overline{OA}$. So $\Sigma\,\overline{AG}=\overline{0}$, since $\overline{OA}+\overline{OB}+\overline{OC}=3\overline{OG}$ So also $\Sigma\,\overline{A'G'}=\overline{0}$ or $\Sigma\,\overline{G'A'}=\overline{0}$. Thus, we have $\Sigma\,\overline{AA'} = \Sigma(\overline{AG}+\overline{GG'}+\overline{G'A'}) = \overline{0}+3\overline{GG'}+\overline{0}$]

2.2.2 Resultant of several forces acting on a particle.

Bookwork 2.4. To find the resultant of coplanar forces using their components.

Let us find the resultant of the forces $\overline{F}_1, \overline{F}_2, \ldots\ldots, \overline{F}_n$. Now the resultant is

$$\overline{F}_1+\overline{F}_2,+\ldots\ldots+\overline{F}_n = X\,\overline{i}+Y\,\overline{j},\text{say}.$$

Multiplying this scalarly by $\bar{i}$,

$$\bar{F}_1\cdot\bar{i}+\bar{F}_2\cdot\bar{i}+\ldots\ldots+\bar{F}_n\cdot\bar{i}=X\,\bar{i}\cdot\bar{i}=X.$$

Now $\bar{F}_1\cdot\bar{i}$ is the component of $\bar{F}_1$ in the $\bar{i}$ direction. So X is the sum of the components of the forces in the $\bar{i}$ direction. Similarly Y is the sum of the components of the forces in the $\bar{j}$ direction. Now the magnitude of the resultant is

$$\left|1X\bar{i}+Y\bar{j}\right|=\sqrt{X^2+Y^2}$$

and the angle between the resultant and the $\bar{i}$ direction is

$$\tan^{-1}\frac{Y}{X}.$$

EXAMPLES

Example 1. Five forces acting at a point are represented in magnitude and direction by the lines joining the vertices of any pentagon to the midpoints of their opposite sides. Show that they are in equilibrium.

(M.K.U)

Let $ABCDE$ be the pentagon and A', B', C', D', E' be the midpoints of sides opposite to A, B, C, D, E. Let

$$\overline{AB}=\bar{a},\ \overline{BC}=\bar{b},\ldots\ldots,\ \overline{EA}=\bar{e}.$$

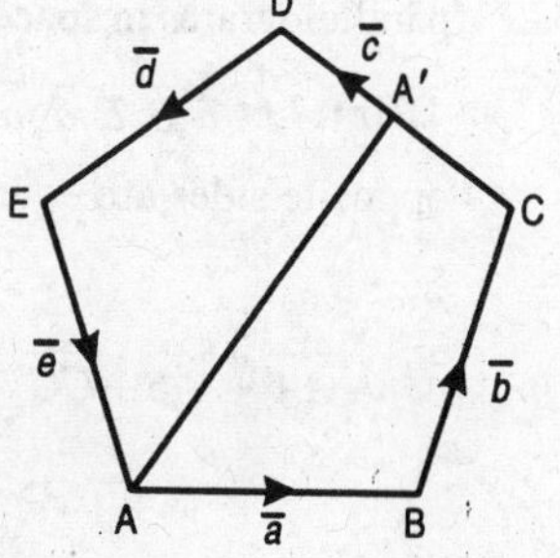

Then

$$\bar{a}+\bar{b}+\bar{c}+\bar{d}+\bar{e}=\bar{0}.$$

Now considering the force $\overline{AA'}$, we have

$$\overline{AA'}=\overline{AB}+\overline{BC}+\overline{CA}=\bar{a}+\bar{b}+\tfrac{1}{2}\bar{c}$$

$$\therefore\quad \Sigma\overline{AA'}=\tfrac{5}{2}\left(\bar{a}+\bar{b}+\bar{c}+\bar{d}+\bar{e}\right)=\bar{0}.$$

Example 2. E is the midpoint of the side CD of a square $ABCD$. Forces 16, 20, $4\sqrt{5}$, $12\sqrt{2}$ act along $\overline{AB}, \overline{AD}, \overline{EA}, \overline{CA}$. Show that they are in equilibrium.

All the forces act through A. Let $\bar{i}, \bar{j}$ be the unit vectors along AB, AD. Then, if $AB = a$,

$$\overline{EA}=\left(-\tfrac{1}{2}\bar{i}-\bar{j}\right)a,$$

$$\overline{CA}=\left(-\bar{i}-\bar{j}\right)a.$$

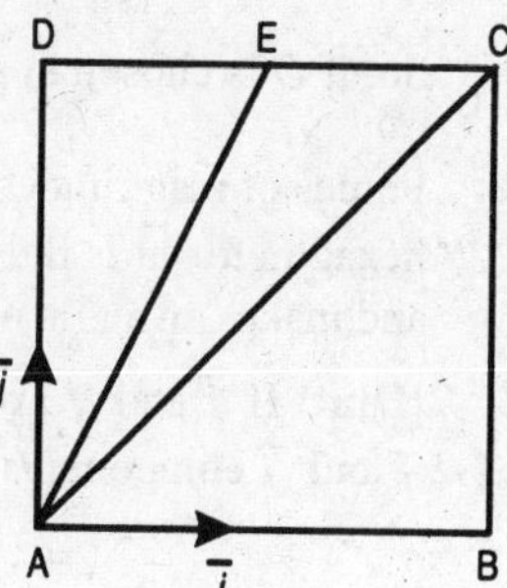

So the unit vectors along $\overline{EA}, \overline{CA}$ are

$$\frac{-\tfrac{1}{2}\bar{i}-\bar{j}}{\sqrt{\tfrac{1}{4}+1}},\ \frac{-\bar{i}-\bar{j}}{\sqrt{2}}.$$

$$\therefore\quad \text{Resultant}=16\bar{i}+20\bar{j}+4\sqrt{5}\frac{-\tfrac{1}{2}\bar{i}-\bar{j}}{\sqrt{\tfrac{1}{4}+1}}+12\sqrt{2}\frac{-\bar{i}-\bar{j}}{\sqrt{2}}$$

$$=16\bar{i}+20\bar{j}-4\sqrt{5}\left(\tfrac{1}{2}\bar{i}+\bar{j}\right)\frac{2}{\sqrt{5}}-12\left(\bar{i}+\bar{j}\right)$$

$$=\bar{i}\,(16-4-12)+\bar{j}\,(20-8-12)=\bar{0}$$

EXERCISES

1. Forces acting at a point are represented in magnitude and direction by $\overline{AB}, 2\overline{BC}, 2\overline{CD}, \overline{DA}, \overline{DB}$ where $ABCD$ is a square. Show that the forces are in equilibrium. **(M.K.U.)**

[Hint: Let $\overline{AB} = \overline{a}, \widehat{AD} = \overline{b}$. Then the resultant is $\overline{a} + 2\overline{b} - 2\overline{a} - \overline{b} + \left(-\overline{b} + \overline{a}\right) = \overline{0}$.]

2. 15 forces act a point and are represented in magnitude and direction by the lines drawn from each of the vertices of a pentagon to the middle points of those sides not passing through the vertex. Show that they are in equilibrium. **(M.U.)**

[Hint: Let $ABCDE$ be the pentagon and let L, M, N be the midpoints of BC, CD, DE, the sides not passing through A. Let $\overline{OA} = \overline{a}$, etc.

$$\overline{AL} + \overline{AM} + \overline{AN} = \left(\overline{OL} - \overline{OA}\right) + \left(\overline{OM} - \overline{OA}\right) + \left(\overline{ON} - \overline{OA}\right)$$

$$= \overline{OL} + \overline{OM} + \overline{ON} - 3\overline{OA} = \tfrac{1}{2}\left(\overline{b} + \overline{c}\right) + \tfrac{1}{2}\left(\overline{c} + \overline{d}\right) + \tfrac{1}{2}\left(\overline{d} + \overline{e}\right) - 3\overline{a}$$

$$= -3\overline{a} + \tfrac{1}{2}\overline{b} + \overline{c} + \overline{d} + \tfrac{1}{2}\overline{e}$$

$\therefore$ Resultant $= \Sigma\left[-3\overline{a} + \tfrac{1}{2}\overline{b} + \overline{c} + \overline{d} + \tfrac{1}{2}\overline{e}\right] = \overline{0}$.]

3. Show that the forces $\overline{AA'}, \overline{B'B}, \overline{CC'}, \overline{D'D}$ acting at a point, where $ABCD$, $A'B'C'D'$ are two parallelograms in space, are in equilibrium. **(M.U.)**

[Hint: Let $\overline{a}, \overline{b}, \overline{c}, \overline{d}, \overline{a'}, \overline{b'}, \overline{c'}, \overline{d'}$ be the P.V's of $A, B, C, D, A', B', C', D'$. In a parallelogram the opposite sides are equal and parallel. So $\overline{AB} = \overline{DC}$. Hence

$$\overline{b} - \overline{a} = \overline{c} - \overline{d} \text{ or } -\overline{a} + \overline{b} - \overline{c} + \overline{d} = \overline{0}. \quad ...(1)$$

$$\overline{AA'} + \overline{B'B} + \overline{CC'} + \overline{D'D} = \left(\overline{a'} - \overline{a}\right) + \left(\overline{b} - \overline{b'}\right) + \left(\overline{c'} - \overline{c}\right) + \left(\overline{d} - \overline{d'}\right)$$

$$= (-\overline{a} + \overline{b} - \overline{c} + \overline{d}) - (-\overline{a'} + \overline{b'} - \overline{c'} + \overline{d'}) = \overline{0} \quad \text{by (1)]}$$

4. $ABCD$ is a quadrilateral. Find a point O such that the forces $\overline{OA}, \overline{OB}, \overline{OC}, \overline{OD}$ acting at O may be in equilibrium. **(M.U.)**

[Hint: Let E, F, M be the midpoints of AC, BD, EF. Then

$$\text{Res} = \left(\overline{OA} + \overline{OC}\right) + \left(\overline{OB} + \overline{OD}\right) = 2\overline{OE} + 2\overline{OF} = 2(2\overline{OM}) = 4\overline{OM}.$$

So, if O is chosen at M then the resultant is $\overline{0}$.]

5. Forces of magnitudes $2, \sqrt{3}, 5, \sqrt{3}, 2$ respectively act at one of the angular points of a regular hexagon towards the other five points in order. Show that their resultant is of magnitude 10 and makes an angle of 60° with the first force. **(M.U.)**

[Hint: If $\overline{i}$ and $\overline{j}$ are the unit vectors parallel and perpendicular to the first force, then the $\overline{i}$ and $\overline{j}$ components of the resultant are

$$2 + \sqrt{3}\cos 30° + 5\cos 60° + \sqrt{3}\cos 90° + 2\cos 120°,$$

$$0 + \sqrt{3}\sin 30° + 5\sin 60° + \sqrt{3}\sin 90° + 2\sin 120°.$$

So the resultant is $5\overline{i} + 5\sqrt{3}\,\overline{j}$. Its magnitude is $\sqrt{5^2 + 5^2 \times 3} = 10$.]

EQUILIBRIUM OF A PARTICLE

3.1 EQUILIBRIUM OF A PARTICLE

When the resultant of the forces acting at a point is zero, then the forces are said to be in equilibrium. In this case the particle is at rest inspite of the forces.

3.1.1 Equilibrium of a particle under three forces.

First we consider cases in which a particle is in equilibrium under the action of three forces.

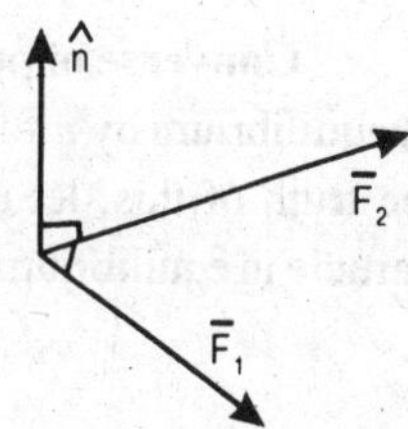

Bookwork 3.1. To show that, if three forces keep a particle in equilibrium, then the forces are coplanar.

Let the forces $\overline{F}_1, \overline{F}_2, \overline{F}_3$, keep a particle in equilibrium. Then the resultant force on the particle is

$$\overline{F}_1 + \overline{F}_2 + \overline{F}_3.$$

Since the particle is in equilibrium,

$$\overline{F}_1 + \overline{F}_2 + \overline{F}_3 = \overline{0}. \qquad ...(1)$$

Let $\hat{n}$ be the unit vector perpendicular to both $\overline{F}_1$ and $\overline{F}_2$. Then

$$\hat{n} \cdot \overline{F}_1 = 0, \qquad \hat{n} \cdot \overline{F}_2 = 0.$$

Now, multiplying (1) scalarly by $\hat{n}$, we see that

$$\hat{n} \cdot \left(\overline{F}_1 + \overline{F}_2 + \overline{F}_3\right) = 0 \text{ or } \hat{n} \cdot \overline{F}_1 + \hat{n} \cdot \overline{F}_2 + \hat{n} \cdot \overline{F}_3 = 0.$$

But $\hat{n} \cdot \overline{F}_1 = 0$ and $\hat{n} \cdot \overline{F}_2 = 0$. So $\hat{n} \cdot \overline{F}_3 = 0$ which means that $\overline{F}_3$ also is perpendicular to $\hat{n}$. Therefore $\overline{F}_1, \overline{F}_2$ and $\overline{F}_3$ are coplanar.

Bookwork 3.2 (Triangle of forces). If three forces acting on a particle can be represented in magnitude and direction by the sides of a triangle, taken in order, then the forces keep the particle in equilibrium.

Let the given forces be represented in magnitude and direction by the sides AB, BC, CA of a triangle ABC. Then the forces are

$$\overline{AB}, \overline{BC}, \overline{CA}.$$

Their resultant is $\overline{AB} + \overline{BC} + \overline{CA}$. But, by vector theory, $\overline{AB} + \overline{BC} + \overline{CA} = \overline{0}$. Hence the resultant force acting on the particle is zero. So the particle is in equilibrium.

Bookwork 3.3 (Converse of triangle of forces). If a particle is kept in equilibrium by three forces, then the forces can be represented in magnitude and direction by the sides of a triangle, taken in order.

Let the given forces be

$$\overline{F}_1, \overline{F}_2, \overline{F}_3.$$

They keep the particle in equilibrium. So their resultant is zero. Hence

$$\bar{F}_1 + \bar{F}_2 + \bar{F}_3 = \bar{0}$$

or

$$\bar{F}_1 + \bar{F}_2 = -\bar{F}_3.$$

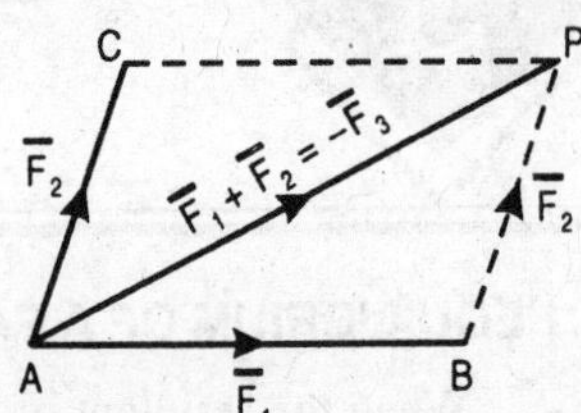

Let AB, AC, denote $\bar{F}_1$, $\bar{F}_2$ in magnitude and direction. Complete the parallelogram $ABPC$. Then BP denotes $\bar{F}_2$ and AP denotes $\bar{F}_1 + \bar{F}_2$ in magnitude and direction. But $\bar{F}_1 + \bar{F}_2 = -\bar{F}_3$. So AP denotes $-\bar{F}_3$. Hence PA denotes $\bar{F}_3$. This completes the proof.

Polygon of forces. It can be easily seen that, if several coplanar forces acting on a particle can be represented in magnitude and direction by the sides of a polygon, taken in order, the forces keep the particle in equilibrium. This result is called the polygon of forces.

Converse of polygon of forces. The converse of polygon of forces is that, "if a particle is kept in equilibrium by n forces, then they can be represented by the sides of a n-sided polygon". To prove the truth of this, let us consider, in particular, the six forces $\bar{F}_1, \bar{F}_2, \bar{F}_3, \bar{F}_4, \bar{F}_5, \bar{F}_6$ which keeps a particle in equilibrium. Because of equilibrium,

$$\bar{F}_1 + \bar{F}_2 + \bar{F}_3 + \bar{F}_4 + \bar{F}_5 + \bar{F}_6 = \bar{0}. \quad ...(1)$$

Take points A, B, C, D, E, F such that

$$\overline{AB} = \bar{F}_1,\ \overline{BC} = \bar{F}_2,\ \overline{CD} = \bar{F}_3,\ \overline{DE} = \bar{F}_4,\ \overline{EF} = \bar{F}_5.$$

Now, from vector theory, we have

$$\overline{AB} + \overline{BC} + \overline{CD} + \overline{DE} + \overline{EF} + \overline{FA} = \bar{0}. \quad ...(2)$$

From (1) and (2) we get $\overline{FA} = \bar{F}_6$. This completes the proof.

Lami's theorem. The following bookwork is an important one. This is called Lami's theorem.

Bookwork 3.4. If a particle is in equilibrium under the action of three forces $\bar{P}, \bar{Q}, \bar{R}$, then to show that

$$\frac{P}{\sin\alpha} = \frac{Q}{\sin\beta} = \frac{R}{\sin\gamma},$$

where α is the angle between $\bar{Q}$ and $\bar{R}$, β is the angle between $\bar{R}$ and $\bar{P}$, and γ is the angle between $\bar{P}$ and $\bar{Q}$ and $|\bar{P}| = P$, etc.

The forces keep the particle in equilibrium. So they are coplanar and their resultant is zero. Hence

$$\bar{P} + \bar{Q} + \bar{R} = \bar{0}.$$

Multiplying this vectorially by $\bar{P}$,

$$\bar{P} \times \bar{P} + \bar{P} \times \bar{Q} + \bar{P} \times \bar{R} = \bar{0}. \quad ...(1)$$

Let $\hat{n}$ be the unit vector perpendicular to the forces such that $\bar{P}, \bar{Q}, \hat{n}$ form a right-handed triad. Then (1) becomes

$$\bar{0} + PQ\sin\gamma\,\hat{n} + PR\sin\beta\,(-\hat{n}) = \bar{0}$$

$$\therefore \quad (PQ\sin\gamma - PR\sin\beta)\,\hat{n} = \bar{0}.$$

$\therefore \qquad PQ \sin\gamma - PR \sin\beta = 0 \quad \text{or} \quad Q \sin\gamma = R \sin\beta.$

$$\therefore \qquad \frac{Q}{\sin\beta} = \frac{R}{\sin\gamma}. \qquad ...(2)$$

Similarly the vectorial multiplication of $\overline{P}+\overline{Q}+\overline{R}=\overline{0}$ by $\overline{Q}$ gives

$$\frac{P}{\sin\alpha} = \frac{R}{\sin\gamma}. \qquad ...(3)$$

From (2) and (3), we get

$$\frac{P}{\sin\alpha} = \frac{Q}{\sin\beta} = \frac{R}{\sin\gamma}.$$

Remark. If four forces $F_1\hat{e}_1$, $F_2\hat{e}_2$, $F_3\hat{e}_3$, $F_4\hat{e}_4$ acting on a particle keep it in equilibrium, where $\hat{e}_1$, $\hat{e}_2$, $\hat{e}_3$, $\hat{e}_4$ are unit vectors, then

$$\frac{F_1}{[\hat{e}_2\ \hat{e}_3\ \hat{e}_4]} = -\frac{F_2}{[\hat{e}_1\ \hat{e}_3\ \hat{e}_4]} = \frac{F_3}{[\hat{e}_1\ \hat{e}_2\ \hat{e}_4]} = -\frac{F_4}{[\hat{e}_1\ \hat{e}_2\ \hat{e}_3]}$$

because multiplying $F_1\hat{e}_1 + F_2\hat{e}_2 + F_3\hat{e}_3 + F_4\hat{e}_4 = \overline{0}$ scalarly by $\hat{e}_3 \times \hat{e}_4$, we get

$$F_1[\hat{e}_1\hat{e}_3\hat{e}_4] + F_2[\hat{e}_2\hat{e}_3\hat{e}_4] = 0 \quad \text{or} \quad \frac{F_1}{[\hat{e}_2\ \hat{e}_3\ \hat{e}_4]} = -\frac{F_2}{[\hat{e}_1\ \hat{e}_3\ \hat{e}_4]}, etc.$$

3.1.2 Equilibrium of a particle under several forces.

Now we study the situation in which a particle is in equilibrium under three or more forces.

Bookwork 3.5. To prove that the necessary and sufficient conditions for a system of coplanar forces to keep a particle in equilibrium, is that the sums of the components of the forces in two mutually perpendicular directions in the plane are zero.

Necessity part. Let the forces be $\overline{F}_1, \overline{F}_2, \ldots, \overline{F}_n$. Then the resultant force acting on the particle is

$$\overline{F}_1 + \overline{F}_2 + \ldots + \overline{F}_n.$$

So, if the particle is in equilibrium, then

$$\overline{F}_1 + \overline{F}_2 + \ldots + \overline{F}_n = \overline{0}. \qquad ...(1)$$

Let $\overline{i}$, $\overline{j}$ be the unit vectors in two perpendicular directions. Multiplying (1) scalarly by $\overline{i}$ and $\overline{j}$,

$$\left(\overline{F}_1 + \overline{F}_2 + \ldots + \overline{F}_n\right)\cdot\overline{i} = 0, \quad \left(\overline{F}_1 + \overline{F}_2 + \ldots + \overline{F}_n\right)\cdot\overline{j} = 0$$

or $\qquad \overline{F}_1\cdot\overline{i} + \overline{F}_2\cdot\overline{i} + \ldots + \overline{F}_n\cdot\overline{i} = 0, \quad \overline{F}_1\cdot\overline{j} + \overline{F}_2\cdot\overline{j} + \ldots + \overline{F}_n\cdot\overline{j} = 0.$

This proves the necessity part that,

if the particle is in equilibrium, then the sums of the components of the forces in two mutually perpendicular directions are zero.

Sufficiency part. Now we have that the sums of the components are zeros. That is,

$$\overline{F}_1\cdot\overline{i} + \overline{F}_2\cdot\overline{i} + \ldots + \overline{F}_n\cdot\overline{i} = 0,$$

$$\overline{F}_1\cdot\overline{j} + \overline{F}_2\cdot\overline{j} + \ldots + \overline{F}_n\cdot\overline{j} = 0.$$

These imply that

$$\left(\overline{F}_1+\overline{F}_2+....+\overline{F}_n\right)\cdot\overline{i}=0,\ \left(\overline{F}_1+\overline{F}_2+....+\overline{F}_n\right)\cdot\overline{j}=0.$$

That is, the resultant force is either perpendicular to both $\overline{i}$ and $\overline{j}$ or is a zero force. The perpendicularity cannot happen. Thus

$$\overline{F}_1+\overline{F}_2+...+\overline{F}_n=\overline{0}.$$

EXAMPLES

Example 1. I is the incentre of a triangle ABC. If forces of magnitudes P, Q, R acting along the bisectors IA, IB, IC are in equilibrium, show that

$$\frac{P}{\cos A/2}=\frac{Q}{\cos B/2}=\frac{R}{\cos C/2}.$$ **(M.U., M.K.U., Bn.U.)**

The forces P, Q, R act at I and are in equilibrium. So we shall use Lami's theorem. The angles opposite to P, Q, R are

$$\angle BIC,\ \angle CIA,\ \angle AIB.$$

$$\therefore\quad \frac{P}{\sin BIC}=\frac{Q}{\sin CIA}=\frac{R}{\sin AIB} \qquad ...(1)$$

Now, from ΔBIC,

$$\angle BIC=180^\circ-\left(B/2+C/2\right).$$

$$\therefore\quad \sin BIC=\sin\left(B/2+C/2\right)=\sin\left(90^\circ-A/2\right)=\cos A/2.$$

Similarly $\sin CIA=\cos B/2$, $\sin AIB=\cos C/2$. Thus (1) becomes

$$\frac{P}{\cos A/2}=\frac{Q}{\cos B/2}=\frac{R}{\cos C/2}.$$

Example 2. I is the incentre of a triangle ABC. If the forces, $\overline{IA}, \overline{IB}, \overline{IC}$ acting at I are in equilibrium, show that ABC is an equilateral triangle. **(M.U.)**

In the previous example we have the forces P, Q, R. Instead of them, now we have AI, BI, CI.

$$\therefore\quad \frac{AI}{\cos A/2}=\frac{BI}{\cos B/2}=\frac{CI}{\cos C/2} \qquad ...(1)$$

But, if r is the radius of the incentre, then

$$\frac{r}{AI}=\sin\frac{A}{2},\ \frac{r}{BI}=\sin\frac{B}{2},\ \frac{r}{CI}=\sin\frac{C}{2}.$$

On eliminating AI, BI, CI from (1), we have

$$\frac{1}{\sin A/2\cos A/2}=\frac{1}{\sin B/2\cos B/2}=\frac{1}{\sin C/2\cos C/2}$$

i.e.,

$$\frac{1}{\sin A}=\frac{1}{\sin B}=\frac{1}{\sin C}.$$

which implies that $A=B=C$ and so the triangle is equilateral.

Example 3. O is the orthocentre of a triangle ABC. If forces of magnitude P, Q, R acting along OA, OB, OC are in equilibrium, show that **(M.U.)**

$$\frac{P}{a}=\frac{Q}{b}=\frac{R}{c}.$$

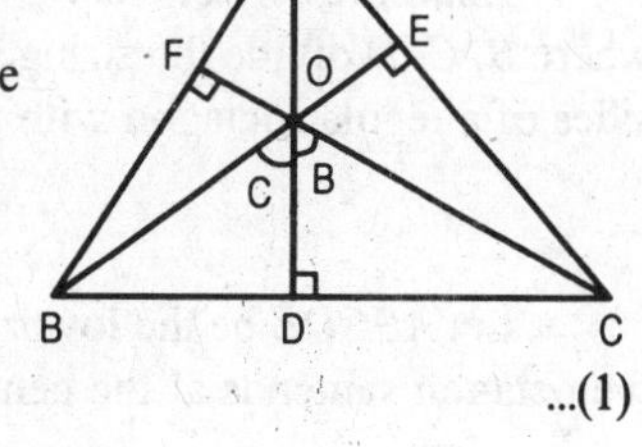

The forces P, Q, R act at O and are in equilibrium. So we shall use Lami's theorem. The angles opposite to P, Q, R are

$$\angle BOC, \angle COA, \angle AOB.$$

$$\therefore \quad \frac{P}{\sin BOC}=\frac{Q}{\sin COA}=\frac{R}{\sin AOB} \quad ...(1)$$

If AD is the altitude through A,

$$\angle BOD = C, \ \angle COD = B$$

since $CBE = 90° - C$, etc.

$$\therefore \quad \angle BOC = B + C.$$

$$\therefore \quad \sin BOC = \sin(B+C) = \sin(180° - A) = \sin A.$$

Similarly $\sin COA = \sin B$, $\sin AOB = \sin C$. Thus (1) becomes

$$\frac{P}{\sin A}=\frac{Q}{\sin B}=\frac{R}{\sin C}.$$

But, by sine formula, $\sin A : \sin B : \sin C = a : b : c$.

$$\therefore \quad \frac{P}{a}=\frac{Q}{b}=\frac{R}{c}.$$

Example 4. Three forces of magnitudes P, Q, R acting at a point being parallel to the sides of a triangle, are in equilibrium. If another set of forces of magnitudes P', Q', R' acting at a point being parallel to the sides of the same triangle, are also in equilibrium, show that

$$\frac{P}{P'}=\frac{Q}{Q'}=\frac{R}{R'}. \quad \textbf{(M.U.)}$$

Let ABC be the triangle. Then the forces acting at the first point are $P\,\widehat{BC}, Q\,\widehat{CA}, R\,\widehat{AB}$. Since they are in equilibrium,

$$P\,\widehat{BC} + Q\,\widehat{CA} + R\,\widehat{AB} = \overline{0}.$$

Similarly, for the second case,

$$P'\,\widehat{BC} + Q'\,\widehat{CA} + R'\,\widehat{AB} = \overline{0}.$$

These two relations can be rewritten as

$$\frac{P}{R}\widehat{BC}+\frac{Q}{R}\widehat{CA}=-\widehat{AB}, \quad \frac{P'}{R'}\widehat{BC}+\frac{Q'}{R'}\widehat{CA}=-\widehat{AB}.$$

So, eliminating $\widehat{AB}$ by subtraction, we get

$$\left(\frac{P}{R}-\frac{P'}{R'}\right)\widehat{BC}+\left(\frac{Q}{R}-\frac{Q'}{R'}\right)\widehat{CA}=\overline{0}.$$

We know that, if $\overline{a}$ and $\overline{b}$ are two non-parallel vectors and if $l\overline{a}+m\overline{b}=\overline{0}$, then $l=0$ and $m=0$. So here

$$\frac{P}{R}-\frac{P'}{R'}=0,\ \frac{Q}{R}-\frac{Q'}{R'}=0.$$

These lead to the result as stated.

Example 5. Weights W, w, W are attached to points B, C, D, respectively of a light string AE where B, C, D divide the string into 4 equal lengths. If the string hangs in the form of 4 consecutive sides of a regular octagon with the ends A and E attached to points on the same level, show that

$$W=\left(\sqrt{2}+1\right)w.$$ **(Bn.U., A.U.)**

Let $ABCDE$ be the lower half of the octagon. Each side of the octagon subtends at the centre O an angle

$$\frac{180°}{4} \text{ or } 45°.$$

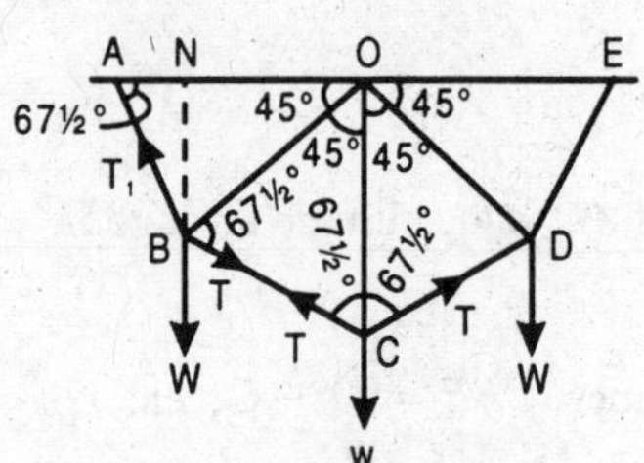

Now $\Delta OAB, \Delta OBC, \Delta OCD, \Delta ODE$ are isosceles triangles with vertical angles $45°$ and the base angles $67\frac{1}{2}°$. The figure is self explanatory.

The forces at C are w and the equal tensions T, T (equal due to symmetry). The angles opposite to w and T are

$$\angle BCD,\ \angle BCw \text{ or } 67\tfrac{1}{2}°+67\tfrac{1}{2}°,\ 180°-67\tfrac{1}{2}°.$$

So, by Lami's theorem,

$$\frac{w}{\sin(67\frac{1}{2}°+67\frac{1}{2}°)}=\frac{T}{\sin(180°-67\frac{1}{2}°)} \text{ or } \frac{w}{\sin 135°}=\frac{T}{\sin 67\frac{1}{2}°}. \quad ...(1)$$

The forces at B are W, T, T_1. The angles opposite to W and T are

$$\angle ABC,\ \angle ABW \text{ or } 67\tfrac{1}{2}°+67\tfrac{1}{2}°,\ 180°-22\tfrac{1}{2}°$$

$$\therefore \quad \frac{W}{\sin 135°}=\frac{T}{\sin 22\frac{1}{2}°}. \quad ...(2)$$

Dividing (2) by (1), we get

$$\frac{W}{w}=\frac{\sin 67\frac{1}{2}°}{\sin 22\frac{1}{2}°}=\frac{\cos 22\frac{1}{2}°}{\sin 22\frac{1}{2}°}=\frac{1}{\tan 22\frac{1}{2}°}$$

$$=\frac{1}{\sqrt{2}-1}=\frac{\sqrt{2}+1}{2-1}=\sqrt{2}+1.$$

$$\therefore \quad W=(\sqrt{2}+1)w.$$

Example 6. A heavy bead of weight W can slide on a smooth circular wire in a vertical plane. The bead is attached to a light thread to the highest point of the wire, and in equilibrium, the thread is taut and makes an angle θ with the vertical. Show that the tension of the thread and the reaction of the wire on the bead are $2W\cos\theta$ and W. **(M.U., C.U.)**

Let A be the highest point of the circle, O the centre and P the bead. It is given that $\angle OAP=\theta$. But $OA = OP$ and so ΔOAP is isosceles. Thus $\angle OPA=\theta$. Now the forces on the bead are

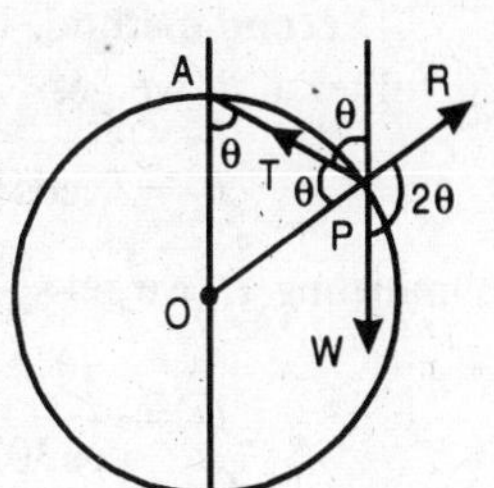

(*i*) Tension T

(*ii*) Normal Reaction R

(*iii*) Weight W.

The angles opposite to them are

$$2\theta,\ 180^\circ-\theta,\ 180^\circ-\theta$$

Therefore, by Lami's theorem, we have

$$\frac{T}{\sin 2\theta}=\frac{R}{\sin(180^\circ-\theta)}=\frac{W}{\sin(180^\circ-\theta)}$$

$$\frac{T}{\sin 2\theta}=\frac{R}{\sin\theta}=\frac{W}{\sin\theta} \quad \text{or} \quad \frac{T}{2\cos\theta}=R=W$$

$\therefore$ $$T=2W\cos\theta,\ R=W.$$

Example 7. A bead of weight W is free to slide on a smooth vertical circle and is connected by a string whose length equals the radius of the circle to the highest point of the circle. Find the tension of the string and the reaction of the circle. **(M.K.U.)**

In the previous example AP was not given. But now AP = radius. So ΔOAP is equilateral and thus $\theta=60^\circ$. Therefore

$$\frac{T}{\sin 120^\circ}=\frac{R}{\sin 120^\circ}=\frac{W}{\sin 120^\circ} \quad \text{or} \quad T=R=W.$$

Example 8. A string $ABCD$ hangs from fixed points A, D carrying a mass of 12 kg. at B and a mass of m kg. at C. AB is inclined at 60° to the horizontal, BC is horizontal and CD is inclined at 30° to the horizontal. Show that $m = 4$. **(M.U.)**

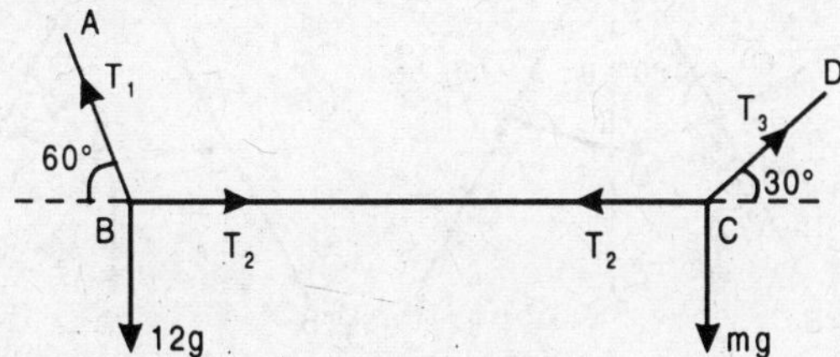

First method. Let the forces acting on the system be $T_1, T_2, T_3, 12g, mg$ as shown in the figure. By Lami's theorem, for the forces at B,

$$\frac{T_2}{\sin(90^\circ+60^\circ)}=\frac{12g}{\sin(180^\circ-60^\circ)} \quad \text{or} \quad T_2=\frac{12g}{\tan 60^\circ}.$$

But, for the forces at C, we have

$$\frac{T_2}{\sin(90^\circ+30^\circ)}=\frac{mg}{\sin(180^\circ-30^\circ)} \quad \text{or} \quad T_2=\frac{mg}{\tan 30^\circ}.$$

$\therefore$ $$\frac{m}{\tan 30^\circ}=\frac{12}{\tan 60^\circ} \quad \text{or} \quad m=\frac{12}{\sqrt{3}\sqrt{3}}=4.$$

Second method. Using the same figure, considering the horizontal and vertical components for the forces at B, we get

$$T_2 = T_1 \cos 60°, T_1 \cos 30° = 12g.$$

Eliminating T_1 ,we get

$$T_2 = \frac{12g}{\cos 30°}. \cos 60°.$$

Similarly, for the forces at C, we have

$$T_2 = T_3 \cos 30°, \ T_3 \cos 60° = mg$$

$$\therefore \qquad T_2 = \frac{mg \cos 30°}{\cos 60°}.$$

Equating the values of T_2, we get $m = 4$.

Example 9. Two fixed smooth bars AB, AC in a vertical plane are each inclined at $30°$ to the vertical. The ends of a light string are tied to two rings each of weight w which slide on the bars. From the midpoint of the string is hung a weight W. Prove that, in the position of equilibrium, each half of the string will make an angle θ with the vertical given by

$$\tan\theta = \frac{W + 2w}{W}\sqrt{3}. \qquad \textbf{(M.U.)}$$

The forces acting on each ring are tension T inclined to the vertical at an angle θ, normal reaction R perpendicular to the rod and weight w. Thus resolving along the rod downward,

$$w \cos 30° + T \cos(\theta + 30°) = 0. \qquad ...(1)$$

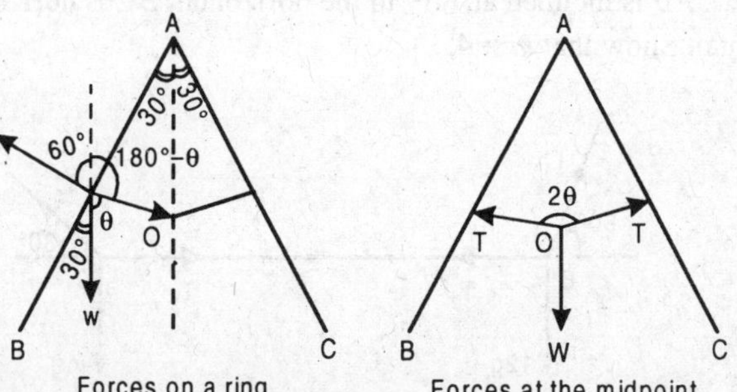

Forces on a ring   Forces at the midpoint

The forces acting at the midpoint of the string are the tensions T and T and the weight W. Resolving them vertically downward,

$$W - 2T \cos\theta = 0. \qquad ...(2)$$

Eliminating T, we get

$$w \cos 30° (2\cos\theta) + W \cos(\theta + 30°) = 0$$

or $\qquad 2w \cos 30° \cos\theta + W [\cos\theta \cos 30° - \sin\theta \sin 30°] = 0$

or $\qquad 2w + W[1 - \tan\theta \tan 30°] = 0$

or $\qquad W \tan\theta \tan 30° = 2w + W. \qquad \therefore \tan\theta = \dfrac{2w + W}{W}\sqrt{3}.$

Example 10. A particle C of weight W is in equilibrium being supported by two strings CA, CB of length $4a$, $3a$ respectively and acted on by a horizontal force W in the plane ABC. If the ends A, B are at the same level and at a distance $5a$ apart, show that the tensions in the strings are $7W/5$, $W/5$. **(M.U.)**

Since $(4a)^2 + (3a)^2 = (5a)^2$,

$$\angle ACB = 90°$$

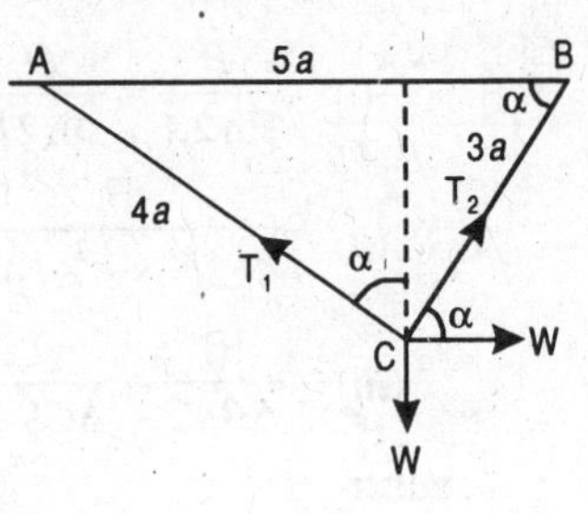

If CA is inclined to the vertical at an angle α, then

$$\cos\alpha = 3/5, \; \sin\alpha = 4/5.$$

If T_1 and T_2 are tensions along CA and CB, resolving horizontally to the right and vertically upwards,

$$T_2 \cos\alpha - T_1 \sin\alpha + W = 0,$$

$$T_2 \sin\alpha + T_1 \cos\alpha - W = 0.$$

Substituting the values of $\cos\alpha$ and $\sin\alpha$ and simplifying,

$$3T_2 - 4T_1 + 5W = 0,$$

$$4T_2 + 3T_1 - 5W = 0.$$

Solving these, we get $T_1 = \dfrac{7W}{5}$, $T_2 = \dfrac{W}{5}$.

Example 11. A weight is supported on a smooth plane of inclination α by a string inclined to the horizon at an angle γ. If the slope of the plane be increased to β and the slope of the string be unaltered, the tension of the string is doubled. Prove that

$$\cot\alpha - 2\cot\beta = \tan\gamma. \qquad \textbf{(M.U., M.K.U.)}$$

The forces acting on the particle are

(*i*) Normal reaction R

(*ii*) Weight W

(*iii*) Tension T

Considering the vertical components, we have

$$R\cos\alpha + T\sin\gamma = W$$

or

$$R\cos\alpha = W - T\sin\gamma. \qquad ...(1)$$

From the horizontal components, we get

$$R\sin\alpha = T\cos\gamma. \qquad ...(2)$$

Dividing (1) by (2), we get

$$\cot\alpha = \frac{W}{T\cos\gamma} - \tan\gamma. \qquad ...(3)$$

When α becomes β, T becomes $2T$. So

$$\cot\beta = \frac{W}{2T\cos\gamma} - \tan\gamma. \qquad ...(4)$$

$(3) - 2(4)$ gives $\cot\alpha - 2\cot\beta = \tan\gamma$.

EXERCISES

1. S is the circumcentre of a triangle ABC. If forces of magnitudes P, Q, R acting along SA, SB, SC are in equilibrium, show that P, Q, R are in the ratio

(i) $$\frac{P}{\sin 2A} = \frac{Q}{\sin 2B} = \frac{R}{\sin 2C}$$ **(Bn.U.)**

(ii) $$\frac{P}{a^2 (b^2 + c^2 - a^2)} = \frac{Q}{b^2 (c^2 + a^2 - b^2)} = \frac{R}{c^2 (a^2 + b^2 - c^2)}$$ **(M.K.U.)**

(iii) $$\frac{P}{\Delta BSC} = \frac{Q}{\Delta CSA} = \frac{R}{\Delta ASB}$$ **(M.U., Bn.U.)**

[Hint:

(i) A is a point on the circumference of the circumcircle. Since BC subtends an angle A at the point A, it subtends an angle $2A$ at the point S. Hence $\angle BSC = 2A$, etc. Use Lami's theorem.

(ii) Use in (i), $\sin 2A = 2\sin A \cos A$ and the results

$$\sin A : \sin B : \sin C = a : b : c,$$

$$\cos A = \frac{b^2 + c^2 - a^2}{2bc} = \frac{a\left(b^2 + c^2 - a^2\right)}{2abc}, \text{ etc.}$$

(iii) $\Delta BSC = \frac{1}{2} SB.\, SC. \sin 2A = \frac{1}{2} R^2 \sin 2A$ etc. So

$$\sin 2A : \sin 2B : \sin 2C = \Delta BSC : \Delta CSA : \Delta ASB.\ ]$$

2. G is the centroid of a triangle ABC. Forces of magnitudes, P, Q, R acting along GA, GB, GC are in equilibrium. Show that

$$\frac{P}{GA} = \frac{Q}{GB} = \frac{R}{GC}.$$ **(M.U., Bn.U.)**

[Hint: $\overline{GA} + \overline{GB} + \overline{GC} = (\overline{OA} - \overline{OG}) + (\overline{OB} - \overline{OG}) + (\overline{OC} - \overline{OG}) = \overline{0}.$

$$\therefore \quad GA\,\widehat{GA} + GB\,\widehat{GB} + GC\,\widehat{GC} = \overline{0}. \quad \text{...(1)}$$

But the forces P, Q, R are in equilibrium. So

$$P\,\widehat{GA} + Q\,\widehat{GB} + R\,\widehat{GC} = \overline{0}. \quad \text{...(2)}$$

Divide (1) by GA and (2) by P and eliminating $G\hat{A}$, equate the coefficients of the other unit vectors to zero.]

3. A string ACB has its extremities tied to two fixed points A and B in the same horizontal line. At C a weight w is knotted. If a, b, c are the sides of ΔABC and Δ is the area find the tension of the string CA in the form

$$\frac{Wb}{4c\Delta}(c^2 + a^2 - b^2).$$ **(M.U, Am.U)**

[Hint: $\dfrac{T}{\sin (90^\circ + B)} = \dfrac{W}{\sin [180^\circ - (A + B)]}$ simplifies to

$$T = W\frac{\cos B}{\sin(A+B)} = W\frac{\cos B}{\sin C}.$$

Use $\cos B = \dfrac{a^2+c^2-b^2}{2ac}$, $\Delta = \dfrac{1}{2}.\ A.\ B.\sin C.$]

4. A and B are two fixed points on a horizontal line at a distance c apart. Two light strings AC and BC of lengths b and a respectively support a mass at C. Show that the tensions of the strings are in the ratio

$$b(a^2+c^2-b^2):a(b^2+c^2-a^2). \qquad \textbf{(M.U.)}$$

[**Hint:** Let M be a point vertically below C. Let $\angle BAC = \alpha$, $\angle ABC = \beta$. Then

$$\angle ACM = 90° + \alpha,\ \angle BCM = 90° + \beta.$$

If the tensions along AC, BC are T_1, T_2, then

$$\frac{T_1}{\sin(90°+\beta)} = \frac{T_2}{\sin(90°+\alpha)}.$$

But $\cos\alpha = \dfrac{b^2+c^2-a^2}{2bc}$, $\cos\beta = \dfrac{a^2+c^2-b^2}{2ca}$.]

5. A heavy body rests on a smooth plane inclined to the horizon at an angle α, being acted on by a force of magnitude S. If the normal reaction of the plane also is S, show that the inclination of the force S to the inclined plane is $90° - 2\alpha$. **(M.U.)**

[**Hint:** The normal reaction S and the force S are equally inclined to the vertical along which the weight acts.]

6. Two heavy particles of weight W and W' are connected by a light inextensible string and placed over a fixed smooth circular cylinder of radius a, the axis of which is horizontal. If θ and θ' are the angles which the radii to the two weights make with the vertical, show that $W\sin\theta = W'\sin\theta'$. **(M.U.)**

[**Hint:** Forces on W are weight W, tension T, normal reaction R. Angles opposite to W, T are 90°, $180° - \theta$. By Lami's theorem,

$$\frac{W}{\sin 90°} = \frac{T}{\sin(180°-\theta)} \text{ or } T = W\sin\theta\ ;\ T = W'\sin\theta'\,]$$

7. A string of length 4m. is attached to two points A and B 2m. apart, in the same horizontal level. A smooth ring of mass 80 gm. threaded to it is acted on by a horizontal force P which holds it in equilibrium at a point vertically below B. Find the tension in the string and the magnitude of P. **(M.U.)**

[**Hint:** If C is the ring and $AC = x$, then, from right-angled the $\Delta ABC, (4-x)^2+2^2 = x^2$ or $x = 5/2$. If $\angle BAC = \alpha$, then $\sin\alpha = 3/5$, $\cos\alpha = 4/5$. Resolving horizontally and vertically, $T\cos\alpha - P = 0, T + T\sin\alpha - 80g = 0; T = 50g, P = 40g.$]

8. A number of particles of equal weight w are attached at various points of a light string, the ends of which are fixed. Show that the cotangents of the angles which the successive portions of the string make with the vertical are in arithmetic progression. **(M.U.)**

[**Hint:** Let any three consecutive tensions in the string be T_1, T_2, T_3 making angles α, β, γ with the vertical. Then

$$\left.\begin{array}{l} T_1 \cos\alpha = T_2 \cos\beta + w \\ T_1 \sin\alpha = T_2 \sin\beta \end{array}\right\} \quad \therefore \cot\alpha = \cot\beta + \frac{w}{T_2 \sin\beta}.$$

$$\left.\begin{array}{l} T_2 \cos\beta = T_3 \cos\gamma + w \\ T_2 \sin\beta = T_3 \sin\gamma \end{array}\right\} \quad \therefore \cot\beta = \cot\gamma + \frac{w}{T_3 \sin\gamma}.$$

So $\cot\alpha - \cot\beta = \cot\beta - \cot\gamma$ since $T_2 \sin\beta = T_3 \sin\gamma$.]

9. Two fixed smooth bars AB, AC in a vertical plane are each inclined at $45°$ to the vertical. The ends of a light string are tied to two rings each of weight w which slide on the bars. From the midpoint of the string is hung a weight W. Prove that in the position of equilibrium, each half of the string will make an angle θ with the vertical given by

$$\tan\theta = \frac{W + 2w}{W}. \qquad \textbf{(M.U.)}$$

[**Hint:** For w, resolving along the bar, $w\cos 45° = T\cos(180° - \theta - 45°)$. For W, resolving vertically, $W = 2T\cos\theta$. Eliminate T]

3.2 LIMITING EQUILIBRIUM OF A PARTICLE ON AN INCLINED PLANE

Bookwork 3.6. Suppose a particle of weight W lying on a rough plane inclined at an angle α to the horizontal is subjected to a force P along the plane in the upward direction. If the equilibrium is limiting, to find P.

Now the following two cases of limiting equilibrium arise :

(*i*) The particle has a tendency to slide up the plane.

(*ii*) The particle has a tendency to slide down the plane.

Case (*i*) Now it is enough to consider the forces acting on the particle along the plane. They are

(*i*) Component of weight $W\sin\alpha$ down the plane

(*ii*) P up the plane

(*iii*) Frictional force F down the plane,

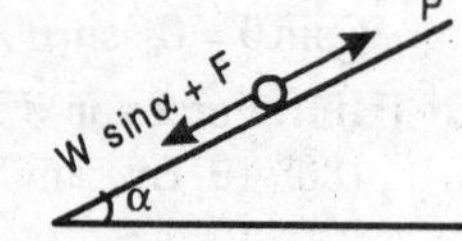

where F has its maximum value so that

$$F = \mu R \quad \text{or} \quad F = \mu(W\cos\alpha),$$

where μ is the coefficient of friction. Thus, in this case, we have

$$P = W\sin\alpha + F \quad \text{or} \quad P = W\sin\alpha + \mu\,(W\cos\alpha).$$

Case (*ii*) In the case in which the particle has a tendency to move downward the frictional force is up the plane and hence we have

$$W\sin\alpha = P + \mu W\cos\alpha$$

or $$P = W(\sin\alpha - \mu\cos\alpha)$$

Bookwork 3.7. Suppose a particle of mass m is placed on a rough inclined plane inclined at an angle α to the horizontal and a force of magnitude S acts on it in a direction making an angle θ with the plane. If the equilibrium is limiting, to find S.

Now the following two cases of limiting equilibrium arise:

(*i*) The particle has a tendency to slide up the plane.

(*ii*) The particle has a tendency to slide down the plane.

Case (*i*) Let the particle have the tendency to move up the plane. In this case the forces acting on the particle are

(*i*) S, the applied force

(*ii*) R, the normal reaction normal to the plane

(*iii*) μR, the frictional force down the plane

(*iv*) mg, the weight,

where μ is the coefficient of friction which is equal to the tangent of the angle of friction, λ. That is,

$$\mu = \tan\lambda.$$

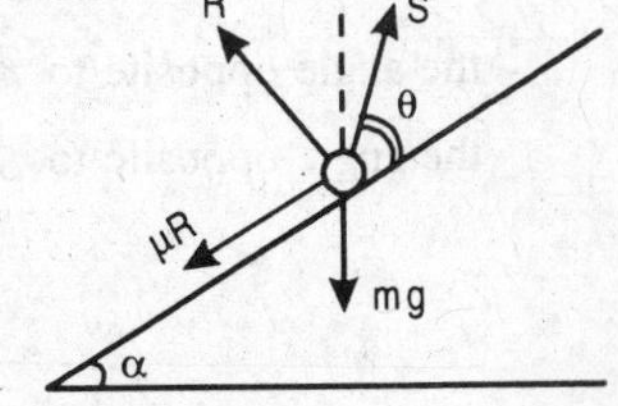

Now considering the components of these forces along the plane and normal to the plane, both in the upward sense,

$$S\cos\theta - \mu R - mg\sin\alpha = 0.$$

$$S\sin\theta + R - mg\cos\alpha = 0.$$

Elimination of R gives

$$S(\cos\theta + \mu\sin\theta) - mg(\sin\alpha + \mu\cos\alpha) = 0$$

$$\therefore \quad S = \frac{mg\,(\sin\alpha + \mu\cos\alpha)}{\cos\theta + \mu\sin\theta} = \frac{mg\,(\sin\alpha + \tan\lambda\cos\alpha)}{\cos\theta + \tan\lambda\sin\theta}$$

$$= \frac{mg\,(\sin\alpha\cos\lambda + \sin\lambda\cos\alpha)}{\cos\theta\cos\lambda + \sin\lambda\sin\theta} = \frac{mg\sin(\alpha+\lambda)}{\cos(\theta-\lambda)}. \qquad ...(1)$$

If θ is unaltered and S is increased, then the particle will slide up the plane.

Minimum *S*. Now we shall obtain the minimum force required to drag the particle up the plane. In (1) m, α, λ are constants. So S is a minimum when the denominator $\cos(\theta-\lambda)$ is a maximum; that is, when $\theta - \lambda = 0$ or $\theta = \lambda$. Hence the force required to drag the particle up the plane will be the least when it is applied in a direction, making an angle, equal to the angle of friction, with the inclined plane.

Case (*ii*) Let the particle have a tendency to move down the plane. In this case the frictional force μR is in the upward sense as in the figure. Here the corresponding value of S can be obtained directly from the above working by simply changing μ into $-\mu$. Thus we get

$$S = \frac{mg\sin(\alpha-\lambda)}{\cos(\theta+\lambda)}.$$

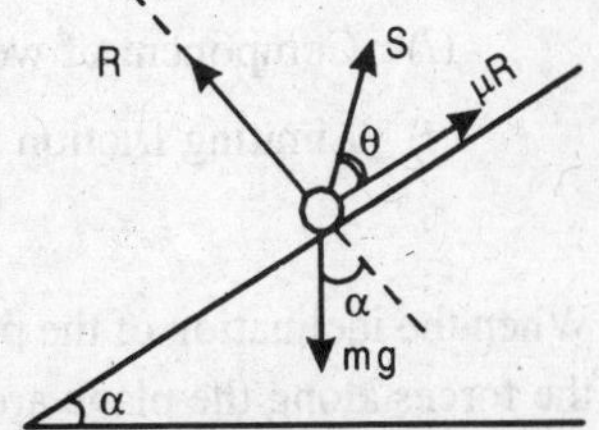

Remark. In the above two cases the involved forces are four in number. If, however, instead of R and μR, their resultant, namely, the *reaction* is considered, then there will be only three forces and so Lami's theorem can be used to find S. The *reaction* is inclined to the normal at an angle λ. In the first case of the above two,

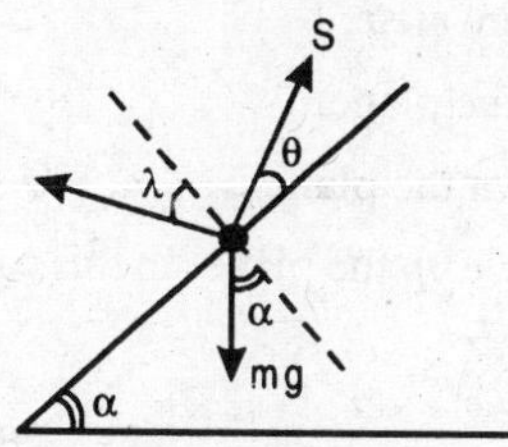

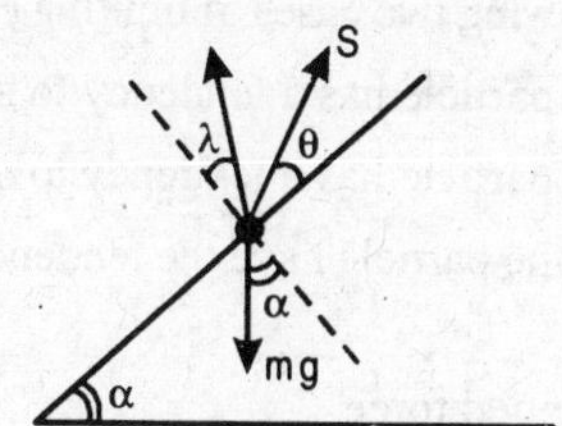

the angle opposite to $mg = (90° - \theta) + \lambda$

the angle opposite to $S = 180° - \lambda - \alpha$.

$$\therefore \qquad \frac{S}{\sin(180° - \alpha - \lambda)} = \frac{mg}{\sin(90° - \theta + \lambda)}$$

i.e.,
$$\frac{S}{\sin(\alpha + \lambda)} = \frac{mg}{\cos(\theta - \lambda)}.$$

Thus, in the limiting equilibrium,

$$S = \frac{mg \sin(\alpha + \lambda)}{\cos(\theta - \lambda)}.$$

In the second case, we have

the angle opposite to $mg = (90° - \theta) - \lambda$

the angle opposite to $S = 180° - \alpha + \lambda$.

Thus, in the limiting equilibrium,

$$S = \frac{mg \sin(\alpha - \lambda)}{\cos(\theta + \lambda)}.$$

EXAMPLES

Example 1. A body of weight 4 kg. rests in limiting equilibrium on a rough plane whose slope is $30°$. If the plane is raised to a slope of $60°$, find the force along the plane required to support the body. **(M.K.U.)**

In the first case the body has a tendency to slide down. So the forces on the body along the plane are

(*i*) Component of weight $4 \sin 30°$ down the plane

(*ii*) Limiting friction μR, that is, $\mu\,(4 \cos 30°)$ up the plane.

$$\therefore \qquad 4 \sin 30° = \mu\,(4 \cos 30°) \text{ or } \mu = 1/\sqrt{3}.$$

When the inclination of the plane is increased to $60°$ also, the body has a tendency to slide down. So the forces along the plane are

(*i*) Component of weight $4 \sin 60°$ down the plane

(*ii*) Limiting friction $\mu\,(4 \cos 60°)$ up the plane

(*iii*) Supporting force P up the plane.

$$\therefore \qquad 4 \sin 60° = \mu(4 \cos 60°) + P \text{ or } P = 4/\sqrt{3} \text{ kg. wt.}$$

Example 2. A particle rests on a plane inclined at $45°$ to the horizontal, being supported by a string along the line of the greatest slope. If the ratio of the maximum and minimum tensions consistent with equilibrium is 2:1, find the coefficient of friction. **(A.U)**

When the body has tendencies to move down and up, let the tensions be T_1, T_2. Then $T_2 = 2T_1$. Also

$$W \sin 45° = \mu \,(W \cos 45°) + T_1,$$

$$W \sin 45° + \mu \,(W \cos 45°) = 2T_1,$$

where W is the weight of the particle and μ, the coefficient of friction. Eliminating T_1,

$$W \sin 45° + \mu \,(W \cos 45° = 2W \sin 45° - 2\mu W \cos 45°$$

i.e., $$1 + \mu = 2 - 2\mu \quad \text{or} \quad \mu = 1/3.$$

Example 3. A particle is placed on a rough plane whose inclination to the horizon is α and is acted on by a force P, parallel to the plane and in a direction making an angle β with the line of greatest slope in the plane. If the coefficient of friction is μ and the equilibrium is limiting, find the direction in which the body will begin to move. **(M.U.)**

Leaving out the normal reaction, we have, along the plane, the forces

(*i*) P along OB, say

(*ii*) Component of weight $W \sin \alpha$ down the plane along OA

(*iii*) Limiting friction.

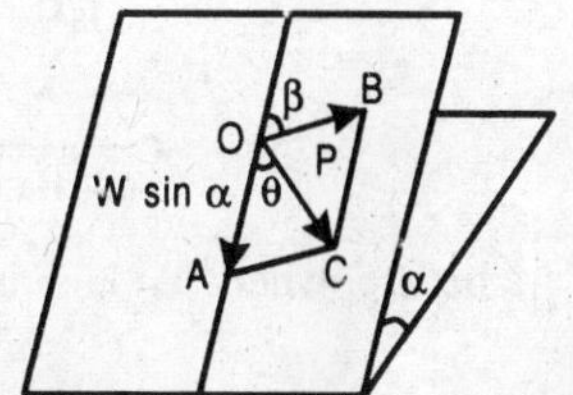

The angle between the first two is $180° - \beta$. So the resultant of these two is along OC inclined to OA at an angle θ, namely,

$$\tan^{-1} \frac{P \sin (180° - \beta)}{W \sin \alpha + P \cos (180° - \beta)} \quad \text{or} \quad \tan^{-1} \frac{P \sin \beta}{W \sin \alpha - P \cos \beta}$$

by (2) of Bookwork 2.1. The third force which is the limiting friction will be opposite to this direction. So the body will have a tendency to move in the direction OC.

Example 4. Find the least force required to drag a particle on a rough horizontal plane and show that the least force acts in a direction making with the horizontal, an angle equal to the angle of friction. **(M.U.)**

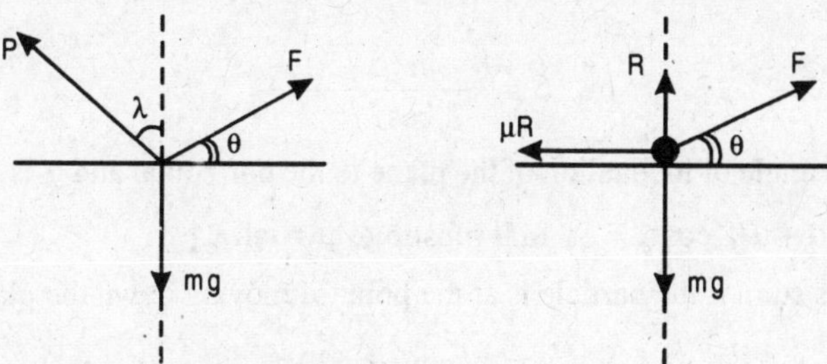

Let a force of magnitude F be applied to the particle in the direction which makes an angle θ with the horizontal. If this force is such that the particle is in the limiting equilibrium, then the other forces acting on the particle are

(*i*) the weight mg vertically downwards,

(*ii*) the reaction P which makes an angle λ with the normal, where λ is the angle of friction.

Now, by Lami's theorem,

$$\frac{F}{\sin(180°-\lambda)} = \frac{mg}{\sin(\lambda+90°-\theta)} = \frac{P}{\sin(90°+\theta)}.$$

$$\therefore \quad F = \frac{\sin(180°-\lambda)}{\sin(90°+\lambda-\theta)} mg = \frac{mg\sin\lambda}{\cos(\lambda-\theta)}.$$

Here λ is a constant. So F is a minimum when $\cos(\lambda-\theta)$ is a maximum. That is, the minimum F is obtained from $\lambda-\theta=0$ or $\theta=\lambda$, the angle of friction.

Alternative method. Instead of the reaction P, we now take the normal reaction R and the frictional force μR, where $\mu=\tan\lambda$ is the coefficient of friction. Then the forces acting on the particle are four in number. Since the particle is in limiting equilibrium, the sums of the components in two perpendicular directions are zero. Therefore, from the horizontal and vertical components,

$$F\cos\theta-\mu R=0, \quad F\sin\theta+R-mg=0.$$

On elimination of R, we get

$$F = \frac{mg\mu}{\cos\theta+\mu\sin\theta} = \frac{mg\tan\lambda}{\cos\theta+\tan\lambda\sin\theta}$$

$$= \frac{mg\sin\lambda}{\cos\theta\cos\lambda+\sin\theta\sin\lambda} = \frac{mg\sin\lambda}{\cos(\theta-\lambda)}.$$

As before, when $\theta=\lambda$, F is a minimum.

EXERCISES

1. Show that the greatest inclination of a rough inclined plane to the horizon so that a particle will remain on it at rest, is equal to the angle of friction. **(M.U.)**

   [Hint: Components of forces along and normal to the plane give

   $mg\sin\alpha=\mu R$, $mg\cos\alpha=R$. So $\tan\alpha=\mu$. But $\mu=\tan\lambda$. Hence $\alpha=\lambda$ **]**

2. A particle of weight W placed on a rough inclined plane is acted on by an external force S which acts along the plane in the upward sense. If the particle is at the point of moving up the plane, show that

   $$S = \frac{W\sin(\alpha+\lambda)}{\cos\lambda}, \qquad \textbf{(Br.U.)}$$

   where α is the angle of inclination of the plane to the horizontal and λ is the angle of friction.

   [Hint: $W\sin\alpha+\mu W\cos\alpha=S$; In it substitute $\mu=\tan\lambda$ **]**

3. In the previous sum, if the particle is at the point of moving down the plane, show that

   $$S = \frac{W\sin(\alpha-\lambda)}{\cos\lambda}.$$

4. A body of weight w rests on a rough inclined plane and is just on the point of slipping down. On applying a force equal to the weight of the body parallel to the plane upwards, the weight is just on the point of moving up. Find the coefficient of friction and the angle of the plane. **(M.U.)**

[**Hint:** (*i*) $W \sin\alpha = \mu (W \cos\alpha)$

(*ii*) $W \sin\alpha + \mu (W \cos\alpha) = W$. Eliminating $\mu\cos\alpha$, $2\sin\alpha = 1$; $\mu = 1/\sqrt{3}$.]

5. A weight is supported on a rough inclined plane by a force acting along the line of the greatest slope. If a force which just supports it when the angle of the plane is α is the same as the force which just moves it up the plane when the angle of the plane is $\alpha/2$, show that the angle of friction is $\alpha/4$. **(M.U.)**

[**Hint:** (*i*) $W \sin\alpha = \mu W \cos\alpha + P$

(*ii*) $W \sin\alpha/2 + \mu W \cos\alpha/2 = P$. Eliminate P and use $\mu = \tan\lambda$ to get $\lambda = \alpha/4$.]

6. A particle is placed on a rough plane inclined at an angle α to the horizontal. If the force, which acting parallel to the plane in the upward sense, is just sufficient to keep the particle at the point of moving up the plane, is n times the force, which acting in the same manner, is just sufficient to keep the particle at the point of moving down the plane, show that

$$\tan\alpha = \mu.\frac{n+1}{n-1},$$

where μ is the coefficient of friction.

[**Hint:** $W \sin\alpha = \mu W \cos\alpha + P$, $W \sin\alpha + \mu W \cos\alpha = nP$. Eliminate P]

7. A force P acting along a rough inclined plane is just sufficient to support a body on the plane. The angle of friction λ is less than α, the inclination of the plane with the horizontal. Prove that the least force P', acting along the plane sufficient to drag the body up the plane is

$$\frac{\sin(\alpha+\lambda)}{\sin(\alpha-\lambda)}P.$$ **(M.U.)**

[**Hint:** (*i*) $W \sin\alpha = \mu W \cos\alpha + P$

(*ii*) $W \sin\alpha + \mu W \cos\alpha = P'$, $\mu = \tan\lambda$. Eliminate W and find P'.]

8. A weight is to be transported from the bottom to the top of an inclined plane whose inclination to the horizontal is α. Show that a smaller force will be required to drag it along the plane than to lift it, provided the coefficient of friction is less than $\tan\left(\pi/4 - \alpha/2\right)$. **(M.U.)**

[**Hint:** To lift a body of weight W directly upward, a force W is needed. But to drag the body up the plane, a force P is needed given by

$$P = W \sin\alpha + \mu (W \cos\alpha).$$

If $P < W$, then $\sin\alpha + \mu\cos\alpha < 1$ or $\mu < \frac{1-\sin\alpha}{\cos\alpha}$. Using Trigonometry, we have

$$\mu < \frac{1-\cos(90°-\alpha)}{\sin(90°-\alpha)} = \frac{2\sin^2(45°-\alpha/2)}{2\sin(45°-\alpha/2)\cos(45°-\alpha/2)} = \tan(45°-\alpha/2)]$$

9. A particle of weight 30 kg. resting on a rough horizontal plane is just at the point of motion when acted on by horizontal forces of 6 kg. wt. and 8 kg. wt. at right angles to each other. Find the coefficient of friction between the particle and the plane and the direction in which the friction acts. **(M.K.U.)**

[**Hint:** The frictional force is μR or 30μ. This equals in magnitude the resultant of 8 and 6, namely 10. So $\mu = 1/3$]

10. Two rough particles of masses m_1 and m_2 connected by a light string rest on an inclined plane with the string lying along a line of greatest slope. If the particles are in limiting equilibrium, show that

$$\tan\alpha = \frac{\mu_1 m_1 + \mu_2 m_2}{m_1 + m_2},$$ **[K.U.]**

where α is the inclination of the plane and μ_1, μ_2 are the coefficients of friction of the particles.

[Hint: Let m_1 be in a level higher than m_2. Eliminate T from

$$m_1 g\sin\alpha + T = \mu_1 m_1 g\cos\alpha,\ \ m_2 g\sin\alpha = T + \mu_2 m_2 g\cos\alpha\ ]$$

11. Two equal weights W of different materials, rest on an inclined plane connected by a string lying along the line of greatest slope. If the coefficient of friction between the lower weight and the plane is $\frac{1}{3}$ and that between the upper weight and the plane is $\frac{2}{3}$ and equilibrium is limiting, find the inclination of the plane and the tension in the string. **(M.U.)**

[Hint: $W\sin\alpha = \frac{1}{3}W\cos\alpha + T$; $W\sin\alpha + T = \frac{2}{3}\ W\cos\alpha$; $\tan\alpha = \frac{1}{2}$]

12. Two equally rough inclined planes inclined at angles α and β, $(\alpha > \beta)$, to the horizon, have a common vertex. A string passing over a small smooth pulley at the vertex supports two particles of equal mass. If the particles are in the limiting equilibrium, show that μ, the coefficient of friction, is

$$\tan\frac{\alpha - \beta}{2}.$$

[Hint: $mg\sin\alpha = T + \mu mg\cos\alpha$, $mg\sin\beta + \mu mg\cos\beta = T$. Eliminate T.]

FORCES ON A RIGID BODY

4.1 MOMENT OF A FORCE

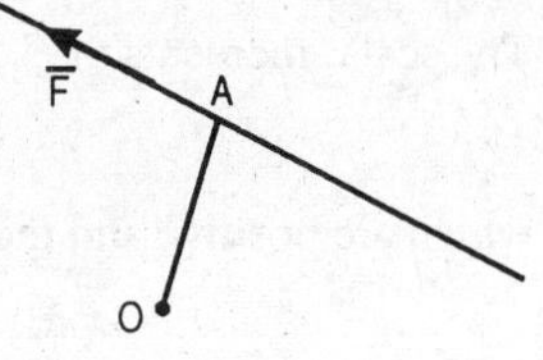

Moment of a force. Let $\bar{F}$ be a force and A, a point on its line of action. Let O be a point in space. Then the vector

$$\overline{OA} \times \bar{F}$$

is called the moment of $\bar{F}$ about O.

Remark 1. The above moment is independent of the position of A on the straight line because, if B is any other point on the line, then

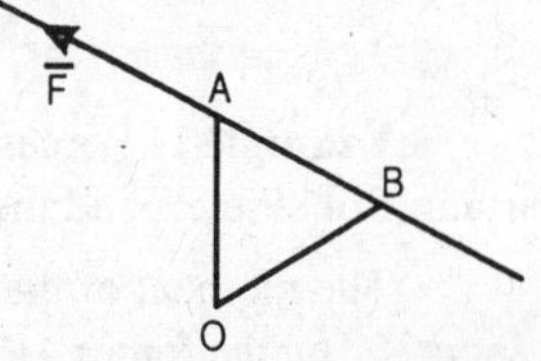

$$\overline{OB} \times \bar{F} = (\overline{OA} + \overline{AB}) \times \bar{F}$$

$$= \overline{OA} \times \bar{F} + \bar{0}.$$

Remark 2. If the moment of $\bar{F}$ about A is zero, then either

(*i*) $\bar{F} = \bar{0}$ or

(*ii*) The line of action of $\bar{F}$ passes through A.

4.1.1 Moment of a force about a line

Let $\bar{F}$ be a force and A, a point on its line of action. Let l be a directed line through a point O, the direction of the line being specified by $\hat{e}$. Then the scalar triple product

$$\left(\overline{OA} \times \bar{F}\right) \cdot \hat{e}$$

is called the moment of the force $\bar{F}$ about l.

4.1.2 Scalar moment

Let $\bar{F}$ be a force in a plane. Let A be a point on its line of action and O, any point in the plane. Let ON be the perpendicular from O to the line and

$$ON = p.$$

Then the moment of $\bar{F}$ about O is

$$\overline{OA} \times \bar{F} = OA \cdot F \cdot \sin\theta \cdot \hat{n} = pF\,\hat{n},$$

where θ is the angle between $\overline{OA}$ and $\bar{F}$, and $\hat{n}$ is the unit vector perpendicular to $\overline{OA}$, $\bar{F}$ such that $\overline{OA}$, $\bar{F}$, $\hat{n}$ form a right - handed triad. Now we call

$$pF$$

the scalar moment of $\bar{F}$ about O.

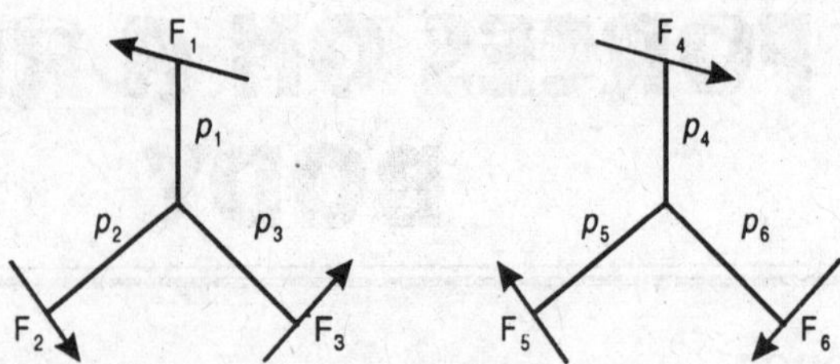

The scalar moments of F_1, F_2, F_3 in the first figure are

$$p_1F_1,\ p_2F_2,\ p_3F_3$$

which are positive and the moments of F_4, F_5, F_6 in the second figure are

$$-p_4F_4,\ -p_5F_5,\ -p_6F_6$$

Which are negative. The first three forces are such as to cause on a rigid body a rotational motion in the anticlockwise sense and the other three to cause a rotational motion in the clockwise sense.

EXAMPLES

Example 1. Forces of magnitudes $3P$, $4P$, $5P$, act along the sides BC, CA, AB of an equilateral triangle of side a. Find the moment of the resultant about A. **(M.U.)**

The moment of the resultant about A equals the sum of the moments of the individual forces about A. But the forces $4P$, $5P$ pass through A. So their moments about A are zero. The moment of $3P$ which passes through B is

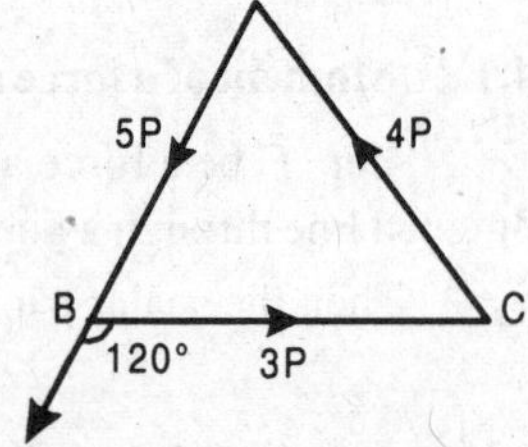

$$\overline{AB}\times(3P\,\widehat{BC}) = AB\cdot 3P\cdot\sin 120°\hat{n}$$

$$= a\cdot 3P\cdot\frac{\sqrt{3}}{2}\hat{n}.$$

So this is the moment of the resultant about A.

Example 2. If l, m, n are the moments of a force F in a plane about three noncollinear points A, B, C in the plane, show that the line of action of F divides AB in the ratio $l : m$. Deduce that, if l, m, n are given, then F can be found completely. **(M.U.)**

Suppose l, m, n are positive. Then A, B, C lie above the line of force if the force is from left to right. Let the line of force meet AB at P and A', B' be the feet of the perpendicular from A, B to the line of force. Then

$$AA'\times F = l,$$
$$BB'\times F = m.$$

$$\therefore \quad \frac{AA'}{BB'}=\frac{l}{m}. \text{ So } \frac{AP}{PB}=\frac{l}{m}.$$

That is, P is the point which divides AB externally in the ratio $l : m$.

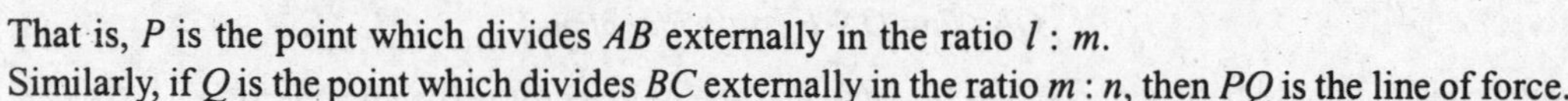
Similarly, if Q is the point which divides BC externally in the ratio $m : n$, then PQ is the line of force.

Since $AA'\times F = l$, finding AA', we get F also.

Example 3. One end of a rope of 20 m. is to be fixed to a telegraph post and the other end is to be pulled by a man on the ground with a constant force F. To cause the maximum effect to overturn the post, at what height the rope is to be fixed? **(M.U.)**

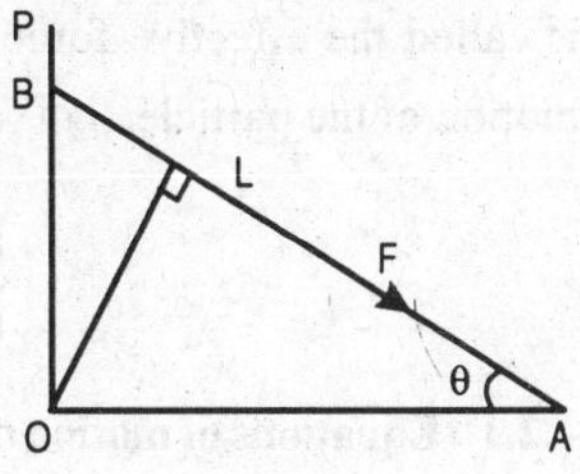

Let OP be the post, AB the rope and

$$\underline{|OAB} = \theta.$$

Let OL be the perpendicular on AB. Now the post is to overturn about O. So the man should aim for the maximum moment of F about O. But the moment is $OL \times F$ and it is a maximum when OL is a maximum. But

$$OL = OA \sin\theta \text{, from } \Delta\, OAL$$

$$= (AB \cos\theta) \sin\theta \text{, from } \Delta\, OAB$$

$$= \tfrac{1}{2} AB \sin 2\theta$$

which is a maximum when $2\theta = 90°$ or $\theta = 45°$. In this situation

$$OB = AB \sin 45° = 20 \times \frac{1}{\sqrt{2}}.$$

Note. Whatever be the length of the rope, θ should be 45°.

EXERCISES

1. Two forces $\overline{F}_1$ and $\overline{F}_2$ act at a point A. P is a moving point such that the moments of $\overline{F}_1$ and $\overline{F}_2$ about P are equal. Find the locus of P. **(M.U.)**

   [Hint: $\overline{PA} \times \overline{F}_1 = \overline{PA} \times \overline{F}_2$ or $\overline{AP} \times (\overline{F}_1 - \overline{F}_2) = \overline{0}$. So $\overline{AP}$ is always parallel to $\overline{F}_1 - \overline{F}_2$. Hence the locus of P is a straight line through A and parallel to $\overline{F}_1 - \overline{F}_2$.**]**

2. Find the locus of all points in a plane such that two forces, given in magnitude and position in the plane, shall have equal moments, in the same sense, about the points. **(M.K.U.)**

   [Hint: This is same as the previous sum**]**

3. The ratio of the moments of a variable force about two given points A, B is a constant, but the magnitudes of these moments vary. Show that the force passes through a fixed point on AB **(M.U.)**

   [Hint: Let the line of force intersect AB at C. Let AM, BN be the perpendiculars to the line of force. Then $\dfrac{AM \cdot F}{BN \cdot F} = \text{const.}, \dfrac{AM}{BN} = \dfrac{AC}{BC}.\ \ \therefore \dfrac{AC}{BC} = \text{const.}$ **]**

4.2 GENERAL MOTION OF A RIGID BODY

In this section we extend the Newton's laws of motion, $N.$ 1, $N.$ 2, $N.$ 3, to the motion of a rigid body.

Rigid body. A system of particles such that the distance between any two of them is always constant, is called a rigid body.

Applied forces. Forces applied on a body by external agencies are called applied forces on the body.

Effective forces. If a particle of mass m has an acceleration $\ddot{\overline{r}}$, then the quantity

$$m\ddot{\overline{r}}$$

is called the effective force of the particle. With this nomenclature we have that the equation of motion of the particle, $m\ddot{\bar{r}} = \bar{F}$, is that

$$\begin{Bmatrix}\text{The effective force}\\ \text{on a particle}\end{Bmatrix} = \begin{Bmatrix}\text{The applied force}\\ \text{on the particle}\end{Bmatrix}.$$

4.2.1 Equations of motion of a rigid body

The general motion of a rigid body is a composition of the motion of translation of the mass centre and the motion of rotation of the body about the mass centre. The equations of these two component motions are obtained in the following bookwork.

Bookwork 4.1. The bookwork has the following two parts:

(*i*) The mass centre of a rigid body of mass M moves as if it is a particle of mass M acted on by the applied forces on the rigid body, moved parallelly and made act on it.

(*ii*) The motion of a rigid body relative to the mass centre G is governed by the equation

$$\begin{Bmatrix}\text{Sum of the moments of}\\ \text{the effective forces, relative}\\ \text{to } G\text{, of the constituent}\\ \text{particles, about } G\end{Bmatrix} = \begin{Bmatrix}\text{Sum of the}\\ \text{moments of the}\\ \text{applied forces}\\ \text{about } G\end{Bmatrix}$$

Let us make the following assumptions :

m_1, m_2, m_3	Masses of the particles constituting the rigid body
M	Total mass $m_1 + m_2 + m_3 +$ ......
$\bar{r}_1, \bar{r}_2, \bar{r}_3$	P.V's of m_1, m_2, m_3...... with reference to a fixed point O
$\bar{F}_{ij} (i \neq j)$	Force exerted on m_i by m_j due to their mutual contact
$\bar{F}_{ii}$	Applied force on m_i including the forces due to external constraints
$\bar{F}$	$\bar{F}_{11} + \bar{F}_{22} + \bar{F}_{33} + \ldots\ldots$
$\bar{R}$	P.V. of the mass centre G of the rigid body, $\dfrac{m_1\bar{r}_1 + m_2\bar{r}_2 + \ldots}{M}$

Proof of (*i*). Now, by N. 3, $\overline{F_{ij}}$ and $\overline{F_{ji}}$ are equal in magnitude but opposite in direction. So

$$\bar{F}_{ij} + \bar{F}_{ji} = \bar{0}. \qquad \ldots(1)$$

The equations of motion of m_1, m_2, m_3,...... are

$$m_1\ddot{\bar{r}}_1 = \bar{F}_{11} + \bar{F}_{12} + \bar{F}_{13} + \ldots\ldots$$

$$m_2\ddot{\bar{r}}_2 = \bar{F}_{21} + \bar{F}_{22} + \bar{F}_{23} + \ldots\ldots$$

$$m_3\ddot{\bar{r}}_3 = \bar{F}_{31} + \bar{F}_{32} + \bar{F}_{33} + \ldots\ldots$$

....

When these equations are added, using (1),

$$m_1\ddot{\bar{r}}_1 + m_2\ddot{\bar{r}}_2 + \ldots\ldots = \bar{F}_{11} + \bar{F}_{22} + \ldots\ldots = \bar{F}.$$

Thus we get that

$$\text{Sum of the effective forces} = \text{Sum of the applied forces.} \qquad \ldots(2)$$

But $m_1\bar{r}_1 + m_2\bar{r}_2 + ... = M\bar{R}$. Therefore

$$M\ddot{\bar{R}} = \bar{F}. \qquad ...(3)$$

Since $\ddot{\bar{R}}$ is the acceleration of the mass centre, we obtain the first result as stated.

Proof of (*ii*). Since $\bar{F}_{ij}$ and $\bar{F}_{ji}$ are equal in magnitude but opposite in direction and act along the same line, their moments about O are equal in magnitude but opposite in direction. So

$$\bar{r}_i \times \bar{F}_{ij} + \bar{r}_j \times \bar{F}_{ji} = \bar{0}. \qquad ...(4)$$

Now the equation of motion of m_i is

$$m_i\ddot{\bar{r}}_i = \bar{F}_{i1} + \bar{F}_{i2} + ... = \sum_j \bar{F}_{ij}.$$

Multiplying this vectorially by $\bar{r}_i$,

$$\bar{r}_i \times m_i\ddot{\bar{r}}_i = \bar{r}_i \times \sum_j \bar{F}_{ij} = \sum_j \bar{r}_i \times \bar{F}_{ij}.$$

Adding all such equations corresponding to m_1, m_2, m_3 ......,

$$\sum_i \bar{r}_i \times m_i \ddot{\bar{r}}_i = \sum_i \sum_j \bar{r}_i \times \bar{F}_{ij}.$$

But, in virtue of (4), the terms in the double summation get cancelled in pairs with the exception of the terms which involve the applied forces. So the equation reduces to

$$\Sigma \bar{r}_i \times m_i\ddot{\bar{r}}_i = \Sigma \bar{r}_i \times \bar{F}_{ii}. \qquad ...(5)$$

Thus, in words,

$$\left\{\begin{matrix}\text{The sum of the moments}\\ \text{of the effective forces}\\ \text{about a fixed point } O\end{matrix}\right\} = \left\{\begin{matrix}\text{The sum of the moments of}\\ \text{the applied forces about } O.\end{matrix}\right\} \qquad ...(6)$$

Suppose $\bar{s}_i$ is the position vector of m_i with reference to G. Then

$$\bar{r}_i = \bar{R} + \bar{s}_i.$$

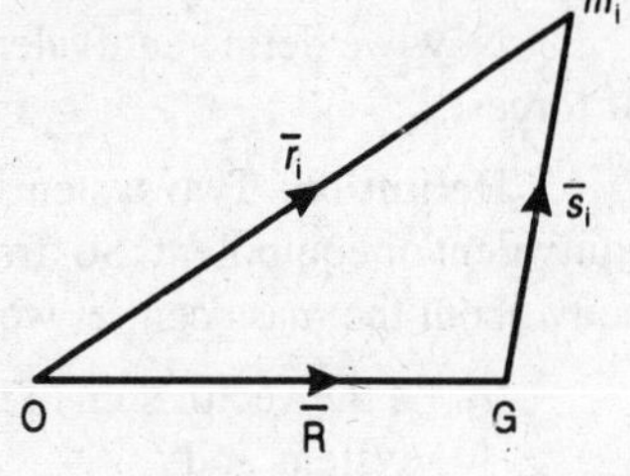

Now $(\Sigma m_i\bar{s}_i)/M$ is the P.V. of the mass centre G with reference to G itself. So it is $\bar{0}$ and hence $\Sigma m_i\bar{s}_i = \bar{0}$. Now (5) becomes

$$\Sigma(\bar{R} + \bar{s}_i) \times m_i(\ddot{\bar{R}} + \ddot{\bar{s}}_i) = \Sigma(\bar{R} + \bar{s}_i) \times \bar{F}_{ii}.$$

i.e., $$(\Sigma m_i)\bar{R} \times \ddot{\bar{R}} + \bar{R} \times (\Sigma m_i\ddot{\bar{s}}_i) + (\Sigma m_i\bar{s}_i) \times \ddot{\bar{R}} + \Sigma(\bar{s}_i \times m_i\ddot{\bar{s}}_i)$$
$$= \bar{R} \times (\Sigma\bar{F}_{ii}) + \Sigma(\bar{s}_i \times \bar{F}_{ii}).$$

Since $\Sigma m_i = M$, $\Sigma\bar{F}_{ii} = \bar{F}$, $M\ddot{\bar{R}} = \bar{F}$, $\Sigma m_i\bar{s}_i = \bar{0}$, $\Sigma m_i\ddot{\bar{s}}_i = \bar{0}$,

$$\Sigma\bar{s}_i \times m_i\ddot{\bar{s}}_i = \Sigma\ddot{\bar{s}}_i \times \bar{F}_{ii}. \qquad ...(7)$$

From (7) and (5) it may be noted that the motion of the body relative to the mass centre is the same as it would be if the mass centre is fixed and the same forces act on the body at the same points.

4.2.2 Conditions following equilibrium of a rigid body

If the applied forces keep the rigid body in equilibrium, then the mass centre of the body is at rest and so the velocity $\dot{\bar{R}}$ and acceleration $\ddot{\bar{R}}$ of G are zero and, thus, from (3), we get that

$$\text{The sum of the applied forces } = \bar{0}. \qquad ...(8)$$

Also the body does not have a rotational motion. Thus, from (5) and (7), we get that

$$\left.\begin{array}{r}\text{The vector sum of the moments of the}\\ \text{applied forces about a fixed point or } G\end{array}\right\} = \bar{0} \qquad ...(9)$$

From (8) and (9) it is evident that, if a system of forces keeps a rigid body in equilibrium, then

(*i*) The sum of the components of the forces in any direction is zero; and ...(10)

(*ii*) The sum of the moments of the forces about any line through a fixed point or G is zero. ...(11)

4.2.3 Kinetic energy of a rigid body

Kinetic energy. The kinetic energy of a particle of mass m moving with a velocity v is $\frac{1}{2}mv^2$. If the position vector of a particle is $\bar{r}$, then this kinetic energy can be written as $\frac{1}{2}m\dot{\bar{r}}.\dot{\bar{r}}$.

Kinetic energy of a rigid body. Let T be the kinetic energy of the rigid body. Then, with the notations used in the previous section, we have

$$T = \tfrac{1}{2}\Sigma m_i \dot{\bar{r}}_i \cdot \dot{\bar{r}}_i = \tfrac{1}{2}\Sigma m_i \cdot (\dot{\bar{R}} + \dot{\bar{s}}_i)\cdot(\dot{\bar{R}} + \dot{\bar{s}}_i)$$

$$= \tfrac{1}{2}\left[(\Sigma m_i)\dot{\bar{R}}\cdot\dot{\bar{R}} + 2\dot{\bar{R}}\cdot(\Sigma m_i \dot{\bar{s}}_i) + \Sigma m_i \dot{\bar{s}}_i \cdot \dot{\bar{s}}_i\right]$$

$$= \tfrac{1}{2}M\dot{\bar{R}}\cdot\dot{\bar{R}} + 0 + \tfrac{1}{2}\Sigma m_i \dot{\bar{s}}_i \cdot \dot{\bar{s}}_i.$$

$$= \begin{Bmatrix}\text{K.E. of a particle of}\\ \text{mass } M \text{ moving with}\\ \text{the mass centre}\end{Bmatrix} + \begin{Bmatrix}\text{K.E. of the body}\\ \text{due to its motion}\\ \text{relative to the mass centre}\end{Bmatrix} \qquad ...(1)$$

4.3 EQUIVALENT (OR EQUIPOLENT) SYSTEMS OF FORCES

Now we define equivalent systems of forces which are otherwise called equipolent systems of forces.

Definition. Two systems of forces which produce the same motion on a given rigid body are equivalent or equipolent. So, from the equations of the motion of the mass centre and motion of the body about the mass centre, we get that two systems of forces are equivalent or equipolent

(*i*) If the vector sum of the forces of one system equals the vector sum of forces of the other system and

(*ii*) If the vector sum of the moments of the forces of one system, about any fixed point or the mass centre, equals the vector sum of the moments of the forces of the other system, about the same point on the mass centre.

In symbols, the system of forces $\bar{F}_i$ acting at $\bar{r}_i$ on a rigid body is equivalent to the system of forces $\bar{F}'_j$ acting at $\bar{r}'_j$ on the rigid body if

$$\sum_i \bar{F}_i = \sum_j \bar{F}'_j, \quad ...(1)$$

$$\sum_i \bar{r}_i \times \bar{F}_i = \sum_j \bar{r}'_j \times \bar{F}'_j. \quad ...(2)$$

Transmissibility of a force. It is evident that two forces equal in magnitude and direction, acting on a rigid body along the same line but at different points, are equivalent. So a force can be transmitted, without altering its effect on the rigid body, to any other point on its line of action. This is known as the principle of transmissibility of force on a rigid body.

Remark 1. Two forces $\bar{F}_1$ and $\bar{F}_2$ acting at the same point on a rigid body is equivalent to a single force $\bar{F}_1 + \bar{F}_2$ acting at that point because the forces satisfy (1) and (2).

Remark 2. By the principle of transmissibility of a force we get that, if the lines of action of two forces $\bar{F}_1$ and $\bar{F}_2$ intersect, the forces are equivalent to a single force $\bar{F}_1 + \bar{F}_2$ at the point of intersection.

4.4 PARALLEL FORCES

Computation of the resultant of two parallel forces is not as simple as the computation of the resultant of two intersecting forces.

Parallel forces. Forces whose lines of action are parallel are called parallel forces. If their directions are in the same sense, then they are called like parallel forces; otherwise, they are called unlike parallel forces.

Bookwork 4.2. To find the resultant of two parallel forces acting on a rigid body.

Case (*i*). Let the forces be like parallel forces, namely $F_1\bar{i}$ and $F_2\bar{i}$ acting at A_1 and A_2 respectively, where $\bar{i}$ is the unit vector in the direction of the forces. Let $\hat{e}$ be the unit vector in the

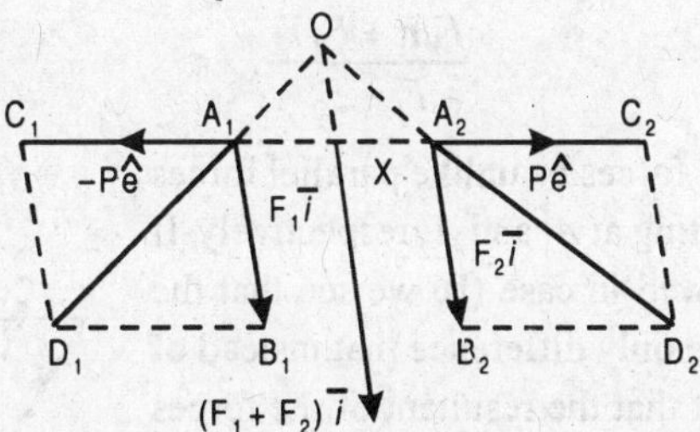

direction of $\overline{A_1A_2}$. Introduce a force $-P\hat{e}$ at A_1 and a force $P\hat{e}$ at A_2. Since these two forces are equal in magnitude and opposite in direction and act along the same line, their introduction will not affect the effects of the given two forces. Let

$$\overline{A_1B_1} = F_1\,\bar{i},\ \overline{A_2B_2} = F_2\,\bar{i},\ \overline{A_1C_1} = -P\hat{e},\ \overline{A_2C_2} = P\hat{e}.$$

Complete the parallelograms $A_1B_1D_1C_1$ and $A_2B_2D_2C_2$. Then the resultant of the two forces $F_1\bar{i}$ and $-P\hat{e}$ acting at A_1 is

$$\overline{A_1D_1} = F_1\,\bar{i} - P\hat{e}$$

and the resultant of the forces $F_2\bar{i}$ and $P\hat{e}$ acting at A_2 is

$$\overline{A_2D_2} = F_2\,\bar{i} + P\hat{e}.$$

If the lines A_1D_1 and A_2D_2 intersect at O, then the resultant of these two resultants is

$$\overline{A_1D_1} + \overline{A_2D_2} = (F_1\overline{i} - P\hat{e}) + (F_2\overline{i} + P\hat{e})$$
$$= (F_1 + F_2)\overline{i}$$

acting at O. Note that this resultant is parallel to the original forces.

Point of intersection of the resultant with A_1A_2. From the similar triangles

$$\Delta OXA_1,\ \Delta A_1B_1D_1,$$

$$\frac{OX}{XA_1} = \frac{F_1}{P}. \quad ...(1)$$

Also from the similar triangles $\Delta OXA_2,\ \Delta A_2B_2D_2$,

$$\frac{OX}{XA_2} = \frac{F_2}{P}. \quad ...(2)$$

Dividing (2) by (1), we get

$$\frac{XA_1}{XA_2} = \frac{F_2}{F_1}.$$

That is, the line of action of the resultant divides internally A_1A_2 in the ratio F_2: F_1

Note. In sums this result may be used in the form

$$F_1 \times XA_1 = F_2 \times XA_2.$$

Position vector of X. Let the P.V's of A_1, A_2 be $\overline{r_1}, \overline{r_2}$. Since X divides A_1A_2 internally in the ratio F_2: F_1, the position vector of X is

$$\frac{F_1\overline{r_1} + F_2\overline{r_2}}{F_1 + F_2}.$$

Case (*ii*). Let the given forces be unlike parallel forces $F_1\overline{i}$ and $F_2(-\overline{i})$, $(F_1 > F_2)$, acting at A_1 and A_2 respectively. If we adopt the procedure followed in case (*i*), we see that the steps of case (*i*) repeat with the only difference that instead of F_2 they have $-F_2$. Thus we get that the resultant of the forces $F_1\overline{i}$ and $-F_2\overline{i}$ acting at A_1 and A_2 is

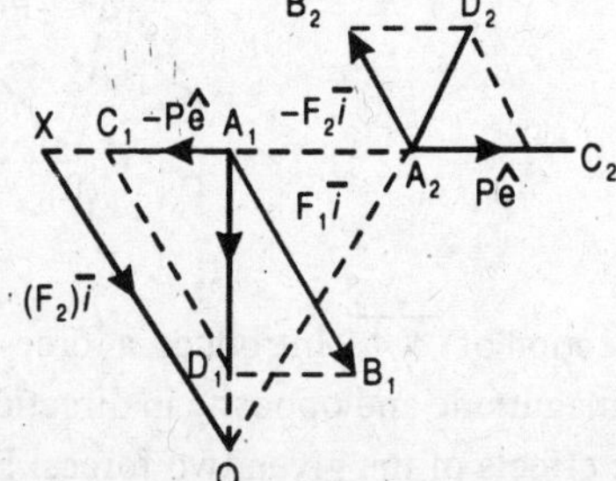

$$\{F_1 + (-F_2)\}\overline{i}.$$

acting at the point which divides A_1A_2 in the ratio $(-F_2)$: F_1, that is, at the point which divides A_1A_2 externally in the ratio F_2: F_1.

4.4.1 Point of application of resultant of many parallel forces

Suppose that a system of parallel forces

$$F_1\overline{i}, F_2\overline{i}, F_3\overline{i}, \ldots\ldots\ldots, F_n\overline{i},$$

not necessarily coplanar, act at points whose position vectors are respectively

$$\overline{r_1}, \overline{r_2}, \overline{r_3}, \ldots\ldots\ldots, \overline{r_n}$$

Then the resultant of $F_1\bar{i}$, $F_2\bar{i}$ is $(F_1+F_2)\bar{i}$ acting at the point whose P.V. is

$$\frac{F_1\bar{r}_1+F_2\bar{r}_2}{F_1+F_2}.$$

The resultant of $F_1\bar{i}$, $F_2\bar{i}$, $F_3\bar{i}$ is $(F_1+F_2+F_3)\bar{i}$ acting at the point whose P.V. is

$$\frac{(F_1+F_2)\dfrac{F_1\bar{r}_1+F_2\bar{r}_2}{F_1+F_2}+F_3\bar{r}_3}{(F_1+F_2)+F_3} \quad \text{or} \quad \frac{F_1\bar{r}_1+F_2\bar{r}_2+F_3\bar{r}_3}{F_1+F_2+F_3}.$$

Similarly, the resultant of the given forces and the P.V. of its point of application are

$$(F_1+F_2+......+F_n)\bar{i},\ \frac{F_1\bar{r}_1+F_2\bar{r}_2+........+F_n\bar{r}_n}{F_1+F_2+....+F_n}.$$

Remark 1. If the forces of earth's gravitation on a system of particles of masses m_1, m_2, m_3,...... whose position vectors are $\bar{r}_1$, $\bar{r}_2$ $\bar{r}_3$,.... supposed to be parallel, then the position vector of the point, the centre of gravity, through which the resultant gravitation acts, is

$$\frac{m_1 g\bar{r}_1+m_2 g\bar{r}_2+........}{m_1 g+m_2 g+......} \quad \text{or} \quad \frac{m_1\bar{r}_1+m_2\bar{r}_2+........}{m_1+m_2+......}.$$

Centre of gravity, that is, the mass centre is dealt with later.

EXAMPLES

Example 1. Two like parallel forces of magnitudes P, Q, *act* on a rigid body. If Q is changed to P^2/Q, with the line of action being the same, show that the line of action of the resultant will be the same as it would be, if the forces were simply interchanged. **(M.K.U.)**

If the forces, P and $\dfrac{P^2}{Q}$, act at A, B, then their resultant divides AB internally in the ratio

$$\frac{P^2}{Q}:P \text{ or } \frac{P}{Q}=1 \text{ or } P:Q. \qquad ...(1)$$

For the second case also, the ratio is the same $P:Q$. Further all the involved forces and the resultants are parallel to one another.

Example 2. If two like parallel forces of magnitudes P, Q, $(P>Q)$, acting on a rigid body at A, B, are interchanged in position, show that the line of action of the resultant is displaced through a distance

$$\frac{AB(P-Q)}{P+Q}. \qquad \textbf{(M.U.)}$$

Let $AB=a$ and let the resultant intersect AB at a distance x_1 from A. Then,

$$x_1P=(a-x_1)Q$$

$$\therefore \qquad x_1=\frac{aQ}{P+Q}. \qquad ...(1)$$

If the distance in the second case is x_2, then replacing P, Q with Q, P in (1),

$$x_2=\frac{aP}{P+Q}. \qquad \therefore \qquad x_2-x_1=\frac{a(P-Q)}{P+Q}.$$

Example 3. A rod AB of length $a+b$ and weight W has its centre of gravity at a distance a from A. It rests on two parallel knife edges C and D at a distance c apart in the same horizontal plane so that equal portions of the rods project beyond each knife edge. Prove that the reactions of the knife edges on the rod, are respectively

$$\frac{b-a+c}{2c}W, \ \frac{a-b+c}{2c}W$$

Let the projected lengths be x, x. Then

$$a+b=x+c+x \quad \text{or} \quad x=\tfrac{1}{2}(a+b-c).$$

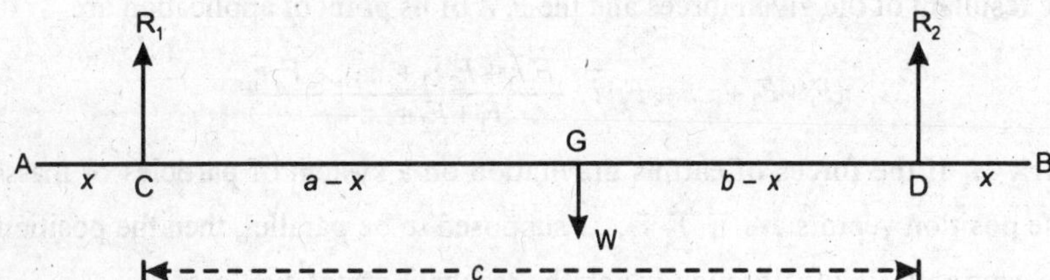

The following forces act on the rod:

(*i*) Reaction R_1 at C vertically upwards

(*ii*) Reaction R_2 at D vertically upwards

(*iii*) Weight W at G vertically downwards.

Since the rod is in equilibrium, the sum of the moments of the forces about any point is zero. Taking moments of these forces about C,

$$-(a-x)W+cR_2=0 \quad \text{or} \quad R_2=\frac{a-x}{c}W.$$

$$\therefore \qquad R_2=\frac{a-\tfrac{1}{2}(a+b-c)}{c}W=\frac{a-b+c}{2c}W.$$

Similarly, taking moments about D, we get R_1 as stated.

Example 4. A uniform plank AB of length $2a$ and weight W is supported horizontally on two horizontal pegs C and D at a distance d apart. The greatest weight that can be placed at the two ends in succession without upsetting the plank are W_1 and W_2 respectively. Show that

$$\frac{W_1}{W+W_1}+\frac{W_2}{W+W_2}=\frac{d}{a}.$$

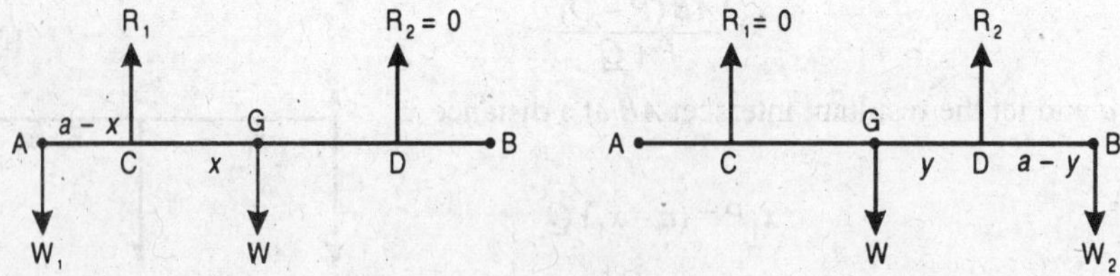

Let G be the mass centre and $CG=x$, $GD=y$. Let R_1, R_2 be the reactions at C, D. When the greatest weight W_1 is placed at A, R_2 is just zero. In this situation taking moments about C,

$$(a-x)W_1-xW=0 \quad \text{or} \quad x=\frac{aW_1}{W+W_1}.$$

Similarly, in the other case, taking moments about D,

$$YW - (a-y)\,W_2 = 0. \quad \therefore \quad y = \frac{aW_2}{W+W_2}$$

But $x + y = d$. So the result as stated.

Example 5. A round table of weight W stands on three legs whose upper ends are attached to its rim, so as to form an equilateral triangle. Show that a body whose weight does not exceed W may be placed anywhere on the table without the risk of tilting it.

Let AA_1, BB_1, CC_1 be the legs. Let the diameter AD meet BC at E. The place where the least weight should be placed to topple the table, is D. Suppose that, when a weight W' is placed at D, the table is at the point of tilting. Under this situation the forces acting on the table are

(i) The weight W at G vertically downward

(ii) The weight W' at D vertically downward

(iii) The reactions of the floor R, R at B_1, C_1 vertically upward.

Though the table is on the point of tilting, it is in equilibrium. So the sum of moments of the forces about any point is zero. If moments are taken about E,

$$\left.\begin{array}{l}\text{Sum of the moments of}\\ \text{the reactions } R, R\end{array}\right\} = 0$$

because $EB = EC$ and, for the moments of W, W',

$$EG \cdot W - ED \cdot W' = 0 \text{ or } W = W'$$

because $EG = ED$ since $AG = r$ and $GE = r/2$.

Example 6. A square table stands on four legs placed at the middle points of its sides; find the greatest weight which can be put at one corner of the table without upsetting it, the total weight of the table and legs being W. **(M.U.)**

Let A, B, C, D be the upper ends of the legs. Let O be the centre of gravity of the table. Let the diagonal QP of the table meet BC at M. Then

$$MB = MC, \; MO = MP.$$

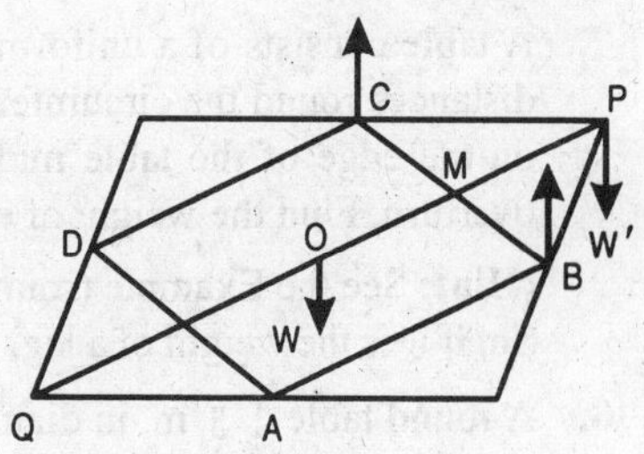

Let W' be the required weight to be put at P. At the moment of tilting the reactions on the legs at A, D are zero. Taking moments of the other forces about M, the sum of the moments of the equal reactions through B, C is zero and

$$MO \cdot W - PM \cdot W' = 0 \text{ or } W' = W.$$

EXERCISES

1. Two like parallel forces of magnitudes P, Q act on a rigid body. If the second force is moved away from the first parallelly through a distance d, show that the resultant of the force moves through a distance

$$\frac{dQ}{P+Q}.$$ **(K.U., Bn.U.)**

[Hint: In the first and second cases $x_1P = (a - x_1)Q$, $x_2P = (a + d - x_2)Q$. Find $x_2 - x_1$.**]**

2. Two unlike parallel forces P and Q $(P > Q)$ acting on a rigid body at A and B, are interchanged in position. Show that the point of application of the resultant on AB will be displaced along AB through a distance

$$\frac{P+Q}{P-Q}AB.$$ **(M.U.)**

[Hint: The resultants divide AB internally in the ratios $Q:-P$ and $P:-Q$.]

3. Find the magnitude and the line of action of the resultant of parallel forces of magnitudes 3, 6, 8 in one direction and of magnitude 12 in the opposite direction acting at the points A, B, C, D in a straight line, where $AB = 10$, $BC = 30$ and $CD = 50$. **(M.U.)**

[**Ans:** 5; at a distance -140 from A.]

4. A heavy uniform rod AB of length 4m. rests horizontally on two pegs C, D which are one metre apart. A weight 10 kg. suspended from one end or a weight 4 kg. suspended from the other end will just tilt the rod up. Find the weight of the rod and the distances of the pegs from the centre of the rod. **(M.U.)**

[Hint: If $CG = x$, then $AC = 2-x$, $GD = 1-x$, $DB = 1+x$. So

$$10(2-x) - xW = 0, 4(1+x) - (1-x)W = 0$$

They give $(3x-2)(x-5) = 0$ or $x = 2/3$, $W = 20$.]

5. A non-uniform horizontal beam $ABCD$ rests on two supports B and C, where $AB = BC = CD$. It is found that the beam will just tilt when a weight of P is hung from A or when a weight of Q is hung from D. Show that the weight of the beam is $P + Q$ and show that its centre of gravity divides AD in the ratio $(2P + Q) : (P + 2Q)$.

6. A uniform rod AB of length $2a$ and weight W rests on two smooth horizontal pegs P and Q at the same level and at a distance a apart. If weights pW and qW are suspended from A and B respectively, then the reactions at P and Q are found to be equal. Show that

$$AP = \frac{a\,(1-p+3q)}{2\,(1+p+q)}.$$ **(M.U.)**

7. A table consists of a uniform circular board supported by three vertical legs fixed at equal distances round the circumference. The board alone weighs 9 kg. A weight of 12 kg, placed on the edge of the table midway between two legs is just sufficient to cause the table to overturn. Find the weight of each leg. **(M.U.)**

[Hint: See the Example (round table) sum. The weight of the table equals the weight placed. So, if w is the weight of a leg, $9 + 3w = 12$ or $w = 1$ kg.]

8. A round table $1 \cdot 5$ m. in diameter has three symmetrically placed legs each $0 \cdot 5$ m from the centre G. If the mass of the table is 200 kg., show that the least mass that can be placed on the edge of the table to tilt the table is 100 kg. and that the greatest mass that can be placed on the edge without tilting, is 400 kg. **(M.U.)**

[Hint: Let A, B, C be the upper ends of the legs. Let $PAGD$ be a diameter (G is $C.G$). Then the least mass should be placed at D and the greatest mass should be placed at P.]

4.4.2 Varignon's theorem.

In this section we bring in the relationship between the sum of the moments of any two coplanar forces and the moment of their resultant.

Bookwork 4.3. (Varignon's theorem). The sum of the moments of two intersecting or parallel forces about any point is equal to the moment of the resultant of the forces about the same point.

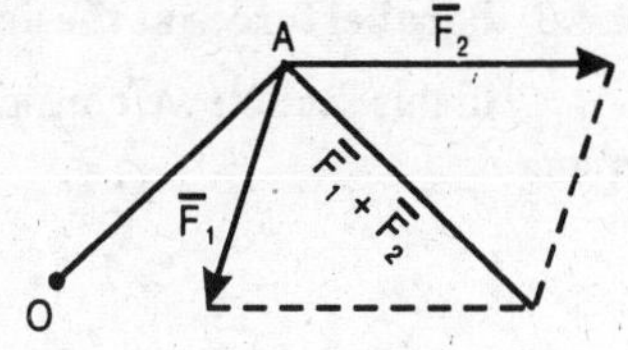

Case (*i*) Intersecting forces. Let the lines of action of the forces $\bar{F}_1$ and $\bar{F}_2$ intersect at A. Then the moments of $\bar{F}_1$ and $\bar{F}_2$ about any point O are

$$\overline{OA}\times\bar{F}_1,\ \overline{OA}\times\bar{F}_2$$

and their sum is

$$\overline{OA}\times\bar{F}_1+\overline{OA}\times\bar{F}_2.$$

But the resultant of $\bar{F}_1$ and $\bar{F}_2$ is $\bar{F}_1+\bar{F}_2$ acting at A. So its moment about O is

$$\overline{OA}\times\left(\bar{F}_1+\bar{F}_2\right).$$

Since $\overline{OA}\times\bar{F}_1+\overline{OA}\times\bar{F}_2=\overline{OA}\times\left(\bar{F}_1+\bar{F}_2\right)$, the theorem follows for the intersecting forces.

Case (*ii*). Parallel forces. Let the parallel forces be $\bar{F}_1=F_1\bar{i}$ and $\bar{F}_2=F_2\bar{i}$ acting at A_1 and A_2. Let $\bar{a}_1,\bar{a}_2$ be the P.V's of A_1, A_2 with respect to O. Then, the moments of $\bar{F}_1$, $\bar{F}_2$ about O are

$$\bar{a}_1\times F_1\bar{i},\ \bar{a}_2\times F_2\bar{i}$$

Their sum is

$$\bar{a}_1\times F_1\bar{i}+\bar{a}_2\times F_2\bar{i}=(F_1\bar{a}_1+F_2\bar{a}_2)\times\bar{i}.$$

...(1)

But the resultant of $F_1\bar{i}$ and $F_2\bar{i}$ is $(F_1+F_2)\,\bar{i}$ acting at X, where X divides A_1A_2 internally in the ratio $F_2\cdot F_1$. So the P.V. of X is

$$\frac{F_1\bar{a}_1+F_2\bar{a}_2}{F_1+F_2}.$$

So the moment of the resultant about O is

$$\overline{OX}\times(F_1+F_2)\bar{i}=\frac{F_1\bar{a}_1+F_2\bar{a}_2}{F_1+F_2}\times(F_1+F_2)\bar{i}$$

$$=(F_1\bar{a}_1+F_2\bar{a}_2)\times\bar{i} \qquad ...(2)$$

From (1) and (2) we get the theorem for parallel forces.

Remark. Varignon's theorem easily extends to any number of coplanar forces. Let $\bar{F}_1,\bar{F}_2,\ldots,\bar{F}_n$ be the given forces. Then

$$\text{Mt. of }(\bar{F}_1+\bar{F}_2)=\text{Mt. of }\bar{F}_1+\text{Mt. of }\bar{F}_2$$

$$\text{Mt. of }\left\{(\bar{F}_1+\bar{F}_2)+\bar{F}_3\right\}=\text{Mt. of }(\bar{F}_1+\bar{F}_2)+\text{Mt. of }\bar{F}_3$$

$$=(\text{Mt. of }\bar{F}_1+\text{Mt. of }\bar{F}_2)+\text{Mt. of }\bar{F}_3$$

$$=\text{Mt. of }\bar{F}_1+\text{Mt. of }\bar{F}_2+\text{Mt. of }\bar{F}_3,\text{ etc.}$$

4.4.3 Parallel forces at the vertices of a triangle

In this section we consider the resultant of three like parallel forces acting at the vertices of a triangle.

EXAMPLES

Example 1. Three like parallel forces P, Q, R act at the vertices of a triangle ABC. Show that their resultant passes through

(*i*) the centroid if $P = Q = R$,

(*ii*) the incentre if $P/a = Q/b = R/c$. **(M.U.)**

Let $\bar{a}, \bar{b}, \bar{c}$ be the P.V's of A, B, C. Then the resultant passes through the point whose P.V. is

$$\frac{P\bar{a}+Q\bar{b}+R\bar{c}}{P+Q+R}.$$

(*i*) If $P = Q = R$, then

$$\frac{P\bar{a}+Q\bar{b}+R\bar{c}}{P+Q+R}=\frac{\bar{a}+\bar{b}+\bar{c}}{3}$$

which is the P.V. of the centroid.

(*ii*) If $\dfrac{P}{a}=\dfrac{Q}{b}=\dfrac{R}{c}=k$, then

$$\frac{P\bar{a}+Q\bar{b}+R\bar{c}}{P+Q+R}=\frac{k(a\bar{a}+b\bar{b}+c\bar{c})}{k(a+b+c)}$$

$$=\frac{a\bar{a}+b\bar{b}+c\bar{c}}{a+b+c}$$

which is the P.V. of the incentre.

Example 2. Three like parallel forces P, Q, R act at the vertices of a triangle ABC. If their resultant passes through the orthocentre O, show that

$$\frac{P}{\tan A}=\frac{Q}{\tan B}=\frac{R}{\tan C}.$$ **(Bn. U.)**

Let AD be the altitude through A. Now P acts at A. So the resultant of Q, R should act at D such that

$$\frac{BD}{DC}=\frac{R}{Q}. \quad ...(1)$$

But, from ΔABD, ΔACD,

$$BD=\frac{AD}{\tan B},\quad CD=\frac{AD}{\tan C}.$$

Substituting these values in (1), we get

$$\frac{Q}{\tan B}=\frac{R}{\tan C}, \text{etc.}$$

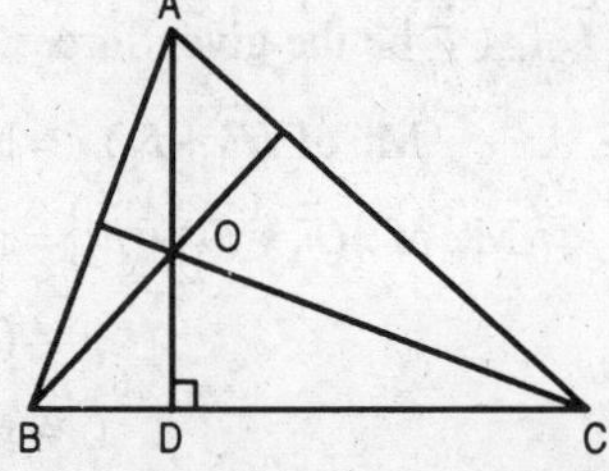

Example 3. Three like parallel forces P, Q, R act at the vertices of a triangle ABC. If

$$\frac{P}{\tan A}=\frac{Q}{\tan B}=\frac{R}{\tan C}=k,$$

show that the resultant of the forces pass through the orthocentre.

Q, R act at B, C. Let their resultant act at X on BC. Then $\overline{AX}$ is given by

$$\overline{AX}=\frac{Q\overline{AB}+R\overline{AC}}{Q+R}=\frac{\tan B\,\overline{AB}+\tan C\,\overline{AC}}{\tan B+\tan C}.$$

$$\therefore \qquad \overline{AX}\cdot\widehat{BC}=\frac{-\tan B\cdot AB\cdot\cos B+\tan C\cdot AC\cdot\cos C}{\tan B+\tan C}$$

$$=\frac{-c\sin B+b\sin C}{\tan B+\tan C}=0 \text{ since } \frac{b}{\sin B}=\frac{c}{\sin C}.$$

So AX is perpendicular to BC. Thus AX is the altitude through A. Now P acts at A and $Q+R$ acts at X. So the resultant acts at a point on the altitude. Similarly the resultant acts at points on the other altitudes also. This implies that the resultant acts at the orthocentre.

EXERCISES

1. Three equal like parallel forces act at the midpoints of the sides of a triangle. Show that their resultant passes through its centroid.
2. Three like parallel forces of magnitudes P, Q, R act at the vertices of a triangle ABC. Show that, if their resultant passes through the circumcentre S of the triangle, then

$$\frac{P}{\sin 2A}=\frac{Q}{\sin 2B}=\frac{R}{\sin 2C}. \qquad \textbf{(Bn.U.)}$$

[**Hint:** The resultant passes through the point whose P.V. w.r.t S is

$$\frac{P\overline{SA}+Q\overline{SB}+R\overline{SC}}{P+Q+R}.$$

But the point is S itself. So this P.V. is zero.

$$\therefore \qquad P\overline{SA}+Q\overline{SB}+R\overline{SC}=\overline{0}.$$

Multiply this vectorially by $\overline{SA}$ and use $\underline{|BSC} = 2A$, etc.]

4.5 FORCES ALONG THE SIDES OF A TRIANGLE

In this section we consider the resultant of forces acting on a rigid body, the forces being along the sides of a triangle.

EXAMPLES

Example 1. P, Q, R are forces along the sides BC, CA, AB of a triangle ABC taken in order. Show that, if their resultant

(*i*) passes through the incentre, then

$$P+Q+R=0$$

(*ii*) passes through the centroid, then

$$\frac{P}{a}+\frac{Q}{b}+\frac{R}{c}=0 \text{ or } \frac{P}{\sin A}=\frac{Q}{\sin B}=\frac{R}{\sin C}. \qquad \textbf{(M.U.)}$$

(*iii*) passes through the circumcentre, then

$$P\cos A+Q\cos B+R\cos C=0 \qquad \textbf{(M.K.U.)}$$

(*iv*) passes through the orthocentre, then

$$\frac{P}{\cos A}+\frac{Q}{\cos B}+\frac{R}{\cos C}=0. \qquad \textbf{(M.U.)}$$

(*i*) **Incentre I.** Let *ID*, *IE*, *IF* be the perpendiculars to the sides. Then

$$ID=IE=IF=r.$$

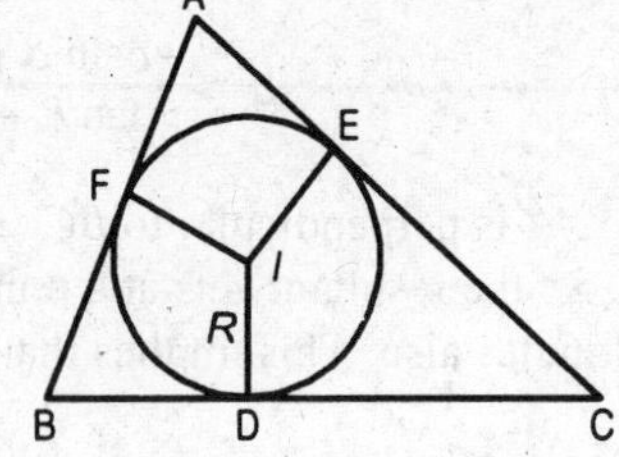

The resultant passes through the incentre and so its moment about *I* is zero. Hence the sum of the moments of the given forces about *I* is zero.

$\therefore$ $$rP+rQ+rR=0 \text{ or } P+Q+R=0.$$

Note. If *P*, *Q*, *R* are positive, then

$$P+Q+R\neq 0$$

and so the resultant cannot pass through the incentre. Therefore one or two of *P*, *Q*, *R* must be negative.

***(ii)* Centroid G.** Let *AD* be a median. Let p_1 be the length of the perpendicular from *G* to *BC*. Then the area of $\Delta\, ABC$ is

$$\Delta=\frac{1}{2}BC\times(3p_1).$$

$\therefore$ $$p_1=\frac{2\Delta}{3a}, \text{etc.}$$

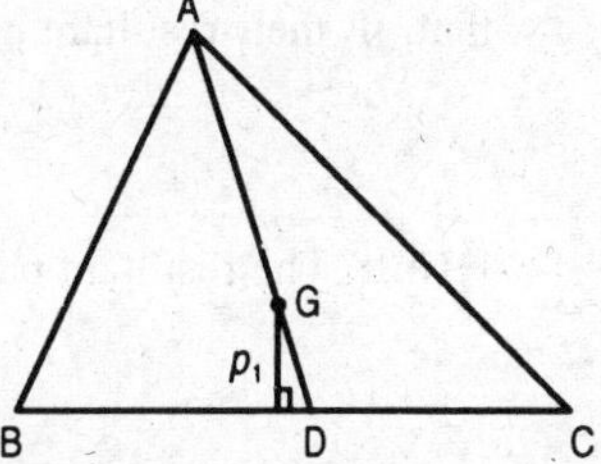

Now the sum of the moments about *G* is 0. Therefore

$$P\frac{2\Delta}{3a}+Q\frac{2\Delta}{3b}+R\frac{2\Delta}{3c}=0 \text{ or } \frac{P}{a}+\frac{Q}{b}+\frac{R}{c}=0.$$

***(iii)* Circumcentre S.** Now *A* is a point on the circumcircle and so *BC* subtends the angle 2*A* at the centre *S*. If *SD* is the perpendicular to *BC*, finding the area of $\Delta\, BSC$, in two different ways,

$$\frac{1}{2}\cdot a\cdot SD=\frac{1}{2}R\cdot R\cdot\sin 2A \text{ or } SD=\frac{R^2\sin 2A}{a}.$$

$\therefore$ $$SD=R^2\cdot 2\cdot\frac{\sin A}{a}\cdot\cos A=k\cos A, \text{etc.}$$

Thus, taking moments of the forces about *S*,

$$SD\cdot P+SE\cdot Q+SF\cdot R=0 \text{ or } k(P\cos A+Q\cos B+R\cos C)=0$$

$\therefore$ $$P\cos A+Q\cos B+R\cos C=0.$$

***(iv)* Orthocentre *O*.** Let *AD*, *BE* be two altitudes. Then

$$\underline{|CBE}=90^\circ-C.$$

So, from ΔBDO,

$$\frac{OD}{BD} = \tan(90^\circ - C) = \cot C \qquad ...(1)$$

But, from ΔABD

$$\frac{BD}{AB} = \cos B. \qquad ...(2)$$

Thus, on multiplying (1) and (2), we get

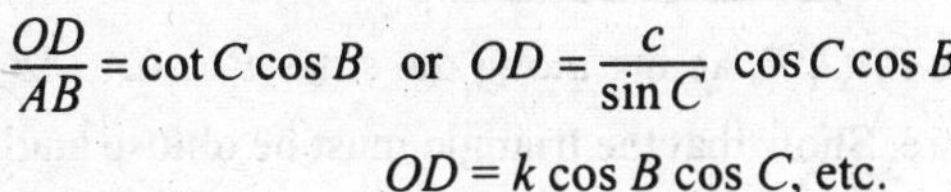

$$\frac{OD}{AB} = \cot C \cos B \quad \text{or} \quad OD = \frac{c}{\sin C} \cos C \cos B$$

$$\therefore \qquad OD = k \cos B \cos C, \text{ etc.}$$

Therefore, taking moments about O,

$$k(P \cos B \cos C + Q \cos C \cos A + R \cos A \cos B) = 0.$$

$$\therefore \qquad \frac{P}{\cos A} + \frac{Q}{\cos B} + \frac{R}{\cos C} = 0.$$

Note. If P, Q, R are positive one of A, B, C must be obtuse so that its cosine is negative.

Example 2. Three forces P, Q, R act along the sides BC, CA, AB of a triangle ABC. If their resultant passes through the incentre and centroid, then show that

$$\frac{P}{a(b-c)} = \frac{Q}{b(c-a)} = \frac{R}{c(a-b)}. \qquad \textbf{(M.U.)}$$

Since the resultant passes through the incentre and centroid, we have respectively

$$P + Q + R = 0 \qquad ...(1)$$

$$\frac{P}{a} + \frac{Q}{b} + \frac{R}{c} = 0 \qquad ...(2)$$

(See the previous example). Solving (1) and (2) for P, Q, R by the method of cross multiplication, we get

$$\frac{P}{\begin{vmatrix} 1 & 1 \\ 1/b & 1/c \end{vmatrix}} = \frac{Q}{\begin{vmatrix} 1 & 1 \\ 1/c & 1/a \end{vmatrix}} = \frac{R}{\begin{vmatrix} 1 & 1 \\ 1/a & 1/b \end{vmatrix}}$$

i.e.,

$$\frac{P}{1/c - 1/b} = \frac{Q}{1/a - 1/c} = \frac{R}{1/b - 1/a}.$$

Multiplying the denominators by abc, we get the result.

Example 3. Forces $P\,\widehat{BC}, Q\,\widehat{CA}, R\,\widehat{AB}$ act respectively at B, C, A, of an equilateral triangle ABC. If their resultant is a force parallel to BC and through the centroid G of the triangle, show that

$$-P = 2Q = 2R. \qquad \textbf{(M.U., Bn. U.)}$$

The forces are $P\,\widehat{BC}, Q\,\widehat{CA}, R\,\widehat{AB}$. Their resultant is

$$P\,\widehat{BC} + Q\,\widehat{CA} + R\,\widehat{AB}$$

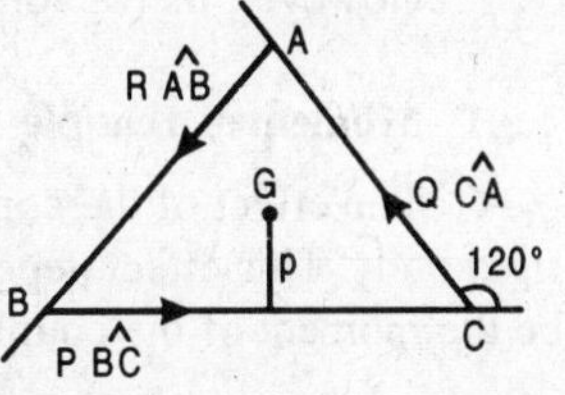

Since this resultant is parallel to $\widehat{BC}$,

$$\widehat{BC} \times (P\,\widehat{BC} + Q\,\widehat{CA} + R\,\widehat{AB}) = \bar{0}$$

i.e., $\bar{0} + (Q\sin 120^{o} - R\sin 120^{o})\hat{n} = \bar{0}$ or $Q = R$.

Since the resultant passes through G, the sum of the moments of the forces about G is zero. Thus

$$p(P+Q+R)=0 \text{ or } P+Q+R=0,$$

where p is the perpendicular distance of the centroid from the sides. But $Q=R$. This leads to the result

$$-P=2Q=2R.$$

EXERCISES

1. The resultant of three forces P, Q, R, acting along the sides BC, CA, AB of a triangle ABC passes through the orthocentre. Show that the triangle must be obtuse angled. If $\angle A = 120^{o}$, and $\angle B = \angle C$, show that $Q + R = P\sqrt{3}$. **(M.U. Bn.U.)**

   [Hint: See Example 1. Now $\angle A = 120^{o}$, $\angle B = \angle C = 30^{o}$.**]**

2. Three forces P, Q, R act along the sides BC, CA, AB of a triangle. Show that, if their resultant passes respectively through

   the incentre and circumcentre,

   the circumcentre and orthocentre,

   the orthocentre and centroid,

   then

$$\frac{P}{\cos B - \cos C} = \frac{Q}{\cos C - \cos A} = \frac{R}{\cos A - \cos B} \quad \textbf{(K.U.)}$$

$$\frac{P}{(b^2 - c^2)\cos A} = \frac{Q}{(c^2 - a^2)\cos B} = \frac{R}{(a^2 - b^2)\cos C} \quad \textbf{(M.U.)}$$

$$\frac{P}{\sin 2A \sin(B - C)} = \frac{Q}{\sin 2B \sin(C - A)} = \frac{R}{\sin 2C \sin(A - B)} \quad \textbf{(M.U.)}$$

4.6 COUPLES

In case (*ii*) of the bookwork of finding the resultant of parallel forces, if $F_1 = F_2$, that is, if the given forces are unlike parallel forces of equal magnitude, then $A_1 D_1$ will be parallel to $A_2 D_2$ and so no point of intersection, as O, will exist. Therefore it becomes impossible to reduce two unlike parallel forces of equal magnitude to a single force. Thus, we are necessiated to keep two such forces as they are. Two such forces are said to constitute a couple.

Couple. A couple, acting on a rigid body, is just a pair of unlike parallel forces of equal magnitude acting on the body along two different lines.

Remark. Since a couple cannot be reduced to a single force, a couple is not equivalent to any single force. So a couple and a force will never keep a rigid body in equilibrium.

However, the vector sum of the constituent forces of a couple is zero.

4.6.1 Moment of a couple

The effect of the constituent forces of a couple on a rigid body is to cause a rotation on the rigid body. This effect depends on the moments of the forces. The sum of these moments is said to be the moment of the couple.

Definition. The sum of the moments of the constituent forces of a couple about any point is called the moment of the couple.

Bookwork 4.4. To show that the moment of a couple, as defined above, is independent of the point about which the moment is obtained.

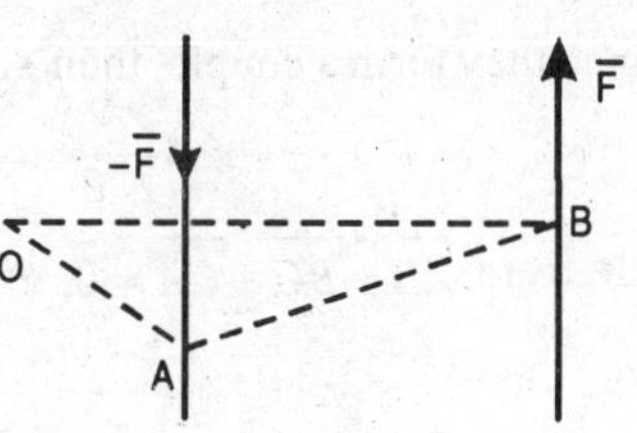

Consider a couple $\left(-\overline{F}, \overline{F}\right)$ constituted by the forces $-\overline{F}$ and $\overline{F}$. Let A be any point on the line of action of the force $-\overline{F}$ and B, any point on the line of action of the force $\overline{F}$. Then the moments of $-\overline{F}$ and $\overline{F}$ about an arbitrarily chosen point O, are

$$\overline{OA}\times\left(-\overline{F}\right),\ \overline{OB}\times\overline{F}.$$

So their sum is

$$\begin{aligned} -\overline{OA}\times\overline{F} + \overline{OB}\times\overline{F} &= \left(-\overline{OA}+\overline{OB}\right)\times\overline{F} \\ &= \overline{AB}\times\overline{F}. \end{aligned}$$

This sum is independent of O.

Furthermore, since $\overline{BA}\times\left(-\overline{F}\right) = \overline{AB}\times\overline{F}$, we get the result

$$\begin{Bmatrix}\text{Moment of}\\ \text{a couple}\end{Bmatrix} = \begin{Bmatrix}\text{Moment of one constituent force about}\\ \text{a point on the line of action of the other.}\end{Bmatrix}.$$

4.6.2 Arm and axis of a couple

If $\hat{n}$ is the unit vector perpendicular to the plane of a couple such that $\overline{AB}, \overline{F}, \hat{n}$ form a right-handed triad, then the moment of the couple is.

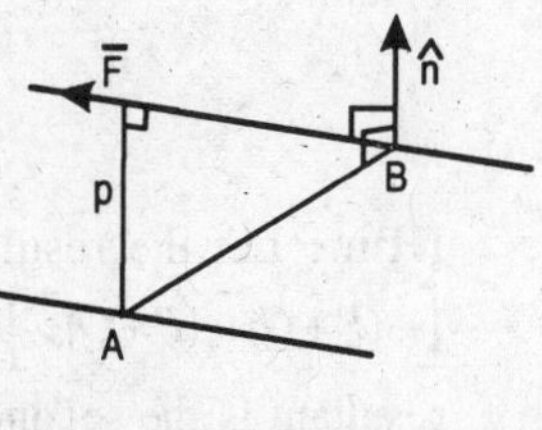

$$\begin{aligned} \overline{AB}, \overline{F} &= AB\cdot F\cdot \sin\theta\,\hat{n} \\ &= (AB\sin\theta)\,F\hat{n} \\ &= pF\hat{n}, \end{aligned}$$

where θ is the angle between $\overline{AB}$ and $\overline{F}$ and p is the perpendicular distance between the lines of action of the forces. p is called the arm of the couple and the direction of $\hat{n}$ is called the axis of the couple. It is important to note that the directions of the constituent forces of the couple in question are such as to cause a rotation in the anticlockwise sense. If, however, the directions of the constituent forces are such as to cause a rotation in the clockwise sense, then the moment of the couple will be

$$pF(-\hat{n}) = -pF\hat{n}.$$

In the above two cases the scalar moments of the couple are respectively pF and $-pF$.

EXAMPLES

Example 1. Three forces acting along the sides of a triangle in the same order are equivalent to a couple. Show that they are proportional to the sides of the triangle. **(M.U.)**

Let the triangle be ABC and the forces be

$$P\widehat{BC}, Q\widehat{CA}, R\widehat{AB}.$$

Since they form a couple, their sum equals zero. So

$$P\widehat{BC}+Q\widehat{CA}+R\widehat{AB}=\overline{0}. \qquad ...(1)$$

But, from $\overline{AB}+\overline{BC}+\overline{CA}=\overline{0}$, we have

$$a\widehat{BC}+b\widehat{CA}+c\widehat{AB}=\overline{0}. \qquad ...(2)$$

Comparing the coefficients of $B\hat{C}$, $C\hat{A}$, $A\hat{B}$ in (1) and (2), we get

$$\frac{P}{a}=\frac{Q}{b}=\frac{R}{c}.$$

EXERCISES

1. A system of forces in the plane of a triangle ABC is equivalent to a single force at A, acting along the internal bisector of the angle A and a couple of moment G_1. If the moments of the system about B and C are G_2 and G_3, show that $(b+c)\,G_1=bG_2+cG_3$. **(M.U.)**

   [Hint: G_2 = Mt. of the force F at A about B + Mt. of the couple
   $=(c\sin A/2)F+G_1$.
   $G_3=-(b\sin A/2)F+G_1$; Eliminate F.**]**

2. P and Q are the magnitudes of two like parallel forces. A couple of moment of magnitude G is combined with them. Show that the resultant of the parallel forces is displaced through a distance

$$\frac{G}{P+Q}. \qquad \textbf{(M.U.)}$$

   [Hint: Let the resultant of the parallel forces be $(P+Q)\overline{i}$ at A. Introduce the couple $\left[-(P+Q)\overline{i},(P+Q)\overline{i}\right]$ whose moment is G such that $-(P+Q)\overline{i}$ acts at A. Then the new resultant is the second constituent force $(P+Q)\overline{i}$. If the distance between A and this constituent force is p, then, considering the moment of about A, $p\,(P+Q)=G$.**]**

3. If three forces of magnitudes P, Q, R acting at the angular points of a triangle ABC along the tangents to the circumcircle, are equivalent to a couple, show that

$$P:Q:R=\sin 2A:\sin 2B:\sin 2C. \qquad \textbf{(M.U.)}$$

   [Hint: R_1: Circumradius; Sides of the triangle formed by the tangents: $kR_1\sin 2A$, $kR_1\sin 2B$, $kR_1\sin 2C$, where $k=\frac{1}{2}(\sec A\sec B\sec C)$. Use the result of Example 1.**]**

4.7 RESULTANT OF SEVERAL COPLANAR FORCES

Reduction of a system of coplanar forces acting on a rigid body to one or two forces, is dealt with in the following bookwork.

Bookwork 4.5. A system of coplanar forces reduce either to a single force or to a couple.

Let n coplanar forces act on a rigid body. Then, choosing two of them which do not form a couple, we can reduce them to a single force. This reduction will reduce the given system to $n-1$ forces. If this process is repeated successively then the system will reduce to just two forces. If these two forces are unlike parallel forces of equal magnitude, then they form a couple. Otherwise, they further reduce to a single force. Thus we achieve that a system of a coplanar forces reduce either to a couple or to a single force.

Remark. Suppose $\overline{F}_1, \overline{F}_2, \overline{F}_3, \ldots\ldots \overline{F}_n$ are forces. Then we have the following results:

(*i*) If $\overline{F}_1 + \overline{F}_2 + \ldots\ldots + \overline{F}_n \neq \overline{0}$, then the system reduces to a single force.

(*ii*) If $\overline{F}_1 + \overline{F}_2 + \ldots\ldots + \overline{F}_n = \overline{0}$, then the system reduces to a couple provided the sum of the moments of $\overline{F}_1, \overline{F}_2, \ldots\ldots, \overline{F}_n$ about any point is not zero.

(*iii*) If $\overline{F}_1 + \overline{F}_2 + \ldots\ldots + \overline{F}_n = \overline{0}$ and also the sum of the moments of $\overline{F}_1, \overline{F}_2, \ldots\ldots, \overline{F}_n$ is zero, then the system is in equilibrium.

EXAMPLES

Example 1. Show that the forces $\overline{AB}, \overline{CD}, \overline{EF}$ acting respectively at A, C, E of a regular hexagon $ABCDEF$, are equivalent to a couple of moment equal to the area of the hexagon. **(Bn.U.)**

Let O be the centre of the hexagon. Now the sum of the forces is

$$\overline{AB} + \overline{CD} + \overline{EF}$$

or

$$\overline{AB} + \overline{BO} + \overline{OA}$$

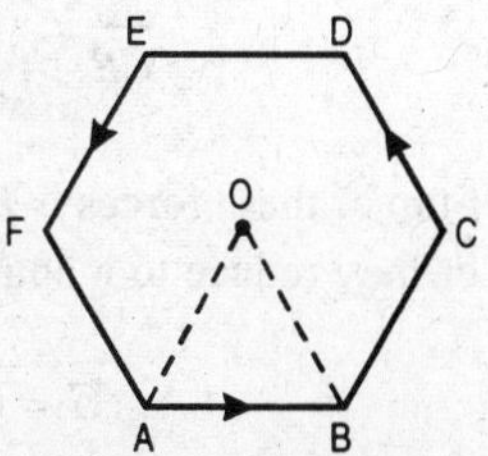

It is evident that it is zero. So, either the system is in equilibrium or it reduces to a couple. But the moment of $\overline{AB}$ about O is

$$\overline{OA} \times \overline{AB} = OA \cdot AB \cdot \sin OAB\, \overline{k} = 2\Delta \overline{k},$$

where Δ is the area of $\Delta\, AOB$. By symmetry the sum of the moments of all the forces is $3\,(2\Delta)\ \overline{k}$ or $60\Delta\, \overline{k}$. So the system reduces to a couple of moment 6Δ. But the area of the hexagon also is 6Δ.

Example 2. $ABCDEF$ is a regular hexagon. Forces P, $2P$, $3P$, $2P$, $5P$, $6P$ act along AB, BC, DC, ED, EF, AF. Show that the six forces are equivalent to a couple and find the moment of the couple. **(M.U., M.K.U., K.U., Bn.U.)**

Let the side of the hexagon be a and let

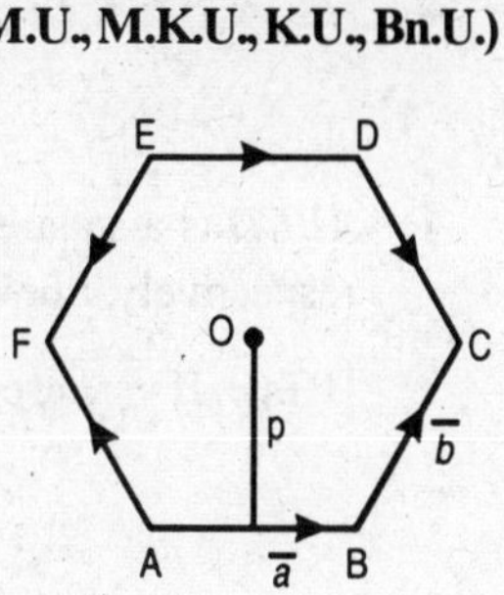

$$\overline{AB} = \overline{a}, \quad \overline{BC} = \overline{b}.$$

Then we have

$$\overline{DC} = \overline{DO} + \overline{OC} = \overline{a} - \overline{b}$$

Similarly,

$$\overline{ED} = \overline{a}, \quad \overline{EF} = -\overline{b}, \quad \overline{AF} = -\overline{a} + \overline{b}.$$

All these six vectors are of length a. So, to get the respective unit vectors, we should divide them by a. Thus the sum of the given forces is

$$P\,\frac{\overline{a}}{a} + 2P\,\frac{\overline{b}}{a} + 3P\,\frac{\overline{a} - \overline{b}}{a} + 2P\,\frac{\overline{a}}{a} + 5P\,\frac{(-\overline{b})}{a} + 6P\,\frac{-\overline{a} + \overline{b}}{a}.$$

This reduces to $\overline{0}$. So, the system reduces to a couple or is in equilibrium. If p is the length of the perpendicular from the centre O to the sides, then the sum of the scalar moments of the forces about O, is

$$p\,[P+2P-3P-2P+5P-6P]=-3pP=-3\frac{\sqrt{3}\,a\,P}{2}.$$

Thus the system reduces to a couple whose moment is $\frac{-3\sqrt{3}}{2}a\,P.$

Example 3. P, Q, R are points on the sides BC, CA, AB of a triangle ABC, dividing them internally in the same ratio $1+\lambda : 1-\lambda$. Show that the forces $\overline{AP}, \overline{BQ}, \overline{CR}$ acting at A, B, C are equivalent to a couple of moment $2\lambda\Delta$, where Δ is the area of the triangle ABC. **(M.U., A.U.)**

P divides BC in the ratio

$$1+\lambda : 1-\lambda.$$

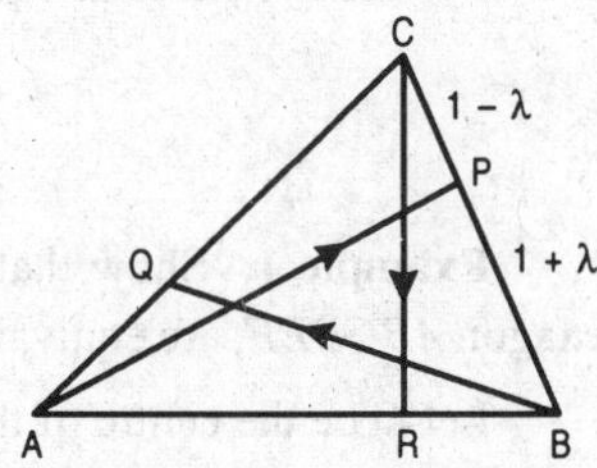

$$\therefore\ \overline{AP}=\frac{(1-\lambda)\overline{AB}+(1+\lambda)\overline{AC}}{(1+\lambda)+(1-\lambda)}$$

$$=\tfrac{1}{2}(1-\lambda)\overline{AB}-\tfrac{1}{2}(1+\lambda)\overline{CA},$$

$$\overline{BQ}=\tfrac{1}{2}(1-\lambda)\overline{BC}-\tfrac{1}{2}(1+\lambda)\overline{AB},$$

$$\overline{CR}=\tfrac{1}{2}(1-\lambda)\overline{CA}-\tfrac{1}{2}(1+\lambda)\overline{BC}.$$

Sum of these forces is zero because $\overline{AB}+\overline{BC}+\overline{CA}$ is zero. So, either the forces are in equilibrium or they reduce to a couple. If the sum of the moments of the forces, say about A is $\overline{G}$, then

$$\overline{G}=\overline{0}+\overline{AB}\times\overline{BQ}+\overline{AC}\times\overline{CR}$$

$$=\overline{AB}\times\left\{\tfrac{1}{2}(1-\lambda)\overline{BC}-\tfrac{1}{2}(1+\lambda)\overline{AB}\right\}+\overline{AC}\times\left\{\tfrac{1}{2}(1-\lambda)\overline{CA}-\tfrac{1}{2}(1+\lambda)\overline{BC}\right\}$$

$$=\tfrac{1}{2}(1-\lambda)\,\overline{AB}\times\overline{BC}-\tfrac{1}{2}(1+\lambda)\,\overline{AC}\times\overline{BC}$$

$$=\tfrac{1}{2}(1-\lambda)\,2\Delta\hat{n}-\tfrac{1}{2}(1+\lambda)2\Delta\hat{n}=-2\lambda\Delta\hat{n},\ \text{since}\ \overline{AB}\times\overline{BC}=2\Delta\hat{n}.$$

So the forces reduce to a couple of moment $2\lambda\Delta$.

EXERCISES

1. $ABCD$ is a square of side a. Forces $5P, 4P, 3P, 6P, 2\sqrt{2}\,P$ act along AB, BC, CD, DA, BD respectively. Show that the system reduces to a couple of moment $9aP$. **(M.U.)**

   [Hint: If $\overline{i}, \overline{j}$ are unit vectors along AB, BC, then the forces are

   $$5P\overline{i},\ 4P\overline{j},\ -3P\overline{i},\ -6P\overline{j},\ 2\sqrt{2}P\left(\frac{-\overline{i}+\overline{j}}{\sqrt{2}}\right).$$

   Their sum $=\overline{0}$. So, a couple; Mt. about $B=a\,(3P)+a\,(6P)$.]

2. Forces of 3,4,5,6 and $2\sqrt{2}$ act along AB, BC, CD, DA and AC of a square $ABCD$ of side a. Show that the system reduces to a couple of moment $9aP$. **(M.K.U.)**

[**Hint:** Forces: $3\bar{i}, 4\bar{j}, -5\bar{i}, -6\bar{j}, 2\sqrt{2}\,\dfrac{\bar{i}+\bar{j}}{\sqrt{2}}$. Their sum is zero. Sum of the moments of the forces about $A = a(4P) + a(5P)$.]

3. *ABC* is an equilateral triangle of side *a*; *D, E, F* divide the sides *BC, CA, AB* respectively in the ratio 2 : 1. Three forces, each of magnitude *P*, act at *D, E, F* perpendicularly to the sides and outward from the triangle. Prove that they are equivalent to a couple of moment $\frac{1}{2}Pa$. **(M.U.)**

[**Hint:** The vector sum of the forces is zero because they are equally inclined at one another. So either they are in equilibrium or they reduce to a couple. The scalar moment of each force about the centroid is *pP*, where $p = a/6$]

4. *P, Q, R* are points on the sides *BC, CA, AB* of a triangle *ABC*, dividing them internally in the same ratio *m*:*n*. Show that the forces $\overline{AP}, \overline{BQ}, \overline{CR}$ acting at *A, B, C* are equivalent to a couple of moment

$$\frac{2(n-m)}{m+n}\Delta$$

where Δ is the area of the triangle *ABC*. **(K.U.)**

5. *ABCD*, are two coplanar parallelograms. Show that the forces $\overline{AA'}, \overline{B'B}, \overline{CC'}, \overline{D'D}$ acting at *A, B, C, D* reduce to a couple.

6. *ABCD* is a quadrilateral lamina *AB* = 5cm; *BC* = *DC* = *DB* = 4 cm; *DA* = 3 cm. Forces 10, 8, 8, 6 gm. wt respectively act along *AB, BC, CD, DA*. Prove that they are equivalent to a couple and find the moment. **(M.K.U.)**

[**Hint:** Force along $AB: 10\widehat{AB} = 2(5\widehat{AB}) = 2\overline{AB}$. The other forces are $2\overline{BC}, 2\overline{CD}, 2\overline{DA}$. Sum of the forces $\bar{0}$. So, a couple. Moment about $B = 4\times6 + 4\cdot\frac{\sqrt{3}}{2}\cdot 8$ since *BD* is perpendicular to *DA* and Δ *BCD* is equilateral]

7. Forces *P, Q, R, S*, $\sqrt{2}T, \sqrt{2}U$ act along *AB, BC, CD, DA, AC, DB* of a square *ABCD* of side 3. If

$$T + U = R - P,\quad T - U = S - Q,$$

show that the forces reduce to a coupe of moment

$$\tfrac{3}{2}(P + Q + R + S).$$ **(M.U.)**

[**Hint:** Equating the sums of $\bar{i}, \bar{j}$ components to 0,

$$P + T + U - R = 0,\ \ -S + Q + T - U = 0.$$

Take moments about the meet of the diagonals]

8. Forces $P_1, P_2, P_3, P_4, P_5, P_6$ acts along *AB, BC, CD, DE, EF, FA* of a regular hexagon. Show that they will be in equilibrium if **(M.K.U.,)**

$$P_1 - P_4 = P_3 - P_6 = P_5 - P_2,\ \ P_1 + P_2 + P_3 + P_4 + P_5 + P_6 = 0.$$

[**Hint:** From components along and perpendicular to *AB*, $2P_1 + P_2 - P_3 - 2P_4 - P_5 + P_6 = 0$, $P_2 + P_3 - P_5 - P_6 = 0$ or $2a + b - c = 0, b + c = 0$ where $a = P_1 - P_4, b = P_2 - P_5, c = P_3 - P_6$. So $a = -b = c$. Take moments about the centre.]

9. If a system of coplanar forces reduces to a couple whose moment is *G* and when each force is turned round its point of application through a right angle, it reduces to a couple of moment

H, prove that,when each force is turned through an angle θ, the system is equivalent to a couple of moment

$$G\cos\theta + H\sin\theta.$$

Show further that, if the forces are turned through an angle $2\tan^{-1} H/G$, the moment of the couple is still *G*.

[Hint: Let $x_r\bar{i} + y_r\bar{j}$ be the P.V. of the point of application of the force $F_r\,(\cos\alpha_r\bar{i} + \sin\alpha_r\bar{j})$ which makes an angle α_r with the $\bar{i}$ direction. Since the systems are couples of moments *G*, *H*,

$$\Sigma F_r(\cos\alpha_r\bar{i} + \sin\alpha_r\bar{j}) = \bar{0},\ \Sigma F_r(-\sin\alpha_r\bar{i} + \cos\alpha_r\bar{j}) = \bar{0} \quad ...(1)$$

$$\Sigma\,(x_r\bar{i} + y_r\bar{j})\times F_r(\cos\alpha_r\bar{i} + \sin\alpha_r\bar{j}) = G\bar{k} \quad ...(2)$$

$$\Sigma\,(x_r\bar{i} + y_r\bar{j})\times F_r(-\sin\alpha_r\bar{i} + \cos\alpha_r\bar{j}) = H\bar{k} \quad ...(3)$$

Show that $\Sigma F_r\left\{\cos(\alpha_r+\theta)\,\bar{i} + \sin(\alpha_r+\theta)\,\bar{j}\right\} = \bar{0}$ and also, by considering (2) × cos θ + (3) × sin θ, that $\Sigma(x_r\bar{i} + y_r\bar{j}) \times F_r\left\{\cos(\alpha_r+\theta)\,\bar{i} + \sin(\alpha_r+\theta)\,\bar{j}\right\} = g\cos\theta + h\sin\theta.$

(*ii*) Set $\cos\frac{\theta}{2} = \frac{G}{\sqrt{G^2+H^2}}$, and $\sin\frac{\theta}{2} = \frac{H}{\sqrt{G^2+H^2}}$ in $G\cos\theta + H\sin\theta$**]**

4.7.1 Moment of a certain couple as an area

In this section we first show that certain three coplanar forces acting on a rigid body are equivalent to a couple whose moment equals a certain area.

Bookwork 4.6. Three coplanar forces represented by and acting along the sides of a triangle, taken in order, reduce to a couple, the magnitude of whose moment being equal to twice the area of the triangle.

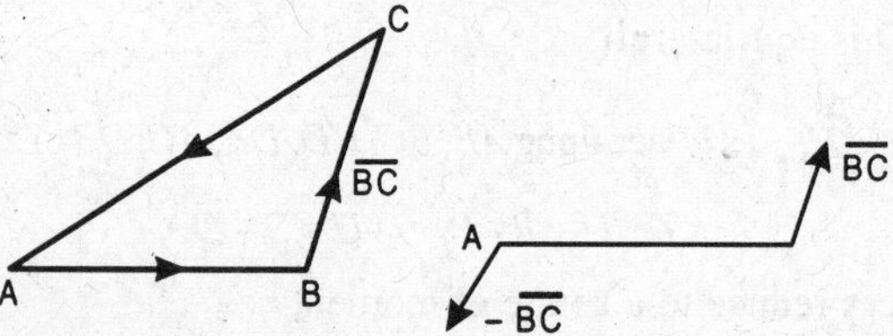

Let *ABC* be the given triangle. Then the given forces are

$\overline{AB}$ acting at *A*, $\overline{BC}$ acting at *B*, $\overline{CA}$ acting at C.

The first and the third forces act at *A*. Their resultant is

$$\overline{AB} + \overline{CA} \text{ or } \overline{CA} + \overline{AB} \text{ or } \overline{CB} \text{ or } -\overline{BC}$$

acting at *A*. So the given three forces are equivalent to the two forces,

(*i*) $-\overline{BC}$ acting at *A*,

(*ii*) $\overline{BC}$ acting at B,

that is, the given forces are equivalent to the couple.

$$\left(-\overline{BC}, \overline{BC}\right).$$

Its moment is $\overline{AB} \times \overline{BC}$. But we know that the

$$\text{area of the triangle } ABC = \tfrac{1}{2}\left|\overline{AB} \times \overline{BC}\right|.$$

Hence the magnitude of the moment of the couple is

$$\left|\overline{AB} \times \overline{BC}\right| = 2\,(\text{area of the triangle } ABC).$$

Hence the result.

An extension. The above bookwork can be extended to any number of coplanar forces acting on a rigid body, that is, n coplanar forces represented by and acting along the sides of a polygon A_1, A_2,......., A_n taken in order, reduce to a couple the magnitude of whose moment is equal to twice the area of the polygon. The proof involves just a division of the polygon into triangles

$$A_1A_2A_3,\ A_1A_3A_4,\ .....,A_1A_{n-1}A_n$$

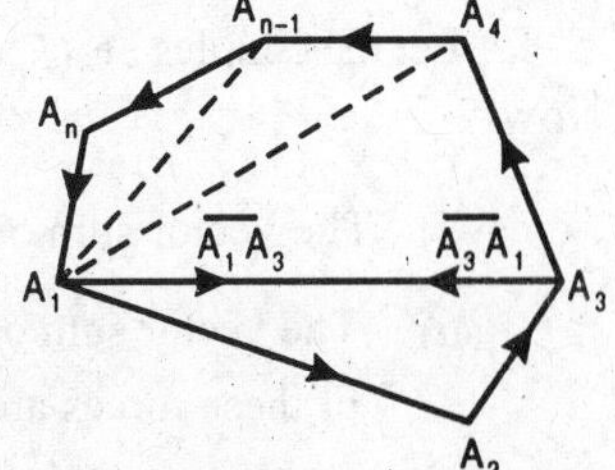

and an introduction of the forces

$$\overline{A_1A_3},\ \overline{A_3A_1}$$

along $\overline{A_1A_3}$, and similar introduction along A_1A_4, A_1A_5,....., A_1A_{n-1}.

EXAMPLES

Example 1. Five equal forces act along the sides AB, BC, CD, DE, EF of a regular hexagon. Show that the sum of moments of these forces about any point Q on FA is a constant. **(M.U.)**

Let the side of the hexagon be a and the equal forces be P. We know that the six forces

$$\overline{AB}, \overline{BC}, \overline{CD}, \overline{DE}, \overline{EF}, \overline{FA}$$

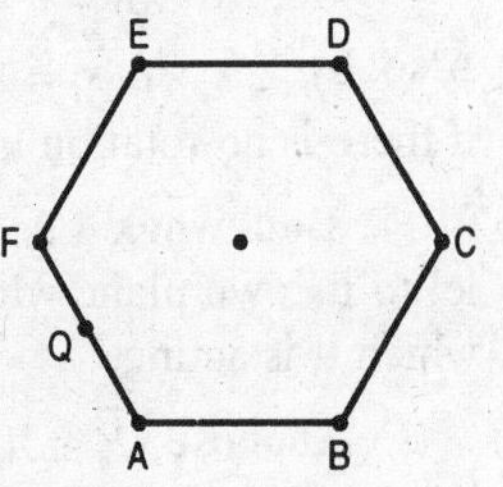

acting at A, B, C, D, E, F reduces to a couple of moment which is equal to the area of the hexagon, namely,

$$6\cdot\tfrac{1}{2}\cdot a\cdot a\cdot\sin 60^\circ \quad\text{or}\quad \frac{3\sqrt{3}}{2}a^2.$$

Therefore taking moments of these six forces about Q,

$$\overline{QA}\times\overline{AB}+\overline{QB}\times\overline{BC}+......+\overline{QF}\times\overline{FA}=\frac{3\sqrt{3}}{2}a^2\,\overline{k}, \qquad ...(1)$$

where $\overline{k}$ is the unit vector perpendicular to the plane of the hexagon. Dividing both sides of (1) by a and multiplying by P,

$$\overline{QA}\times(P\,\widehat{AB})+\overline{QB}\times(P\,\widehat{BC})+......+\overline{QF}\times(P\,\widehat{FA})=\frac{3\sqrt{3}}{2}a\,P\overline{k}.$$

In the sixth term of this, $\overline{QF}$ and $\widehat{FA}$ are parallel and so it vanishes, that is,

$$\overline{QF}\times(P\,\widehat{FA})=\overline{0}.$$

$$\therefore \qquad \overline{QA}\times(P\,\widehat{AB})+\overline{QB}\times(P\,\widehat{BC})+......+\overline{QE}\times(P\,\widehat{EF})=\frac{3\sqrt{3}}{2}a\,P\overline{k}.$$

Thus, in words, we have

$$\left.\begin{array}{l}\text{Sum of the scalar moments of}\\ \text{the given five forces about } Q\end{array}\right\}=\frac{3\sqrt{3}}{2}a\,P,\ \text{a constant.}$$

4.7.2 Couples in a parallel planes

The vector moment of a couple is perpendicular to the plane of the couple. So, if two couples have parallel vector moments, then they should be in the same plane or in parallel planes.

Bookwork 4.7. Two couples of equal moments are equivalent.

The vector sum of the constituent forces of each couple is zero. So the couples satisfy the first condition of equivalence. Since the moment of a couple is equal to the sum of the moments of the constituent forces about any point, by hypothesis, the couples satisfy the second condition of equivalence. So the couples are equivalent.

Bookwork 4.8. Two coplanar couples whose moments are equal in magnitude but opposite in direction keep a rigid body in equilibrium.

Let the couples be $(\overline{F_1}, -\overline{F_1})$ and $(\overline{F_2}, -\overline{F_2})$. Then there are four forces acting on the rigid body. Now

(*i*) The vector sum of these forces $= \overline{0}$,

(*ii*) The vector sum of the moments of these forces about the mass centre $\Big\}$ = sum of the moments of the couples

$= \overline{0}$ by the hypothesis.

So, by $M\ddot{\overline{R}} = \overline{F}$ (See (3) in section 4.2.1.), the mass centre is at rest if it is initially at rest. Also, by $\Sigma\, \overline{s_i} \times m_i \ddot{\overline{s_i}} = \Sigma \overline{s_i} \times \overline{F_{ii}}$ (see (7) in section 4.2.1.), there is no rotation about the mass centre if there is no rotation initially. Thus the four forces can keep the rigid body in equilibrium.

Bookwork 4.9. A couple can be transfered to a plane parallel to its own plane without altering its effect on the rigid body on which it is acting.

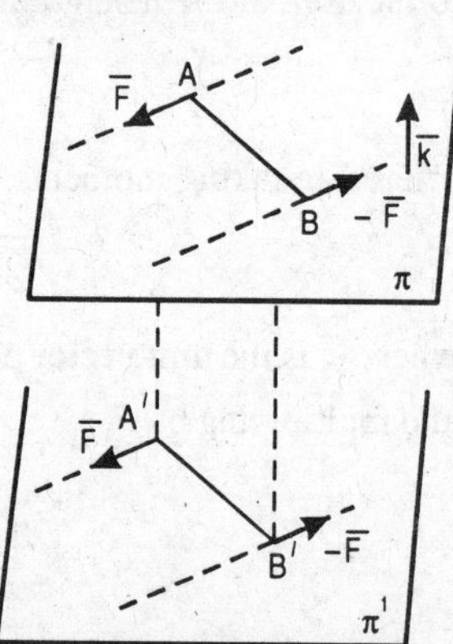

Suppose ($\overline{F}$ at A, $-\overline{F}$ at B) is a given couple in the plane π with AB as its arm. Let π' be a plane parallel to π and $A'B'$, the projection of AB on π'. Let $\overline{k}$ be the unit vector perpendicular to π as shown in the figure.

Consider the couple ($\overline{F}$ at A', $-\overline{F}$ at B'). The moment of the given couple is $(AB)(F)\overline{k}$ and that of the other is $(A'B')(F)\,\overline{k}$. But $AB = A'B'$. So these moments are equal and consequently the couples are equivalent.

Remark. Couples in a set of parallel planes can be compounded into a single couple in a plane parallel to the given planes.

Bookwork 4.10. Given a couple, to find an equivalent couple having its constituent forces along two given parallel lines in the plane of the couple.

Let l_1 and l_2 be the given parallel lines. Let $-\overline{F}$ and $\overline{F}$ be the constituent forces of the given couple and let them meet l_1 and l_2 at A_1 and A_2. Suppose

$$\overline{A_1P_1} = -\overline{F}, \quad \overline{A_2P_2} = \overline{F}.$$

Draw the parallelograms

$$A_1B_1P_1C_1,\ A_2B_2P_2C_2$$

having A_1P_1, A_2P_2 as diagonals and the sides being parallel to A_1A_2 and l_1.

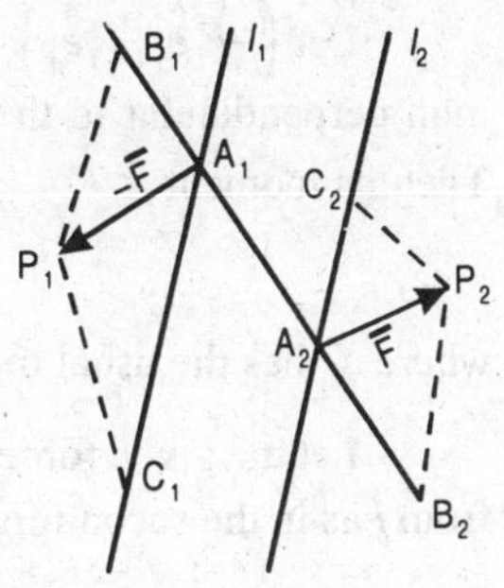

Since $A_1P_1 = A_2P_2$, the parallelograms are equal so that $A_1B_1 = A_2B_2$, $A_1C_1 = A_2C_2$. Now the forces $-\overline{F}$ at A_1 and $\overline{F}$ at A_2 are equivalent to

$$\overline{A_1B_1},\ \overline{A_1C_1} \text{ at } A_1,$$

$$\overline{A_2B_2},\ \overline{A_2C_2} \text{ at } A_2.$$

Of these four forces, $\overline{A_1B_1}$, $\overline{A_2B_2}$ are equal and opposite and act along the same line and so they cancel themselves, leaving out only $\overline{A_1C_1}, \overline{A_2C_2}$ along l_1, l_2. But $\overline{A_1C_1}$, $\overline{A_2C_2}$ are equal and opposite. So they form the couple $(\overline{A_1C_1},\ \overline{A_2C_2})$.

Bookwork 4.11. A system of coplanar couples acting on a rigid body is equivalent to a couple in the same plane whose moment is equal to the sum of the moments of the given couples.

Let

$$\left(-\overline{F}_1, \overline{F}_1\right),\ \left(-\overline{F}_2, \overline{F}_2\right),\ \ldots\ldots,\ \left(-\overline{F}_n, \overline{F}_n\right)$$

be n given coplanar couples and let their moments be $\overline{G}_1, \overline{G}_2, \ldots, \overline{G}_n$. Suppose that l_1 and l_2 are two arbitrarily chosen parallel lines in the plane of the couples and that A and B are two points on them. Let the couples

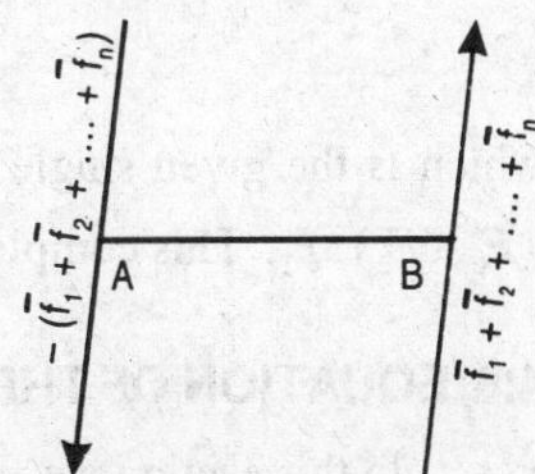

$$\left(-\overline{f}_1, \overline{f}_1\right),\ \left(-\overline{f}_2, \overline{f}_2\right), \ldots\ldots,\ \left(-\overline{f}_n, \overline{f}_n\right)$$

having the constituent forces $-\overline{f}_1, -\overline{f}_2, \ldots\ldots, -\overline{f}_n$ along l_1 and the constitutent forces $\overline{f}_1, \overline{f}_2, \ldots\ldots, \overline{f}_n$ along l_2, be respectively equivalent to the given couples. Then

$$\overline{AB} \times \overline{f}_1 = \overline{G}_1,\ \overline{AB} \times \overline{f}_2 = \overline{G}_2, \ldots\ldots, \overline{AB} \times \overline{f}_n = \overline{G}_n.$$

Now the resultants of the n forces along l_1 and that of the n forces along l_2 are respectively

$$-\left(\overline{f}_1 + \overline{f}_2 + \ldots. + \overline{f}_n\right),\ \left(\overline{f}_1 + \overline{f}_2 + \ldots. + \overline{f}_n\right).$$

They form a couple which is equivalent to the given n couples. The moment of this couple is

$$\overline{AB} \times \left(\overline{f}_1 + \overline{f}_2 + \ldots\ldots + \overline{f}_n\right) = \overline{AB} \times \overline{f}_1 + \ldots\ldots + \overline{AB} \times \overline{f}_n$$

$$= \overline{G}_1 + \overline{G}_2 + \ldots\ldots + \overline{G}_n$$

= the sum of the moments of the given couples.

Hence the result.

4.7.3 Resultant of a couple and a force

We now proceed to reduce a system of three forces, of which two form a couple, to a single force.

Bookwork 4.12. To show that a couple and a force in the same plane reduce to a single force. This single force is the same as the given force, but has a different parallel line of action.

Let $\left(-F_1\hat{e}_1, F_1\hat{e}_1\right)$ be the given couple and let AB be a common perpendicular to the lines of action of its constituent forces. Then its moment is

$$\overline{AB}\times F_1\hat{e}_1 = AB\cdot F_1\cdot\hat{n}, \qquad \text{...(1)}$$

where $\hat{n}$ has the usual meaning.

Let the given force be $F_2\hat{e}_2$ acting along the line l. Take a line l' parallel to l at a distance AB from l as in the second figure. Suppose CD is a common perpendicular to l' and l. Then

$$CD = AB.$$

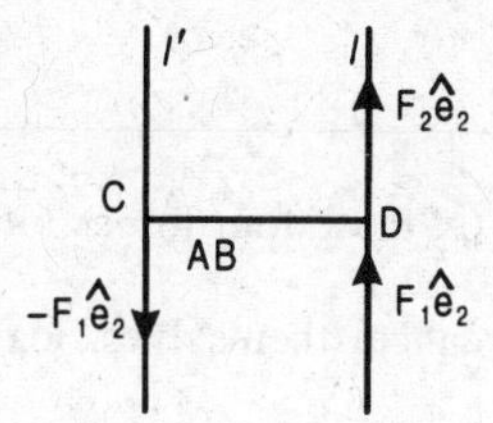

Consider the couple $\left(-F_1\hat{e}_2, F_1\hat{e}_2\right)$ having its constituent forces along l' and l. It is evident that its moment is same as (1). So this new couple $\left(-F_1\hat{e}_2, F_1\hat{e}_2\right)$ is equivalent to the given couple. Hence the given couple and the given force are equivalent to the new couple $\left(-F_1\hat{e}_2, F_1\hat{e}_2\right)$ and the force $F_2\hat{e}_2$, acting along l. So the given couple and the given force are equivalent to the parallel forces.

$$(F_1+F_2)\hat{e}_2,\ -F_1\hat{e}_2$$

acting along l, l'. Their resultant is

$$(F_1+F_2)\hat{e}_2 + \left(-F_1\hat{e}_2\right) = F_2\hat{e}_2$$

which is the given single force but acting at the point which divides CD externally in the ratio $(F_1+F_2):F_1$. This completes the proof.

4.8 EQUATION OF THE LINE OF ACTION OF THE RESULTANT

In this section we find the equation of the line of action of the resultant force when a given system of coplanar forces reduce to a single force.

Bookwork 4.13. When a system of coplanar forces $\overline{F}_1, \overline{F}_2, \ldots\ldots, \overline{F}_n$, acting at $A_1, A_2, \ldots\ldots, A_n$, reduce to a single force, to find the equation of its line of action.

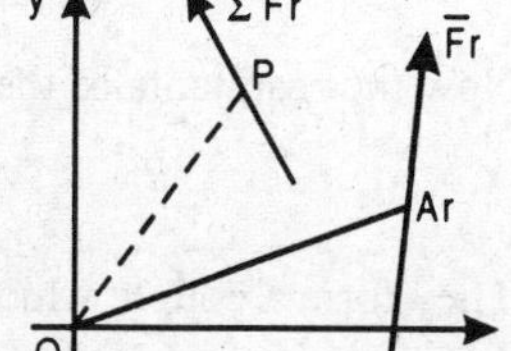

Choose any two perpendicular lines Ox, Oy in the plane of the forces as the x, y axes and let $\overline{i}$, $\overline{j}$ be the unit vectors in their directions. Let $P(x, y)$ be any point on the line of action of the resultant force $\Sigma\overline{F}_r$ of the system. Then any relation in x, y is the equation of the line. Now

$$\overline{OP} = x\overline{i} + y\overline{j}.$$

Let P_r, Q_r be the components of $\overline{F}_r$ in the $\overline{i}$, $\overline{j}$ directions. Then

$$\overline{F}_r = P_r\overline{i} + Q_r\overline{j}.$$

Since the sum of the moments of the forces about any point, say O, equals the moment of their resultant about O,

$$\Sigma(\overline{OA}_r\times\overline{F}_r) = \overline{OP}\times(\Sigma\overline{F}_r) \quad\text{or}\quad \overline{OP}\times(\Sigma\overline{F}_r) - \Sigma(\overline{OA}_r\times\overline{F}_r) = \overline{0}$$

i.e., $$(x\overline{i} + y\,\overline{j})\times\Sigma(P_r\overline{i} + Q_r\,\overline{j}) - \Sigma(\overline{OA}_r\times\overline{F}_r) = \overline{0}$$

i.e., $$(x\bar{i}+y\,\bar{j})\times\{(\Sigma P_r)\bar{i}+(\Sigma Q_r)\,\bar{j}\}-\Sigma\,(\overline{OA_r}\times\bar{F}_r)=\bar{0}$$

i.e., $$x\,(\Sigma Q_r)\,\bar{k}-y(\Sigma P_r)\,\bar{k}-(\Sigma\, p_r\, F_r)\,\bar{k}=\bar{0}$$

with the usual meaning for $\bar{k}$ and p_r being the perpendicular distance of O from $\bar{F}_r$ such that its value is positive or negative according as the sense of rotation of $\bar{F}_r$ about O is anticlockwise or not. Thus the equation of the line of action of the resultant is

$$(\Sigma Q_r)x-(\Sigma P_r)y-\Sigma\, p_r\, F_r=0$$

or $$(\Sigma Q_r)x-(\Sigma P_r)y-\Sigma G_r=0, \qquad ...(1)$$

where $G_r=p_rF_r$. This equation can be put in the elegant form

$$Yx-Xy-G=0, \qquad ...(2)$$

where

$X=\Sigma P_r$ = sum of the components of the forces in the x direction,

$Y=\Sigma Q_r$ = sum of the components of the forces in the y direction

$G=\Sigma G_r=\Sigma\, p_rF_r$ = sum of the scalar moments of the forces about the origin.

Now we have that the resultant force is

$$\bar{F}_1+\bar{F}_2+....+\bar{F}_n \text{ or } X\,\bar{i}+Y\,\bar{j}$$

whose magnitude is $\sqrt{X^2+Y^2}$ and the line of action is

$$Yx-Xy=G.$$

The slope of the line is Y/X.

Note. The convenient form of (2) to remember is

$$\begin{vmatrix} X & Y \\ x & y \end{vmatrix}+G=0,$$

where (x,y) is any point on the line of action of the resultant.

4.8.1 Sum of the moments about an arbitrary point

We shall consider the same system of forces as in the previous section. We obtain now the sum of the moments of the forces about an arbitrary point $A(a, b)$ in terms of X, Y, G. This sum is

$$\begin{aligned}\Sigma\,\overline{AA_r}\times\bar{F}_r &=\Sigma(\overline{OA_r}-\overline{OA})\times\bar{F}_r\\ &=-\Sigma\,\overline{OA}\times\bar{F}_r+\Sigma\,\overline{OA_r}\times\bar{F}_r\\ &=\Sigma[(-a\,\bar{i}-b\bar{j})\times(P_r\bar{i}+Q_r\,\bar{j})]+(\Sigma G_r)\,\bar{k}\\ &=-a(\Sigma Q_r)\,\bar{k}+b\,(\Sigma P_r)\,\bar{k}+\Sigma G_r\,\bar{k}\\ &=\{-a(\Sigma Q_r)+b\,(\Sigma P_r)+(\Sigma G_r)\}\,\bar{k}\\ &=(-aY+bX+G)\,\bar{k}.\end{aligned}$$

The sum of the scalar moments about A is

$$-aY+bX+G \text{ or } \begin{vmatrix} X & Y \\ a & b \end{vmatrix}+G,$$

where (a,b) is the arbitrary point.

EXAMPLES

Example 1. Forces 3, 2, 4, 5 kg. wt. act along the sides AB, BC, CD, DA of a square. Find their resultant and its line of action. **(M.U., Bn.U.)**

Let $\overline{i}, \overline{j}$ be the unit vectors parallel to $\overline{AB}, \overline{AD}$ and $AB = a$. Let AB, AD be the x, y axes. The vector sum of the forces is

$$(3\overline{i}) + (2\overline{j}) + (-4\overline{i}) + (-5\overline{j}) = -\overline{i} - 3\overline{j}.$$

Let X, Y be the sums of the $\overline{i}, \overline{j}$ components of the forces and G, the sum of the moments about the origin A. Then

$$X = -1, \quad Y = -3.$$

The magnitude of the resultant force is

$$\sqrt{X^2 + Y^2} = \sqrt{(-1)^2 + (-3)^2} = \sqrt{10}.$$

$$G = 0 \times 3 + a\,(2) + a\,(4) + 0 \times 5 = 6a.$$

The equation of line of action of the resultant force is

$$\begin{vmatrix} X & Y \\ x & y \end{vmatrix} + G = 0 \text{ or } \begin{vmatrix} -1 & -3 \\ x & y \end{vmatrix} + 6a = 0$$

i.e., $$-y + 3x + 6a = 0.$$

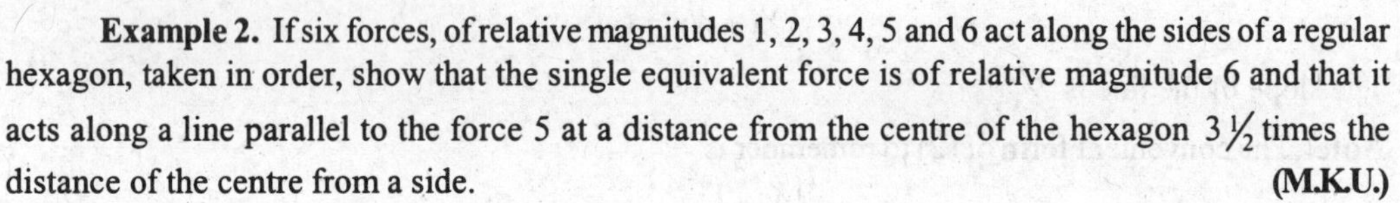

Example 2. If six forces, of relative magnitudes 1, 2, 3, 4, 5 and 6 act along the sides of a regular hexagon, taken in order, show that the single equivalent force is of relative magnitude 6 and that it acts along a line parallel to the force 5 at a distance from the centre of the hexagon $3\frac{1}{2}$ times the distance of the centre from a side. **(M.K.U.)**

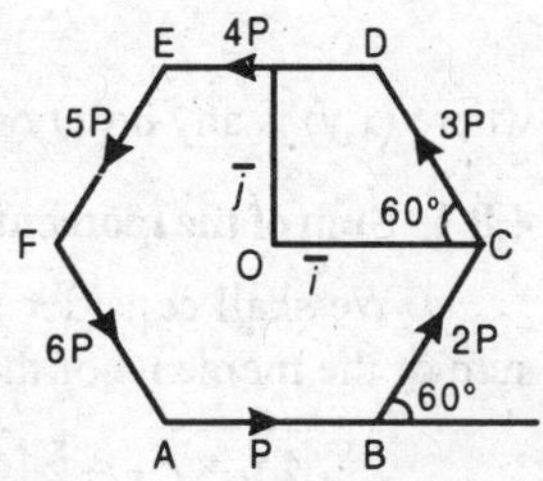

Let the forces be $P, 2P, 3P, 4P, 5P, 6P$ along the sides AB, BC, CD, DE, EF, FA of the regular hexagon $ABCDEF$ whose centre is O. Choose OC as the x axis and the perpendicular line through O as the y axis. Let $\overline{i}, \overline{j}$ be the unit vectors in their directions. Then we have the unit vectors along the sides, taken in order,

$$\widehat{AB} = \overline{i}$$
$$\widehat{BC} = \cos 60°\,\overline{i} + \sin 60°\,\overline{j} = \tfrac{1}{2}\overline{i} + \tfrac{\sqrt{3}}{2}\overline{j}$$
$$\widehat{CD} = -\cos 60°\,\overline{i} + \sin 60°\,\overline{j} = -\tfrac{1}{2}\overline{i} + \tfrac{\sqrt{3}}{2}\overline{j}$$
$$\widehat{DE} = -\widehat{AB}$$
$$\widehat{EF} = -\widehat{BC}$$
$$\widehat{FA} = -\widehat{CD}$$

Denoting the sum of the $\overline{i} \cdot \overline{j}$ components of the forces by X, Y and the sum of the moments of the forces about O by G, we get

$$X = P + 2P\left(\tfrac{1}{2}\right) + 3P\left(\tfrac{-1}{2}\right) + 4P(-1) + 5P\left(\tfrac{-1}{2}\right) + 6P\left(\tfrac{1}{2}\right) = -3P.$$

$$Y = 2P\left(\tfrac{\sqrt{3}}{2}\right) + 3P\left(\tfrac{\sqrt{3}}{2}\right) + 5P\left(\tfrac{-\sqrt{3}}{2}\right) + 6P\left(\tfrac{-\sqrt{3}}{2}\right) = -3\sqrt{3}\,P.$$

$\therefore$ Resultant force $= x\,\bar{i} + Y\,\bar{j} = -3P\bar{i} - 3\sqrt{3}\,P\,\bar{j}$

$$= 6P\left(-\frac{\bar{i}}{2} - \frac{\sqrt{3}}{2}\bar{j}\right) = 6P\,\widehat{EF}.$$

It is parallel to EF and its magnitude is $6P$. Let p be the perpendicular distances of the sides from O. The sum of the moments G of the six forces about O is

$$G = p\cdot P + p\cdot 2P + p\cdot 3p + p\cdot 4P + p\cdot 5P + p\cdot 6P = 21p\,P.$$

So the equation of the line, $Yx - Xy = G$, becomes

$$-3\sqrt{3}\,Px + 3Py = 21Pp \quad \text{or} \quad 3\sqrt{3}\,x + y = 7p.$$

$\therefore$ Distance of this line from O $\left.\right\} = \dfrac{7p}{\sqrt{(-\sqrt{3})^2 + 1}} = \dfrac{7p}{2}.$

Example 3. Forces with components (1, 0), (– 2, 0), (1, 1) act respectively at the points (0, 0), (1, 1), (1,0). What is the system equivalent to? **(M.K.U.)**

Let X, Y be the sums of $\bar{i}$, $\bar{j}$ components and G, the sum of the moments about the origin. Now the forces, having components (1, 0), (– 2, 0), (1, 1), are

$$\bar{i},\ -2\bar{i},\ \bar{i} + \bar{j}.$$

$$\therefore \quad X = 1 - 2 + 1 = 0,\ Y = 1.$$

The magnitude of the resultant force is $\sqrt{X^2 + Y^2}$ or 1.

The P.V.'s of the points of application of the forces are

$$\bar{0},\ \bar{i} + \bar{j},\ \bar{i}.$$

So the sum of their moments about the origin is

$$\bar{0}\times\bar{i} + (\bar{i} + \bar{j})\times(-2\bar{i}) + \bar{i}\times(\bar{i} + \bar{j}) = \bar{0} + 2\bar{k} + \bar{k} = 3\bar{k}.$$

So $G = 3$. Thus the equation of motion of the line of action of the resultant force is

$$\begin{vmatrix} X & Y \\ x & y \end{vmatrix} + G = 0 \text{ or } \begin{vmatrix} 0 & 1 \\ x & y \end{vmatrix} + 3 = 0 \text{ or } x = 3.$$

Example 4. The sums of moments of a given system of coplanar forces about the three points (– 2, 0), (0, 3), (2, 4) are 6, 3, – 2 units. Find the magnitude of the resultant force of the system and the equation to its line of action. **(M.U.)**

Let X, Y be the sums of the $\bar{i}$, $\bar{j}$ components of the forces and G, the sum of the moments of the forces about the origin. Then, considering the moments about (– 2, 0), (0, 3), (2, 4) namely 6, 3, – 2, we get

$$6 = \begin{vmatrix} X & Y \\ -2 & 0 \end{vmatrix} + G = 2Y + G, \qquad \text{...(1)}$$

$$3 = \begin{vmatrix} X & Y \\ 0 & 3 \end{vmatrix} + G = 3X + G, \qquad \text{...(2)}$$

$$-2 = \begin{vmatrix} X & Y \\ 2 & 4 \end{vmatrix} + G = 4X - 2Y + G. \qquad \text{...(3)}$$

$$\left.\begin{aligned} (2)-(1): \quad & 3X - 2Y = -3 \\ (3)-(2): \quad & X - 2Y = -5 \end{aligned}\right\} \therefore X = 1,\ Y = 3,\ G = 0.$$

So the magnitude of the resultant is

$$\sqrt{1^2 + 3^2} \quad \text{or} \quad \sqrt{10}.$$

The equation of the line of action of the force is

$$\begin{vmatrix} X & Y \\ x & y \end{vmatrix} + G = 0 \quad \text{or} \quad \begin{vmatrix} 1 & 3 \\ x & y \end{vmatrix} + 0 = 0$$

i.e., $$3x - y = 0.$$

EXERCISES

1. Forces of magnitudes $3P$, $4P$, $5P$ act along the sides AB, BC, CA of an equilateral triangle taken in order. Find the magnitude, the direction and the line of action of the resultant. **(M.U.)**

   [Hint: Choose B as the origin and BC as the x axis; $AB = a$; $X = 0$; $Y = \sqrt{3}P$; $G = \frac{5\sqrt{3}}{2} aP$;

   Resultant: $\sqrt{3}P$. Line of action: $x = \frac{5a}{2}$.]

2. $ABCD$ is a square lamina of side 24 cm. E is the middle point of AB. Forces of 7, 8, 12, 5, 9, 6 kg. wt. act at A, E, B, D, A, D parallel to $\overline{AB}, \overline{EC}, \overline{BC}, \overline{BD}, \overline{CA}$ and $\overline{DE}$. Find the magnitude of the resultant force. **(M.U.)**

   [Hint: Resolving the forces into components along AB, AD, we get the magnitude as

   $$\sqrt{\left\{\left(7 - 7\sqrt{2} + 14/\sqrt{5}\right)^2 + \left(12 - 2\sqrt{2} + 4/\sqrt{5}\right)^2\right\}}.]$$

3. Forces $P\,\widehat{AB}, 4P\,\widehat{BC}, 2P\,\widehat{CD}, 6P\,\widehat{DA}$ act at A, B, C, D of a square of side a. Show that the magnitude of their resultant is $P\sqrt{5}$ and that the equation of its line of action, referred to AB, AD, as the x, y axes, is $2x - y + 6a = 0$. **(M.U., Bn.U.)**

4. Forces $\widehat{AB}, 2\,\widehat{BC}, 4\,\widehat{CD}, 4\,\widehat{DA}$ act at A, B, C, D of a square. Show that the magnitude of its resultant is $\sqrt{13}$ and that it is inclined at $\tan^{-1}(3/2)$ to CB. **(M.U.)**

5. $ABCD$ is a rectangle such that $CD : AC = 3{:}5$ and forces of 3 kg., 5 kg., 5 kg., act along AB, AC, DB respectively. Show that their resultant is parallel to AB; also find its magnitude and position. **(M.U.)**

   [Hint: Origin: A; If $AB = 3a$, $\angle BAC = \theta$, then $\cos\theta = 3/5$, $\sin\theta = 4/5$.

   Forces: $3\bar{i}$, $5(3/5\,\bar{i} + 4/5\,\bar{j})$, $5(3/5\,\bar{i} - 4/5\,\bar{j})$.

   So $X = 9, Y = 0$; Equation of $BD: 4x + 3y = 12a$, $G = -12a$; Line of action: $Y = 4a/3$.]

6. Forces P, $2P$, $3P$, $4P$, $5P$, $6P$ act along the sides taken in order of a regular hexagon which circumscribes a circle of radius 2 decimetres. Prove that the resultant is a single force and find the distance from the centre of the hexagon of its line of action. **(M.U.)**

[Hint: See the Example (hexagon) sum. Now $p = \sqrt{3}$.]

7. If six forces of magnitudes 3, 4, 5, 6, 7, 8 act along the sides taken in order of a regular hexagon of side 4 units, show that the single equivalent force is of magnitude 6 and that it acts along a line parallel to the force of magnitude 7 at a distance of $11\sqrt{3}$ units from the centre of the hexagon. **(M.K.U., Bn.U.)**

8. $ABCDEF$ is a regular hexagon. Forces P, $3P$, $5P$ act at the vertices A, C, E in the direction parallel to AD. Forces $2P$, $4P$, $6P$ act at the vertices B, D, F in the opposite direction. Find the magnitude of the resultant and where its line of action cuts AB. **(M.K.U.)**

[Hint: If $\bar{i}$ is along AD and A, the origin, then

$$X = (P + 3P + 5P) - (2P + 4P + 6P) = -3P; \; Y = 0.$$

$$G = 0 - p(2P) + p(3P) + 0 - p(5P) + p(6P) = 2\,pP,$$

where p is the distance of the sides from the centre. The line of action is $y = {}^{2p}\!/_3$.]

9. Three forces each equal to P act along the sides of a triangle ABC in order. Prove that the resultant is $P\,(1 - 8\sin {}^A\!/_2 \, \sin {}^B\!/_2 \sin {}^C\!/_2)^{1/2}$ and that its line of action divides BC externally in the ratio $c : b$ **(M.U., Bn.U.)**

[Hint: $(\text{Magnitude})^2 = [P(\widehat{BC} + \widehat{CA} + \widehat{AB}) \cdot P(\widehat{BC} + \widehat{CA} + \widehat{AB})]^{1/2}$. Use

$$\cos A + \cos B + \cos C = 1 + 4 \sin {}^A\!/_2 \, \sin {}^B\!/_2 \, \sin {}^C\!/_2.$$

The resultant of the equal forces P along CA and AB bisects the external angle at A and so divides BC externally in the ratio of the sides AB, AC.]

10. G_1, G_2, G_3 denote the sums of the moments of a system of coplanar forces about the points $A(x_1, y_1)$, $B(x_2, y_2)$, $C(x_3, y_3)$. Show that, if the resultant of the system is a single force through the origin, then

$$\begin{vmatrix} x_1 & x_2 & x_3 \\ y_1 & y_2 & y_3 \\ G_1 & G_2 & G_3 \end{vmatrix} = 0.$$ **(M.U.)**

[Hint: $G = 0$ since the resultant passes through the origin.

$$\begin{vmatrix} X & Y \\ x_1 & y_1 \end{vmatrix} + 0 = G_1, \text{etc.} \;\; \therefore \;\; x_1Y - y_1X = G_1, \;\; x_2Y - y_2X = G_2, \;\; x_3Y - y_3X = G_3.$$

The eliminant of Y, X leads to the given, result.]

11. Forces with components (2, 0), (– 1, 0), (1, 0) act at the points (0, 0), (0, 1), (1, 0). What is the system equivalent to? **(M.U.)**

[Hint: $X = 2, Y = 0, G = 1$; Mag $= 2$; Line: $2y + 1 = 0$.]

12. A system of coplanar forces has moments – 60, –156, 84 units about the origin, (8,0), (0,10). Find the magnitude of the resultant and the equation to its line of action. **(M.U., M.K.U.)**

[Hint: $X = 14\cdot4, Y = 12, G = -60$; Magnitude $= \sqrt{351\cdot36}$. Line of action : $5x - 6y + 25 = 0$.]

13. A variable system of forces in a plane has constant moments G, G_1 about two fixed points A, B $(AB = a)$. Show that the resultant passes through a fixed point on AB and that the minimum magnitude of the resultant is $\frac{G - G_1}{a}$. **(M.U.)**

[**Hint:** Choose A, AB as the origin and x axis. Then

$$\begin{vmatrix} X & Y \\ a & 0 \end{vmatrix} + G = G_1 \Rightarrow Y = \frac{G - G_1}{a},$$

a constant. So x only varies. When $X = 0$, $\sqrt{X^2 + Y^2}$ is a minimum. The line $-Yx + Xy + G = 0$ meets the x axis at $\left(G/_Y, 0\right)$.]

4.9 EQUILIBRIUM OF A RIGID BODY UNDER THREE COPLANAR FORCES

The following book work gives the nature of a set of three coplanar forces which keep a rigid body in equilibrium.

Bookwork 4.14. If three coplanar forces keep a rigid body in equilibrium, then either they all are parallel to one another or they are concurrent.

Let the forces be $\overline{F}_1, \overline{F}_2, \overline{F}_3$. Considering only $\overline{F}_1$ and $\overline{F}_2$, we get the following two cases :

(*i*) $\overline{F}_1$ and $\overline{F}_2$, are parallel.

(*ii*) $\overline{F}_1$ and $\overline{F}_2$, are not parallel.

We shall now study the nature of $\overline{F}_3$ in these cases.

Case (*i*). Suppose $\overline{F}_1 = F_1\overline{i}$ and $\overline{F}_2 = F_2\overline{i}$ act at A_1 and A_2. Then their resultant is $(F_1 + F_2)\,\overline{i}$. Consequently this resultant $(F_1 + F_2)\,\overline{i}$ and $\overline{F}_3$ keep the body in equilibrium. This implies not only that these two forces act along the same line but also that $\overline{F}_3 = -(F_1 + F_2)\overline{i}$. So $\overline{F}_3$ is parallel to $\overline{F}_1$ and $\overline{F}_2$. That is, the given three forces are parallel to one another.

Case (*ii*). Suppose the lines of action of $\overline{F}_1$ and $\overline{F}_2$ intersect at A. Then their resultant is

$$\overline{F}_1 + \overline{F}_2 \quad \text{acting at } A.$$

This resultant and the third force keep the body in equilibrium. It means that necessarily $\overline{F}_1 + \overline{F}_2$ and $\overline{F}_3$ should act along the same line. This implies that $\overline{F}_3$ also passes through A. So the forces are concurrent at A.

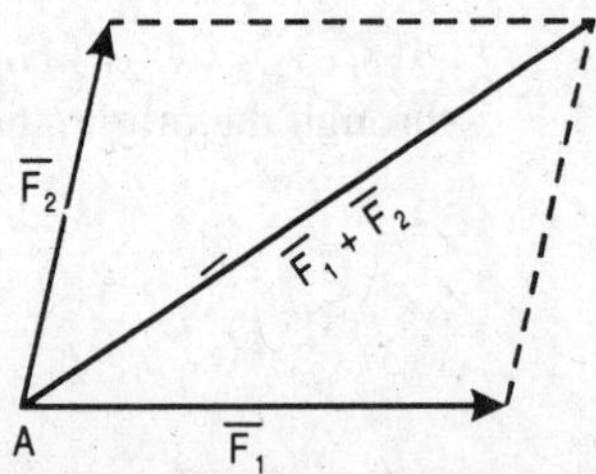

Thus, in conclusion, we get that either the forces are all parallel to one another or they are concurrent.

4.9.1 Cotangent formulae

To solve sums wherein a rigid body is in equilibrium, acted on by three coplanar concurrent forces, we will, in general, require to use simple relations between the involved distances. In some cases, in which the inclination of the body to the horizontal or to the vertical is required, the inclination can be obtained directly by using one of the following trigonometric formulae

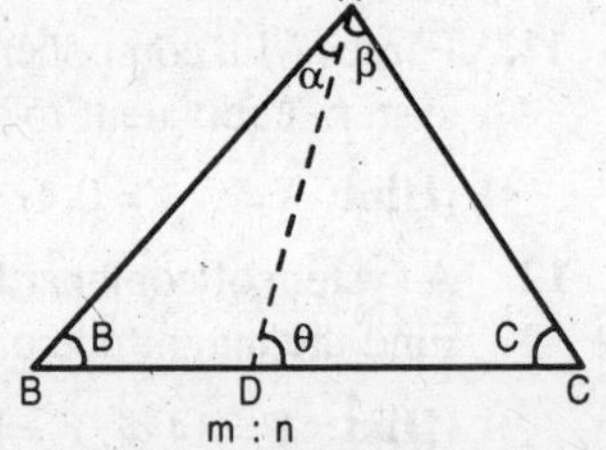

$$(m + n)\cot\theta = m\cot\alpha - n\cot\beta$$

$$\left(\frac{1}{m}+\frac{1}{n}\right)\cot\theta = \frac{1}{m}\cot B - \frac{1}{n}\cot C,$$

where ABC is a triangle in which D divides BC internally in the ratio $m : n$ and angle is θ.

EXAMPLES

Example 1. A solid hemisphere of radius a and weight W is placed with its curved surface on a smooth table and a string of length $l\,(< a)$ is attached to a point on its rim and to a point on the table. Show that, in the equilibrium position, the tension of the string and the inclination θ of the plane base to the horizon are

$$\frac{3W}{8}\frac{a-l}{\sqrt{2al-l^2}},\quad \tan^{-1}\frac{a-l}{\sqrt{2al-l^2}}.$$

Let A be the point of contact of the hemisphere with the table, OB the middle radius and CD the string. The forces acting on the hemisphere are

1. Reaction R of the table
2. Weight W of the hemisphere
3. Tension T of the string.

Since they are three in number they should be either all parallel or concurrent. But the reaction at A, being normal to the spherical surface, is vertical. The weight also is vertical. Thus the reaction and the weight are parallel. Consequently the tension also should be parallel to them. Hence the string CD is vertical.

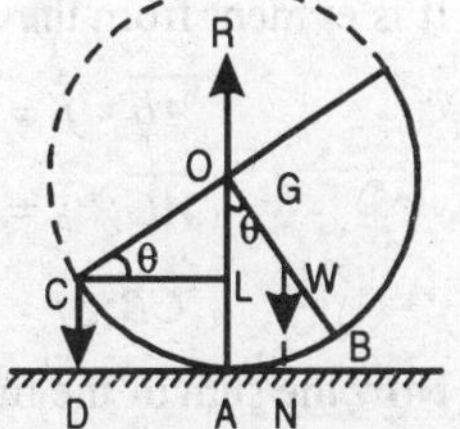

Draw CL perpendicular to OA. Then

$$\sin\theta = \frac{OL}{a} = \frac{OA-CD}{a} = \frac{a-l}{a} \quad\text{or}\quad \tan\theta = \frac{a-l}{\sqrt{2al-l^2}}.$$

Further, if N is the foot of the perpendicular from G to the table, taking moments about A of the three forces,

$$CL\cdot T - AN\cdot W = 0 \;\text{ or }\; CL\cdot T - OG\sin\theta\, W = 0$$

$$\therefore\quad a\cos\theta\cdot T - {}^{3a}\!/_{8}\sin\theta\, W = 0$$

$$\therefore\quad T = \frac{3W}{8}\tan\theta \quad\text{or}\quad T = \frac{3W}{8}\frac{a-l}{\sqrt{2al-l^2}}.$$

Example 2. A uniform solid hemisphere of weight W rests with its curved surface on a smooth horizontal plane. A weight w is suspended from a point on the rim of the hemisphere. If the plane base of the rim is inclined to the horizontal at an angle θ, prove that

$$\tan\theta = \frac{8w}{3W}.$$

With the notations used in the previous example, taking moments about A,

$$CL\cdot w - AN\cdot W = 0 \;\text{ or }\; \left({}^{3a}\!/_{8}\sin\theta\right)W = (a\cos\theta)w$$

$$\therefore\quad \tan\theta = \frac{8w}{3W}.$$

Example 3. A triangular lamina ABC, obtuse-angled at C, stands with its plane vertical and the side AC in contact with a table. Show that the least weight w, which suspended from B, will tilt the triangle, is $\frac{W}{3}\frac{a^2+3b^2-c^2}{c^2-a^2-b^2}$, where W is the weight of the triangle and a, b, c the sides. **(M.U.)**

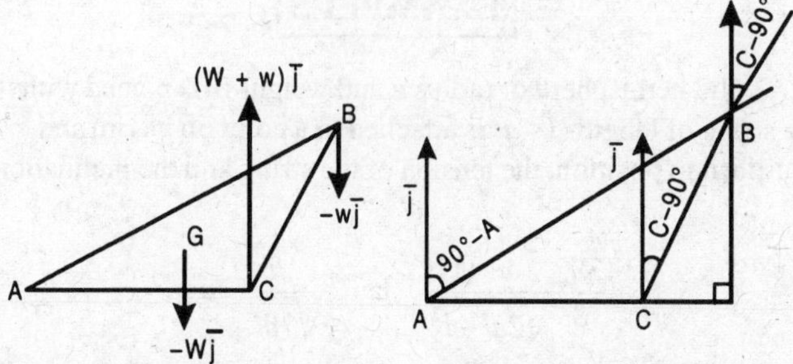

Let $\bar{j}$ be the unit vector vertically upward. Then, at the moment of tilting, the forces acting on the triangular lamina are the three parallel forces

$$-W\,\bar{j},\ -w\,\bar{j},\ \text{Reaction } R\bar{j}=(W+w)\bar{j}$$

acting at G, B, C.

It is evident from the second figure that

$$\overline{AB}\times\bar{j}=c\cos A\,\bar{k}$$

$$\overline{AC}\times\bar{j}=b\,\bar{k}$$

$$\overline{CB}\times\bar{j}=a\sin(C-90°)\,\bar{k}=-a\cos C\,\bar{k}.$$

Now the sum of the moments about C is 0. So

$$(\overline{CG}\times(-W\,\bar{j})+\overline{CB}\times(-w\,\bar{j})+\bar{0}=\bar{0}$$

or $$W(\overline{CG}\times\bar{j})+w(\overline{CB}\times\bar{j})=\bar{0}$$

or $$W(\overline{CA}+\overline{AG})\times\bar{j}+w(\overline{CB}\times\bar{j})=\bar{0}$$

or $$W\left[\overline{CA}+\tfrac{1}{3}(\overline{AC}+\overline{AB})\right]\times\bar{j}+w(\overline{CB}\times\bar{j})=\bar{0}$$

or $$\tfrac{W}{3}\left[(2\overline{CA}+\overline{AB})\times\bar{j}\right]+w(\overline{CB}\times\bar{j})=\bar{0}$$

or $$\tfrac{W}{3}\left[-2b\bar{k}+c\cos A\,\bar{k}\right]+w(-a\cos\bar{C}\,\bar{k})=\bar{0}.$$

$$\therefore\quad w=\frac{\tfrac{1}{3}[-2b+c\cos A]}{a\cos C}W=\frac{W}{3}\frac{\left[-2b+c.\dfrac{b^2+c^2-a^2}{2bc}\right]}{a.\dfrac{a^2+b^2-c^2}{2ab}}$$

$$=\frac{W}{3}.\frac{-3b^2+c^2-a^2}{a^2+b^2-c^2}=\frac{W}{3}\frac{a^2+3b^2-c^2}{c^2-a^2-b^2}$$

Example 4. A right circular cone of height h and vertical angle 2α is placed with its vertex A in contact with a smooth vertical wall and its slant side resting against a smooth horizontal rail P fixed parallel to the wall at a distance c from it. Show that, if the axis makes an angle θ with the horizontal, in the equilibrium position, then

$$3h = 4c \sec^2 (\theta - \alpha) \sec \theta. \qquad \textbf{(M.K.U.)}$$

The following are the forces acting on the cone as in the figure:

(*i*) Weight vertically downward through the centre of gravity G

(*ii*) Horizontal normal reaction of the wall along AB

(*iii*) Reaction of the peg perpendicular to the slant side AP.

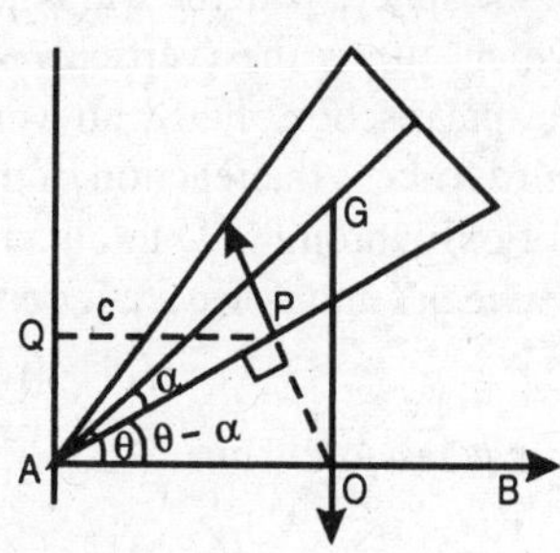

Since these forces are three in number, they should concur. Now the weight and the reaction of the wall meet at O. So the reaction of the peg should pass through O.

The given result is a relation between $c = PQ$ and $\frac{3}{4}h = AG$. To obtain this relation we shall consider in succession PQ, AP, AO, AG, where Q is the foot of the perpendicular drawn from P to the wall.

$$c = PQ = AP \cos (\theta - \alpha) \text{ from } \Delta APQ$$

$$= \{AO \cos (\theta - \alpha)\} \cos (\theta - \alpha) \text{ from } \Delta AOP$$

$$= AG \cos \theta - \cos^2 (\theta - \alpha) \text{ from } \Delta AOG$$

$$= \frac{3}{4} h \cos \theta \cos^2 (\theta - \alpha).$$

Example 5. A uniform rod of length $16a$ rests in equilibrium against a smooth vertical wall and upon a peg P at a distance a from the wall. Show that the inclination of the rod to the vertical is $30°$.

Let AG be one half of the rod and P, the peg. The forces on the rod are

1. Normal reaction of the wall at A
2. Reaction of the peg normal to the rod
3. Weight of the rod.

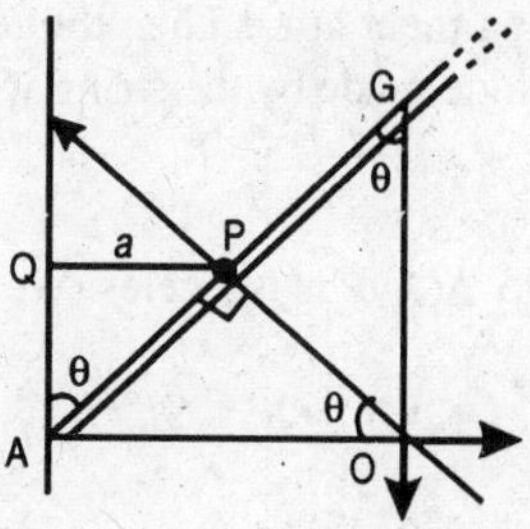

Let them meet at O. Let θ be the angle made by the rod with the vertical and $QP = a$. Then

$$\angle PAQ = \angle AGO = \angle POA = \theta.$$

$$\therefore \qquad AP = \frac{a}{\sin \theta} \text{ from } \Delta PAQ.$$

Finding PO differently in two ways and denoting $\cos \theta, \sin \theta$ by c, s, we have

$$PO = AP \cot \theta \text{ from } \Delta APO$$

$$= \frac{a}{\sin \theta} \cot \theta = \frac{ac}{s^2}, \qquad \text{...(1)}$$

$$PO = GP \tan \theta = (GA - PA) \tan \theta \text{ (from } \Delta GPO)$$

$$= \left(8a - \frac{a}{\sin \theta}\right) \tan \theta = \frac{8as}{c} - \frac{a}{c}. \qquad \text{...(2)}$$

Equating (1), (2), we get $s^3 = 1/8$ or $s = 1/2$ or $\theta = 30°$.

Example 6. A uniform rod AB rests on a fixed smooth sphere with its lower end A pressing against a smooth vertical wall which touches the sphere. If θ is the angle which the rod makes with the vertical, show that $a = 2l \sin \theta/2 \cos^3 \theta/2$, where l is the length of the rod and a the radius of the sphere. **(M.U.)**

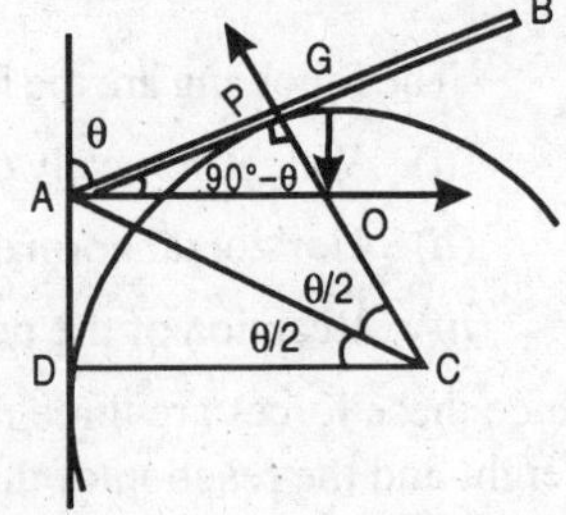

Let C be the centre of the sphere and D, P the points of contact of the sphere with the wall and the rod. Three forces act on the rod, of which one is the (vertical) weight through G and the other is the normal reaction of the wall which is horizontal. Let them meet at O. The third force is the reaction of the sphere normal to the rod. This passes not only through O but also through G. To obtain the given relation between l and a, we shall consider

$$AG,\ AO,\ AP$$

in succession. Thus

$$l/2 = AG = AO \operatorname{cosec}\theta \text{ from } \Delta AOG$$

$$= \{AP \operatorname{cosec}\theta\} \operatorname{cosec}\theta \text{ from } \Delta AOP$$

$$= \{a \tan \theta/2\} \operatorname{cosec}^2\theta \text{ from } \Delta ACP$$

since angle ACP = angle $ACD = \theta/2$. Therefore

$$a = \tfrac{1}{2}l \cot \theta/2 \sin^2\theta = \tfrac{1}{2}l.\frac{\cos\theta/2}{\sin\theta/2}.4\sin^2\theta/2\cos^2\theta/2$$

$$= 2l\sin\theta/2\cos^3\theta/2.$$

Example 7. A uniform rod AB rests with a point P on it ($AP = \tfrac{3}{4}AB$) in contact with a fixed smooth peg and the end A attached to a light string which is fastened to a fixed point. If the rod makes an angle of 45° with the horizontal, show that the string makes with the horizontal an angle whose tangent is 2. **(M.U.)**

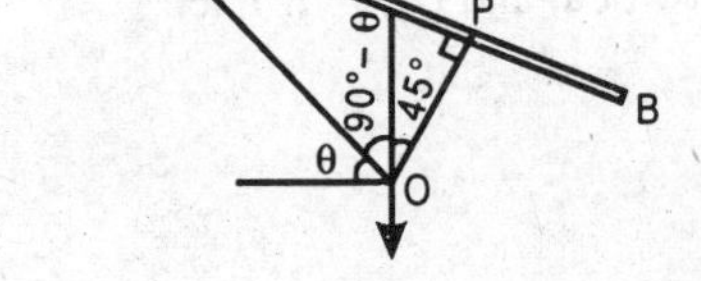

Let AB be the rod, AC the string and G the centre of mass of the rod. Let the weight of the rod and the normal reaction of the peg meet at O. Then the tension acts along OAC. Let θ be the angle made by the string with the horizontal. Now

$$\angle AOG = 90° - \theta, \angle GOP = 45°$$

So ΔGOP is isosceles. We shall find OP in two different ways:

(i) $OP = GP = l/4,\ (AB = l)$ ...(1)

(ii) $OP = AP \tan(\theta - 45°)$, since $\angle PAO = \theta - 45°$

$$= \frac{3l}{4}\frac{\tan\theta - 1}{1+\tan\theta}. \quad ...(2)$$

Equating (1) and (2), we get $\tan\theta = 2$.

Example 8. A square plate $ABCD$ of side $2a$ and centre G is placed with its plane vertical between two smooth pegs P, Q which are in the same horizontal line at a distance c apart. Show that, in the position of equilibrium the inclination of one of its edges to the horizontal is either

$$45° \text{ or } \frac{1}{2}\sin^{-1}\frac{a^2 - c^2}{c^2}. \quad \textbf{(M.U., A.U.)}$$

Let the sides AB, AD be in contact with P, Q. Then the reactions of the pegs P, A are normal to AB, AD. Let them intersect at O. Then $APOQ$ is a rectangle and the weight of the plate acts through O.

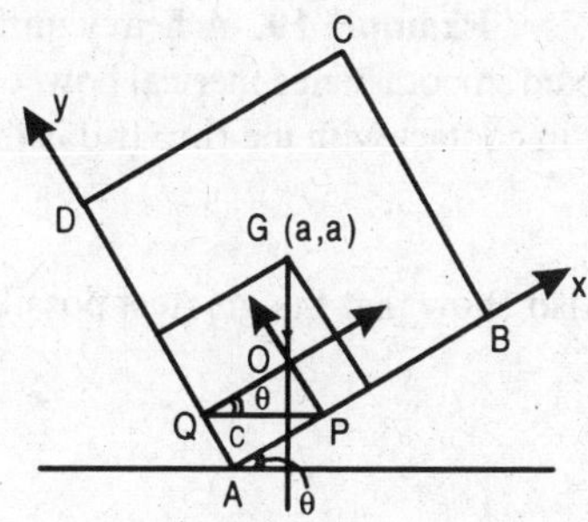

Let AB be inclined to the horizontal at an angle θ. Now PQ is horizontal. So angle PQO also is θ and

$$QO = c\cos\theta, \quad PO = c\sin\theta.$$

To obtain θ we shall use the fact that GO, the vertical line, is perpendicular to PQ, the horizontal line. Choosing AB, AD as the x, y axes,

$$\text{Slope of } PQ = \tan(180° - \theta) \text{ since } \angle BPQ = 180° - \theta$$
$$= -\tan\theta.$$

But G is (a, a) and O is $(c\cos\theta, c\sin\theta)$. By $\dfrac{y_1 - y_2}{x_1 - x_2}$,

$$\therefore \quad \text{Slope of } GO = \frac{a - c\sin\theta}{a - c\cos\theta}.$$

Since PQ and GO are perpendicular,

$$(-\tan\theta)\,\frac{a - c\sin\theta}{a - c\cos\theta} = -1$$

or $\quad \sin\theta\,(a - c\sin\theta) = \cos\theta\,(a - c\cos\theta)$

i.e., $\quad a(\sin\theta - \cos\theta) - c(\sin^2\theta - \cos^2\theta) = 0$

i.e., $\quad (\sin\theta - \cos\theta)\{a - c(\sin\theta + \cos\theta)\} = 0.$

The first factor gives $\theta = 45°$; the second factor gives

$$\sin\theta + \cos\theta = a/c \quad \text{or} \quad (\sin\theta + \cos\theta)^2 = a^2/c^2$$

i.e., $\quad \sin^2\theta + \cos^2\theta + 2\sin\theta\cos\theta = a^2/c^2 \quad \text{or} \quad 1 + \sin 2\theta = a^2/c^2.$

i.e., $\quad \sin 2\theta = \dfrac{a^2 - c^2}{c^2} \quad \text{or} \quad \theta = \dfrac{1}{2}\sin^{-1}\dfrac{a^2 - c^2}{c^2}.$

Example 9. A uniform rectangular board rests vertically in equilibrium with its sides $2a$ and $2b$ on two smooth pegs in the same horizontal, distance c apart. Prove that the side of length $2a$ makes with the horizontal an angle θ given by

$$c\cos 2\theta = a\cos\theta - b\sin\theta.$$

With the notations used in the previous example,

$AB = 2a$, $BC = 2b$, G is (a, b), O is $(c\cos\theta, c\sin\theta)$. By $\dfrac{y_1 - y_2}{x_1 - x_2}$,

$$\text{Slope of } GO = \frac{b - c\sin\theta}{a - c\cos\theta}.$$

But the slope of PQ is $-\tan\theta$ and PQ is perpendicular to GO.

$$\therefore \quad (-\tan\theta)\,\frac{b - c\sin\theta}{a - c\cos\theta} = -1$$

which gives the required result.

Example 10. A heavy uniform rod AB of length $2a$ rests partly within and partly without a fixed smooth hemispherical bowl of radius r. The rim of the bowl is horizontal and one point of the rod is in contact with the rim. If θ is the inclination of the rod to the horizon, show that

$$2r \cos 2\theta = a \cos\theta.$$

Also show that the greatest possible inclination of the rod is

$$\sin^{-1} \frac{1}{\sqrt{3}}.$$ **(M.K.U.,M.U.)**

Two reactions of the bowl and the weight of the rod act on the rod. The reaction of the bowl at the lower end A is normal to the bowl .So it should be along the radius AC. The other reaction is perpendicular to the rod at D. These two reactions should meet at a point O on the circumference since angle ADO is $90°$. The weight should act along OG which is vertical. Let AE be the perpendicular drawn from A on OG. Then E also lies on the circle. Now

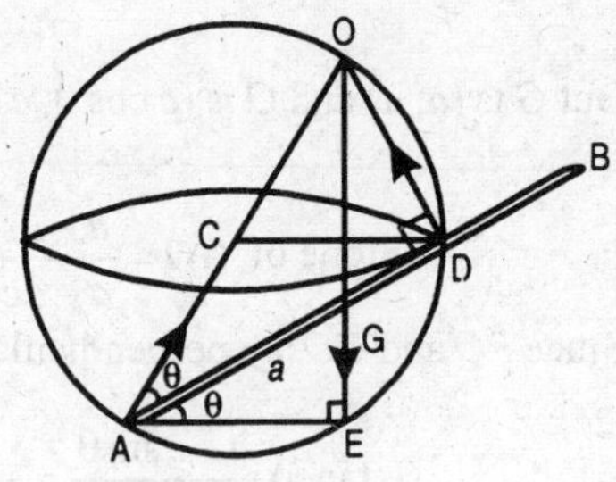

$$\underline{|CAD} = \underline{|CDA} \text{ since } \Delta CAD \text{ is isosceles}$$

$$= \underline{|EAD} \text{ since } CD, AE \text{ are parallel.}$$

But, from the right angled triangle GAE,

$$AE = AG \cos\theta = a \cos\theta.$$

Again, from the right angled triangle AEO,

$$AE = AO \cos 2\theta = 2r \cos 2\theta$$

$$\therefore \qquad a \cos\theta = 2r \cos 2\theta. \qquad ...(1)$$

To prove the second part of the result, we have to show that AD is less than AB. That is,

$$2r \cos\theta < 2a \text{ or } \frac{r}{a} \cos\theta < 1 \text{ i.e., } \frac{\cos^2\theta}{2\cos 2\theta} < 1 \text{ by (1)}$$

i.e., $\quad 1 - \sin^2\theta < 2(1 - 2\sin^2\theta)$ or $\sin^2\theta < 1/3$.

So the maximum possible value for θ is $\sin^{-1} 1/\sqrt{3}$.

Remark. The portion of the rod projected outside the bowl is

$$DB = AB - AD = 2a - 2r \cos\theta = 2(a - r \cos\theta).$$

Example 11. A uniform rod of length $4a$ is placed with an end inside a smooth hemispherical bowl whose rim is horizontal and whose radius is $a\sqrt{3}$. Show that a quarter of the rod will project over the edge of the bowl. **(M.K.U.,M.U.)**

Replacing a by $2a$ and r by $a\sqrt{3}$ in (1) of the previous example, we get

$$2\sqrt{3} \cos^2\theta - \cos\theta - \sqrt{3} = 0 \text{ or } \cos\theta = \sqrt{3}/2.$$

The length of the projected portion of the rod is

$$DB = AB - AD = AB - AO \cos\theta = 4a - 2a\sqrt{3} \cos\theta = a.$$

Example 12. A uniform rod ADB of length $4a$ rests with one end A in contact with the inside smooth surface of a hemispherical bowl of radius r and D in contact with its horizontal rim. If $DB=a$, show that the inclination of the rod to the horizontal is $30°$ and $r=a\sqrt{3}$. **(M.U.)**

Again as in the first bowl example, finding AE in two different ways, we get

$$AE = AG\cos\theta = 2a\cos\theta, \quad AE = AO\cos 2\theta = 2r\cos 2\theta.$$

$$\therefore \qquad a\cos\theta = r\cos 2\theta. \qquad ...(1)$$

But $AD = 3a$ and, in triangle AOD,

$$AD = AO\cos\theta = 2r\cos\theta.$$

$$\therefore \qquad 3a = 2r\cos\theta. \qquad ...(2)$$

Dividing (1) by (2) and simplifying, we get $\theta = 30°, r = a\sqrt{3}$.

Example 13. A uniform rod of length $32a$ rests partly within and partly without a smooth cylindrical cup of radius a. Show that in the position of equilibrium, the rod makes an angle of $60°$ with the horizon, and prove also that the cylinder will topple over unless its weight is at least six times that of the rod. **(C.U.)**

To avoid unwieldness the rod is shown in the figure partially. As in the figure, the forces on the rod are

(*i*) The normal reaction of the curved surface at A

(*ii*) The reaction of the rim at B perpendicular to the rod

(*iii*) The weight at G.

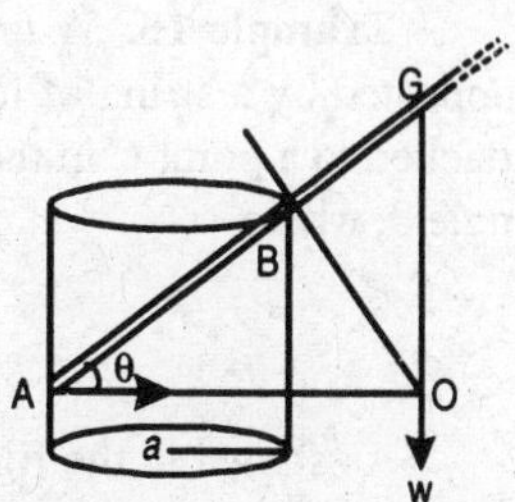

Let them meet at O. Let θ be the angle made by the rod with the horizontal. Now, considering the diameter of the base

$$\begin{aligned} 2a &= AB\cos\theta \\ &= (AO\cos\theta)\cos\theta \quad \text{from } \Delta AOB \\ &= (AG\cos\theta)\cos^2\theta \quad \text{from } \Delta AOG \\ &= 16a\cos^3\theta. \end{aligned}$$

$$\therefore \qquad \cos^3\theta = 1/8 \text{ or } \cos\theta = 1/2 \text{ or } \theta = 60°.$$

At the point of toppling, let the point of contact of the cylinder on the floor be D. Considering the cylinder and the rod as a rigid body the forces acting on it are

(*i*) Weight W of the cylinder at C

(*ii*) Weight w of the rod at G

(*iii*) Reaction of the floor at D.

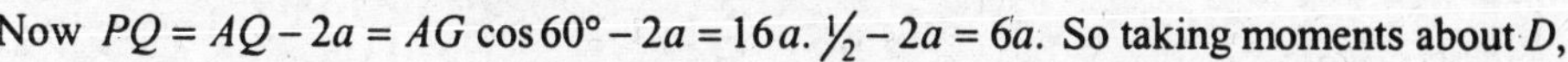

Now $PQ = AQ - 2a = AG\cos 60° - 2a = 16a \cdot 1/2 - 2a = 6a$. So taking moments about D,

$$aW = PQ\,w \text{ or } aW = 6a\,w \text{ or } W = 6w.$$

Example 14. A solid hemisphere is supported by a string fixed to a point on its rim and to a point on a smooth vertical wall with which the curved surface of the hemisphere is in contact. If θ, ϕ are the inclinations of the string and the plane base of the hemisphere to the vertical, prove that

$$\tan\phi = \tfrac{3}{8} + \tan\theta. \qquad \textbf{(M.U.)}$$

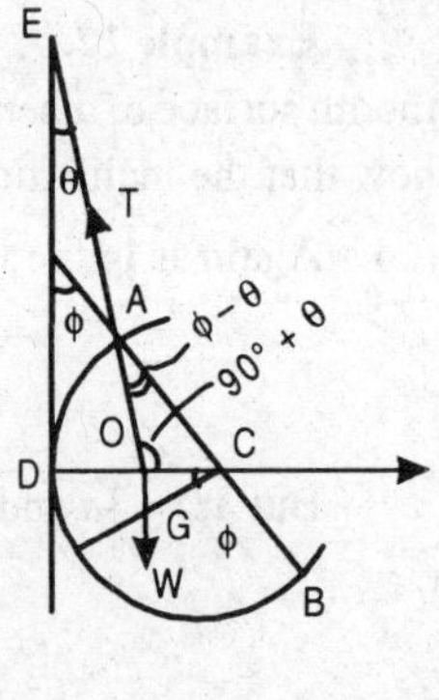

In the figure the meanings of AB, C, D, E, G are evident. Two of the forces on the solid are

(*i*) The normal reaction of the wall along the horizontal radius DC.

(*ii*) The weight through G, vertically downwards.

Let them meet at O. Then the tension, the third force, will act along OA, that is, along OAE, where AE is the string. Now the radius through G is perpendicular to AB. In the $\Delta\, AOC$

$$\angle A = \phi - \theta,\ \angle C = 90° - \phi,\ \angle O = 90° + \theta.$$

Then from the sine formula

$$\frac{OC}{\sin(\phi - \theta)} = \frac{AC}{\sin(90° + \theta)} \text{ or } OC = \frac{a}{\cos\theta}\sin(\phi - \theta), \quad \text{...(1)}$$

where a is the radius. Also from the right-angled triangle OCG

$$OC = CG\cos\phi \text{ or } OC = {}^{3a}/_{8}\cos\phi. \quad \text{...(2)}$$

Equating (1) and (2) and simplifying we get the result as stated.

Example 15. A uniform rod AB of length $2a$ hangs against a smooth vertical wall, being supported by a string of length $2l$ tied to one end of the rod with the other end of the string being attached to a point C in the wall above the rod. Show that the rod can rest inclined to the wall at an angle θ, where

$$\cos^2\theta = \frac{l^2 - a^2}{3a^2}.$$

(M.U., M.K.U., Bn.U.)

As shown in the figure, the forces acting on the rod are

1. Weight of the rod at G
2. Tension of the string at B
3. Normal reaction of the wall at A.

Let these three forces concur at O. From the similar triangles GBO, ABC, if

$$AC = 2y,\ OG = y.$$

From the right angled triangle AGO,

$$\cos\theta = \frac{OG}{AG} = \frac{y}{a} \text{ or } \cos^2\theta = \frac{y^2}{a^2}. \quad \text{...(1)}$$

Finding AO^2 from the right angled triangles AOC, AOG,

$$AO^2 = l^2 - (2y)^2 = l^2 - 4y^2, \quad \text{...(2)}$$

$$AO^2 = a^2 - y^2. \quad \text{...(3)}$$

Equating (2) and (3), we get

$$y^2 = \frac{l^2 - a^2}{3}. \quad \therefore \cos^2\theta = \frac{l^2 - a^2}{3a^2} \text{ by (1).}$$

Example 16. A solid cone of height h and semivertical angle α is placed with its base against a smooth vertical wall and is supported by a string attached to its vertex and to a point in the wall. Show that the greatest possible length of the string is

$$h\sqrt{1+{}^{16}\!/_{9}\tan^2\alpha}.$$ **(M.U., M.K.U., C.U., Bn.U.)**

Let the string CE be of length l. The cone is in limiting equilibrium with the tip A as the point of contact. The following are the forces acting on the cone as in the figure:

(*i*) Weight through G

(*ii*) Normal reaction of the wall at A perpendicular to the wall

(*iii*) Tension of the string.

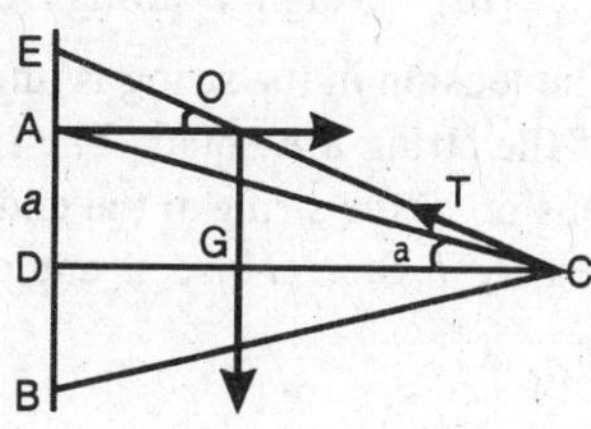

Let them meet at O. Let a be the base radius of the cone and l, the length of the string. Then, from the right angled triangle CDE,

$$CE^2 = CD^2 + DE^2.$$

$$\therefore \qquad l^2 = h^2 + (DA + AE)^2 = h^2 + (a^2 + AE)^2. \qquad ...(1)$$

But, from the similar triangles EAO, EDC,

$$\frac{EA}{ED} = \frac{AO}{DC} \text{ or } \frac{EA}{a + EA} = \frac{DG}{DC} = \frac{h/4}{h} = \frac{1}{4}.$$

Thus $EA = a/3$. When this and $a/h = \tan\alpha$ are used, (1) becomes

$$l^2 = h^2 + \left(a + \tfrac{1}{3}a\right)^2 = h^2\left\{1 + {}^{16}\!/_{9}\tan^2\alpha\right\}.$$

Example 17. A square board rests in a vertical plane with one corner against a smooth vertical wall, the adjacent upper corner being attached to the wall by a string of same length as the side of the square. Show that, if the string makes an angle θ with the vertical then

$$\tan\theta = \tfrac{1}{3}.$$ **(M.U.)**

Let $ABCD$ be the square board of side a with A touching the wall. Let PD be the string. The forces acting on the board are

(*i*) Tension along DP,

(*ii*) Normal reaction at A perpendicular to the wall

(*iii*) Weight through G.

Let them all meet at O. Let DL be the perpendicular to the wall. Then

$$PL = a\cos\theta. \qquad \therefore\ PA = 2a\cos\theta. \qquad ...(1)$$

From the triangle PAO, we get AO as

$$AO = PA\tan\theta = (2a\cos\theta)\tan\theta = 2a\sin\theta \text{ by (1)}$$

But, from the triangle AOG,

$$AO = AG\cos(45° - \theta) = a/\sqrt{2}\,(\cos 45°.\cos\theta + \sin 45°.\sin\theta) = a/2\,(\cos\theta + \sin\theta)$$

$$\therefore \qquad 2a\sin\theta = a/2\,(\cos\theta + \sin\theta) \text{ or } \tan\theta = \tfrac{1}{3}.$$

Example 18. A string of length $2l$ has one end attached to the extremity of a smooth heavy rod AB of length $2a$ and the other end carries a weightless ring C which slides on the rod. The string is hung over a smooth peg O. Show that, if θ is the angle which the rod makes with the vertical, then

$$l\cos\theta = a\sin^3\theta.$$ **(M.U.)**

The forces acting on the rod are

(*i*) Tension T at A along AO

(*ii*) Reaction R of the ring along CO and perpendicular to AB

(*iii*) Weight W along OG.

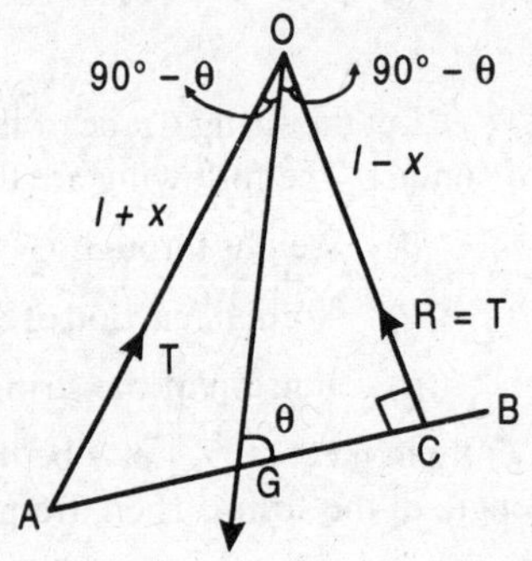

The tension in the string is uniform. So the tension at both the ends of the string are equal. The ring is at rest. So $R = T$. That is, the tension of the string at the end is T and the tension on either side of peg are T. So OG bisects angle AOC.

$$\therefore \qquad \angle AOG = \angle COG = 90° - \theta.$$

Let $AO = l + x$ and $OC = l - x$. Then, from the triangle AOC,

$$\frac{OC}{OA} = \sin(2\theta - 90°) \text{ or } \frac{l-x}{l+x} = -\cos 2\theta.$$

$$\therefore \qquad x = l\frac{1+\cos 2\theta}{1-\cos 2\theta} = l\,\frac{2\cos^2\theta}{2\sin^2\theta} = l\cot^2\theta. \qquad ...(1)$$

Also, from triangle AOG, using the sine formula,

$$\frac{AO}{\sin AGO} = \frac{AG}{\sin AOG} \text{ or } \frac{l+x}{\sin(180° - \theta)} = \frac{a}{\sin(90° - \theta)}.$$

$$\therefore \qquad \frac{l+x}{\sin\theta} = \frac{a}{\cos\theta} \text{ or } x = a\tan\theta - l. \qquad ...(2)$$

Thus, from (1), (2),

$$l\cot^2\theta = a\tan\theta - l \text{ or } l\operatorname{cosec}^2\theta = a\tan\theta$$

$$l\cos\theta = a\sin^3\theta.$$

Example 19. A uniform beam of length l and weight W hangs from a fixed point by two strings of lengths a and b. Prove that the inclination θ of the rod to the horizon is given by

$$\sin\theta = \frac{a^2 - b^2}{l\sqrt{2(a^2+b^2) - l^2}}. \qquad \textbf{(M.U.)}$$

Let AB be the rod. Let G be the mass centre. The tensions of the strings are along AO, BO and the weight of the rod is through G. All meet at O. Let

$$\overline{OA} = \bar{a},\ \overline{OB} = \bar{b}.$$

Then $|\bar{a}| = a,\ |\bar{b}| = b$ and

$$\overline{OG} = \tfrac{1}{2}(\bar{a} + \bar{b}),\ \overline{BA} = \bar{a} - \bar{b}$$

and the angle between $\overline{OG}$ and $\overline{BA}$ is $90° - \theta$.

$$\therefore \qquad \cos(90° - \theta) = \frac{\overline{OG}\cdot\overline{BA}}{|\overline{OG}||\overline{BA}|} = \frac{\tfrac{1}{2}(\bar{a}+\bar{b})\cdot(\bar{a}-\bar{b})}{OG\cdot l}.$$

$$\therefore \qquad \sin\theta = \frac{\tfrac{1}{2}(a^2 - b^2)}{OG\,l}.$$

$$OG = \sqrt{\overline{OG} \cdot \overline{OG}} = \sqrt{\tfrac{1}{2}(\bar{a}+\bar{b}) . \tfrac{1}{2}(\bar{a}+\bar{b})}$$

$$= \tfrac{1}{2}\sqrt{a^2+b^2+2\bar{a}\cdot\bar{b}} = \tfrac{1}{2}\sqrt{a^2+b^2+2ab\cos AOB}$$

$$= \tfrac{1}{2}\sqrt{a^2+b^2+2ab\frac{a^2+b^2-l^2}{2ab}} \quad \text{by cosine formula}$$

$$= \tfrac{1}{2}\sqrt{2(a^2+b^2)-l^2}. \qquad ...(2)$$

Substituting the values of OG in (1), we get the result as stated.

Example 20. A smooth rod AB of length $2a$ has the end A resting on a smooth plane of inclination α to the horizon and is supported at B by a smooth horizontal rail P parallel to the plane at a perpendicular distance c from the plane. Show that the inclination θ of the rod to the inclined plane is given by $a \sin^2\theta = c \sin\alpha \sec(\theta - \alpha)$. **(M.U.)**

The forces acting on the rod are

(*i*) The reaction along AO, normal to the inclined plane

(*ii*) The reaction along PO, normal to the rod

(*iii*) The weight, along the vertical OG.

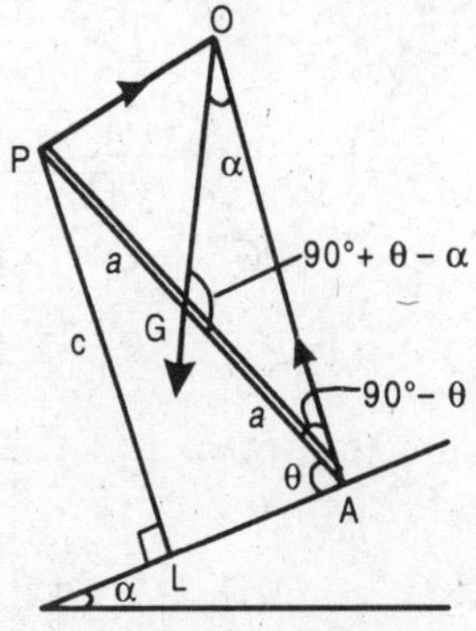

Now α is the angle between horizontal line and the plane so the angle between the vertical line and the perpendicular to the plane is α, that is, angle $AOG = \alpha$. Considering PL, AP, OA, AG in succession, where L is the perpendicular from p to the plane, we have

$$c = PL = AP\sin\theta \quad \text{from } \Delta LPA$$

$$= [OA\cos(90° - \theta)]\sin\theta \text{ from } \Delta APO$$

$$= OA\sin^2\theta$$

But, from $\Delta\, AGO$, $\dfrac{OA}{\sin(90°+\theta-\alpha)} = \dfrac{AG}{\sin\alpha}$. Therefore

$$c = \left[AG\frac{\cos(\theta-\alpha)}{\sin\alpha}\right]\sin^2\theta = \frac{a\cos(\theta-\alpha)\sin^2\theta}{\sin\alpha}$$

Thus, $c\sin\alpha\sec(\theta-\alpha) = a\sin^2\theta$.

Example 21. *A* rod AB rests within a smooth hemispherical bowl. The centre of gravity G divides it into two portions of lengths a, b. Show that, if 2α is the angle subtended by the rod at the centre of the bowl and θ is the inclination of the rod to the horizon in the equilibrium position, then

$$\tan\theta = \frac{b-a}{b+a}\tan\alpha.$$

The forces acting on the rod are

1. The reaction at A along AO,
2. The reaction at B along BO,
3. The weight along the vertical OG.

In the triangle OAB, $AG : GB = a : b$ and ΔOAB is isosceles. Also

$$\angle OGB = 90° - \theta, \ \angle OAB = \angle OBA = 90° - \alpha.$$

So, by the cotangent formula,

$$\left(\frac{1}{a}+\frac{1}{b}\right)\cot(90°-\theta)=\frac{1}{a}\cot(90°-\alpha)-\frac{1}{b}\cot(90°-\alpha)$$

or $\quad (a+b)\tan\theta = b\tan\alpha - a\tan\alpha.$

$$\therefore \qquad \tan\theta=\frac{b-a}{b+a}\tan\alpha.$$

Example 22. A rod rests wholly within a smooth hemispherical bowl of radius r, its centre of gravity dividing the rod into two portions a and b. Show that, if θ is the inclination of the rod to the horizontal in the position of equilibrium, then

$$\sin\theta=\frac{b-a}{2\sqrt{r^2-ab}}. \qquad \text{(M.U.)}$$

The physical situation of this example is same as that of the previous example. Let M be the midpoint of AB. Then, from the ΔGMO, we get

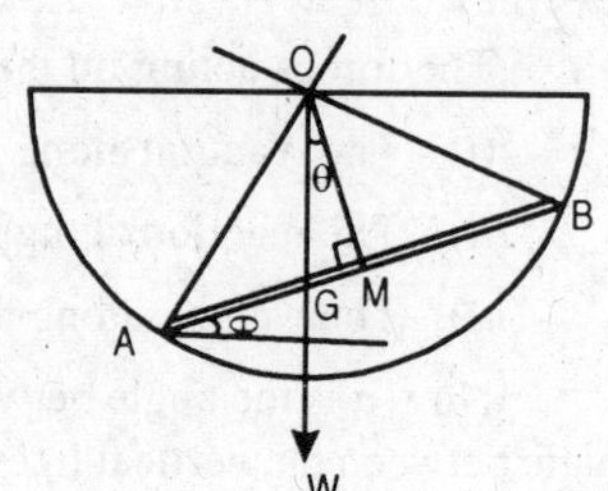

$$\sin\theta=\frac{GM}{OG}. \qquad \text{...(1)}$$

$$OG^2 = OM^2+GM^2, \text{ from } \Delta OGM$$
$$= (OA^2-AM^2)+GM^2, \text{ from } \Delta OAM$$

But $GM = AM - AG = \dfrac{a+b}{2}-a=\dfrac{b-a}{2}$. Therefore

$$OG^2=\left[r^2-\left(\frac{a+b}{2}\right)^2\right]+\left(\frac{b-a}{2}\right)^2=r^2-\frac{1}{4}[4ab].$$
$$=r^2-ab$$

Thus (1) becomes $\sin\theta=\dfrac{b-a}{2\sqrt{r^2-ab}}.$

Example 23. A heavy sphere rests touching two smooth inclined planes one of which is inclined at 60° to the horizontal. If the pressure on this plane is one-half of the weight of the sphere, prove that the inclination of the other plane to the horizontal is 30°. **(M.U.)**

Let α be the inclination of the second inclined plane. Let the points of contact of the sphere with the planes be A, B as in the figure. Let G be the centre of the sphere. The forces acting on the sphere are

(*i*) Normal reaction $R_1 = W/2$ along AG.

(*ii*) Normal reaction R_2 along BG

(*iii*) Weight W through G.

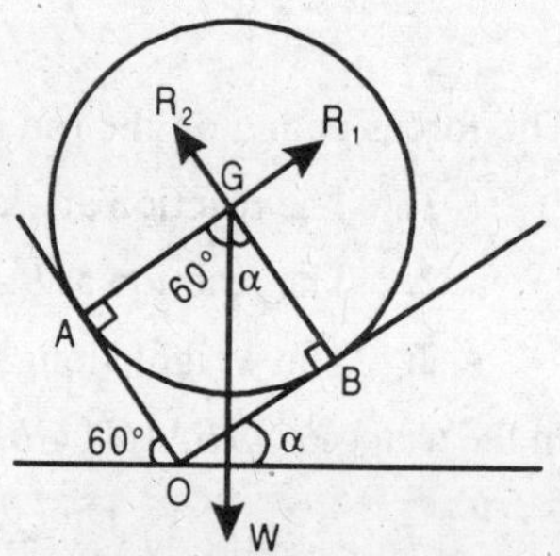

For the forces R_1, R_2, W, the angles opposite to R_1 and W are $180°-\alpha$, $60°+\alpha$. So, by Lami's theorem,

$$\frac{R_1}{\sin(180°-\alpha)}=\frac{W}{\sin(60°+\alpha)} \quad\text{or}\quad \frac{W/2}{\sin\alpha}=\frac{W}{\sin(60°+\alpha)}. \qquad \text{...(1)}$$

i.e., $$\sin(60° + \alpha) = 2\sin\alpha.$$

By expansion and division by $\cos\alpha$, we get

$$\tan\alpha = \frac{1}{\sqrt{3}} \text{ or } \alpha = 30°.$$

Example 24. A uniform sphere rests on two smooth inclined planes whose inclinations to the horizontal are α and β. If the pressure on the former plane is half the weight of the sphere, prove that $\beta = \tan^{-1}\dfrac{\sin\alpha}{2 - \cos\alpha}$. **(M.U., M.K.U.)**

Instead of (1) in the previous example, now we have

$$\frac{R_1}{\sin(180° - \beta)} = \frac{W}{\sin(\alpha + \beta)},\quad R_1 = \frac{W}{2}$$

which lead to the result in the same way.

Example 25. A uniform beam AB rests with its extremities on two smooth inclined planes which meet in a horizontal line and whose inclinations to the horizontal are α and β. Show that, if θ is the angle made by the rod with the vertical, then

(*i*) $2\cot\theta = \cot\alpha - \cot\beta$. **(M.U.)**

(*ii*) Find the reactions of the plane. **(M.U.)**

(*iii*) If $\alpha = 30°, \beta = 45°$, show that the rod must be inclined to the horizontal at an angle $\cot^{-1}(\sqrt{3} + 1)$. **(M.U.)**

(*i*) The forces acting on the rod are

1. The reaction R_A along AO normal to the plane AQ
2. The reaction R_B along BO normal to the plane BQ
3. The weight W along the vertical OG.

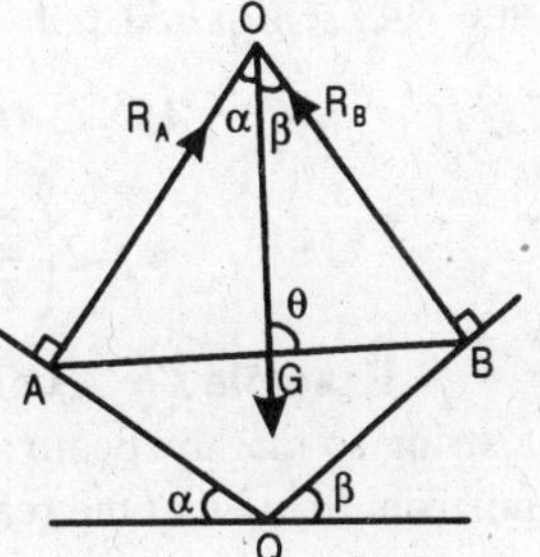

In the triangle OAB, $AG : GB = 1 : 1$ and angles AOG and BOG are α and β. So by the cotangent formula,

$$(1+1)\cot\theta = 1 \times \cot\alpha - 1 \times \cot\beta. \quad ...(1)$$

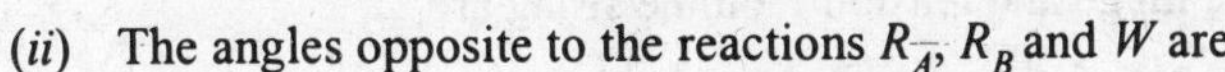

(*ii*) The angles opposite to the reactions R_A, R_B and W are

$$180° - \beta,\quad 180° - \alpha,\quad \alpha + \beta.$$

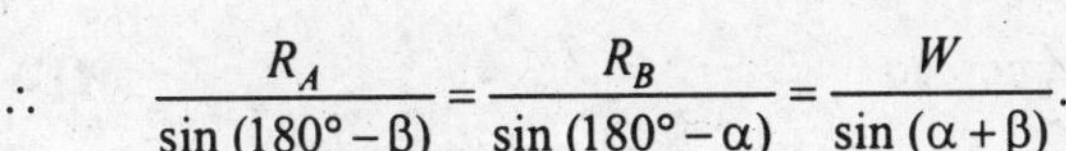

$$\therefore \quad \frac{R_A}{\sin(180° - \beta)} = \frac{R_B}{\sin(180° - \alpha)} = \frac{W}{\sin(\alpha + \beta)}.$$

$$\therefore \quad R_A = \frac{W\sin\beta}{\sin(\alpha + \beta)},\quad R_B = \frac{W\sin\alpha}{\sin(\alpha + \beta)}.$$

(*iii*) If $\alpha = 30°$, $\beta = 45°$, then, from (1),

$$2\cot\theta = \sqrt{3} - 1 \text{ or } \cot\theta = \frac{\sqrt{3} - 1}{2}.$$

If λ is the angle made by the rod with the horizontal, then $\theta = 90° - \lambda$ and so

$$\cot(90° - \lambda) = \frac{\sqrt{3} - 1}{2} \text{ or } \tan\lambda = \frac{\sqrt{3} - 1}{2}.$$

$$\therefore \quad \cot\lambda = \frac{2}{\sqrt{3} - 1} = \frac{2(\sqrt{3} + 1)}{3 - 1} = \sqrt{3} + 1.$$

$$\therefore \qquad \lambda = \cot^{-1}(\sqrt{3}+1).$$

Example 26. A smooth hemispherical bowl of diameter a is fixed so that its horizontal rim touches a smooth vertical wall. A uniform rod is in equilibrium inclined at 60° to the horizon with one end resting on the inner surface of the bowl and the other end resting against the wall. Show that the length of the rod is equal to $a+\dfrac{a}{\sqrt{13}}$. **(M.U.)**

Let AB be the rod, G its mass centre, B the upper end, C the centre of the sphere and D, the point of contact of the bowl with the wall. Let the horizontal line through A meet the wall at E. Let the vertical line through C meet AE at F. Let α be the angle made by AC with the vertical. Now the forces on the rod are

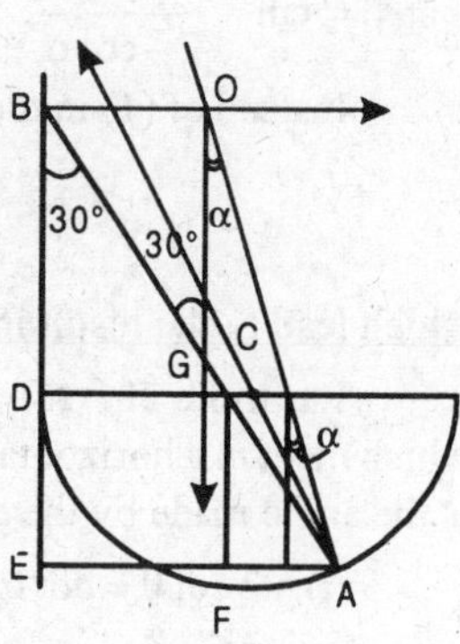

(*i*) The reaction of the wall at B normal to it

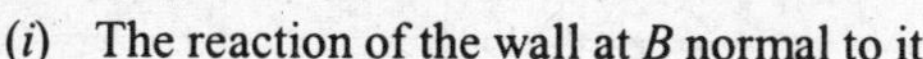

(*ii*) The reaction of the sphere along AC

(*iii*) The weight of the rod acting at G vertically.

Let them meet at O. Now, in the triangle ABO,

$$AG:GB = 1:1,\ \underline{|OGB} = 30°,\ \underline{|GOB} = 90°,\ \underline{|GOC} = \alpha.$$

So, by the cotangent formula,

$$(1+1)\cot 30° = 1\times\cot\alpha - 1\times\cot 90° \text{ or } \cot\alpha = 2\sqrt{3}$$

and $\sin\alpha = 1/\sqrt{13}$. Also, from ΔEAB, $AE = AB\sin 30° = AB/2$.

$$\therefore \qquad AB = 2AE = 2(CD+FA) = 2(\tfrac{1}{2}a + CA\sin\alpha)$$

$$= 2\left(\frac{a}{2}+\frac{a}{2}\frac{1}{\sqrt{13}}\right) = a\left(1+\frac{1}{\sqrt{13}}\right).$$

Example 27. A uniform beam of weight W hinged at one end is supported at the other end by a string so that the beam and the string are in a vertical plane and make the same angle α with the horizon. Show that the reaction R at the hinge and tension T on the string are

$$R = W/4\,\sqrt{8+\operatorname{cosec}^2\alpha}$$ **(M.U., Bn.U.)**

$$T = W/4\,\operatorname{cosec}\alpha.$$ **(M.U.)**

Let AB be the beam and G its centre of mass. Let BP be the string. Let the weight and tension meet at O. Then the reaction of the hinge passes through O. Since the rod and the string are equally inclined to the horizontal at an angle α, they are equally inclined to the vertical OG at an angle 90°– α. Let angle AOG be θ. Then, by cotangent formula,

$$(1+1)\cot(90°-\alpha) = \cot\theta - \cot(90°-\alpha)$$

$$\therefore \qquad 3\tan\alpha = \cot\theta$$

$$\text{or} \qquad \cot\theta = \frac{3}{\cot\alpha}.$$

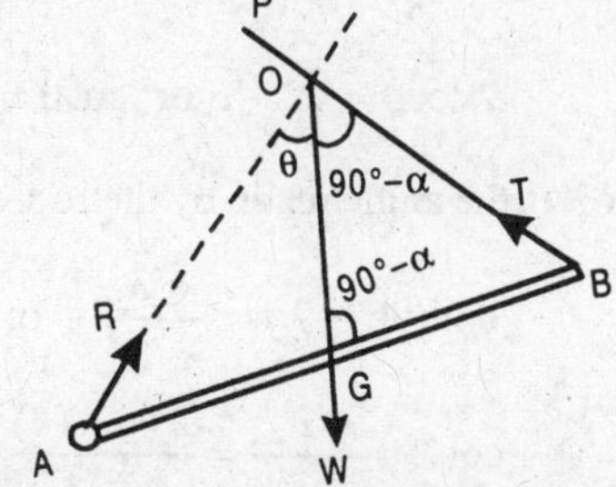

Denote $\sqrt{9+\cot^2\alpha}$ by λ.

Then, from the figure,

$$\sin\theta = \frac{\cot\alpha}{\lambda}, \quad \cos\theta = \frac{3}{\lambda}.$$

Now the angles opposite to R, T, W are

$$90° + \alpha,\ 180° - \theta,\ 90° + \theta - \alpha.$$

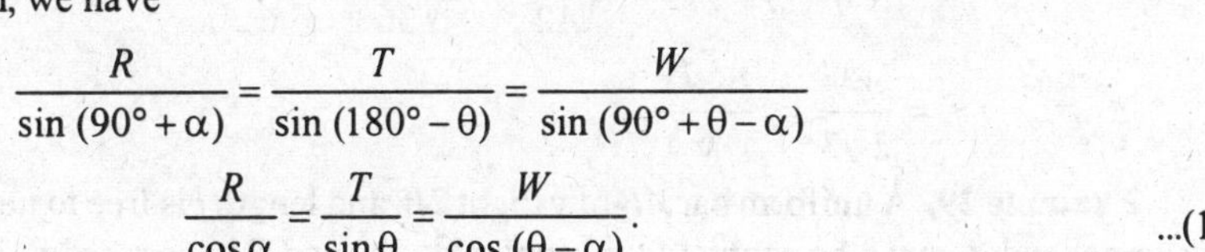

Thus, by Lami's theorem, we have

$$\frac{R}{\sin(90° + \alpha)} = \frac{T}{\sin(180° - \theta)} = \frac{W}{\sin(90° + \theta - \alpha)}$$

or

$$\frac{R}{\cos\alpha} = \frac{T}{\sin\theta} = \frac{W}{\cos(\theta - \alpha)}. \qquad ...(1)$$

In this, considering $\cos(\theta - \alpha)$ seperately

$$\cos(\theta - \alpha) = \cos\theta\cos\alpha + \sin\theta\sin\alpha$$

$$= \frac{3\cos\alpha}{\lambda} + \frac{\cot\alpha\sin\alpha}{\lambda} = \frac{4\cos\alpha}{\lambda}.$$

Thus, from the first and the third of (1),

$$R = \frac{W\cos\alpha}{\frac{4\cos\alpha}{\lambda}} = \frac{W\lambda}{4} = \frac{W}{4}\sqrt{9 + \cot^2\alpha}$$

$$= \frac{W}{4}\sqrt{8 + (1 + \cot^2\alpha)} = \frac{W}{4}\sqrt{8 + \operatorname{cosec}^2\alpha}.$$

$$T = \frac{W\sin\theta}{\frac{4\cos\alpha}{\lambda}} = \frac{W}{4}\,\frac{\lambda}{\cos\alpha}\,\frac{\cot\alpha}{\lambda} = \frac{W}{4}\operatorname{cosec}\alpha.$$

Example 28. A uniform rod AB of weight W and length $2a$, is hinged at A by a smooth hinge. It is kept at rest inclined at an angle α to the vertical by means of a force of magnitude F applied horizontally at B. Find the magnitude and direction of the reaction of the hinge on the rod. Show that

$$F = \tfrac{1}{2} W \tan\alpha.$$

If $\alpha = 30°$, show that R and F are

$$\frac{W\sqrt{39}}{6}, \frac{W\sqrt{3}}{6}.$$

The horizontal applied force, the vertical weight of the rod and the reaction of the hinge are the only forces on the rod. So they should be concurrent, say at O. In the triangle AOB, the centre of gravity G divides AB in the ratio 1:1, angle OGB=α and angle GOB=90°. If angle GOA is θ, then, by cotangent formula,

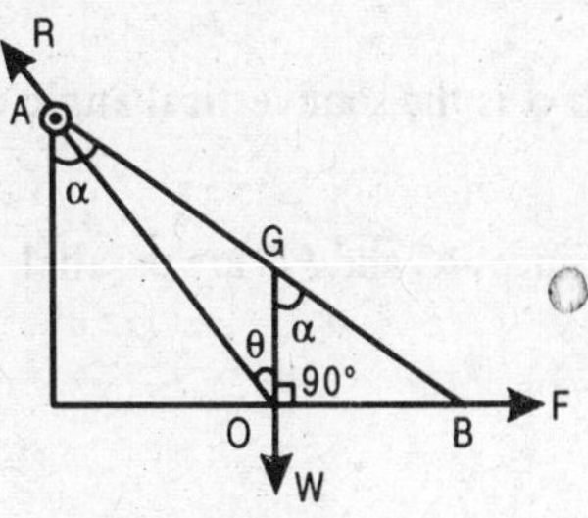

$$(1 + 1)\cot\alpha = \cot\theta - \cot 90° = \cot\theta$$

i.e.,

$$\tan\theta = \tfrac{1}{2}\tan\alpha.$$

Since the forces are in equilibrium, considering Lami's theorem,

$$\frac{R}{\sin 90°} = \frac{W}{\sin(90° + \theta)} = \frac{F}{\sin(180° - \theta)}.$$

$$\therefore \qquad R = W\sec\theta = W\sqrt{1+\tan^2\theta} = W\sqrt{1+\tfrac{1}{4}\tan^2\alpha}, \qquad \text{...(1)}$$

$$\therefore \qquad F = W\tan\theta = \tfrac{1}{2}W\tan\alpha. \qquad \text{...(2)}$$

When $\alpha=30°$, we get, from (1) and (2),

$$R = W\sqrt{1+\tfrac{1}{4}\cdot\tfrac{1}{3}} = W\sqrt{\frac{13}{12}} = W\sqrt{\frac{39}{36}} = \frac{W\sqrt{39}}{6}.$$

$$F = \frac{W}{2\sqrt{3}} = \frac{W\sqrt{3}}{6}.$$

Example 29. A uniform bar AB of weight $2W$ and length l is free to turn about a smooth hinge at its upper end A, and a horizontal force applied to the end B keeps the bar in equilibrium with B at a distance a from the vertical through A. Prove that the reaction at the hinge is equal to

$$W\sqrt{\frac{4l^2-3a^2}{l^2-a^2}}. \qquad \textbf{(M.U.)}$$

With the notations used in the previous example, for the weight of the bar $2W$, the reaction of the hinge is

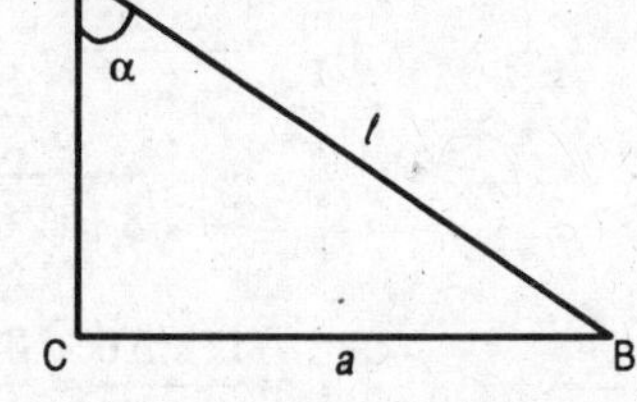

$$R = (2W)\sqrt{1+\tfrac{1}{4}\tan^2\alpha}.$$

Now $AB = l$, $CB = a$. Hence

$$\tan\alpha = \frac{CB}{AC} = \frac{a}{\sqrt{l^2-a^2}}.$$

Therefore the reaction is

$$R = 2W\sqrt{1+\frac{1}{4}\frac{a^2}{l^2-a^2}} = W\sqrt{\frac{4l^2-4a^2+a^2}{l^2-a^2}} = W\sqrt{\frac{4l^2-3a^2}{l^2-a^2}}.$$

Example 30. The altitude of a right cone is h and the radius of its base is a. A string of length l is fastened to the vertex and to a point on the circumference of the circular base and is then put over a smooth peg. The cone rests with its axis horizontal. Show that the length of the string is $\sqrt{h^2+4a^2}$. **(M.U.)**

As in the figure, the two equal tensions and the weight meet at the peg O. The vertical line bisects angle AOB. Let

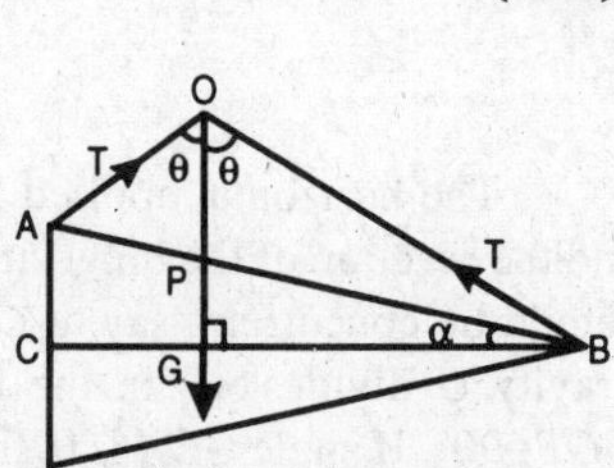

$$\angle AOP = \angle BOP = \theta.$$

If α is the semivertical angle of the cone, Then

$$\angle APO = 90° - \alpha.$$

Since AC and PG are parallel,

$$\frac{AP}{PB} = \frac{CG}{GB} = \frac{1}{3} \text{ since } GB = \tfrac{3h}{4}.$$

Thus, by the cotangent formula, we get

$$(1+3)\cot(90°-\alpha) = 3\cot\theta - \cot\theta$$

$$4\tan\alpha = 2\cot\theta \text{ or } \cot\theta = 2\tan\alpha = \frac{2a}{h}. \qquad ...(1)$$

Considering the projections of the strings OB, OA on the altitude

$$GB = OB\sin\theta, \quad GC = OA\sin\theta.$$

$$\therefore \quad GB + GC = (OB + OA)\sin\theta \text{ or } h = l\sin\theta.$$

$$\therefore \quad l = h\operatorname{cosec}\theta = h\sqrt{1+\cot^2\theta} = h\sqrt{1+\frac{4a^2}{h^2}} \text{ by (1)}$$

$$= \sqrt{h^2+4a^2}.$$

EXERCISES

1. AB and AC are two rods of length 10 cm. smoothly jointed at A. BD is a weight less bar of length 6 cm. smoothly jointed at B and fastened at D to a small smooth ring P sliding on AC. The system is hung on a smooth pin A. Prove that the rods make with the vertical an angle $\tan^{-1} \frac{1}{3}$. **(M.K.U.)**

[Hint: The reaction of the ring P on AC is perpendicular to AC and is along BP. So the angle BPA is 90° with $AP = \sqrt{10^2-6^2} = 8$. If 2α is the angle BAC,

$$\tan 2\alpha = \frac{6}{8} \text{ or } \frac{2\tan\alpha}{1-\tan^2\alpha} = \frac{3}{4} \text{ or } \tan\alpha = \frac{1}{3}.]$$

2. A uniform rod of length $2r$ rests with one end against the inside of a smooth hemispherical bowl of radius r whose rim is horizontal, and with one point of its length in contact with the rim. Show that, if θ is the inclination of the rod to the horizontal, then

$$\cos\theta = \tfrac{1}{8}(1+\sqrt{33}). \qquad \textbf{(M.U.)}$$

[Hint: In bowl-example 10, replace $2a$ by $2r$. Then $2\cos 2\theta = \cos\theta$]

3. A smooth hemispherical bowl of radius r is held with its rim horizontal. A uniform rod rests with one end against the inner surface of the bowl. If the portion of the rod within the bowl is of length c, show that the total length of the rod is $\frac{4}{c}(c^2-2r^2)$. **(M.U.)**

[Hint: If $2a$ is the length of the rod and θ is the inclination of the rod to the horizon, then $2r\cos 2\theta = a\cos\theta$.] ...(1)

4. A uniform rod AB of length $2l$ rests partly within and partly without a smooth cylindrical cup of radius a. Show that in the position of equilibrium the rod makes with the horizon an angle θ given by $\cos^3\theta = \frac{2a}{l}$. **(M.U.)**

[Hint: O: Pt of concurrence of the forces; Forces: Normal reaction of the cylinder along the horizontal AO, weight along GO, reaction of the rim normal to AB at the point of contact C along CO. If AO meets the cylinder at D, relate successively $AD = 2a$, AC, AO, $AG = l$, one with the other]

5. A sphere of radius a and weight W rests on a smooth vertical wall being suspended by a string of length l with one end attached to a point A on the surface of the sphere and the other end to a point B on the wall. Find the inclination θ of the string to the vertical and its tension in the position of equilibrium.

[**Hint:** Let C, D be the centre and the point of contact of the sphere. The forces on the sphere are concurrent and they are the reaction along DC, the weight through C and the tension along CAB, $\sin\theta = \frac{a}{a+l}$; $T = \frac{W}{\cos\theta}$.]

6. A sphere of radius a and weight W rests on a smooth inclined plane supported by a string of length l with one end attached to a point A on the surface of the sphere and the other end fastened to a point D on the plane. If α is the inclination of the plane to the horizontal, prove that the tension T of the string is

$$\frac{W(a+l)\sin\alpha}{\sqrt{l^2+2al}}.$$ **(M.U., K.U., M.K.U.)**

[**Hint:** Forces acting on the sphere are the reaction of the plane normal to it, the weight and the tension. The first two intersect at O, the centre of the sphere. So DA passes through O. If B is the point of contact and angle BOD is θ, from ΔOBD,

$$\cos\theta = \frac{a}{a+l}, \quad \sin\theta = \sqrt{1-\frac{a^2}{(a+l)^2}}.$$

The angle opposite to T, W are $180° - \alpha$, $180° - \theta$. Use Lami's theorem.]

7. A cylindrical rough roller of weight W has a base radius r. When it is at rest, show that the horizontal force, through the centre, necessary to pull it over an obstacle on the ground of height h is equal to or greater than

$$\frac{W}{r-h}\sqrt{h(2r-h)}.$$

[**Hint:** Let O be the centre, P the tip of the bstacle, θ, the angle made by OP with vertical. When the roller just rises, the forces, namely weight W, the pulling force F and the reaction of the obstacle, meet at O. Then, by Lami's theorem,

$$\frac{F}{\sin(180°-\theta)} = \frac{W}{\sin(90°+\theta)} \quad \text{or} \quad F = W\tan\theta.$$

If PN is the perpendicular to the vertical through O,

$$\cos\theta = \frac{ON}{r} = \frac{r-h}{r}, \quad \tan\theta = \frac{\sqrt{h(2r-h)}}{r-h}.]$$

8. Equal weights P and P are attached to two strings ACP and BCP passing over a smooth peg C and hangs on either side of C. AB is a heavy beam of weight W, whose centre of gravity a ft from A and b ft from B. Show that AB is inclined to the horizon at an angle

$$\tan^{-1}\left[\frac{a-b}{a+b}\tan\left(\sin^{-1}\frac{W}{2P}\right)\right].$$ **(M.K.U.)**

[**Hint:** The forces on the beam are the equal tensions P, P equally inclined to the vertical, say at α, and its own weitht. If θ is the inclination of the rod to the horizontal, by cotangent formula,

$$(a+b)\cot(90°-\theta) = a\cot\alpha - b\cot\alpha$$

or $$\tan\theta = \frac{a-b}{a+b}\cot\alpha = \frac{a-b}{a+b}\tan(\pi/2 - \alpha).$$

Resolving the forces vertically, $2P \cos \alpha = W$. So

$$\alpha = \cos^{-1} \frac{W}{2P}. \therefore \frac{\pi}{2} - \alpha = \sin^{-1} \frac{W}{2P}]$$

9. A rod AB whose centre of gravity divides it into two parts of lengths a and b, has its ends A and B tied to a string which passes over a small smooth fixed peg O and the rod rests inclined to the vertical at an angle θ. Show that

$$\cot \theta = \frac{a-b}{a+b} \cot \alpha,$$

where 2α is the angle between the parts of the strings.

[**Hint:** The tensions along AO and BO are equal. So AO and BO are equally inclined to the vertical OG, at an angle α. By cotangent formula, $(a+b) \cot \theta = a \cot \alpha - b \cot \alpha$.]

10. A body of weight $2W$ is attached to the end A and another body of weight W to the end B of a rod AB of negligible weight and of length $2a$. The rod hangs from a point O to which it is attached by light strings AO, BO each of length b. Prove that in equilibrium position, the inclination θ of the rod to the horizontal is given by

$$\tan \theta = \frac{a}{3\sqrt{b^2 - a^2}}.$$

[**Hint:** The resultant weight divides the rod in the ratio 1 : 2. The strings are equally inclined to the rod, say at an angle α. By Cotangent formula,

$$\left(\frac{1}{1} + \frac{1}{2}\right) \cot (90° - \theta) = \frac{1}{1} \cot \alpha - \frac{1}{2} \cot \alpha.$$

Considering the sum of the projections of the string on the rod, $2b \cos \alpha = 2a$. Eliminate α.]

A SPECIFIC REDUCTION OF FORCES

5.1 REDUCTION OF COPLANAR FORCES INTO A FORCE AND A COUPLE

Earlier we saw a system of coplanar forces to reduce to either a single force or a single couple. But in the following bookwork we reduce a system of coplanar forces to a force acting at an arbitrarily chosen point and a couple.

Bookwork 5.1. To show that a system of coplanar forces acting on a rigid body can be reduced to a force at an arbitrarily chosen point and a couple in the plane.

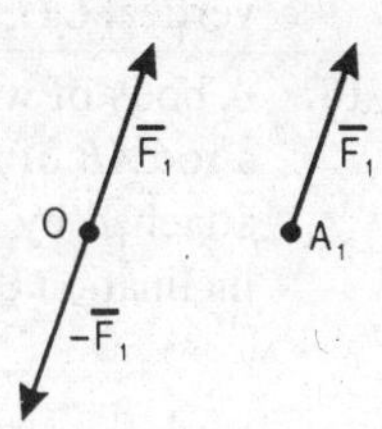

Let $\overline{F}_1, \overline{F}_2, \ldots, \overline{F}_n$ be the given forces acting on the rigid body at $A_1, A_2, \ldots, A_n$. Let O be an arbitrarily chosen point in the plane. First introduce two forces $\overline{F}_1$ and $-\overline{F}_1$ at this point. This introduction does not alter the effects of the given forces because the resultant of these two forces is a zero force. Now the force $\overline{F}_1$ at A_1 and the force $-\overline{F}_1$ at O form a couple whose moment is $\overline{OA_1} \times \overline{F}_1$. So the force $\overline{F}_1$ at A_1 is equivalent to

(*i*) A force $\overline{F}_1$ at O and

(*ii*) A couple with a moment $\overline{OA_1} \times \overline{F}_1$ in the plane.

Similarly the force $\overline{F}_2$ at A_2 is equivalent to a force $\overline{F}_2$ at O and a couple with a moment $\overline{OA_2} \times \overline{F}_2$ and so on. Thus we see that the given force system is equivalent to the system which consists of

(*i*) n forces. $\overline{F}_1, \overline{F}_2, \ldots, \overline{F}_n$ at O and

(*ii*) n couples with moments $\overline{OA_1} \times \overline{F}_1, \ldots, \overline{OA_n} \times \overline{F}_n$ in the plane.

But the resultant of the n forces at O is the single force

$$\overline{F}_1 + \overline{F}_2 + \ldots + \overline{F}_n \text{ at } O.$$

The resultant of the n couples is a single couple in the plane with a moment

$$\overline{OA_1} \times \overline{F}_1 + \overline{OA_2} \times \overline{F}_2 + \ldots + \overline{OA_n} \times \overline{F}_n.$$

So the given force system is equivalent to the single force

$$\overline{F}_1 + \overline{F}_2 + \ldots + \overline{F}_n$$

at O and a couple with the moment

$$\overline{OA_1} \times \overline{F}_1 + \overline{OA_2} \times \overline{F}_2 + \ldots + \overline{OA_n} \times \overline{F}_n.$$

But $\overline{OA_1} \times \overline{F}_1$, $\overline{OA_2} \times \overline{F}_2, \ldots, \overline{OA_n} \times \overline{F}_n$ are the moments of the given forces about O. So the moment of the above couple is the sum of the moments of given forces about O. So, in conclusion, we get that any system of coplanar forces $\overline{F}_1, \overline{F}_2, \ldots, \overline{F}_n$ is equivalent to a single force

$$\overline{F}_1 + \overline{F}_2 + \ldots + \overline{F}_n$$

acting at any point in the plane and a couple whose moment is equal to the sum of the moments of $\overline{F}_1, \overline{F}_2, \ldots, \overline{F}_n$ about that point.

Invariance of the single force. The single force is the vector sum of the given forces. As such it is independent of O. For brevity we shall denote

$$\overline{F}_1 + \overline{F}_2 + \overline{F}_3 + ... + \overline{F}_n \text{ by } \overline{F}.$$

Then $\overline{F} \cdot \overline{F}$ or F^2 and the direction of $\overline{F}$ are independent of O.

Invariance of $\overline{\mathbf{F}} \cdot \overline{\mathbf{G}}$. The single couple depends on the base point O. So it is not an invariant. We shall denote the moment of this couple by $\overline{G}$. Than

$$\overline{G} = \Sigma \overline{OA_i} \times \overline{F}_i.$$

We shall show that $\overline{F}.\overline{G}$ is an invariant. Suppose we reduce the given system to a single force $\overline{F}$ at a different point P whose position vector is $\overline{r}$ with reference to O and a couple $\overline{G'}$. Then

$$\begin{aligned} \overline{G'} &= \Sigma\, \overline{PA_i} \times \overline{F}_i = \Sigma\left(\overline{OA_i} - \overline{OP}\right) \times \overline{F}_i \\ &= \Sigma\, \overline{OA_i} \times \overline{F}_i - \overline{OP} \times \left(\Sigma\, \overline{F}_i\right) = \overline{G} - \overline{r} \times \overline{F}. \end{aligned}$$

$$\begin{aligned} \therefore \quad \overline{F} \cdot \overline{G'} &= \overline{F} \cdot \left(\overline{G} - \overline{r} \times \overline{F}\right) = \overline{F} \cdot \overline{G} - \overline{F} \cdot \left(\overline{r} \times \overline{F}\right) \\ &= \overline{F} \cdot \overline{G} - \left[\overline{F}\, \overline{r}\, \overline{F}\right] = \overline{F} \cdot \overline{G} - 0 = \overline{F}.\overline{G}. \end{aligned}$$

Thus $\overline{F} \cdot \overline{G}$ is the same for all positions of the point P.

5.1.1 Conditions of equilibrium under coplanar forces

Bookwork 5.2. To show that set of necessary and sufficient conditions for a system of coplanar forces to keep a rigid body in equilibrium are

(*i*) The sum of the components of the forces along any line in the plane is zero. **C. 1.**

(*ii*) The sum of the components of the forces along a line in the plane perpendicular to the former is zero. **C. 2.**

(*iii*) The sum of the moments of the forces about any one point in the plane is zero. **C. 3.**

Necessity part. In this part we have to assume that the system of forces of keep the body in equilibrium and then show that C. 1, C. 2, C. 3 are true.

Let $\overline{F}_1, \overline{F}_2, ..., \overline{F}_n$ be the given forces and let O be an arbitrarily chosen point in the plane. Then the given system is equivalent to a force $\overline{F}_1 + \overline{F}_2 + ... + \overline{F}_n$ in the plane at O and a couple in the plane whose moments is the sum of the moments of the forces about O. Now the system keeps the body in equilibrium. So the force at O and the couple must vanish. This leads to the results,

(*i*) $\overline{F}_1 + \overline{F}_2 + ... + \overline{F}_n = \overline{0}$ ...(1)

(*ii*) Sum of the moments of the forces about $O = \overline{0}$. ...(2)

Choose arbitrarily a line in the plane through O and let $\overline{i}$, be the unit vector along it. Then multiplying (1) scalarly by $\overline{i}$,

$$\overline{F}_1 \cdot \overline{i} + \overline{F}_2 \cdot \overline{i} + ... + \overline{F}_n \cdot \overline{i} = 0.$$

This proves C. 1. Similarly, taking the unit vector $\overline{j}$ in the plane, perpendicular to $\overline{i}$, and multiplying (1) scalarly by $\overline{j}$, we see that C. 2 is true. Furthermore, we get, from (2), that C. 3 is true.

Sufficiency part. In this part we have to assume that C.1, C. 2, C.3 are true and then show that the forces keep the body in equilibrium.

As before reduce the system to a single force at O and a single couple. Now, by C.1,

$$\overline{F}_1 \cdot \overline{i} + \overline{F}_2 \cdot \overline{i} + ... + \overline{F}_n \cdot \overline{i} = 0. \quad \therefore \left(\overline{F}_1 + \overline{F}_2 + ... + \overline{F}_n\right) \cdot \overline{i} = 0.$$

Similarly, by C.2,

$$\left(\overline{F}_1 + \overline{F}_2 + ... + \overline{F}_n\right) \cdot \overline{j} = 0.$$

Now $\overline{F}_1 + \overline{F}_2 + ... + \overline{F}_n$ cannot be perpendicular to both $\overline{i}$ and $\overline{j}$. So the only possibility for the above dot products to vanish, is that $\overline{F}_1 + \overline{F}_2 + ... + \overline{F}_n = \overline{0}$, that is, the single force at O vanishes. The moment of the couple is the sum of the moments of the given forces about any point. So, by C.3, the couple also vanishes. Hence the body is in equilibrium.

Two more sets of sufficient conditions. The following two bookworks provide two other sets of sufficient conditions for a system of coplanar forces to keep a body in equilibrium.

Bookwork. 5. 3. A set of sufficient conditions for a system of coplanar forces to keep a rigid body in equilibrium is that the sums of the moments of the forces about any three noncollinear points in the plane are zero.

Let the given system consist of forces $\overline{F}_1, \overline{F}_2, ..., \overline{F}_n$ at $A_1, A_2, ..., A_n$. Let the sum of the moments of $\overline{F}_1, \overline{F}_2, ..., \overline{F}_n$ about each of the noncollinear points A, B, C, be zero. Then

$$\Sigma \overline{AA_i} \times \overline{F}_i = \overline{0}, \ \Sigma \overline{BA_i} \times \overline{F}_i = \overline{0}, \ \Sigma \overline{CA_i} \times \overline{F}_i = \overline{0}. \qquad ...(1)$$

Reduce the given system to a force acting at A and a couple. Then the force at A is

$$\overline{F}_1 + \overline{F}_2 + ... + \overline{F}_n, \text{ say } \overline{F}$$

and the couple has the moment

$$\Sigma \overline{AA_i} \times \overline{F}_i.$$

But, by (1), this moment is zero. So the couple vanishes and the given system reduces to the single force $\overline{F}$ acting at A, that is, the resultant of the given n forces is the single force $\overline{F}$ acting at A. But we know that the sum of the moments of a system of forces about any point equals the moment of their resultant about the same point. So the sum of the moments of the given forces $\overline{F}_1, \overline{F}_2, ..., \overline{F}_n$, about B equals the moment of $\overline{F}$ about B. That is,

$$\overline{BA_1} \times \overline{F}_1 + \overline{BA_2} \times \overline{F}_2 + ... = \overline{BA} \times \overline{F}.$$

In this, the left-hand side expression is $\overline{0}$ by (1). So

$$\overline{BA} \times \overline{F} = \overline{0}.$$

Similarly, considering the moments about C, we get

$$\overline{CA} \times \overline{F} = \overline{0}.$$

These two equations imply that either $\overline{F} = \overline{0}$ or $\overline{F}$ is parallel to both $\overline{BA}, \overline{CA}$. The latter case is not possible because A, B, C are noncollinear. So $\overline{F} = \overline{0}$. Hence the body is in equilibrium.

Bookwork 5.4. A set of sufficient conditions for a system of coplanar forces to keep a rigid body in equilibrium is that the sums of moments of the forces about any two points A and B are individually zero and that the sum of the components of the forces in any direction not perpendicular to AB is zero.

The first two conditions are the same as the first two conditions of the previous bookwork. So we get that the given system reduces to a single force $\overline{F}$ at A and $\overline{BA} \times \overline{F} = \overline{0}$. The third condition is $\overline{F}_1 \cdot \hat{e} + \overline{F}_2 \cdot \hat{e} + ... + \overline{F}_n \cdot \hat{e} = 0$ or $\overline{F} \cdot \hat{e} = 0$ where $\hat{e}$ is a unit vector not perpendicular to AB. Now considering $\overline{BA} \times \overline{F} = \overline{0}$ and $\overline{F} \cdot \hat{e} = 0$ together, we see that either $\overline{F} = \overline{0}$ or $\overline{F}$ is parallel to $\overline{AB}$. and considering perpendicular to $\hat{e}$. But $\hat{e}$ is not perpendicular to AB. So $\overline{F} = 0$. Hence the body is in equilibrium.

EXAMPLES

Example 1. Prove that, if four forces acting along the sides of a square are in equilibrium, they must be equal in magnitude. **(M.U.)**

Let the square be $ABCD$ and the unit vectors in the directions of AB, AD be $\bar{i}, \bar{j}$. Let the forces and their points of action be

$$\begin{matrix} P\bar{i}, & Q\bar{j}, & R\bar{i}, & S\bar{j}; \\ A, & B, & C, & D \end{matrix}$$

and let $P > 0$. Due to equilibrium the sum of the forces is $\bar{0}$.

$\therefore \quad P\bar{i} + Q\bar{j} + R\bar{i} + S\bar{j} = \bar{0}$ or $(P+R)\bar{i} + (Q+S)\bar{j} = \bar{0}$.

$\therefore \quad P+R=0,\ Q+S=0$ or $R=-P, S=-Q$.

Thus the forces are

$$P\bar{i},\ Q\bar{j},\ -P\bar{i},\ -Q\bar{j}$$

Also the sum of the moments of the forces about any point, say A, is $\bar{0}$. Thus, if a is the side of the square,

$$\bar{O} + \overline{AB}\times(Q\bar{j}) + \overline{AD}\times(-P\bar{i}) + \bar{O} = \bar{0}$$

i.e., $\quad a\bar{i}\times(Q\bar{j}) + a\bar{j}\times(-P\bar{i}) = \bar{0}$

i.e., $\quad aQ\bar{k} + aP\bar{k} = \bar{0} \qquad$ or $\qquad Q = -P$.

Thus the forces are

$$P\bar{i},\ -P\bar{j},\ -P\bar{i},\ P\bar{j}.$$

It is evident that their magnitudes are equal.

Example 2. A ladder of length $2a$ and weight W, with its centre of gravity three-eighths of the way up, stands on a smooth horizontal plane resting against a smooth vertical wall and the midpoint is tied to a point in the wall by a horizontal rope of length l. Find the tension of the rope. **(M. K.U.)**

The figure is self explanatory. The forces on the ladder are

(*i*) Reaction R_1 at A

(*ii*) Reaction R_2 at B

(*iii*) Weight W at G

(*iv*) Tension T at M along ML.

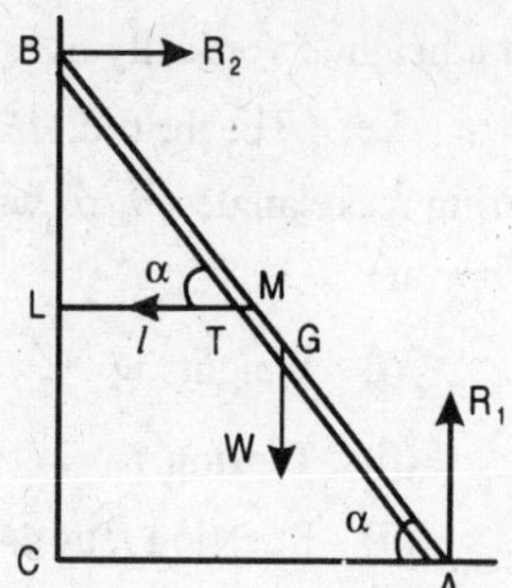

Considering the horizontal components, we get

$$T = R_2.$$

We shall not consider the vertical components. Let α be the angle made by the ladder with the horizontal. Now the perpendicular distances of the forces W, T, R_2 from A are

$$AG\cos\alpha,\ AM\sin\alpha,\ AB\sin\alpha$$

or $$2a\cdot\tfrac{3}{8}\cdot\cos\alpha,\ a\sin\alpha,\ 2a\sin\alpha.$$

Taking moments of all the four forces about A

$$\left(2a\cdot \tfrac{3}{8}\cdot \cos\alpha\right)W+\left(a\sin\alpha\right)T=\left(2a\sin\alpha\right)R_2$$

i.e., $\quad \tfrac{3}{4}\cot\alpha\, W+T=2R_2$ or $\tfrac{3}{4}\cot\alpha\, W+T=2T$

i.e., $\quad T=\dfrac{3}{4}\cot\alpha\, W=\dfrac{3}{4}\dfrac{l}{\sqrt{a^2-l^2}}W$ from ΔBLM.

Example 3. A uniform rod of length $2a$ and weight W is resting on a fixed rail parallel to a smooth vertical wall with one of its ends pressing the wall and to its other end is attached a weight w. The distance of the rail from the wall is b. If the rod is in equlibrium in a vertical plane, show that the angle θ made by the rod with the vertical is given by

$$\sin\theta=\left[\frac{b}{a}\frac{W+w}{W+2w}\right]^{1/3} \qquad \textbf{(A.U)}$$

The figure is self explanatory. We can avoid R_1 by resolving the forces vertically and taking moments about A. Thus, resolving vertically,

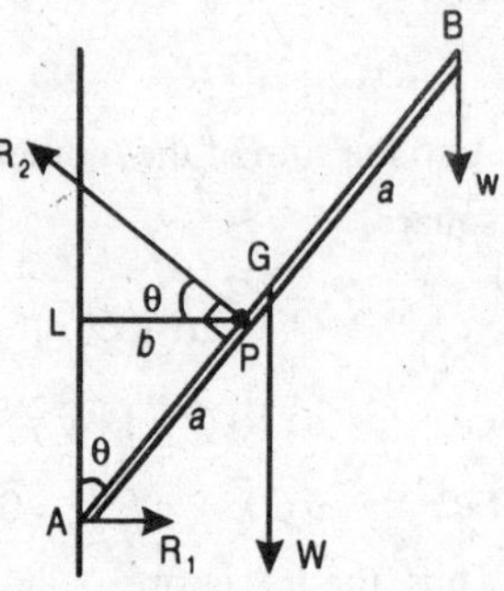

$$R_2\sin\theta=W+w. \qquad ...(1)$$

Taking moments about A,

$$AP\cdot R_2=AG\sin\theta\cdot W+AB\sin\theta\cdot w,\quad AP=\frac{LP}{\sin\theta}=\frac{b}{\sin\theta}.$$

$$\therefore \quad \frac{b}{\sin\theta}R_2=a\sin\theta\, W+2a\sin\theta\, w$$

$$\therefore \quad \frac{b}{\sin\theta}\,\frac{W+w}{\sin\theta}=a\sin\theta\, W+2a\sin\theta\, w \text{ by (1).}$$

This gives $\sin\theta$ as in the result.

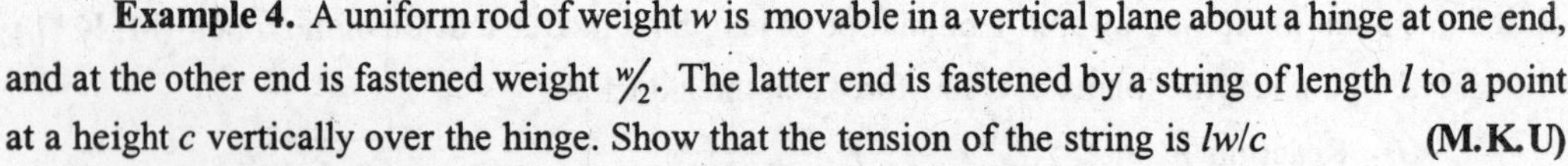

Example 4. A uniform rod of weight w is movable in a vertical plane about a hinge at one end, and at the other end is fastened weight $w/2$. The latter end is fastened by a string of length l to a point at a height c vertically over the hinge. Show that the tension of the string is lw/c **(M.K.U)**

Let AB be the rod, $AB=2a$ and BP, the string. Let the rod and the string make angles θ, α with the vertical. Four forces act on the rod. They are

(*i*) Weights w. $w/2$

(*ii*) Tension T

(*iii*) Reaction R at A.

Let AL be the perpendicular from A to the string. Taking moments about A, thus avoiding R,

$$-a\sin\theta\, w-2a\sin\theta(w/2)+T\cdot AL=0.$$

$$\therefore \quad T=\frac{2a\sin\theta}{AL}\cdot w. \qquad ...(1)$$

From the right angled Δ *APL*,

$$AL = c\sin\alpha. \qquad ...(2)$$

Also, using the sine formula for ΔABP,

$$\frac{l}{\sin(180^\circ - \theta)} = \frac{2a}{\sin\alpha} \text{ or } 2a\sin\theta = l\sin\alpha. \qquad ...(3)$$

When (2) and (3) are used, (1) becomes

$$T = \frac{(l\sin\alpha)w}{(c\sin\alpha)} \quad \text{or} \quad T = \frac{lw}{c}.$$

Example 5. Two equal uniform rods, each of weight W and length a are freely jointed at one extremity, and rest symmetrically in a vertical plane in contact with a smooth horizontal cylinder of radius b, the axis of the cylinder being at right angles to the plane of the rods. Their other extremities are connected by an inextensible string of length $2C$. Show that the tension of the string is

$$W\left(\frac{ab}{c^2} - \frac{c}{2\sqrt{a^2 - c^2}}\right).$$

(A.U)

Let AB be one rod touching the cylinder at P. Let O be the centre of the cylinder. Let G be the midpoint of AB and GN, the perpendicular from G to the vertical through A. The forces on AB are

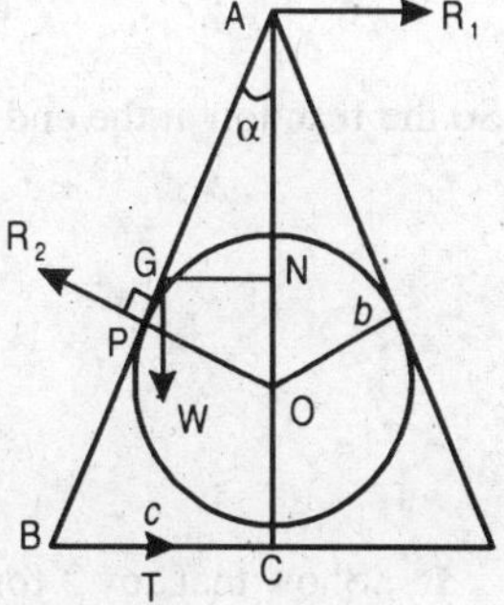

(*i*) Reaction R_1 at A

(*ii*) Reaction R_2 at P

(*iii*) Weight W at G

(*iv*) Tension T at B

Let α be the angle BAC. Now the perpendicular distances of the forces R_2, W, T from A are

$$AP, \quad GN, \quad AC$$

i.e., $$OP\cot\alpha, \quad AG\sin\alpha, \quad AB\cos\alpha$$

i.e., $$b\cot\alpha, \quad a/_2\, a\sin\alpha, \quad a\cos\alpha.$$

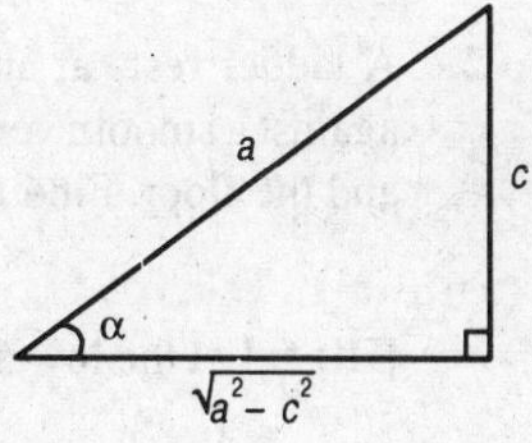

So, taking moments of the forces about A,

$$-b\cot\alpha\ R_2 + a/_2\, a\sin\alpha, W + a\cos\alpha\ T = 0$$

$$T = \frac{b\cot\alpha\ R_2 - a/_2\, a\sin\alpha W}{a\cos\alpha} = \frac{b}{a}\operatorname{cosec}\alpha\ R_2 - 1/_2 \tan\alpha\ W$$

Due to symmetry the reaction on the rod at A is horizontal. Resolving the forces vertically, thus avoiding R_1,

$$R_2\sin\alpha = W \quad \text{or} \quad R_2 = \frac{W}{\sin\alpha}.$$

$$\therefore \quad T = \frac{b}{a}\operatorname{cosec}^2\alpha\ W - \frac{1}{2}\tan\alpha\ W = \left(\frac{b}{a}\frac{a^2}{c^2} - \frac{1}{2}\frac{c}{\sqrt{a^2 - c^2}}\right)W$$

$$= \left(\frac{ab}{c^2} - \frac{1}{2}\frac{c}{\sqrt{a^2 - c^2}}\right)W.$$

Example 6. Three equal uniform rods, each of weight W, are smoothly jointed so as to form an equilateral triangle ABC. The system is supported at the middle point of the rod BC. Show that the reaction at the hinge at A is $\frac{W\sqrt{3}}{6}$. **(M.U)**

Show also that the action at each of the other hinges is $W\sqrt{\frac{13}{12}}$. **(M.U)**

The reactions at the end A on the rods BA, CA should be similar and opposite. So they should be only horizontal . Let them be R, R. We shall consider the forces on the rod AB only. The weight W of the rod acts at G vertically downward. But there are only three forces on the rod AB. Since the rod is in equilibrium the third force, the reaction at B, should have its horizontal and vertical components as R, W as shown in the figure.

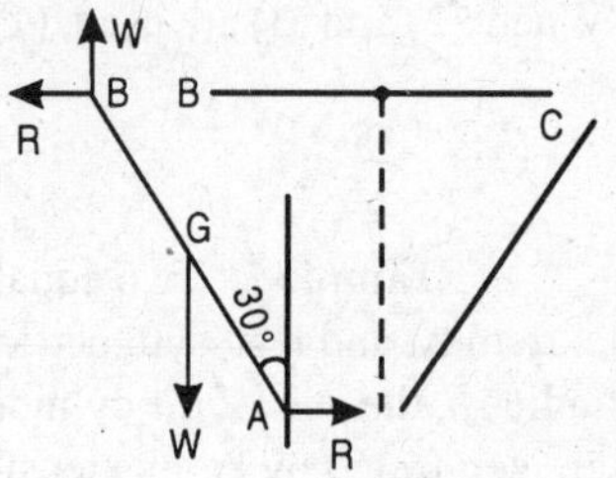

If $BC = a$, then the vertical through G meets BC at a distance $a/4$ from A.

Taking moments about B,

$$-\frac{a}{4}W + (a\cos 30^\circ)R = 0 \text{ or } R\frac{\sqrt{3}}{2} = \frac{W}{4} \text{ or } R = \frac{W}{2\sqrt{3}}.$$

So the reaction at the end A is $\frac{W}{2\sqrt{3}}$. The reaction at the end B and also at the end C is

$$\sqrt{R^2 + W^2} \text{ or } \sqrt{\frac{W^2}{12} + W^2} \text{ or } \sqrt{\frac{13}{12}}\,W.$$

EXERCISES

1. Show that any 3 forces along the sides of a triangle cannot be in equilibrium. **(M.U.)**

   [Hint: If ABC is the Δ, two forces pass through A. Their moments about A are zero. The moment of the third force about A is not zero . So the sum of the moments $\neq 0$]

2. A ladder rests at an angle α to the horizontal, with its ends resting on a smooth floor and against a smooth vertical wall, the lower end being joined by a string to the junction of the wall and the floor. Find the tension of the string and reactions of the wall and the ground. **(M.U.)**

   [Hint: Let the lower end of the ladder AB be A, $AB = 2a$; Let the forces be

   $$\text{At } A: -T\bar{i} + R_1\bar{j}; \quad \text{At } G: -W\bar{j}; \quad \text{At } B: R_2\bar{i}.$$

   So $R_2 = T$, $R_1 = W$. Taking moments about A,

   $$a\cos\alpha\, W = 2a\sin\alpha\, R_2 \quad \text{or} \quad T = \tfrac{1}{2}\cot\alpha\, W \,]$$

3. A ladder of weight W rests at an angle α to the horizontal, with its ends resting on a smooth floor and against a smooth vertical wall, the lower end being joined by a string to the junction of the wall and the floor. A man whose weight is one-half of the ladder has ascended the ladder through two-thirds of its length. Show that the tension of the string is

   $$\frac{5}{6}W\cot\alpha.$$ **(M.K.U)**

[Hint: As in the previous sum $R_2 = T$. Taking moments about A,

$$a\cos\alpha\, W + 2a.\tfrac{2}{3}\cdot \cos\alpha.\, \tfrac{W}{2} = 2a\sin\alpha\, R_2]$$

4. A ladder of length $2l$ and weight W rests against a smooth vertical wall. Its lower end is in contact with a smooth floor and is prevented from slipping by a string of length a connecting it with the junction of the wall and the floor. If a person of weight $2W$ stands on the rung of the ladder, $\tfrac{l}{2}$ from the lower end, determine the reaction at the ends of the ladder and the tension of the string. **(M.U)**

[Ans. With the notations used in the previous sum,

(*i*) $R_1 = 3W$, (*ii*) $T = \dfrac{Wa}{\sqrt{4l^2 - a^2}}$, (*iii*) $R_2 = \dfrac{Wa}{\sqrt{4l^2 - a^2}}$.

5. A heavy uniform rod AB of weight w hinged at a is kept inclined at an angle of 30° to the vertical by a horizontal force P applied at the end B. Find the magnitude of the force P and the reaction at the hinge. **(M.U.)**

[Hint: Rod $AB = a$; Forces: $P\bar{i}$ at B, $-W\bar{j}$ at G, $-P\bar{i}$ and $W\bar{j}$ at A. Taking moments about A,

$\dfrac{a}{2}\cdot\dfrac{1}{2}\cdot W = \dfrac{a\sqrt{3}}{2} P$ or $P = \dfrac{W}{2\sqrt{3}}$.

Reaction at the hinge $= \sqrt{P^2 + W^2} = W\sqrt{\dfrac{13}{12}}$.]

6. Two smooth bars AB, AC, fixed in a vertical plane are each inclined at 45° to the vertical. The ends of a light string are tied to two rings each of weight w which slide without friction on the bars. From the middle point of the string is hung a weight W. Prove that, if the parts of the string make angles θ with the vertical, then

$$\tan\theta = 1 + \frac{2w}{W}. \quad \textbf{(M.U.)}$$

[Hint: Resolving the forces on one ring, along the rod,

$$w\cos 45° = T\cos(180° - 45° - \theta),$$

and resolving the forces at the midpoint of the string vertically,

$$W = 2T\cos\theta.$$

Eliminating T, $\dfrac{w\cos 45°}{W} = -\dfrac{\cos(45° + \theta)}{2\cos\theta}$.]

7. Forces acting along the sides of a cyclic quadrilateral are in equilibrium. Show that each force is proportional to the side opposite to it. **(M.U.)**

[Hint: Quadrilateral : $ABCD$; Forces along AB, BC, CD, DA : P, Q, R, S. Let AL, AM be the perpendiculars on BC, CD. Then

$$AL = AB\sin B, \qquad AM = AD\sin B.$$

Taking moments about A,

$$0 + (AB\sin B)Q + (AD\sin B)R + 0 = 0.$$

Thus, numerically $\dfrac{Q}{AD} = \dfrac{R}{AB}$, etc.]

8. Forces P_1, P_2, P_3 act along the sides BC, CA, AB of a triangle ABC, and forces Q_1, Q_2, Q_3 act along SA, SB, SC, where S is the circumcentre. Prove that, if the six forces are in equilibrium, then

(*i*) $P_1 \cos A + P_2 \cos B + P_3 \cos C = 0$ **(M.U.)**

(*ii*) $\dfrac{P_1 Q_1}{BC} + \dfrac{P_2 Q_2}{CA} + \dfrac{P_3 Q_3}{AB} = 0.$ **(M. K. U.)**

[Hint:

(*i*) If R is the circumradius, the sum of the moments about S is

$$P_1 (R \cos A) + P_2 (R \cos B) + P_3 (R \cos C) = 0.$$

(*ii*) $\underline{|ACS} = 90° - B$, $\underline{|ABS} = 90° - C$, Sum of the moments about A is

$$P_1\, c \sin B + Q_3\, b \sin(90° - B) - Q_2\, c \sin(90° - C).$$

Multiplying it by Q_1 and adding the similar results,

$$\Sigma P_1 Q_1\, c \sin B + \Sigma [Q_1 Q_3\, b \cos B - Q_1 Q_2\, c \cos C] = 0.$$

$$\therefore \quad \Sigma P_1 Q_1\, c \sin B = 0 \text{ or } \Sigma P_1 Q_1\, bc = 0 \text{ or } \Sigma \frac{P_1 Q_1}{a} = 0.]$$

5.2 PROBLEMS INVOLVING FRICTIONAL FORCES

We know that, when a body is simply in equilibrium, that is, not in limiting equilibrium, the friction called into play is less than μR, where μ is the coefficient of friction and R is the normal reaction. But, if the equilibrium is limiting, then

$$F = \mu R, \qquad \tan \lambda = \mu,$$

where

(*i*) $F = \mu R$ is the frictional force

(*ii*) R is the normal reaction

(*iii*) μ is the coefficient of friction

(*iv*) λ is the angle of friction.

The angle of friction is the angle made by the reaction with the normal.

In problems involving limiting friction the method of solving them is two-fold; one is to keep the reaction as a single force as such and the other is to resolve it into its components, namely, the normal reaction and the limiting friction.

EXAMPLES

Example 1. A uniform ladder AB rests against a smooth wall at B and upon a rough ground at A. Boy whose weight is twice that of the ladder, climbs it. Prove that, the force of friction when he is at the top of the ladder, is five times as great as when he is at the bottom. **(M.K.U.)**

The ladder is not in limiting equilibrium. So, in the first case, the forces at A are

(*i*) Friction F_1 horizontally

(*ii*) Normal reaction R_1 vertically

(*iii*) Weight of the boy $2W$,

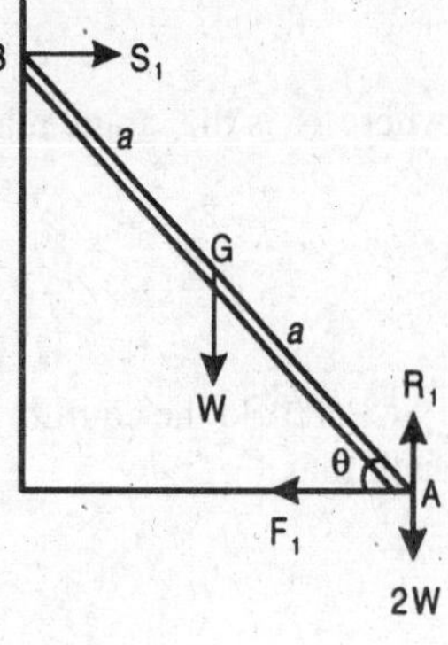

as in the figure. The vertical components of the forces give

$$R_1 = 3W. \quad \text{...(1)}$$

If θ is the angle of inclination of the ladder to the horizontal and $AB = 2a$, taking moments about B,

$$a\cos\theta\, W + 4a\cos\theta\, W + 2a\sin\theta\, F_1 - 2a\cos\theta\, R_1 = 0.$$

$$\therefore \quad 5W + 2\tan\theta\, F_1 = 2R_1 \quad \text{or} \quad 5W + 2\tan\theta\, F_1 = 6W \text{ by (1)}$$

$$\therefore \quad F_1 = \frac{W}{2\tan\theta}. \quad \text{...(2)}$$

In the second case, the forces at A are

(*i*) Friction F_2 horizontally,

(*ii*) Normal reaction R_2 vertically.

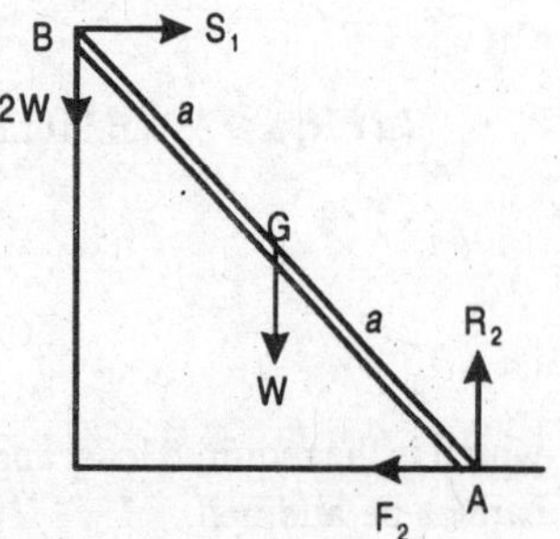

Now the vertical components of the forces gives.

$$R_2 = 3W. \quad \text{...(3)}$$

Taking moments about B, and dividing by $a\cos\theta$,

$$W + 2\tan\theta\, F_2 = 2R_2 \quad \text{or} \quad W + 2\tan\theta\, F_2 = 6W \text{ by (3)}$$

$$\therefore \quad F_2 = \frac{5W}{2\tan\theta}. \quad \text{...(4)}$$

From (2) and (4), we get the required result.

Example 2. A solid hemisphere rests on a rough horizontal plane and against a smooth vertical wall. Show that, if the coefficient of friction μ is greater than $3/8$, then the hemispheres can rest in any position and if it is less, the least angle that the base of the hemisphere can make with the vertical is

$$\cos^{-1}\frac{8\mu}{3}. \qquad \textbf{(M.U., C.U., M.K.U.)}$$

Let, in the equilibrium position, the points of contact with the plane and the wall be A, B. The forces on the body are

(*i*) Friction F at A

(*ii*) Reaction R at A

(*iii*) Reaction S at B

(*iv*) Weight W at G

as in the figure. Then, from the horizontal and vertical components,

$$S - F = 0, \quad R - W = 0 \quad \text{or} \quad S = F, \quad R = W.$$

Now $CG = 3a/8$, where a is the radius of the sphere and the distance of G from the vertical through A is

$$CG \cos\theta \quad \text{or} \quad {}^{3a}\!/_8 \cos\theta,$$

where θ is the angle made by the base with the vertical. Thus, taking moments about A,

$$ {}^{3a}\!/_8 \cos\theta\, W - aS = 0 \quad \text{or} \quad {}^{3a}\!/_8 \cos\theta\, R = aF.$$

$$\therefore \qquad \frac{F}{R} = \frac{3}{8}\cos\theta.$$

(*i*) So the equilibrium is possible for any inclination so long the coefficient of friction is large such that

$$\mu > \frac{3}{8}\cos\theta \quad \text{or} \quad \frac{8\mu}{3} > \cos\theta. \qquad \text{...(1)}$$

But the maximum value for $\cos\theta$ is 1. Thus (1) becomes

$$\frac{8\mu}{3} > 1 \quad \text{or} \quad \mu > \frac{3}{8}.$$

(*ii*) If $\mu < {}^3\!/_8$ and if the equilibrium is limiting, then $F = \mu R$ and (1) gives

$$\mu = \frac{3}{8}\cos\theta \quad \text{or} \quad \cos\theta = \frac{8\mu}{3}$$

i.e,
$$\theta = \cos^{-1}\frac{8\mu}{3}$$

which is the required least angle because, for a still smaller angle, the friction required is larger which cannot be attained.

Example 3. A sphere of weight W resting on a rough inclined plane of inclination α is kept in equilibrium by a horizontal string attached to the highest point of the sphere. Show that the angle of friction is greater than ${}^\alpha\!/_2$ and that the tension of the string is $W \tan {}^\alpha\!/_2$. **(M.U.)**

Let A be the point of contact, C the centre and P the topmost point. Forces on the sphere are

(*i*) Friction F at A up the plane

(*ii*) Reaction R at A normal to the plane

(*iii*) Tension T horizontally at P

(*iv*) Weight W vertically downward.

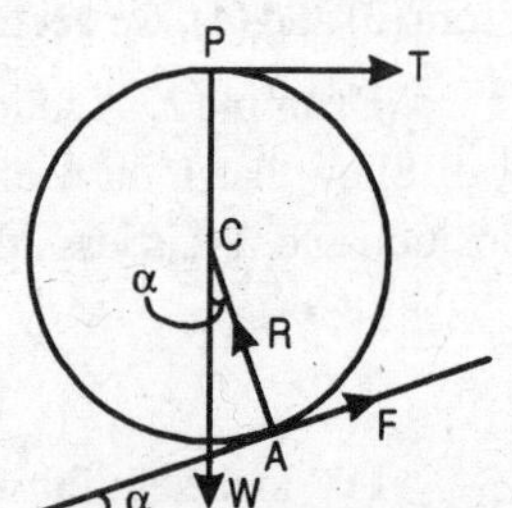

Taking moments about C,

$$aF - aT = 0$$

$$\therefore \qquad F = T. \qquad \text{...(1)}$$

Resolving the forces horizontally and vertically,

$$T + F\cos\alpha = R\sin\alpha, \qquad \text{...(2)}$$

$$R\cos\alpha + F\sin\alpha = W. \qquad \text{...(3)}$$

From (1) and (2),

$$\frac{F}{R} = \frac{\sin\alpha}{1+\cos\alpha} = \frac{2\sin{}^\alpha\!/_2 \cos{}^\alpha\!/_2}{2\cos^2{}^\alpha\!/_2} = \tan{}^\alpha\!/_2$$

μ should be large enough so that ${}^F\!/_R < \mu$. That is,

$$\tan{}^\alpha\!/_2 < \tan\lambda \quad \text{or} \quad {}^\alpha\!/_2 < \lambda.$$

Remembering that $F = T$ and solving for T, we get

$$T = \frac{\sin\alpha}{1+\cos\alpha} W = W \tan\frac{\alpha}{2}.$$

Example 4. A uniform ladder AB rests in limiting equilibrium with the end A on a rough floor, the coefficient of friction being μ and with the other end B against a smooth vertical wall. Show that, if θ is the inclination of the ladder to the vertical then $\tan\theta = 2\mu$. **(M.U.)**

If $\theta = 30°$, find μ. **(M.K.U.)**

Method 1. (*i*) Now A has a tendency to move away from the wall. So the frictional force at A is towards the wall. Thus, if $\bar{i}$, $\bar{j}$ are the unit vectors along CA and CB, the forces acting on the ladder are

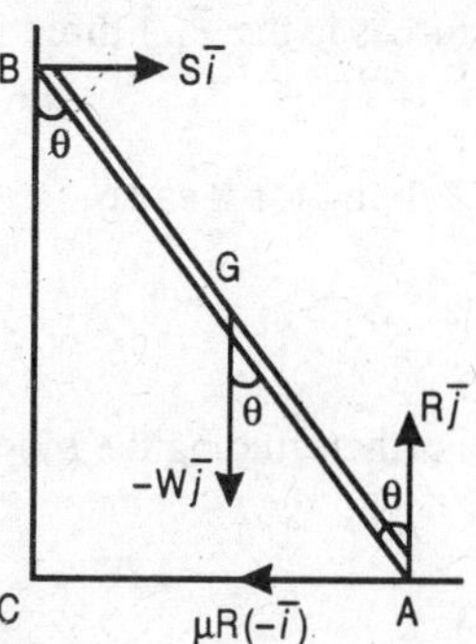

(*i*) $-\mu R\bar{i}$, $R\bar{j}$ at A

(*ii*) $S\bar{i}$ at B

(*iii*) $-W\bar{j}$ at G

The sum of the $\bar{i}$ components and the sum of $\bar{j}$ components are zero. Therefore

$$S - \mu R = 0, \quad R - W = 0.$$

Solving these two equations,

$$R = W, \quad S = \mu W.$$

If $AB = 2a$, taking moments about A of the forces,

$$a\sin\theta\, W - 2a\cos\theta\, S = 0 \quad \text{or} \quad \tan\theta = \frac{2S}{W} = \frac{2\mu W}{W} = 2\mu.$$

(*ii*) When $\theta = 30°$,

$$\tan 30° = 2\mu \quad \text{or} \quad \mu = \frac{1}{2\sqrt{3}}.$$

Remark. The magnitude of the reaction acting on the rod at A, is

$$\sqrt{R^2 + \mu^2 R^2} = R\sqrt{1+\mu^2} = W\sqrt{1+\mu^2}.$$

Method 2. Let the weight and the reaction at B intersect at O. Then the reaction at A passes through O. The reaction is inclined to the normal to the floor, that is, to the vertical at an angle λ, where λ is the angle of friction and

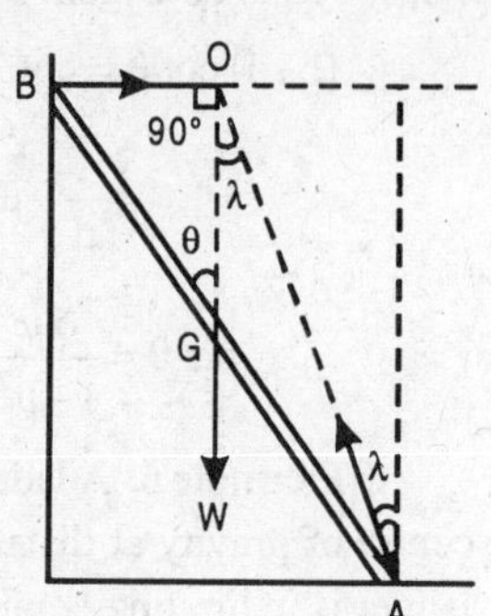

$$\mu = \tan\lambda.$$

In the triangle AOB, $BG : GA = 1:1$ and

$$\angle OGB = \theta; \ \angle GOB = 90°; \ \angle GOA = \lambda.$$

So, by cotangent formula,

$$(1+1)\cot\theta = \cot\lambda - \cot 90°.$$

i.e.,
$$2\cot\theta = \cot\lambda \quad \text{or} \quad \tan\theta = 2\tan\lambda = 2\mu.$$

Example 5. Find the inclination θ to the vertical of a uniform ladder AB of length $2a$ and weight W which is in limiting equilibrium having contact with a rough horizontal floor and a rough vertical wall, the coefficients of friction being μ. **(M.U)**

Show that the greatest inclination of the ladder to the vertical is 2λ. **(M.K.U)**

(i) Now A has a tendency to move away from the wall and B has a tendency to move downwards. Let the forces acting on the ladder be

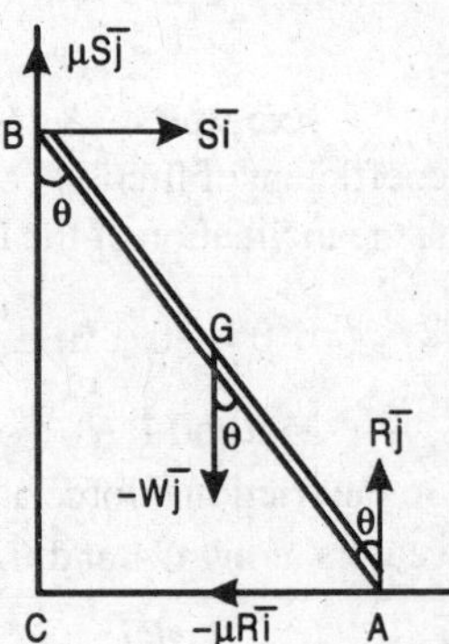

(i) $-\mu R\bar{i}$, $R\bar{j}$ at A

(ii) $S\bar{i}$, $\mu\, S\bar{j}$ at B

(iii) $-W\bar{j}$ at G

Since the ladder is in equilibrium, the sums of the components of these forces in the $\bar{i}$, $\bar{j}$ directions are zero. So

$$S - \mu R = 0, \quad R + \mu S - W = 0.$$

Solving for R and S,

$$R = \frac{W}{1+\mu^2}, \quad S = \frac{\mu W}{1+\mu^2}.$$

Further, finding the moments of the forces about A,

$$a \sin\theta\, W - 2a \sin\theta\, \mu\, S - 2a \cos\theta\, S = 0$$

i.e.,

$$(W - 2\,\mu S) \sin\theta - (2S) \cos\theta = 0$$

$$\therefore \quad \tan\theta = \frac{2S}{W - 2\mu S} = \frac{2\mu}{1-\mu^2}.$$

(ii) Since $\mu = \tan\lambda$, $\tan\theta = \dfrac{2\mu}{1-\mu^2} = \dfrac{2\tan\lambda}{1-\tan^2\lambda} = \tan 2\lambda$ or $\theta = 2\lambda$.

Method 2. Now the forces on the rod are the reactions of the floor and the wall at A and B and the weight. Let them meet at O.Then AO is inclined to the normal AD to the floor at the angle λ and BO is inclined to the normal BD to the wall at the angle λ . So, in the ΔOAB,

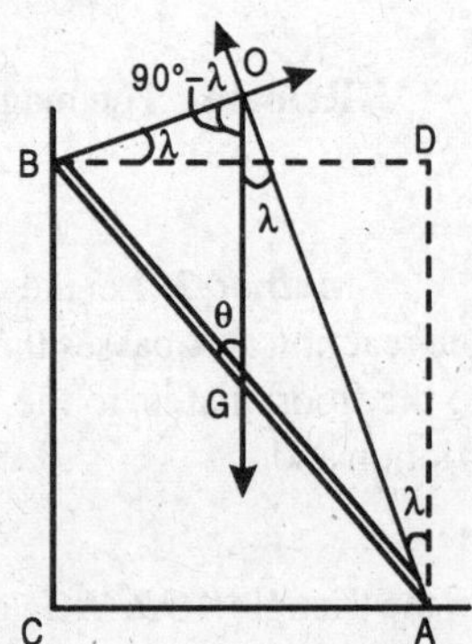

$$BG : GA = 1 : 1,$$

$$\angle OGB = \theta, \qquad \angle BOG = 90^\circ - \lambda, \qquad \angle AOG = \lambda.$$

Thus, by the cotangent formula,

$$(1+1)\cot\theta = \cot\lambda - \cot(90^\circ - \lambda) = \cot\lambda - \tan\lambda$$

$$= \frac{1}{\mu} - \mu = \frac{1-\mu^2}{\mu}.$$

$$\therefore \quad \tan\theta = \frac{2\mu}{1-\mu^2}.$$

Example 6. A ladder which stands on a horizontal ground leaning against a vertical wall, has its centre of gravity at distances a and b from its lower and upper ends respectively.Show that, if the ladder is in limiting equibrium,and if μ and μ' are the coefficients of friction at the lower and upper contacts, its inclination θ to the vertical is given by **(M.U.)**

$$\tan\theta = \frac{(a+b)\mu}{a - b\mu\mu'}.$$

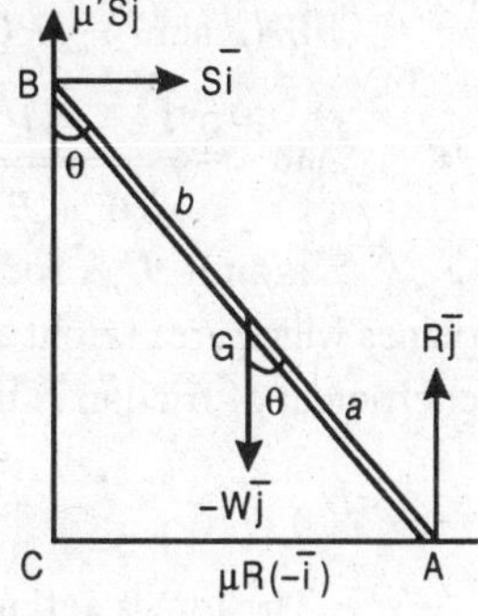

The figure is self explanatory. The sums of the $\bar{i}$ components and $\bar{j}$ components are zero. So we have

$$S-\mu R=0,$$
$$R+\mu' S-W=0.$$

Solving these, we get

$$R=\frac{1}{1+\mu\mu'}W,$$

$$S=\frac{\mu}{1+\mu\mu'}W.$$

Further moments taking about A,

$$a \sin\theta\, W-(a+b)\cos\theta\, S-(a+b)\sin\theta\, \mu' S=0$$

or $\quad aW\tan\theta-(a+b)S-(a+b)\mu' S\tan\theta=0.$

$$\therefore \quad \tan\theta=\frac{(a+b)S}{aW-(a+b)\mu' S}=\frac{(a+b)\mu}{a(1+\mu\mu')-(a+b)\mu'\mu}=\frac{(a+b)\mu}{a-b\mu'\mu}$$

Example 7. A ladder of length $2a$ is in contact with a wall and a horizontal floor, the angle of friction being λ at each contact. If the centre of gravity of the ladder is at a distance ka below the midpoint, show that in the limiting equilibrium, the inclination θ to the vertical is given by

$$\cot\theta=\cot 2\lambda-k\operatorname{cosec}2\lambda.$$ **(M.U.,Bn.U.)**

The forces acting on the ladder are the reactions of the floor and the wall inclined to the normals to them at an angle λ and the weight. If they meet at O, then both AO and BO are inclined to the vertical and horizontal at the same angle λ. So, in the triangle ABO,

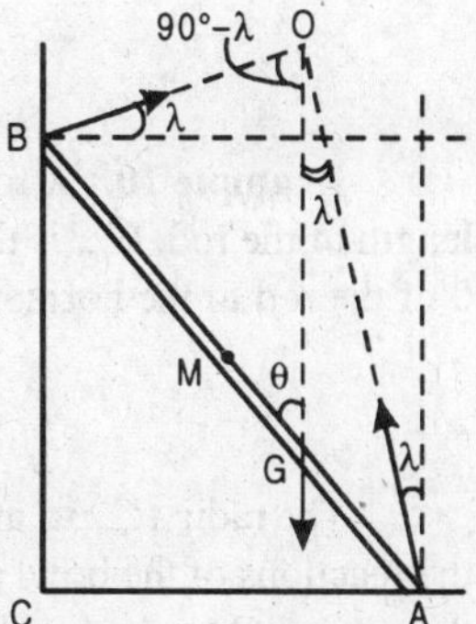

$$\angle BGO=\theta,\ \angle AOG=\lambda,\ \angle BOG=90^\circ-\lambda.$$

$$BG:GA=a+MG:a-MG=a+ka:a-ka=1+k:1-k.$$

So, by cotangent formula,

$$\{(1+k)+(1-k)\}\cot\theta=(1-k)\cot\lambda-(1+k)\cot(90^\circ-\lambda).$$

or $\quad 2\cot\theta=(1-k)\cot\lambda-(1+k)\tan\lambda$

$$=(\cot\lambda-\tan\lambda)-k(\cot\lambda+\tan\lambda).$$

So the result follows as stated since it can be shown that

$$\cot\lambda-\tan\lambda=2\cot 2\lambda,\quad \cot\lambda+\tan\lambda=2\operatorname{cosec}2\lambda.$$

Example 8. A solid hemisphere of weight W rests in limiting equilibrium with its curved surface on a rough inclined plane, its plane face being kept horizontal by a weight P attached to a point A in its rim. Prove that the coefficient of friction is **(M.U.,M.K.U.,Bn.U.)**

$$\mu=\frac{P}{\sqrt{W(2P+W)}}.$$

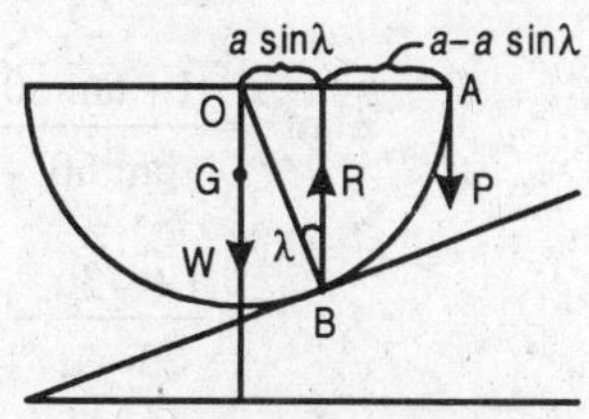

Let O be the centre and a, the radius of the sphere and B, the point of contact of the hemisphere with the inclined plane. The forces acting on the hemisphere are its weight W along OG, the attached weight P at A and the reaction R of the plane. Since W and P are vertical, R also should be vertical. R should be inclined to BO, the normal to the plane at B at an angle equal to the angle friction λ where $\mu=\tan\lambda$. Now taking moments about B,

$$W(a \sin \lambda) - P(a - a \sin \lambda) = 0 \quad \text{or} \quad \sin \lambda = \frac{P}{W + P}.$$

$$\therefore \quad \tan \lambda = \frac{P}{\sqrt{(W+P)^2 - P^2}} \quad \text{or} \quad \mu = \frac{P}{\sqrt{W^2 + 2WP}}.$$

Example 9. A rod is in limiting equilibrium resting horizontally with its ends on two inclined planes which are at right angles and one of which makes an angle α ($< 45^\circ$) with the horizontal. If the coefficient of friction is the same for both the ends, show that

$$\mu = \frac{1 - \tan \alpha}{1 + \tan \alpha}. \qquad \textbf{(M.U.)}$$

The forces acting on the rod are the reactions of the planes and its own weight. Let the reactions meet at O. Then the weight should act through O so that OG is vertical. But AB is horizontal and $AO = OB$. So ΔAOB is isosceles and

$$\underline{|OAG} = \underline{|OBG}.$$

But A has a tendency to slide downwards and B has a tendency to slide upwards because $\alpha < 45^\circ$. As such AO and BO are inclined to the normals AD and BD to the plane at the same angle of friction λ as shown in the figure. Now

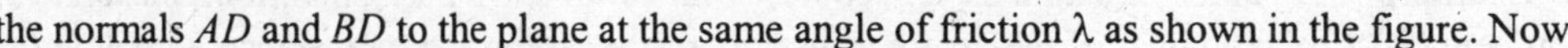

$$\underline{|OAG} = \alpha + \lambda, \qquad \underline{|OBG} = 90^\circ - (\alpha + \lambda).$$

$$\therefore \quad \alpha + \lambda = 90^\circ - (\alpha + \lambda) \quad \text{or} \quad \alpha + \lambda = 45^\circ.$$

$$\therefore \quad \tan(\alpha + \lambda) = 1 \quad \text{or} \quad \tan \alpha + \tan \lambda = 1 - \tan \alpha \tan \lambda.$$

$$\therefore \quad \tan \alpha + \mu = 1 - \mu \tan \alpha \quad \text{or} \quad \mu(1 + \tan \alpha) = 1 - \tan \alpha.$$

$$\therefore \quad \mu = \frac{1 - \tan \alpha}{1 + \tan \alpha}.$$

Example 10. A rod AB rests within a fixed hemispherical bowl whose radius is equal to the length of the rod. If μ is the coefficient of friction, show that, in limiting equilibrium, the inclination θ of the rod to the horizontal is given by

$$\tan \theta = \frac{4\mu}{3 - \mu^2}. \qquad \textbf{(M.K.U.)}$$

The radii AC, BC and the rod AB form an equilateral triangle. If the reactions of the bowl at A, B and the weight of the rod meet at O, then AO, BO are inclined to AC, BC at the same angle of friction λ. Now in the triangle AOB, $AG : GB = 1 : 1$ and

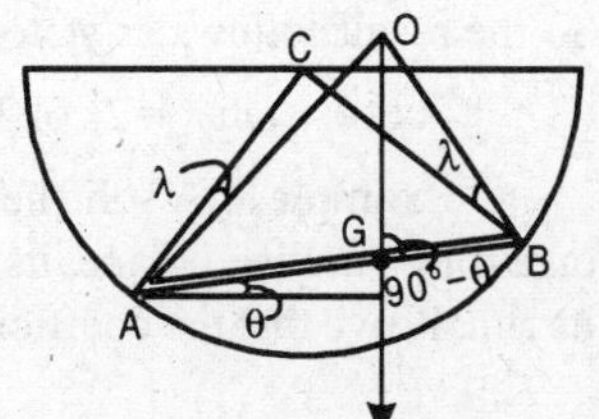

$$\underline{|OGB} = 90^\circ - \theta, \quad \underline{|GAO} = 60^\circ - \lambda, \quad \underline{|GBO} = 60^\circ + \lambda.$$

Therefore, by cotangent formula,

$$(1+1)\cot(90^\circ - \theta) = \cot(60^\circ - \lambda) - \cot(60^\circ + \lambda).$$

$$\therefore \quad 2 \tan \theta = \frac{1 + \tan 60^\circ \tan \lambda}{\tan 60^\circ - \tan \lambda} - \frac{1 - \tan 60^\circ \tan \lambda}{\tan 60^\circ + \tan \lambda}$$

$$= \frac{1 + \sqrt{3}\mu}{\sqrt{3} - \mu} - \frac{1 - \sqrt{3}\mu}{\sqrt{3} + \mu} = \frac{8\mu}{3 - \mu^2}.$$

$$\therefore \quad \tan\theta = \frac{4\mu}{3-\mu^2}.$$

Example 11. A uniform ladder of length l rests on a rough horizontal ground with its upper end projecting slightly over a smooth horizontal rod at a height h above the ground. If the ladder is about to slip, show that the coefficient of friction is equal to

$$\frac{h\sqrt{l^2-h^2}}{l^2+h^2}. \qquad \textbf{(M.U.,M.K.U.,Bn.U.)}$$

Let the three forces acting on the ladder meet at O. Then the direction BO of the reaction of the peg B is perpendicular to AB and the direction of AO of the reaction of the ground is inclined to the vertical at λ, the angle of friction. So, in the triangle ABO,

$$AG : GB = 1 : 1.$$

If angle OGB is θ, then

$$\underline{|OBA} = 90^\circ, \quad \underline{|OAB} = \theta - \lambda.$$

So, by cotangent formula,

$$(1+1)\cot\theta = \cot(\theta-\lambda) - \cot 90^\circ = \cot(\theta-\lambda).$$

$$\therefore \quad \tan\theta = 2\tan(\theta-\lambda) = 2\frac{\tan\theta - \tan\lambda}{1+\tan\theta\tan\lambda} = 2\frac{\tan\theta-\mu}{1+\mu\tan\theta}$$

This gives $\mu = \dfrac{\tan\theta}{2+\tan^2\theta}$. But $\tan\theta = \dfrac{\sqrt{l^2-h^2}}{h}$. So the result as stated.

Example 12. A rod AB is supported at an inclination α to the horizontal with its lower end B on a rough, horizontal plane by a string AC attached to A. Show that, if μ is the coefficient of friction, then the greatest inclination θ of the string to the vertical is given by

$$\cot\theta = \frac{1}{\mu} + 2\tan\alpha \quad \text{or} \quad \cot\theta = \frac{1}{\mu} - 2\tan\alpha,$$

according as the end B has a tendency to move closer to the string or not.

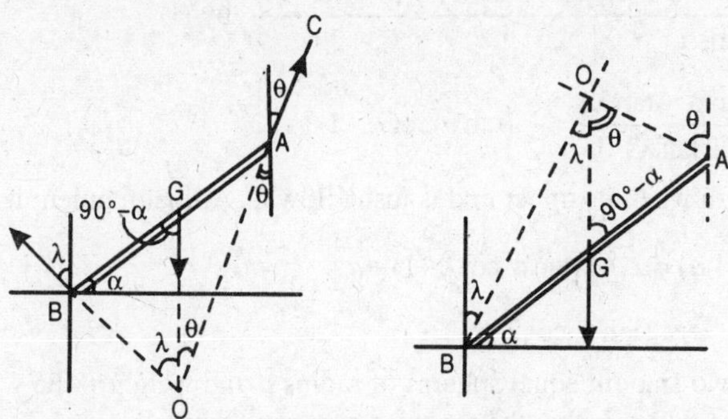

The figures correspond to the first and second cases respectively. Let λ be the angle of friction. Then $\mu = \tan\lambda$. Now the tension acts along AC and the weight along the vertical through G. Let them meet at O. Then the reaction of the plane acts along OB. It should be inclined to the plane at an angle λ. In triangle AOB, $AG : GB = 1 : 1$ and

$$\angle AOG = \theta, \ \angle BOG = \lambda.$$

Also in the first and second figures

$$\angle OGB = 90^\circ - \alpha, \ \angle OGA = 90^\circ - \alpha$$

respectively. So, in these cases, by cotangent formula,

$$(1+1) \cot (90^\circ - \alpha) = \cot\theta - \cot\lambda = \cot\theta - \frac{1}{\mu},$$

$$(1+1) \cot (90^\circ - \alpha) = \cot\lambda - \cot\theta = \frac{1}{\mu} - \cot\theta]$$

which lead to the required results.

Example 13. Two equally rough pegs *A, B* are at a distance *a* apart in a straight line inclined at an angle α to the horizontal. A rod passes over *A* but under *B* and rests in limiting equilibrium. Show that, if λ is the angle of friction, then the distance *x* between the mass centre *G* of the rod and *A* is

$$x = a/2\,(\cot\lambda \tan\alpha - 1). \qquad \textbf{(M.U.)}$$

Show that the length of the shortest rod which will rest in such a position is

$$a\,(\cot\lambda \tan\alpha + 1). \qquad \textbf{(M.U.)}$$

The reactions *R,S* and the friction μR, μS are perpendicular to and along the rod as in the figure. The components of *W* in these directions are

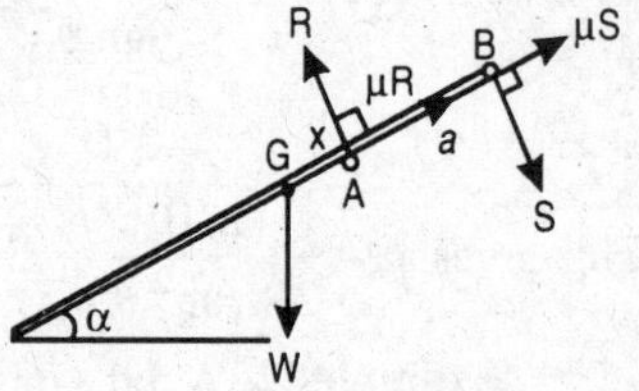

$$W\cos\alpha, \ W\sin\alpha.$$

$\therefore \qquad W\cos\alpha + S = R, \ W\sin\alpha = \mu R + \mu S$

$$\therefore \qquad S = \frac{W(\sin\alpha - \mu\cos\alpha)}{2\mu}. \qquad ...(1)$$

Taking moments about *A*,

$$(x\cos\alpha)W = aS \quad \text{or} \quad x = \frac{aS}{W\cos\alpha}.$$

$$\therefore \qquad x = \frac{a}{W\cos\alpha}\frac{W(\sin\alpha - \mu\cos\alpha)}{2\mu} = \frac{a(\tan\alpha - \mu)}{2\mu} \text{ by (1)}$$

$$= \frac{a(\tan\alpha - \tan\lambda)}{2\tan\lambda} = \frac{a}{2}(\tan\alpha\cot\lambda - 1).$$

The rod is of least length when its upper end is just below *B*. At that moment its length is

$$2GB = 2(x+a) = 2\left[a/2\,(\tan\alpha\cot\lambda - 1) + a\right]$$

$$= a\,(\tan\alpha\cot\lambda + 1).$$

Example 14. Two smooth equal spheres of radius *a* and weight *W* lie within a fixed smooth spherical bowl of radius *b*. Prove that the pressure between them is

$$\frac{aW}{\sqrt{b^2 - 2ab}}. \qquad \textbf{(M.U.)}$$

If $b = 3a$, show that the ratio of reaction between the spheres to the reaction between a sphere and the bowl is $1/2$. **(M.K.U.)**

The figure is self explanatory. In it the forces on the left sphere only are marked. Now

$$AC = b - a,\ AM = a.$$

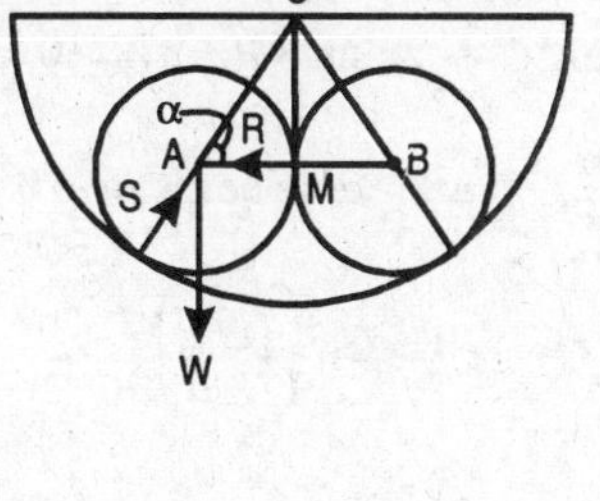

If angle CAM is α, then

$$\cos\alpha = \frac{a}{b-a}.$$

The horizontal and vertical components of the forces give

$$R - S\cos\alpha = 0,\ W - S\sin\alpha = 0. \quad \therefore\ S = \frac{W}{\sin\alpha}.$$

$$\therefore \quad R = W\cot\alpha = W\frac{a}{\sqrt{(b-a)^2 - a^2}} = \frac{aW}{\sqrt{b^2 - 2ab}}.$$

(*ii*) From $R - S\cos\alpha = 0,\ \dfrac{R}{S} = \cos\alpha = \dfrac{a}{b-a} = \dfrac{a}{3a-a} = \dfrac{1}{2}.$

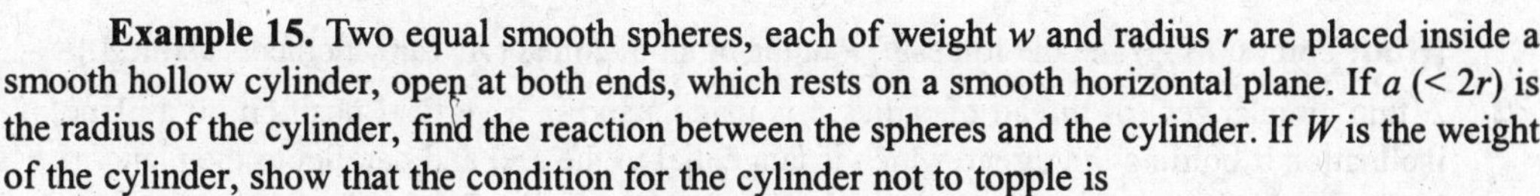

Example 15. Two equal smooth spheres, each of weight w and radius r are placed inside a smooth hollow cylinder, open at both ends, which rests on a smooth horizontal plane. If a ($< 2r$) is the radius of the cylinder, find the reaction between the spheres and the cylinder. If W is the weight of the cylinder, show that the condition for the cylinder not to topple is

$$W > 2w\left(1 - \frac{r}{a}\right). \qquad \textbf{(A.U.)}$$

The figure is self explanatory. The forces on the lower sphere are

$$w,\ P,\ S,\ Q$$

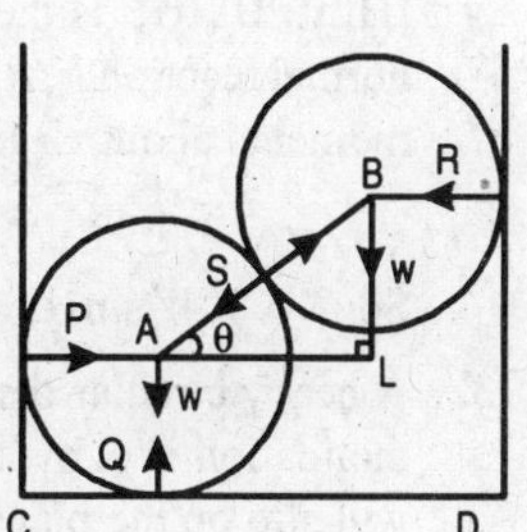

as in the figure. The horizontal components give

$$P = S\cos\theta.$$

But the forces on the upper sphere are

$$w, R, S.$$

$$\therefore \quad S\cos\theta = R,$$

$$w = S\sin\theta.$$

$$\therefore \quad P = R = S\cos\theta = \frac{w}{\sin\theta}\cos\theta = w\cot\theta.$$

$$\therefore \quad S = \frac{w}{\sin\theta}, \quad P = R = w\cot\theta.$$

But $AL = CD - 2r = 2a - 2r$, $AB = 2r$ and so

$$\cos\theta = \frac{AL}{AB} = \frac{a-r}{r}.$$

Thus S, P, R are known in terms of w, r, a.

If the cylinder topples, it will topple about D. Now the forces on the cylinder are

$$P, R, W, R_1.$$

Their distances from D are

$$r,\ r + AB\sin\theta,\ a,\ 0.$$

Taking moments about D and using $P = R$,

$$r.P - (r + 2r \sin\theta).R + aW > 0$$

i.e., $-2r\sin\theta\, R + aW > 0$ or $aW > 2r\sin\theta\, W\cot\theta$.

i.e., $aW > 2rW\cos\theta$ or $aW > 2rW\dfrac{a-r}{r}$.

$\therefore$ $W > 2w\left(1 - \dfrac{r}{a}\right)$.

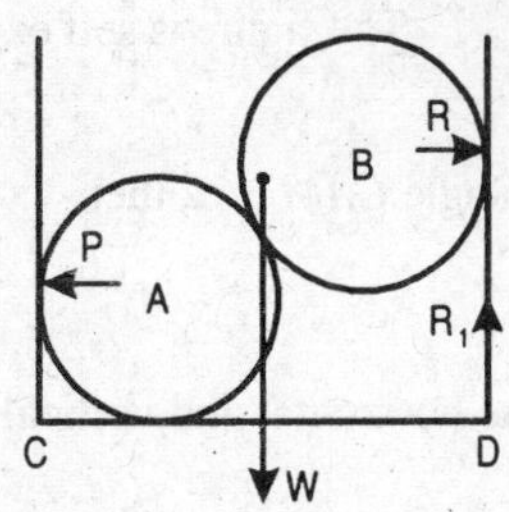

EXERCISES

1. A sphere of weight W is held in equilibrium on a rough inclined plane of inclination α to the horizontal by a force P applied tangentially to its circumference and parallel to the plane. Show that $P = {}^{W}\!/_{2} \sin\alpha$.

   [Hint: Forces : W, P and the forces F, R at the point of contact A. Take moments about A.]

2. A thin circular reel of thread of radius a is made stand in a vertical position on a plane of inclination α holding the thread which is tangential to the reel and parallel to the plane. If W is the weight of the reel including the thread, find the tension of the thread and the friction between the reel and the plane. Find also the coefficient of friction for which this reel will rest in equilibrium. **(M.U.)**

   [Hint: If AGB is the diameter normal to the plane, the forces are tension T at B, friction and normal reaction F, R at A, weight W at G. Components along and perpendicular to the plane and moments about G give

   $$W\sin\alpha = T + F,\ W\cos\alpha = R,\ F = T.$$

   So $T = \frac{1}{2} W\sin\alpha$, $\mu = F/R = \frac{1}{2}\tan\alpha$]

3. A heavy circular disc whose plane is vertical is kept at rest on a rough inclined plane whose inclination is α by a string parallel to the plane and touching the circle. Show that, the disc will slip on the plane if the coefficient of friction is less than

   $$\tfrac{1}{2}\tan\alpha.$$ **(M.U.,Bn.U.)**

4. A sphere of weight W is held in equilibrium on a rough inclined plane of angle α by a force $\frac{1}{2} W\sin\alpha$ applied tangentially to its circumference. Prove that the force must act parallel to the plane and that the coefficient of friction should be greater than $\frac{1}{2}\tan\alpha$. **(C.U.)**

   [Hint: If a is the radius and d is the distance of the applied force from A, the point of contact, taking moments about A.

   $$a\sin\alpha\, W - d\left(\tfrac{1}{2}\right) W\sin\alpha = 0 \text{ or } d = 2a]$$

5. A rough circular hoop of weight 3 kg. hangs over a horizontal peg and a weight of $8/3$ kg.hangs tangentially from it. Show that, if the hoop is about to slip on the peg, then the coefficient, of friction is $8/15$. **(M.U.)**

   [Hint: Let C be the centre and A be the peg above the horizontal radius CB. The forces are 3 kg. wt. at C, $8/3$ kg.wt. at B and the reaction R at A. All are vertical forces. The angle between the vertical R and CA is λ. If the angle of friction so that $\tan\lambda = \mu$. If a is the radius,taking moments about A,

   $$(a\sin\lambda)3 = (a - a\sin\lambda)\, 8/3 \text{ or } \sin\lambda = 8/17 \text{ or } \tan\lambda = 8/15]$$

6. A ladder rests with one end on a rough horizontal ground, the coefficient of friction being $\frac{5}{8}$ and the other end against a smooth vertical wall. If the inclination of the ladder is $45°$, show that a man whose weight is equal to that of the ladder can ascend only three quarters of the length of the ladder. **(M.U.)**

[**Hint:** Lower and upper ends : A, B; Distance of the man from B : x; Forces at A : $R, \frac{5R}{8}$. Vertical components give $R = 2W$. Taking moments about A and dividing by cos $45°$,

$$xW + aW + 2a\,{}^{5R}\!/_{8} = 2aR \text{ or } x = {}^{a}\!/_{2}.]$$

7. A rod rests with one end A on a rough horizontal plane and the other end B against a smooth vertical wall. If l is the length of the rod and a, the distance of its centre of gravity from A, show that the inclination of the rod to the wall when on the point of slipping is $\tan^{-1}\frac{l\mu}{a}$ where μ is the coefficient of friction. **(M.U., Bn.U.)**

[**Hint:** $AG = a$, $BG = l - a$. Consider vertical components of forces. Take moments of the forces about B.]

8. A ladder is kept such that one end rests on a rough horizontal plane and the other end on a smooth vertical plane. Inclination of the ladder to the horizontal is θ. If a man of weight n times that of the ladder ascends it and if the ladder is just on the point of slipping when he reaches the top, calculate the coefficient of friction. **(M.K.U.)**

[**Ans.** $\mu = \frac{1+2n}{2(1+n)\tan\theta}$]

9. A ladder is in limiting equilibrium having contacts with a rough horizontal floor and a rough vertical wall whose coefficients of friction are μ, μ'. If θ is the inclination of the ladder to the vertical, then show that,

$$\tan\theta = \frac{2\mu}{1-\mu\mu'}.$$ **(Bn.U.)**

When $\mu = \mu'$, show that $\theta = 2\lambda$, where λ is the angle of friction.

[**Hint:** $S - \mu R = 0, R + \mu' S - W = 0$. $AB = 2a$; Taking moments about the lower end $a \sin\theta\, W - 2a \sin\theta \mu' S - 2a \cos\theta\, S = 0$. When $\mu = \mu' = \tan\lambda$,

$$\tan\theta = \frac{2\tan\lambda}{1-\tan^2\lambda} = \tan 2\lambda \text{ or } \theta = 2\lambda.]$$

10. (*i*) A ladder is in equilibrium with one end resting on the ground and the other end against a vertical wall; if the ground and the wall are both rough, the coefficient of friction being μ and μ' and if the ladder is on the point of slipping, show that the inclination of the ladder to the horizon is given by

$$\tan\theta = \frac{1-\mu\mu'}{2\mu}$$ **(M.K.U., M.U.Bn.U.)**

(*ii*) When $\mu = \mu'$, show that $\theta = 90° - 2\lambda$, where λ is the angle of friction. **(M.U.)**

[**Hint:** (*ii*) $\tan\theta = \frac{1-\mu^2}{2\mu} = \frac{1-\tan^2\lambda}{2\tan\lambda} = \cot 2\lambda = \tan(90° - 2\lambda).$]

11. A ladder on a horizontal floor leans against a vertical wall. Show that the greatest inclination to the wall which is consistent with equilibrium is

$$\tan^{-1}\frac{2\mu}{1-\mu^2},$$

where μ is the coefficient of friction for contact with the floor and with the wall. Prove that the lines of action of the resultant forces acting at the foot and top of the ladder are at right angles to one another. **(M.K.U.,M.U.)**

[Hint: Forces at the lower and upper ends : $-\mu R\bar{i}+R\bar{j},\ S\bar{i}+\mu S\bar{j}$. Show that $(-\mu R\bar{i}+R\bar{j})\cdot(S\bar{i}+\mu S\bar{j})=0$.**]**

12. A ladder AB rests with A on a rough horizontal ground and B against an equally rough vertical wall. The centre of gravity of the ladder divides AB in the ratio $a:b$. If the ladder is on the point of slipping, show that the inclination θ of the ladder to the ground is given by

$\tan\theta=\dfrac{a-b\mu^2}{\mu(a+b)}$, where μ is the coefficient of friction. **(M.K.U.)**

[Hint: See Example 6. Now $\mu'=\mu$ and θ is the angle made by the ladder to the horizontal.**]**

13. A ladder AB rests with A resting on the ground and B against a vertical wall, the coefficient of friction of the ground and the wall being μ and μ' respectively. The centre of gravity G of the ladder divides AB in the ratio $1:n$. If the ladder is on the point of slipping at both ends, show that its inclination to the ground is given by

$$\tan\theta=\frac{1-n\mu\mu'}{(n+1)\mu}.$$ **(M.U.)**

[Hint: This sum is similar to Example 6.**]**

14. A uniform ladder rests at an angle $45°$ with the horizon, with its upper end against a vertical wall and its lower end on the ground. If μ and μ' are the coefficients of friction of the ground and the wall, show that the least horizontal force which will move the lower extremity towards the wall is

$$\frac{1}{2}W\left(\frac{1+2\mu-\mu\mu'}{1-\mu'}\right).$$ **(M.U.)**

[Hint: If the least force is P and the normal reactions at the lower and upper ends A, B are R, S, then considering the $\bar{i}$ and $\bar{j}$ components and taking moments about A,

$$\left.\begin{aligned}\mu R+S-P&=0\\ \mu'S+W-R&=0\\ W+2\mu'S-2S&=0\end{aligned}\right\}\ \therefore\ \begin{vmatrix}1 & \mu & -P\\ \mu' & -1 & W\\ 2\mu'-2 & 0 & W\end{vmatrix}=0$$**]**

15. An equilateral triangular plate rests in a vertical plane with one end A of its base on a rough horizontal floor and the other end B against a smooth vertical wall; show that, if μ is the coefficient of friction and the equilibrium is limiting, the inclination θ of the base AB to the horizontal, is given by

$$\cot\theta=2\mu+\frac{1}{\sqrt{3}}.$$ **(M.K.U., Bn.U.)**

[Hint: If R, μR are the normal reaction and the friction at A, and S is the normal reaction at B, then $S-\mu R=0$, $R-W=0$. Taking moments about A, $W\cdot AG\cdot\cos(\theta+30°)-S\cdot AB\cdot\sin\theta=0$ where $AG=AB/\sqrt{3}$.**]**

16. A square lamina rests with the ends of a side against a rough vertical wall and a rough horizontal ground. If the coefficient of friction for the ground and the wall are μ and μ', show that when the lamina is on the point of slipping, the inclination of the side in question to the horizontal is

$$\tan^{-1}\frac{1-\mu\mu'}{1+2\mu+\mu\mu'}.$$

(M.U.)

17. A square lamina rests with the ends of a side against a rough vertical wall and a rough horizontal ground with the coefficient of friction μ. Show that, when equilibrium is limiting the inclination of the side in question to the horizontal is

$$\tan^{-1}\frac{1-\mu}{1+\mu}.$$

(M.U.)

18. One end of a uniform ladder of weight W rests against a smooth wall and the other end on a rough plane which slopes down from the wall at an angle α to the horizon.Find the inclination θ of the ladder to the horizontal when it is on the point of sliding. Show that, if λ is the angle of friction and S and R, the reactions of the wall and the plane, then

$$S = W\tan(\lambda-\alpha), \quad R = W\sec(\lambda-\alpha).$$

(M.U.)

[**Hint:** If A, B are the lower and upper ends of the rods and O, the meet of the reaction S at B and the vertical through G, then the reaction at A is along AO and AO is inclined to the normal to the plane at an angle λ. In triangle AOB, $AG : BG = 1 : 1$; $\underline{|OGB} = 90° - \theta$, $\underline{|GOB} = 90°$, $\underline{|GOA} = \lambda - \alpha$. By cotangent formula, $2\tan\theta = \cot(\lambda-\alpha)$. By Lami's theorem,

$$\frac{W}{\sin[90^\circ+(\lambda-\alpha)]} = \frac{R}{\sin 90^\circ} = \frac{S}{\sin[180^\circ-(\lambda-\alpha)]}.$$

19. A solid hemisphere rests in equilibrium on a rough horizontal plane and against a rough vertical wall, the coefficients of friction being μ, μ'. Show that, if the equilibrium is limiting, the inclination of the base to the vertical is **(M.U.)**

$$\cos^{-1}\frac{8\mu(1+\mu')}{3(1+\mu\mu')}.$$

[**Hint:** Using horizontal and vertical components, $S=\mu R$, $R+\mu' S = W$. Taking moments about the lower point of contact,

$$Sa + \mu' Sa = W.{}^{3a}\!/_{8}\cos\theta\ .]$$

20. A solid hemisphere rests in equilibrium on a rough ground and against an equally rough vertical wall, the coefficient of friction being μ. Show that, if the equilibrium is limiting, the inclination of the base to the horizon is

$$\sin^{-1}\frac{8\mu(1+\mu)}{3(1+\mu^2)}.$$

(M.U., Bn.U.)

21. A uniform thin hemispherical bowl rests with its curved surface on a rough horizontal plane (coefficient of friction μ) and leans against a smooth vertical wall. Prove that, when the bowl is on the point of slipping, the inclination of the axis of the bowl to the vertical is $\sin^{-1}(2\mu)$. **(M.U.)**

[**Hint:** G bisects the middle radius (length a). Horizontal and vertical components give $S=\mu R$, $R=W$ and moments about the lower point of contact give ${}^{a}\!/_{2}\sin\theta\cdot W = aS$.]

22. A rod, 12 d.m.long, one end of which is rough and the other end is smooth rests, within a fixed circular hoop of radius 10 d.m.in limiting equilibrium with its rough end at the lowest point of the hoop. Show that the coefficient of friction is $24/23$. **(M.U., A.U.)**

[Hint: Forces at the rough end A : R, μR; Forces at the other end B: S; If C is the centre of the hoop, G is the centre of mass of the rod and angle ACG is α, then $\sin\alpha = 3/5$. Horizontal and vertical components give

$$\left.\begin{aligned} S\sin 2\alpha &= \mu R \\ S\cos 2\alpha + R &= W \end{aligned}\right\} \therefore\ R = \frac{W\sin 2\alpha}{\sin 2\alpha + \mu\cos 2\alpha}.$$

Taking moments about C, $5\mu R = 3\cos\alpha\, W$. Find μ **]**

23. A thin rod of length $2l$ rests in limiting equilibrium inside a rough vertical hoop of radius a. Prove that, if μ is the coefficient of friction and θ is the inclination of the rod to the horizontal, then

$$\theta = \cot^{-1}\frac{a^2 - l^2 - \mu^2 l^2}{a^2\,\mu}. \qquad \textbf{(M.U.)}$$

[Hint: If AB is the rod and C is centre of the hoop and angle $ABC = \alpha$ then,

$$(1+1)\cot(90^\circ - \theta) = \cot(\alpha - \lambda) - \cot(\alpha + \lambda),$$

where $\tan\lambda = \mu$ and $\cos\alpha = l/a$ **]**

5.2.1 Tilting of a body

When a gradually increasing force acts on a body which is in equilibrium, resting on a rough surface, the body either slips or tilts at some moment. This situation depends on the roughness of the surface, that is, the coefficient of friction (cof) . If the cof is fairly small, slipping takes place and if the cof is fairly large, tilting takes place. For an intermediate particular value of cof, both slipping and tilting take place simultaneously. For any value of cof less than this particular value, the body slips and for any value of cof greater than this particular value the body tilts.

Now we shall consider physical situations in which the value of cof has the value such that the slipping and tilting take place simultaneously. In these cases the tilting is about a point of the rigid body and the forces at this point are

(*i*) The normal reaction R

(*ii*) The frictional force μR in the direction opposite to that in which the body has a tendency to move.

The respective value of cof can be obtained by considering the components in two perpendicular directions and moments about a point in the preceeding equilibrium position.

EXAMPLES

Example 1. A rectangular thin plate $ABCD$ ($AB = a$, $BC = h$) stands vertically with its side AB resting on a rough horizontal plane. A string attached to C is pulled horizontally with a gradually increasing force. Show that, if μ is the coefficient of friction, the plate will tilt if

$$\mu > \frac{a}{2h}. \qquad \textbf{(M.U.)}$$

Suppose that the plate will be in limiting equilibrium in a slightly tilted position with B alone being in contact with the horizontal plane whose coefficient of friction is μ. Then the forces acting on the plate will be

(*i*) Weight W at G

(*ii*) Force P at C

(*iii*) Normal reaction R and friction μR at B.

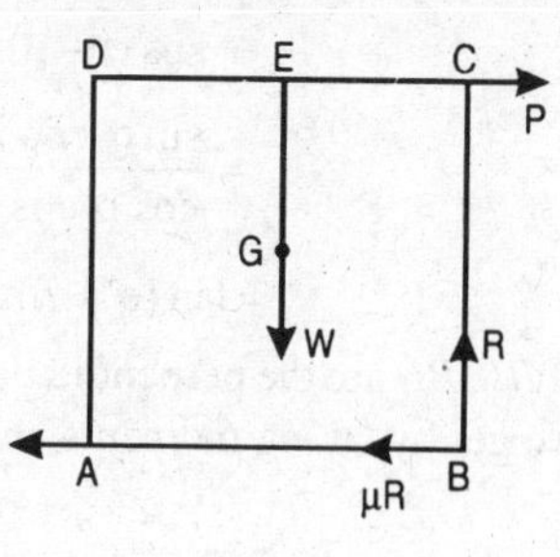

Horizontal and vertical components and moments about B give

$$P = \mu R, \; R = W, \; \tfrac{a}{2} W = hP.$$

Eliminating P and R, we get

$$\mu = \frac{a}{2h}.$$

So, if the cof is greater than $\frac{a}{2h}$, then the body tilts.

Example 2. A square lamina $ABCD$ of side $2a$ is standing upright on a horizontal plane with the side AB having contact with the plane. A string is attached to C and pulled with a slowly increasing force P in a direction at right angles to the diagonal through the corner. Show that the lamina tilts if the coefficient of friction is greater than $\tfrac{1}{3}$. **(M.U.)**

Let μ be the cof. Now tilting takes place at B. The force P at C has components

(*i*) $\frac{P}{\sqrt{2}}$ horizontally and

(*ii*) $\frac{P}{\sqrt{2}}$ vertically downward.

The other forces on the Lamina are

(*i*) Weight W at G

(*ii*) Normal reaction R and friction μR at B

Thus the horizontal and the vertical components and moments about B give

$$\frac{P}{\sqrt{2}} = \mu R, \; R = W + \frac{P}{\sqrt{2}}, \; aW = \frac{2aP}{\sqrt{2}}.$$

Eliminating P and R, we get $\mu = \tfrac{1}{3}$. So, if the cof is greater than $\tfrac{1}{3}$ then the body tilts.

Example 3. $ABCD$ is a uniform square plate of side $2a$ resting with its plane vertical with the side AB on a rough inclined plane of angle α. C is the highest point of the plate. A gradually increasing force is applied at C horizontally. Prove that, if λ is the angle of friction, then the plate tilts if

$$1 + \tan\alpha < 2\tan(\alpha + \lambda).$$ **(M.U.)**

Suppose the plate will be in limiting equilibrium in a slightly tilted position standing on B on the inclined plane whose coefficient and angle of friction are μ and λ. Then the forces acting on the plate are

(*i*) μR along BA and R along BC at B

(*ii*) W vertically at G

(*iii*) P horizontally at C

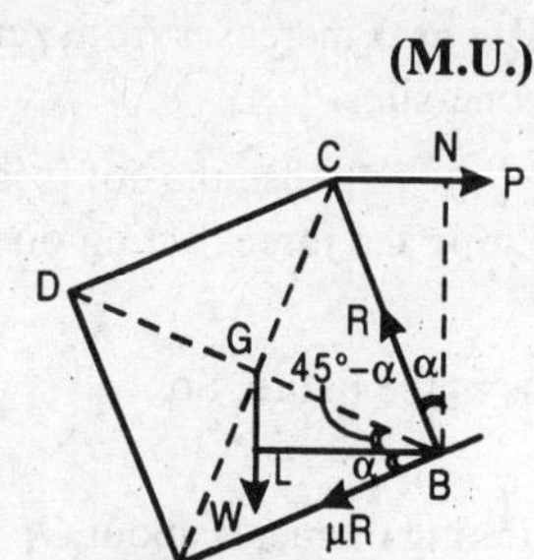

Horizontal and vertical components give

$$P = R\sin\alpha + \mu R\cos\alpha,$$

$$W = R\cos\alpha - \mu R\sin\alpha.$$

$$\therefore \quad \frac{P}{W} = \frac{\sin\alpha + \mu\cos\alpha}{\cos\alpha - \mu\sin\alpha} = \frac{\sin\alpha + \tan\lambda\cos\alpha}{\cos\alpha - \tan\lambda\sin\alpha}$$

$$= \frac{\sin\alpha\cos\lambda + \cos\alpha\sin\lambda}{\cos\alpha\cos\lambda - \sin\alpha\sin\lambda} = \frac{\sin(\alpha+\lambda)}{\cos(\alpha+\lambda)}$$

$$= \tan(\alpha+\lambda). \quad \text{...(1)}$$

If BL, BN are the perpendiculars drawn from B to the vertical through G and the horizontal through C, we get by taking moments about B,

$$W{\cdot}BL - P{\cdot}BN = 0$$

or

$$\frac{P}{W} = \frac{BL}{BN} = \frac{\sqrt{2}\, a\cos(45^\circ - \alpha)}{2a\cos\alpha} = \frac{\cos\alpha + \sin\alpha}{2\cos\alpha}$$

$$= \tfrac{1}{2}(1+\tan\alpha). \quad \text{...(2)}$$

Equating (1) and (2), we get

$$\tan(\alpha+\lambda) = \tfrac{1}{2}(1+\tan\alpha)$$

This gives a value for λ. If the angle of friction is greater than this value, that is, if

$$\tan(\alpha+\lambda) > \tfrac{1}{2}(1+\tan\alpha)$$

then the body tilts.

Example 4. A solid cone of height h and base radius a is placed with its base on a rough inclined plane whose coefficient of friction is μ. The inclination of the plane is increased gradually. Show that the cone slips or topples according as

$$\mu < \frac{4a}{h} \quad \text{or} \quad \mu > \frac{4a}{h}.$$

(M.U.,Bn.U.)

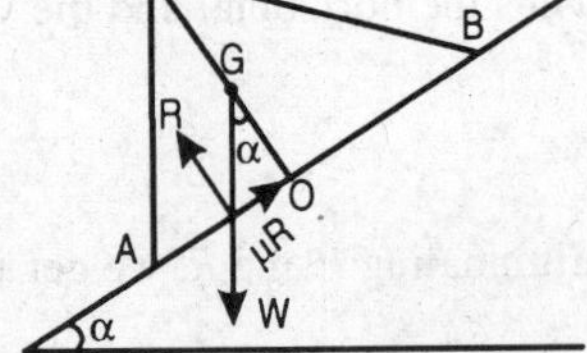

We shall assume that the cof μ is small so that, as α increases, the cone slips and does not topple. At the moment of slipping the forces on the cone are

$$R,\ \mu R,\ W$$

as in the figure. The components along and perpendicular to the plane give

$$W\sin\alpha = \mu R, \quad W\cos\alpha = R.$$

$$\therefore \quad \tan\alpha = \mu. \quad \text{...(1)}$$

But as α increases from zero, $\tan\alpha$ also increases from zero. So, when $\tan\alpha$ attains the value μ, the cone slips.

Suppose the cof μ is large so that the cone tilts about A and does not slip. At the moment of tilting the forces acting on the cone are

$$R,\ F,\ W$$

as in the figure. So

$$R = W\cos\alpha.$$

Taking moments about O

$$OG\sin\alpha\, W - aR > 0$$

or $\quad \frac{h}{4} \sin\alpha\, W - a\, W \cos\alpha > 0$

or $\quad \tan\alpha > \dfrac{4a}{h}$. ...(2)

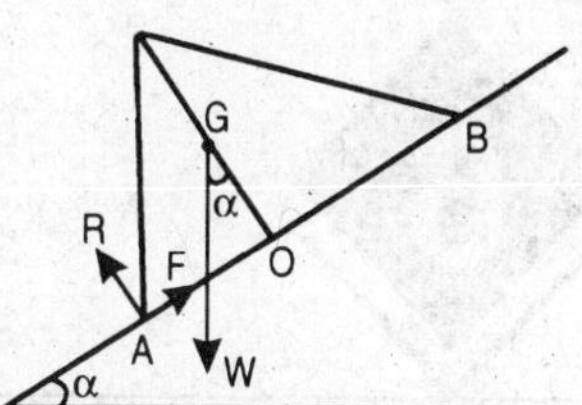

From (1) and (2) we get the critical values for tan α as

$$\mu, \ \frac{4a}{h}.$$

Thus, in conclusion, we have

(*i*) If $\mu < \frac{4a}{h}$, tan α attains the smaller value μ first and so the cone slips.

(*ii*) If $\mu > \frac{4a}{h}$, tan α attains the smaller value $\frac{4a}{h}$ first and so the cone tilts.

Note. If $\mu = \frac{4a}{h}$, slipping and tilting take place simultaneously when tan α attains this equal value.

EXERCISES

1. A square plate *ABCD* stands vertically with its side *AB* resting on a rough horizontal plane. A string attached to *C* is pulled horizontally in the direction *DC* with a gradually increasing force. Show that the plate will tilt if the coefficient of friction is greater than $\frac{1}{2}$.
2. A solid cylinder of radius *r* and height *h* rests on a rough horizontal plane with one base on the plane. It is acted by a gradually increasing horizontal force through the centre of its upper end. Prove that, if μ is the coefficient of friction, the equilibrium will be broken by sliding or tilting according as
$$r > \mu h \quad \text{or} \quad r < \mu h. \qquad \textbf{(M.U.)}$$
3. A cone of vertical angle 2α, rests with its base on a rough plane inclined to the horizon. As the inclination of the plane is gradually increased, show that the cone will slide and not topple if the coefficient of friction is less than 4 tan α. **(M.U.)**
[Hint: Slips if "$\mu < \frac{4a}{h}$" or $\mu < 4\tan\alpha$ since $\frac{a}{h} = \tan\alpha$ **]**
4. A cone is placed with its base on a rough inclined plane. If $\dfrac{1}{\sqrt{3}}$ is the coefficient of friction, find the angle of the cone when it is on the point of both slipping and toppling. **(M.U.)**
[Hint: If θ is the semivertical angle, then $\tan\theta = \frac{a}{h}$. But "$\mu = \dfrac{4a}{h}$" gives $\dfrac{1}{\sqrt{3}} = \dfrac{4a}{h}$ or $\dfrac{1}{4\sqrt{3}} = \tan\theta$**]**
5. A cone, resting with its base in contact with a rough inclined plane inclined at an angle α is on the point of both slipping and toppling. If the angle of friction is λ, find α and the vertical angle of the cone in terms of λ. **(M.U.)**
[Hint: "$\tan\alpha = \mu = \frac{4a}{h}$". Now $\tan\alpha = \mu$ gives $\tan\alpha = \tan\lambda$ or $\alpha = \lambda$. If θ is the semivertical angle, then $\tan\theta = \frac{a}{h}$ and so $\tan\alpha = \frac{4a}{h}$ gives $\tan\lambda = 4\tan\theta$ or $2\theta = 2\tan^{-1}(\frac{1}{4}\tan\lambda)$**]**
6. A rectangular plate of length *a* and height *h* rests on a rough inclined plane whose inclination is gradually increased. The coefficient of friction is μ. Show that it slides or tilts according as
$$\mu < \frac{a}{h} \quad \text{or} \quad \mu > \frac{a}{h}. \qquad \textbf{(M.U.)}$$
7. A cylinder of height *h* is placed with its base of radius *r* on a rough inclined plane and the inclination of the plane to the horizon is gradually increased. Show that, if μ is the coefficient of friction, the cylinder slides or topples according as
$$\mu < \frac{2r}{h} \ \text{or} \ \mu > \frac{2r}{h}.$$
What happens if $\mu = \frac{2r}{h}$?

CENTRE OF MASS

6.1 CENTRE OF MASS

First we define centre of mass.

Definition. Centre of mass. If $m_1, m_2, m_3,$........are the masses of a system of particles situated respectively at points whose position vectors are $\overline{r_1}, \overline{r_2}, \overline{r_3},$ ...., then the point G whose P.V. is

$$\overline{R} = \frac{m_1 \overline{r_1} + m_2 \overline{r_2} + ...}{m_1 + m_2 + ...} = \frac{\Sigma m_i \overline{r_i}}{\Sigma m_i}$$

is called the *centre of mass* or *mass centre* of the system of particles.

Note. Centre of mass of a system is unique.

If the Position vectors of the mass centres of several systems of masses $M_1, M_2,$........are $\overline{R}_1, \overline{R}_2,$ ...., then the position vector of the mass centre of all the systems considered together is

$$\overline{R} = \frac{M_1 \overline{R}_1 + M_2 \overline{R}_2 + ...}{M_1 + M_2 + ...}$$

because $M_1 \overline{R}_1 = m_1 \overline{r_1} + m_2 \overline{r}_2 + ...,$ and so on.

6.1.1 Centre of gravity

It is evident that the resultant of the forces of earth's gravitation acting on a system of particles (supposed to be parallel), act always through the mass centre of the system. As such, the mass centre is also called *centre of gravity* (C. G.) of the system.

Remark 1. The C. G. of two particles of masses m_1, m_2 is the point which divides the line joining them in the ratio $m_2 : m_1$.

Remark 2. For a distribution of mass symmetrical about a point, the mass centre is the point itself. For example, the mass centres of a uniform sphere and a uniform thin circular lamina are their centres; the mass centre of a uniform rod is its midpoint.

Remark 3. Suppose that several bodies of masses $M_1, M_2,$......have their mass centres on a straight line. Then the mass centre of all the bodies lies on the same straight line because, if the position vectors of the individual mass centres are $x_1 \overline{i}, x_2 \overline{i},$ ...., then the P.V. $\overline{R}$ of the entire system is

$$\overline{R} = \frac{M_1 x_1 \overline{i} + M_2 x_2 \overline{i} + ...}{M_1 + M_2 + ...} = \frac{M_1 x_1 + M_2 x_2 + ...}{M_1 + M_2 + ...} \overline{i}.$$

Remark 4. If $(x_1, y_1, z_1), (x_2, y_2, z_2)$........ are the mass centres of bodies of masses $m_1\ m_2,$......., then the mass centre $(\overline{x}, \overline{y}, \overline{z})$ of all the bodies considered together is given by

$$\overline{x} = \frac{m_1 x_1 + m_2 x_2 + ...}{m_1 + m_2 + ...}, \quad \overline{y} = \frac{m_1 y_1 + m_2 y_2 + ...}{m_1 + m_2 + ...}, \quad \overline{z} = \frac{m_1 z_1 + m_2 z_2 + ...}{m_1 + m_2 + ...}$$

Remark 5. For a continuous mass distribution of total mass M, the $P.V.$ $\overline{R}$ of its mass centre is

$$\overline{R} = \frac{\int \overline{r}\, dm}{\int dm} = \frac{\int \overline{r}\, dm}{M},$$

where $\overline{r}$ is the position vector of an element of mass dm. If $\overline{r}$ is $x\overline{i} + y\overline{j} + z\overline{k}$, and if the position vector of the mass centre is $\overline{x}\,\overline{i} + \overline{y}\,\overline{j} + \overline{z}\,\overline{k}$, then

$$\overline{x} = \frac{\int x\, dm}{\int dm}, \quad \overline{y} = \frac{\int y\, dm}{\int dm}, \quad \overline{z} = \frac{\int z\, dm}{\int dm}.$$

6.2 FINDING MASS CENTRE

Mass centre can be found by using integration or without using integration.

6.2.1 Finding mass centre (not using integration)

We proceed now to find the mass centres of certain simple systems.

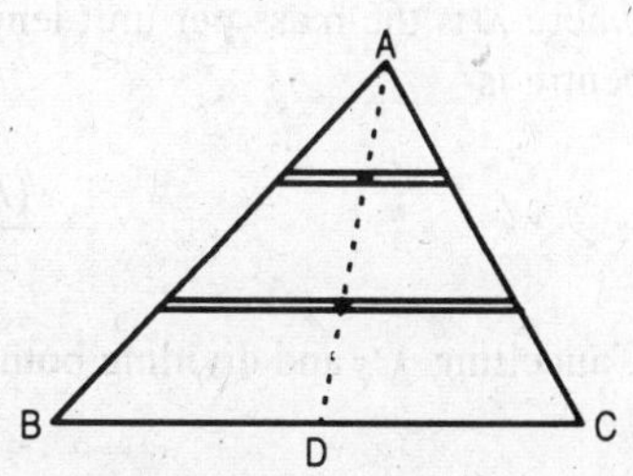

***(i)* Triangular lamina.** Divide the lamina ABC into thin strips, all parallel to the side BC. The mass centres of the strips are their midpoints. But these midpoints lie on the median AD. So the mass centre of all the strips also lies on AD. Similarly it lies on the median BE also. Hence the mass centre of the lamina is the point of intersection of the medians, namely, the centroid of the triangle.

***(ii)* Three particles of same mass.** Suppose three particles of masses m, m, m are situated at the points A, B, C whose P.V's are $\overline{a}, \overline{b}, \overline{c}$. By definition, the position vector of their mass centre is

$$\frac{m\,\overline{a} + m\,\overline{b} + m\,\overline{c}}{m + m + m} \quad \text{or} \quad \frac{\overline{a} + \overline{b} + \overline{c}}{3}.$$

But this vector is the position vector of the centroid of the triangle ABC. So the mass centre of three particles of equal mass placed at A, B, C is at the centroid of the triangle ABC. The mass centre of a triangular lamina ABC is also the centroid of the triangle ABC. As such, in finding the mass centre of a system containing a triangular lamina, the triangular lamina can be replaced by three particles placed at the angular points such that the mass of each particle equals one-third of the mass of the lamina.

The mass centre of three particles of equal mass situated at the mid-points of the sides of a triangle also is at the centroid of the triangle because, with the above assumptions, the P.V's of the midpoints of the sides of the triangle are

$$\tfrac{1}{2}(\overline{b} + \overline{c}), \quad \tfrac{1}{2}(\overline{c} + \overline{a}), \quad \tfrac{1}{2}(\overline{a} + \overline{b})$$

and the P. V. of the mass centre is

$$\frac{\tfrac{1}{2}m(\overline{b} + \overline{c}) + \tfrac{1}{2}m(\overline{c} + \overline{a}) + \tfrac{1}{2}\, m(\overline{a} + \overline{b})}{m + m + m} = \frac{\overline{a} + \overline{b} + \overline{c}}{3}.$$

***(iii)* Three particles of certain masses.** Suppose the positions of three given particles are A, B, C and their masses are proportional to the lengths $AB = c$, $BC = a$, $CA = b$. Then the masses are ka, kb, kc. Now the P.V. of the mass centre of the particles, is

$$\frac{(ka)\,\overline{OA} + (kb)\,\overline{OB} + (kc)\,\overline{OC}}{ka + kb + kc} \text{ or } \frac{a\,\overline{OA} + b\,\overline{OB} + c\,\overline{OC}}{a + b + c}.$$

We know that this vector is the position vector of the incentre of the triangle ABC. So the mass centre of the three particles is the incentre of the triangle ABC.

***(iv)* Three uniform rods forming a triangle.** Let the rods be

$$BC,\ CA,\ AB$$

and their midpoints be

$$D,\ E,\ F.$$

Let the masses of the rods be

$$\lambda BC,\ \lambda CA,\ \lambda AB,$$

where λ is the mass per unit length. Then the P.V. of their mass centre is

$$\frac{(\lambda BC)\,\overline{OD} + (\lambda CA)\,\overline{OE} + (\lambda AB)\,\overline{OF}}{\lambda BC + \lambda CA + \lambda AB}$$

Cancelling λ's and dividing both the numerator and denominator by 2, we get

$$\frac{EF\,(\overline{OD}) + FD\,(\overline{OE}) + DE\,(\overline{OF})}{EF + FD + DE}$$

since $EF = \frac{1}{2} BC$ and so on. This shows that the mass centre of the triangular frame is the incentre of the triangle DEF.

***(v)* Lamina in the form of a trapezium.** Let us have the following assumptions:

AB, CD	:	parallel sides ($AB = 2a$, $CD = 2b$)
h	:	distance between AB and CD
M, N	:	midpoints of AB, CD
σ	:	mass per unit area.

Divide the trapezium into the triangles AMD, DMC, CMB. Their masses are

$$(\tfrac{1}{2}ah)\sigma,\ (\tfrac{1}{2}\cdot 2b\cdot h)\sigma,\ (\tfrac{1}{2}ah)\sigma$$

or

$$3ka,\ 6kb,\ 3ka,$$

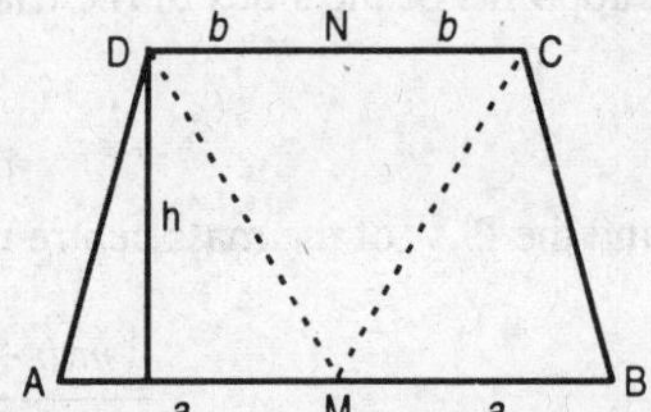

where $k = \frac{1}{6}h\sigma$. We know that a triangular lamina can be replaced with three equal particles, each of mass equal to one-third of the mass of the triangle, placed at the angular points. Such replacements for the triangles

$$AMD,\ DMC,\ CMB$$

and for the trapezium can be carried out successively as shown in the table.

FIG	*A*	*M*	*B*	*D*	*N*	*C*
AMD	*ka*	*ka*	...	*ka*	...	...
MBC	...	*ka*	*ka*	...	...	*ka*
DMC	...	$2kb$	...	$2kb$	...	$2kb$
ABCD	*ka*	$2k(a+b)$	*ka*	$k(a+2b)$	...	$k(a+2b)$
ABCD	...	$2k(2a+b)$	...	...	$2k(a+2b)$	...

Thus we see that the mass centre of the trapezium divides *MN* in the ratio

$$2k(a+2b): 2k(2a+b) \text{ or } a+2b : 2a+b.$$

(*vi*) Solid tetrahedron. Let *ABCD* be the tetrahedron and G_1, G_2, G_3, G_4 be the centroids of the face *BCD, ACD, ABD, ABC*. Divide the tetrahedron into thin triangular laminae, all parallel to the face *BCD*. Due to symmetry, their centroids, that is, their mass centres lie on AG_1. Similarly, it also lies on BG_2, CG_3, DG_4. So it follows that

$$AG_1,\ BG_2,\ CG_3,\ DG_4$$

concur, the point of concurrence being the mass centre.

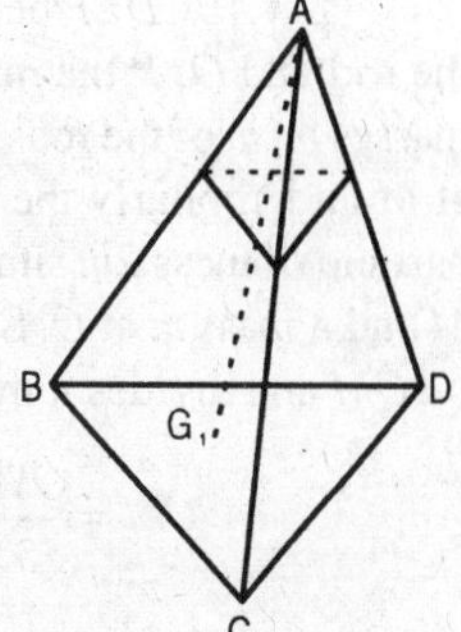

Let Q_1, Q_2, Q_3, Q_4 be the points which divide AG_1, BG_2, CG_3, DG_4 in the same ratio 3:1. Suppose $\bar{a},\bar{b},\bar{c},\bar{d}$ are the P.V's of A, B, C, D. Then the P.V. of G_1 is $\frac{1}{3}(\bar{b}+\bar{c}+\bar{d})$ and consequently the position vector of Q_1 is

$$\frac{3\{\frac{1}{3}(\bar{b}+\bar{c}+\bar{d})\}+1(\bar{a})}{3+1} \text{ or } \frac{\bar{a}+\bar{b}+\bar{c}+\bar{d}}{4}.$$

From symmetry we see that $Q_1,\ Q_2,\ Q_3,\ Q_4$ coincide and the point of coincidence is the mass centre of the tetrahedron. Thus, in conclusion, we get that the point which divides the line joining one vertex and the centroid of the opposite face in the ratio 3:1 is the mass centre of the tetrahedron.

Remark. When one face of the tetrahedron is horizontal, the mass centre is at a height equal to one-fourth of the height of the opposite vertex. So the mass centre of a pyramid is at a height equal to one-fourth of the height of the pyramid because the base of the pyramid can be divided into several triangles and consequently the pyramid can be divided into tetrahedrons with the same height as the pyramid. Furthermore, considering a right circular cone to be a limiting case of a pyramid, we see that the mass centre of a cone divides the axis in the ratio 3 : 1.

EXAMPLES

Example 1. *D, E, F* are the midpoints of the sides *BC, CA, AB* of a ΔABC. Masses m_1, m_2, m_3 are placed at *A, B, C* and masses M_1, M_2, M_3 are placed at *D, E, F*. If the two systems have the same mass centre, show that

$$\frac{m_1}{M_2+M_3} = \frac{m_2}{M_3+M_1} = \frac{m_3}{M_1+M_2}. \qquad \textbf{(M.U.)}$$

Let $\bar{a},\ \bar{b},\ \bar{c}$, be the P.V.'s of *A, B, C*. Then the P.V.'s of *D, E, F* are

$$\tfrac{1}{2}(\bar{b}+\bar{c}),\ \tfrac{1}{2}(\bar{c}+\bar{a}),\ \tfrac{1}{2}(\bar{a}+\bar{b}).$$

Since the mass centres of the two systems coincide,

$$\frac{m_1\bar{a}+m_2\bar{b}+m_3\bar{c}}{m_1+m_2+m_3}=\frac{M_1\cdot\frac{1}{2}(\bar{b}+\bar{c})+M_2\cdot\frac{1}{2}(\bar{c}+\bar{a})+M_3\cdot\frac{1}{2}(\bar{a}+\bar{b})}{M_1+M_2+M_3}.$$

The coefficients of $\bar{a}$, $\bar{b}$, $\bar{c}$ from the left and right sides are equal. Equating the coefficients of $\bar{a}$,

$$\frac{m_1}{m_1+m_2+m_3}=\frac{M_2+M_3}{2(M_1+M_2+M_3)} \quad \text{or} \quad \frac{m_1}{M_2+M_3}=\frac{m_1+m_2+m_3}{2(M_1+M_2+M_3)}, \text{ a constant.}$$

$$\therefore \quad \frac{m_1}{M_2+M_3}=\frac{m_2}{M_3+M_1}=\frac{m_3}{M_1+M_2}.$$

Example 2. A rod of length $5a$ is bent so as to form five sides of a regular hexagon. Show that its centre of mass is at a distance $a\sqrt{1\cdot 33}$ from either end of the rod. **(M.U.)**

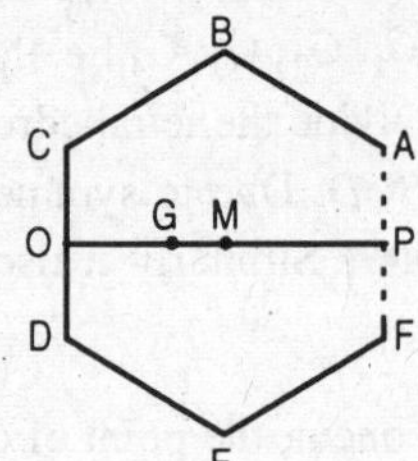

Let $ABCDEF$ be the hexagon formed, M the centre, A, F the free ends of the rod and O, P the midpoints of CD, AF and m the mass of each side. The masses m, m of the rods AB, DE are equivalent to a particle of mass $2m$ situated at M and similarly the masses m, m of the rods BC, EF are equivalent to a particle of mass $2m$ situated at M. So the system is equivalent to a mass $4m$ at M and a mass m at O. So, if G is the mass centre of the whole rod, then G lies on OM and divides it in the ratio 4 : 1. So

$$GM=\frac{OM}{5}=\frac{1}{5}\frac{\sqrt{3}\,a}{2} \quad \text{since } \Delta\, CDM \text{ is equilateral}$$

$$\therefore \quad GA^2=(GM+MP)^2+PA^2=\left(\frac{\sqrt{3}\,a}{10}+\frac{\sqrt{3}\,a}{2}\right)^2+\frac{a^2}{4}$$

$$=3a^2\left(\frac{36}{100}\right)+\frac{a^2}{4}=\frac{133}{100}a^2.$$

$$\therefore \quad GA=\sqrt{1\cdot 33}\,a.$$

Example 3. OA and OB are two uniform rods of lengths $2a$, $2b$. If angle $AOB=\alpha$, show that the distance of the mass centre of the rods from O, is

$$\frac{(a^4+2a^2b^2\cos\alpha+b^4)^{1/2}}{a+b}.$$ **(M.U.)**

If $\hat{a}$, $\hat{b}$ are the unit vectors along OA, OB, then the P. V's of the midpoints of OA, OB are

$$a\hat{a}, \; b\hat{b}.$$

If σ is the mass per unit length, then the masses of the rods are

$$2a\sigma, \; 2b\sigma.$$

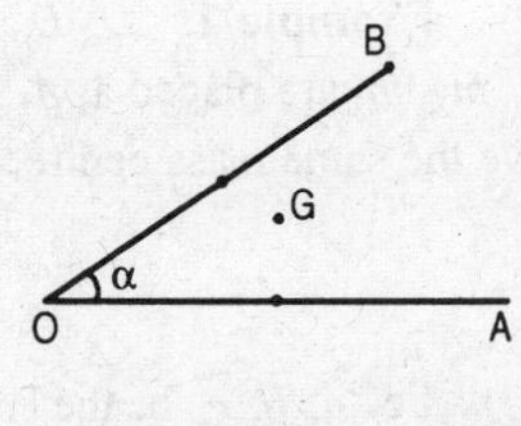

So, if G is the mass centre, then

$$\overline{OG}=\frac{(2a\sigma)a\hat{a}+(2b\sigma)b\hat{b}}{2a\sigma+2b\sigma}=\frac{a^2\hat{a}+b^2\hat{b}}{a+b}.$$

$$\therefore \quad OG^2=\frac{1}{(a+b)^2}(a^2\hat{a}+b^2\hat{b})\cdot(a^2\hat{a}+b^2\hat{b})$$

$$=\frac{a^4+2a^2b^2\hat{a}\cdot\hat{b}+b^4}{(a+b)^2}=\frac{a^4+2a^2b^2\cos\alpha+b^4}{(a+b)^2}.$$

Hence the result.

Example 4. D, E, F are the midpoints of the sides BC, CA, AB of a triangular lamina ABC. The lamina is folded across the line joining E, F and the vertex A is made to lie on the base BC. Show that the distance of the mass centre of the lamina in this position from BC, is three-fourths of the distance of the mass centre of the unfolded lamina from BC. **(M.U.)**

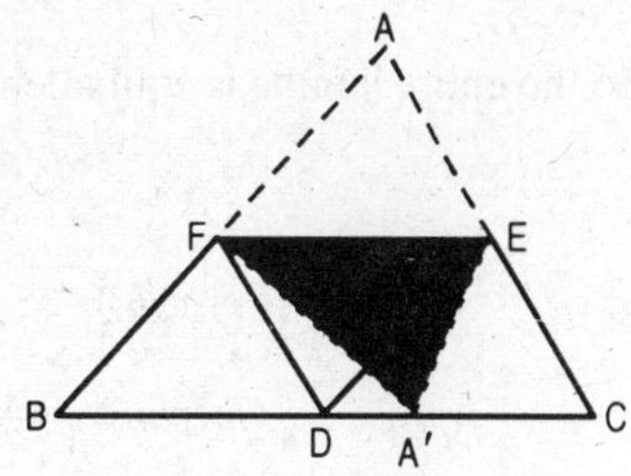

Let $BC = a$ and the distance of A from BC be h. Let A' be the position of A when the lamina is folded. Now the triangles

$$BDF, FDE, DEC, FA'E$$

are of equal areas each having same base and same height.

So each of them can be seen to be equivalent to three particles of certain masses, say m, m, m, placed at the angular points. So the lamina in the folded position is equivalent to particles of masses

$$m, 3m, m, m, 3m, 3m,$$

respectively placed at

$$B, D, A', C, F, E$$

since each of D, F, E is a vertex for three triangles. If $\bar{y}$ is the distance of the mass centre of the folded lamina from BC then,

$$\bar{y} = \frac{m\,(0) + 3m\,(0) + m\,(0) + m(0) + 3m\,(\tfrac{1}{2}h) + 3m\,(\tfrac{1}{2}h)}{m + 3m + m + m + 3m + 3m}$$

$$= \frac{3mh}{12m} = \frac{h}{4} = \frac{3}{4}\left(\frac{h}{3}\right)$$

$$= \frac{3}{4} \text{ (distance of the mass centre of the unfolded lamina from } BC).$$

Example 5. Show that the mass centre of a quadrilateral lamina is the same as the mass centre of a system of four particles of equal masses placed at the angular points and an equal negative mass placed at the point of intersection of the diagonals. **(M.U.)**

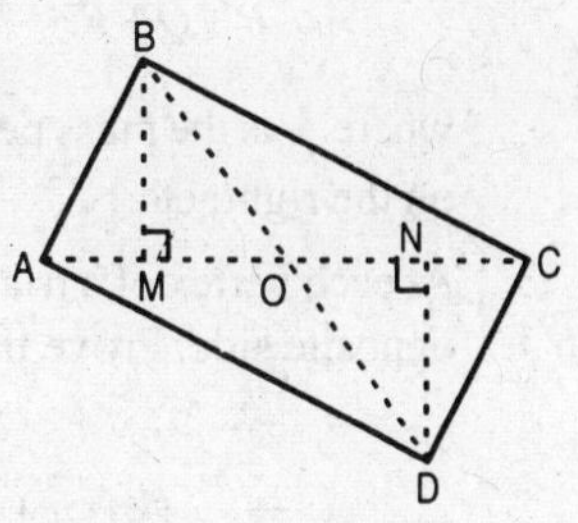

Let $ABCD$ be the quadrilateral. Let the diagonals intersect at O. Let the areas of ΔABC, ΔADC be s, s' and their masses be m, m'. If σ is the mass per unit area, then

$$m = s\sigma, \quad m' = s'\sigma.$$

If BM, DN are perpendiculars from B, D to AC, then

$$\frac{m}{m'} = \frac{s\sigma}{s'\sigma} = \frac{s}{s'} = \frac{\tfrac{1}{2}AC \cdot BM}{\tfrac{1}{2}AC \cdot DN} = \frac{BM}{DN} = \frac{BO}{DO}.$$

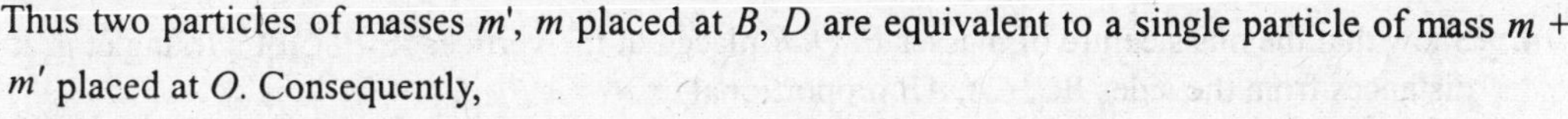

Thus two particles of masses m', m placed at B, D are equivalent to a single particle of mass $m + m'$ placed at O. Consequently,

$$\left.\begin{array}{l}\text{two particles of negative masses } -m', -m \\ \text{placed at } B, D \text{ are equivalent to a particle} \\ \text{of negative mass } -(m+m') \text{ placed at } O.\end{array}\right\} \quad \text{...(1)}$$

Now the lamina ABC is equivalent to three particles of masses

$$\tfrac{1}{3}m,\ \tfrac{1}{3}m,\ \tfrac{1}{3}m \text{ at } A, B, C$$

and the lamina ADC is equivalent to three particles of masses

$$\tfrac{1}{3}m',\ \tfrac{1}{3}m',\ \tfrac{1}{3}m' \text{ at } A, D, C.$$

So the entire lamina is equivalent to particles at A, B, C, D, O as shown below.

	A	***B***	***C***	***D***	***O***
	$\frac{1}{3}(m+m')$	$\frac{1}{3}m$	$\frac{1}{3}(m+m')$	$\frac{1}{3}m'$	....
or	$\frac{1}{3}(m+m')$	$\frac{1}{3}(m+m')-\frac{1}{3}m'$	$\frac{1}{3}(m+m')$	$\frac{1}{3}(m+m')-\frac{1}{3}m$	....
or	$\frac{1}{3}(m+m')$	$\frac{1}{3}(m+m')$	$\frac{1}{3}(m+m')$	$\frac{1}{3}(m+m')$	$-\frac{1}{3}(m+m')$

of which the last step follows from (1). Hence the result.

EXERCISES

1. A given particle is placed anywhere on a uniform triangular lamina. Show that the mass centre of the lamina and the particle lies within a triangle similar to the lamina. **(M.U.)**

[Hint: Let G be the centroid of the lamina ABC of mass M. Let a particle of mass m be placed at a point P on BC. As P moves on BC, the mass centre of the system moves on a line parallel to BC dividing GP in the ratio $m : M$]

2. Three uniform rods form a triangle ABC. If the mass centre of three particles of masses P, Q, R situated at A, B, C coincides with the mass centre of the rods, show that

$$\frac{P}{b+c}=\frac{Q}{c+a}=\frac{R}{a+b}. \qquad \textbf{(M.U., C.U.)}$$

[Hint: $$\frac{P\bar{a}+Q\bar{b}+R\bar{c}}{P+Q+R}=\frac{(a\lambda)\cdot\tfrac{1}{2}(\bar{b}+\bar{c})+(b\lambda)\cdot\tfrac{1}{2}(\bar{c}+\bar{a})+(c\lambda)\cdot\tfrac{1}{2}(\bar{a}+\bar{b})}{a\lambda+b\lambda+c\lambda},$$

where λ is the mass per unit length. The coefficient of $\bar{a}$ on the left equals the coefficient of $\bar{a}$ on the right, etc.]

3. At each vertex of a triangle, a particle is placed, its mass being proportional to the length of the opposite side. Prove that the mass centre of the particles will be the incentre of the triangle. **(M.U.)**

[Hint: $\overline{OG}=\dfrac{(ka)\,\bar{a}+(kb)\,\bar{b}+(kc)\,\bar{c}}{ka+kb+kc}$]

4. Show that the mass centre of masses P, Q, R placed at the vertices A, B, C of a triangle, is at distances from the sides BC, CA, AB proportional to

$$\frac{P}{a},\ \frac{Q}{b},\ \frac{R}{c}. \qquad \textbf{(M.U.)}$$

[Hint: Let h_1, d_1 be the distances of A and G from BC. Then, choosing BC as the x axis, the distances of P, Q, R from the x axis are $h_1, 0, 0$. So

$$d_1 = \frac{Ph_1 + Q(0) + R(0)}{P+Q+R} = \frac{P(2\Delta)}{a(P+Q+R)} = \frac{P}{a}k,$$

since $\Delta = \frac{1}{2} BC \cdot h_1 = \frac{1}{2} a\, h_1$, where k is a constant.]

5. A triangle formed by three rods of different densities has its C.G. at the centre of the circum-circle. Show that the densities are proportional to the secants of the opposite angles. **(M.U.)**

[Hint: Circumcentre of $\Delta\, ABC : S$; Densities: $\lambda_1, \lambda_2, \lambda_3$; Midpoints of BC, CA, AB: D, E, F; P.V. of C.G. with reference to S: $\overline{0}$.

$$\therefore \qquad a\lambda_1\, \overline{SD} + b\lambda_2\, \overline{SE} + c\lambda_3\, \overline{SF} = \overline{0}.$$

Multiply this scalarly by $\overline{BC}$ and then use $SE = R\cos B$, $SF = R\cos C$, the sine formula and $\overline{BC} \cdot \overline{SD} = 0, \overline{BC} \cdot \overline{SE} = a\, SE \sin C, \overline{BC} \cdot \overline{SF} = -\, a\, SF \sin B$**]**

6. $ABCD$ is a rectangle whose diagonals intersect at G. A uniform wire bent into the form $GABCDG$ has its centre of gravity at G. Show that $AB = \sqrt{3}\, BC$. **(M.U.)**

[Hint: Let $AB = 2a$, $BC = 2b$. Let P, Q, S be the midpoints of AD, BC, PG. Masses of AB and DC are equivalent to mass $4a$ at G. Masses of DG and AG are equivalent to mass $2\sqrt{a^2+b^2}$ at S. The fifth mass is $2b$ at Q. So $SG \cdot 2\sqrt{a^2+b^2} = GQ \cdot 2b$ gives $a = \sqrt{3}\, b$.**]**

7. The form of a lamina is a trapezium $ABCD$ in which AB, CD are parallel and $AB = a$, $CD = b$. Show that, if h is the distance between AB, CD, then the distance of its mass centre from AB is

$$\frac{a+2b}{3(a+b)} h.$$ **(M.U., M.K.U.)**

[Hint: The areas of $\Delta\, ABD, \Delta\, BDC$ are $\frac{1}{2}ah, \frac{1}{2}bh$. Their centroids (C.G.'s) are at heights $h/3, 2h/3$, from AB. So, if AB is the x axis and $\overline{y}$ is the distance of the centre of mass of the lamina from AB,

$$\overline{y} = \frac{h/3 \cdot \frac{1}{2}ah + 2h/3 \cdot \frac{1}{2}bh}{\frac{1}{2}ah + \frac{1}{2}bh} = \frac{1}{3}\frac{a+2b}{a+b} h.]$$

8. If one of the parallel sides of a trapezium is double the other, show that the ratio of the distances of the mass centre from the parallel sides is 5 : 4. **(M.U.)**

[Hint: Use the previous sum. Set $a = 2b$. The distances are $4h/9, h - 4h/9$.**]**

9. If the mass centre of a quadrilateral lamina is the point of intersection of the diagonals, show that the quadrilateral is a parallelogram.

[Hint: Let $ABCD$ be the quadrilateral, O the point of intersection of the diagonals and M, N the midpoints of AC, BD. If the quadrilateral is replaced with the five particles of masses $m, m, m, m, -m$, they further reduce to three particles of masses $2m$, $2m$ at M, N and $-m$ at O. But O is the mass centre. So $\overline{0} = (-m)\,\overline{0} + 2m\,(\overline{OM}) + 2m\,(\overline{ON})$ which implies that $\overline{ON} = \overline{0}, \overline{OM} = \overline{0}$, *i.e.*, M, N coincide with O. So O bisects the diagonals. Thus, a parallelogram.**]**

10. The distances of the angular points and the point of intersection of the diagonals of a quadrilateral lamina from a line in its plane are a, b, c, d, e. Show that the distance of the mass centre of the lamina from the same line is

$$\frac{1}{3}(a+b+c+d-e).$$ **(M.U.)**

[Hint: Replace the lamina with five particles of equal mass of which one is negative.**]**

6.2.2 Finding mass centre using integration.

Using the formula for the position vector of the mass centre, namely,

$$\frac{\int \bar{r}\, dm}{\int dm} \text{ or } \frac{\int \bar{r}\, dm}{M},$$

we now obtain the mass centers of a few homogeneous bodies.

***(i)* Thin wire in the form of a circular arc.** Suppose a is the radius of the circle and 2α is the angle subtended by the wire at the centre O. Let us have the following assumptions:

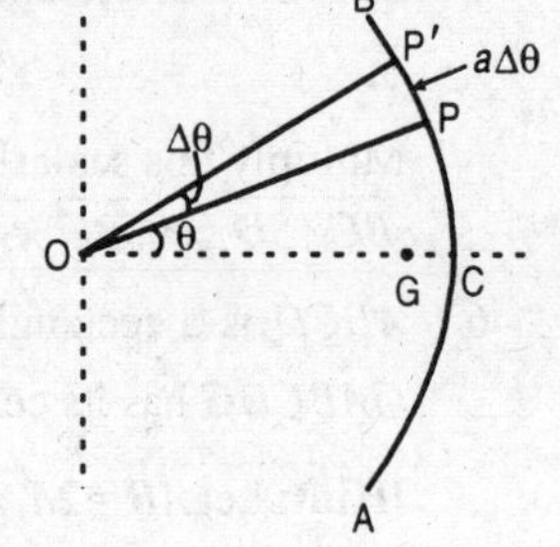

OC	:	Middle radius (chosen as x axis)
(x, y), (r, θ)	:	Cartesian and polar coordinates of P, a point on the wire
PP'	:	Elementary length of the wire
$\Delta\theta$	:	Angle subtended by PP' at O
λ	:	Mass per unit length.

Now the total length of the wire is $a\,(2\alpha)$ and so its mass is $M = a\,(2\alpha)\,\lambda$. Due to symmetry of the wire about OC, the mass centre G of the wire lies on OC. The length of PP' is $a\Delta\theta$ and its mass is $dm = (a\Delta\theta)\lambda$. Its x coordinate is $a \cos\theta$. Thus we get

$$OG = \bar{x} = \frac{\int x\, dm}{\int dm} = \frac{\int_{-\alpha}^{\alpha} (a\cos\theta)\,(a\lambda)\, d\theta}{a\,(2\alpha)\,\lambda}$$

$$= \frac{a}{2\alpha}\int_{-\alpha}^{\alpha} \cos\theta\, d\theta = \frac{a}{2\alpha}[\sin\theta]_{-\alpha}^{\alpha} = \frac{a\sin\alpha}{\alpha}.$$

Corollary. When the wire is semicircular, $\alpha = \frac{\pi}{2}$ and correspondingly we have

$$OG = \frac{a\sin \pi/2}{\pi/2} = \frac{2a}{\pi}.$$

***(ii)* Lamina in the form of a sector of a circle.** We shall have the same assumptions as in the previous case and the assumption that σ is the mass per unit area. Then the area of the lamina is $a^2\,\alpha$ and its mass is $M = (a^2\,\alpha)\sigma$. The area of the elementary area OPP' is

$$\tfrac{1}{2}\, OP \cdot OP' \sin\Delta\theta \simeq \tfrac{1}{2}\, a^2\, \Delta\theta.$$

The mass of this area is $(\frac{1}{2} a^2\, \Delta\theta)\sigma$ and the x-coordinate of its mass centre is $\frac{2}{3}\, a\cos\theta$. So

$$OG = \frac{\int_{-\alpha}^{\alpha} \left(\frac{2}{3} a\cos\theta\right)\left(\frac{1}{2} a^2\sigma\right) d\theta}{a^2\,\alpha\sigma} = \frac{a}{3\alpha}\int_{-\alpha}^{\alpha}\cos\theta\, d\theta$$

$$= \frac{a}{3\alpha}[\sin\theta]_{-\alpha}^{\alpha} = \frac{2a\sin\alpha}{3\alpha}.$$

Corollary. In the case of a quadrant of a circle, $\alpha = \frac{1}{4}\pi$ and the distance of the mass centre from the centre is

$$\frac{2a \sin \frac{1}{4}\pi}{3.(\frac{1}{4}\pi)} = \frac{8a(1/\sqrt{2})}{3\pi} = \frac{8a}{3\pi\sqrt{2}} = \frac{4\sqrt{2}}{3\pi}a.$$

In the case of a semicircular lamina the distance of the mass centre from the centre is

$$\frac{2a \sin \frac{1}{2}\pi}{3.\frac{1}{2}\pi} = \frac{4a}{3\pi}.$$

***(iii)* Lamina in the form of a quadrant of an ellipse of axes 2*a*, 2*b*.** Corresponding to the elementary strip of area $y\,\Delta x$ as shown in the figure, to use the formula

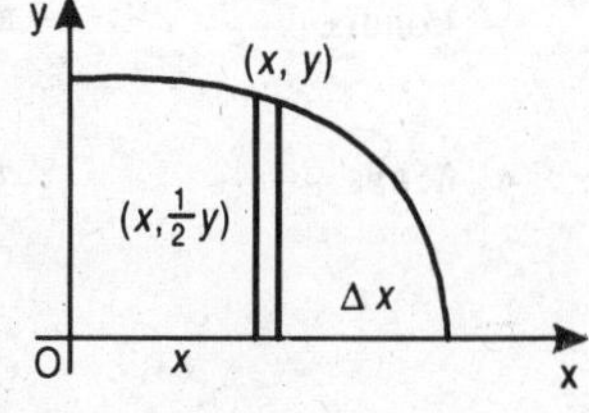

$$\bar{x} = \int \frac{x\,dm}{M},$$

we have $dm = (y\,\Delta x)\sigma$ and $M = (\frac{1}{4}\pi ab)\alpha$, where α is the mass per unit area. So

$$\bar{x} = \frac{\int_0^a x(y\sigma\,dx)}{\frac{1}{4}\pi ab\sigma} = \frac{4}{\pi ab}\int_0^a xy dx.$$

But $x = a\cos\theta$, $y = b\sin\theta$ and when $x = 0, \theta = \frac{\pi}{2}$ and when $x = a, \theta = 0$. Thus

$$\bar{x} = \frac{4}{\pi ab}\int_{\pi/2}^{0} (a\cos\theta)(b\sin\theta)(-a\sin\theta)\,d\theta$$

$$= \frac{4a}{\pi}\int_0^{\pi/2} \sin^2\theta\cos\theta\,d\theta = \frac{4a}{\pi}.\frac{1}{3} = \frac{4a}{3\pi}.$$

Similarly, $\bar{y} = \dfrac{4b}{3\pi}.$

***(iv)* Solid hemisphere of radius *a*.** Divide the hemisphere into thin circular laminae perpendicular to the middle radius OA, where O is the centre of the sphere. Consider the lamina whose distance from O is x and thickness is Δx. For this lamina we have the following :

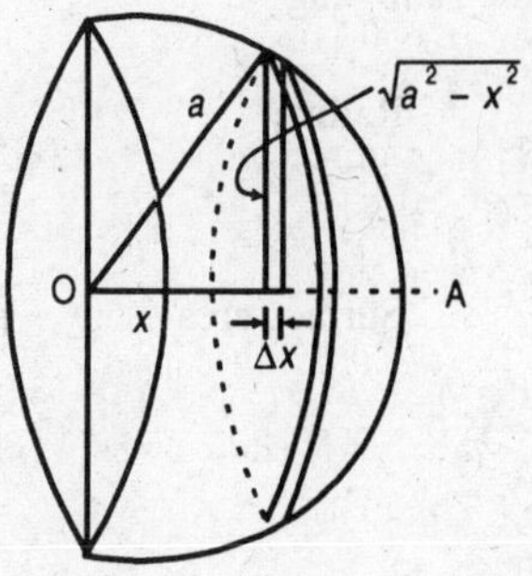

Radius : $\sqrt{a^2 - x^2}$

Volume : $\pi(a^2 - x^2)\,\Delta x$

Mass : $dm = \pi\,(a^2 - x^2)\,\Delta x\rho$. where ρ is mass per unit volume.

Mass centre : Point on OA at a distance x from O.

Thus, if the mass centre of the hemisphere is G, then

$$OG = \frac{\int x\,dm}{M} = \frac{\int_0^a x[\pi(a^2 - x^2)\rho]dx}{\frac{1}{2}\left(\frac{4}{3}\pi a^3\right)\rho}$$

$$= \frac{3}{2a^3}\int_0^a (a^2 x - x^3)\,dx = \frac{3}{2a^3}\left(\frac{1}{2}-\frac{1}{4}\right)a^4 = \frac{3a}{8}.$$

(*v*) Solid right circular cone of height *h*. Divide the cone into thin circular laminae perpendicular to its axis OA. Consider the lamina whose distance from the vertex O is x and thickness is Δx. For this lamina we have the following :

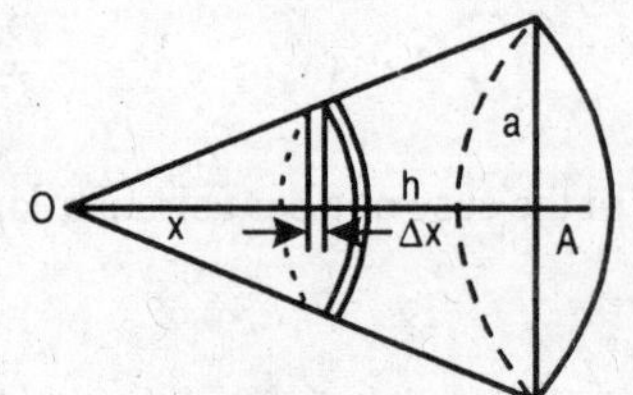

Radius : $\frac{ax}{h}$ from similar triangles, where a is the base radius.

Volume : $\pi\left(\frac{ax}{h}\right)^2 \Delta x$

Mass : $dm = \pi\left(\frac{ax}{h}\right)^2 \Delta x\rho$, where ρ is the mass per unit volume

$$= \frac{\rho\pi a^2 x^2}{h^2}\Delta x$$

Mass centre : Point on the axis at a distance x from O. Thus, if the mass centre of the cone is G, then

$$OG = \frac{\int x\,dm}{M} = \frac{\frac{\rho\pi a^2}{h^2}\int_0^h x\cdot x^2\cdot dx}{M}$$

$$= \frac{\rho\pi a^2}{h^2}\cdot\frac{1}{\frac{1}{3}\pi a^2 . h\rho}\int_0^h x^3\,dx = \frac{3}{h^3}\cdot\frac{h^4}{4} = \frac{3h}{4}.$$

(*vi*) Hemispherical shell. Divide the sphere into thin rings whose planes are perpendicular to the middle radius OA. Consider the ring whose centre is at a distance x from O and breadth is Δs. For this ring we have the following :

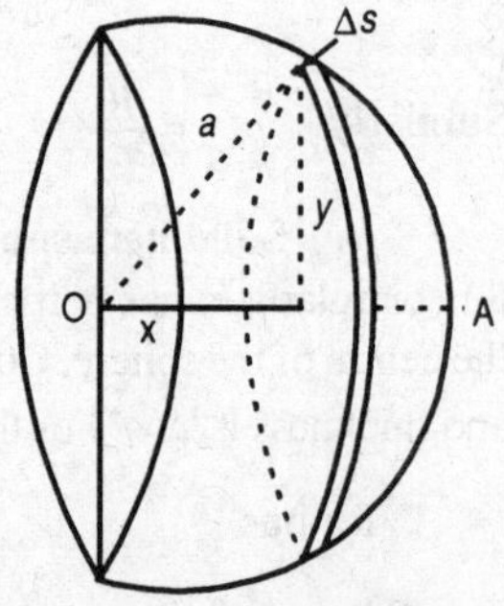

Radius : $y = \sqrt{a^2 - x^2}$, a being the radius of the sphere.

Surface area : $(2\pi y)\,\Delta s = (2\pi y)\sqrt{1 + y_1^2}\cdot\Delta x$

$$= 2\pi y\sqrt{1 + \left(\frac{-x}{y}\right)^2}\,\Delta x = 2\pi y\sqrt{\frac{y^2 + x^2}{y^2}}\,.\,\Delta x$$

$$= 2\pi y\sqrt{\frac{a^2}{y^2}}\,.\,\Delta x = 2\pi a\,\Delta x.$$

Mass : $dm = (2\pi a\,\Delta x)\,\sigma$, σ being mass per unit area

Mass centre : Point on OA at a distance x from O.

Thus, if G is the mass centre of the hemispherical shell, then

$$OG = \frac{\int x\, dm}{M} = \frac{\int_0^a x\,(2\pi a\sigma)\, dx}{\frac{1}{2}(4\pi a^2\sigma)} = \frac{1}{a}\int_0^a x\, dx = \frac{1}{2}a\,.$$

Method using polar coordinates.

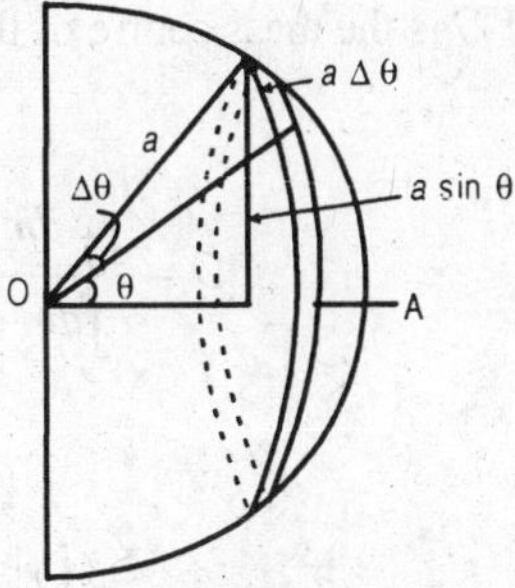

For the typical ring we have

Radius : $a \sin\theta$

Surface area : $(2\pi a \sin\theta)(a\,\Delta\theta)$

$= 2\pi a^2 \sin\theta\, \Delta\theta$

Mass : $= 2\pi a^2\, \sigma \sin\theta\, \Delta\theta$

Mass centre : Point at a distance $a\cos\theta$ from O.

$$\therefore \qquad OG = \frac{\int_0^{\pi/2} (a\cos\theta)(2\pi a^2\,\sigma\sin\theta)\, d\theta}{\frac{1}{2}(4\pi a^2)\,\sigma} = a\int_0^{\pi/2} \sin\theta\cos\theta\, d\theta = \frac{a}{2}$$

(*vii*) Hollow right circular cone of height *h*. Now we consider a hollow cone without the base, whose slant side and base radius are l and a. On division into rings, as was done in case (*vi*),

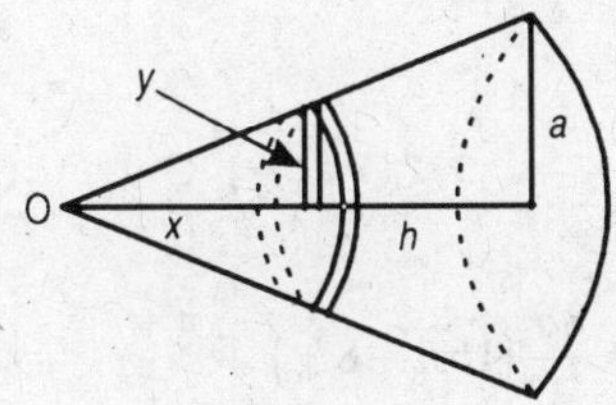

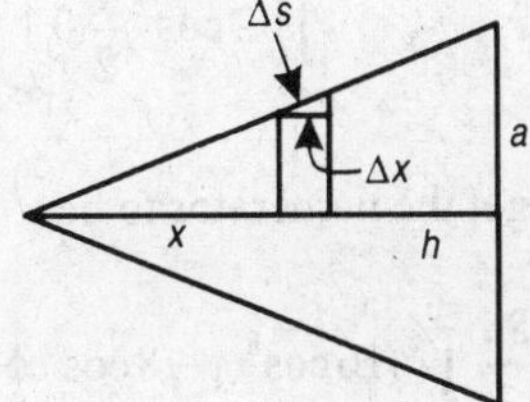

Radius : $y = \dfrac{ax}{h}$

Surface area : $2\pi\,\dfrac{ax}{h}\,\Delta s = \dfrac{2\pi a x}{h}\cdot\dfrac{l}{h}\,\Delta x$ since $\dfrac{\Delta s}{l} = \dfrac{\Delta x}{h}$

Mass : $dm = \left(\dfrac{2\pi a}{h^2}\, lx\,\Delta x\right)\sigma$

$$\therefore \qquad OG = \frac{\frac{2\pi a l}{h^2}\,\sigma \int_0^h x^2\, dx}{\pi a l \sigma} = \frac{2}{3}h.$$

(*viii*) Cardioidal Lamina. Let the equation of the cardioid be

$$r = a(1 + \cos\theta)$$

with O as the pole and the line of symmetry OA as the initial line. Let $P(r, \theta)$ and $P'(r + \Delta r, \theta + \Delta\theta)$ be two neighbouring points on the cardioid. Then, for the sector OPP', we have the following:

Area : $\frac{1}{2}r(r+\Delta r)\sin\Delta\theta \simeq \frac{1}{2}r^2\,\Delta\theta$

Mass : $dm = \frac{1}{2}(r^2\,\Delta\theta)\,\sigma = \frac{1}{2}r^2\,\sigma\,\Delta\theta$

Mass centre : $\left(\frac{2}{3}r, \theta\right)$ nearly.

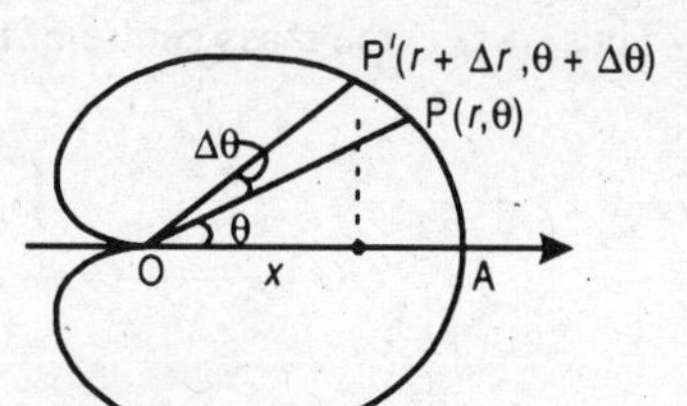

If G is the mass centre of the cardioidal lamina, then

$$OG = \frac{\int x\,dm}{\int dm} = \frac{\int \frac{2}{3}r\cos\theta\,dm}{\int dm} = \frac{\frac{2}{3}\int_{-\pi}^{\pi} r\cos\theta.\frac{1}{2}r^2\,\sigma d\theta}{\int_{-\pi}^{\pi}\frac{1}{2}r^2\,\sigma d\theta}$$

$$= \frac{\frac{2}{3}\int_{-\pi}^{\pi} r^3\cos\theta\,d\theta}{\int_{-\pi}^{\pi} r^2\,d\theta} = \frac{\frac{2a}{3}\int_{-\pi}^{\pi}(1+\cos\theta)^3\cos\theta\,d\theta}{\int_{-\pi}^{\pi}(1+\cos\theta)^2\,d\theta}$$

$$= \frac{\frac{2a}{3}\int_{-\pi}^{\pi}\left(2\cos^2\frac{1}{2}\theta\right)^3\left(2\cos^2\frac{1}{2}\theta-1\right)d\theta}{\int_{-\pi}^{\pi}\left(2\cos^2\frac{1}{2}\theta\right)^2 d\theta}.$$

Putting $\frac{1}{2}\theta = \phi$, we get the numerator to be

$$\frac{8a}{3}\int_0^{\pi/2}(16\cos^8\phi - 8\cos^6\phi)\,d\phi = \frac{8a}{3}(16I_8 - 8I_6)$$

$$= \frac{8a}{3}\left(16\cdot\frac{7}{8}\cdot\frac{5}{6}\cdot\frac{3}{4}\cdot\frac{1}{2}\frac{\pi}{2} - 8\cdot\frac{5}{6}\cdot\frac{3}{4}\cdot\frac{1}{2}\frac{\pi}{2}\right) = \frac{5\pi a}{2}.$$

Similarly the denominator is

$$16I_4 = 16\frac{3}{4}\cdot\frac{1}{2}\cdot\frac{\pi}{2} = 3\pi\cdot$$

$$\therefore \qquad OG = \frac{5\pi a}{2}\cdot\frac{1}{3\pi} = \frac{5a}{6}\cdot$$

6.2.3 Mass centre of a nonhomogeneous solid

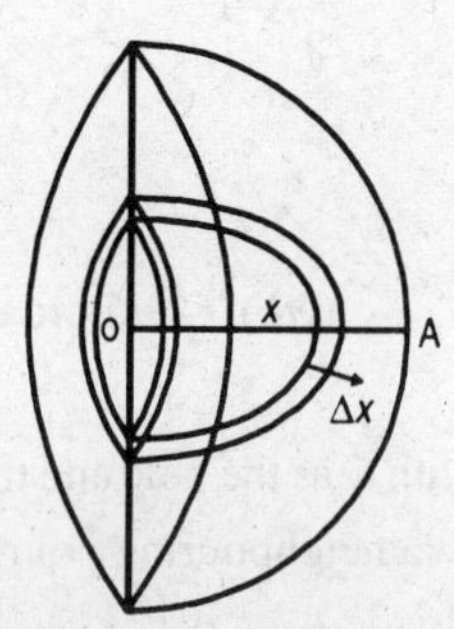

As an illustration of finding the mass centre of a nonhomogeneous body we shall now find the mass centre of a hemisphere of radius a whose density varies inversely as the distance from the centre.

Let O be the centre of the sphere and OA, the middle radius. Divide the solid into hemispherical shells as shown in the figure. For the shell whose radius is x and thickness is Δx we have the following:

Surface area	:	$\frac{1}{2}(4\pi x^2) = 2\pi x^2$
Volume	:	$(2\pi x^2)\Delta x$
Mass	:	$dm = (2\pi x^2 \Delta x)\,\rho$, where $\rho = k/x$
		$= 2\pi k x\,\Delta x$
Mass centre	:	The point on OA at a distance $x/2$ from O.

So, if G is the mass centre of the solid hemisphere,

$$OG = \frac{\int_0^a (\frac{1}{2}x)(2\pi kx\,dx)}{\int_0^a 2\pi kx\,dx} = \frac{\frac{1}{2}\int_0^a x^2\,dx}{\int_0^a x\,dx}$$

$$= \frac{1}{2}\cdot\frac{a^3}{3}\cdot\frac{2}{a^2} = \frac{1}{3}a\cdot$$

6.2.4 Moment of a mass.

As we take moments of weights, now ignoring "g", we can take moments of a system of masses. Thus the sum of the moments of a system of masses on a line about a point on the line equals the moment of the sum of the masses at the C.G. about that point.

As an application, suppose G is the C.G. of a body of mass M and a portion of it of mass M_1 whose C.G. is G_1 is removed. Then the mass of the remainder is $M - M_1$ and its C.G., say G_2, lie on the line G_1G such that G_1, G_2 are on either side of G. Taking moments about G, we get

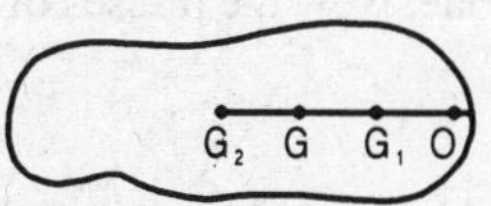

$$GG_2\,(M - M_1) - GG_1\cdot M_1 = 0 \quad\text{or}\quad GG_2\,(M - M_1) = GG_1\cdot M_1.$$

From this we get GG_2, that is, the distance of G_2 from G.

However, in general, taking moments about a point O, as in the figure, we have

$$OG_2\,(M - M_1) + O\,G_1\cdot M_1 = OG\cdot M.$$

EXAMPLES

Example 1. Show that the vertical angle α of a cone which is such that the C.G. of its whole surface area including the base coincides with the C.G. of its volume, is

$$2\sin^{-1}\tfrac{1}{3}.$$ **(M.K.U., M.U.)**

For the cone, let

a	:	Base radius
h	:	Height
l	:	Slant side
O	:	Vertex
G_1	:	C.G. of curved surface
G_2	:	C.G. of base

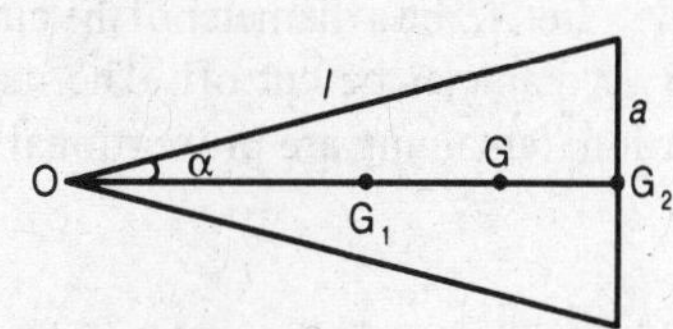

If G is the C.G. of the solid cone, then

$$OG = \frac{3h}{4}. \quad \therefore \quad GG_2 = \frac{h}{4}.$$

$$OG_1 = \frac{2h}{3}. \quad \therefore \quad GG_1 = \frac{3h}{4} - \frac{2h}{3} = \frac{h}{12}.$$

If σ is the mass per unit area, then

$$\text{Mass at } G_1 = \pi a l \,\sigma,$$

$$\text{Mass at } G_2 = \pi a^2 \,\sigma.$$

Taking moments about G,

$$GG_1(\pi a l\,\sigma) = GG_2(\pi a^2 \sigma) \quad \text{or} \quad GG_1 \cdot l = GG_2 \cdot a.$$

$$\therefore \quad \frac{h}{12} \cdot l = \frac{h}{4} a \quad \text{or} \quad \frac{a}{l} = \frac{1}{3}.$$

$$\therefore \quad \sin\alpha = 1/3 \quad \text{or} \quad \alpha = \sin^{-1} 1/3.$$

Example 2. From a solid cylinder of height H, a cone whose base coincides with the base of the cylinder is scooped out so that the mass centre of the remaining solid coincides with the vertex of the cone. Find the height of the cone. **(M.U., M.K.U.)**

Let h, a be the height and radius of the cone. Let AB be the axis of the cylinder whose midpoint is G. Let G_1 be the C.G. of the cone and G_2 be the C.G. of the residual. Then G_2 is the vertex of the cone. Now the masses of the cone and the residual are proportional to

$$1/3\, \pi a^2 h, \ \pi a^2 H - 1/3\, \pi a^2 h$$

or

$$h/3, \quad H - h/3$$

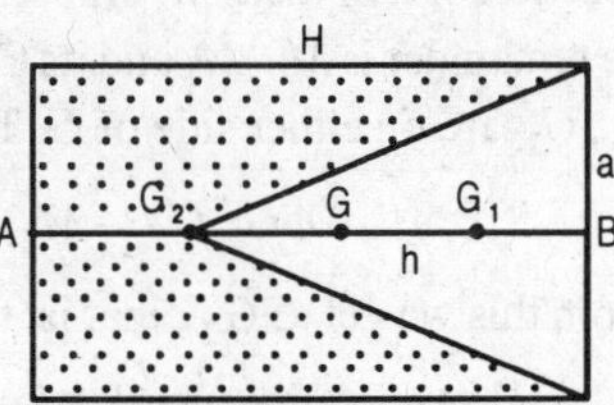

$$GG_1 = GB - G_1B = H/2 - h/4,$$

$$GG_2 = G_2B - GB = h - H/2.$$

Taking moments of the masses about G,

$$\frac{h}{3}\left(\frac{H}{2} - \frac{h}{4}\right) = \left(H - \frac{h}{3}\right)\left(h - \frac{H}{2}\right) \quad \text{or} \quad h^2 - 4Hh + 2H^2 = 0.$$

$$\therefore \quad h = (2+\sqrt{2})H \quad \text{or} \quad h = (2-\sqrt{2})H$$

of which only $h = \left(2-\sqrt{2}\right)H$ is admissible.

Example 3. From the circular lamina of radius a, a circular portion of radius $1/2\, a$ is so stamped out that its centre bisects a radius of the given lamina. Find the C.G. of the remaining portion. **(M.U., M.K.U.)**

Let AB be a diameter of the circular lamina, centre G. Let the circle on GB as diameter be cut off. The masses of the portion removed and the portion remaining are proportional to the areas

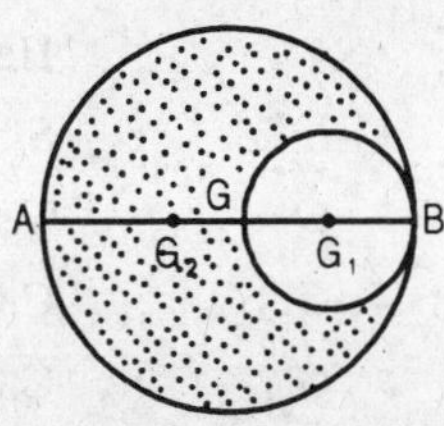

$$1/4\, \pi a^2, \ 3/4\, \pi a^2.$$

Their C.G.'s G_1, G_2 lie on AB. Taking moments of the masses about G,

$$GG_2\left(\tfrac{3}{4}\,\pi a^2\right) = GG_1\left(\tfrac{1}{4}\,\pi a^2\right) \text{ or } GG_2 = \tfrac{1}{3}\,GG_1$$

$$\therefore \quad GG_2 = \tfrac{1}{3}\cdot\tfrac{a}{2} = \tfrac{a}{6}.$$

The C.G. of the residual is at a distance $a/6$ from G.

Example 4. A square hole is punched out of a circular lamina of radius a, having a radius as its diagonal. Show that the distance of C.G. of the remainder from the centre of the circle is

$$\frac{a}{4\pi-2}.$$

(M.U., K.U., M.K.U.)

Let us assume

AB	:	A diameter
GB	:	A diagonal of the square
G	:	C.G. of circular lamina
G_1	:	C.G. of square lamina
G_2	:	C.G. of residual

Since the length of the diagonal is a, the side of the square is $\dfrac{a}{\sqrt{2}}$.

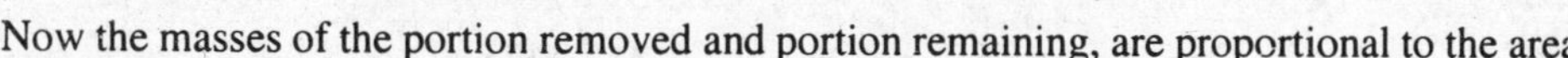

Now the masses of the portion removed and portion remaining, are proportional to the areas

$$\frac{a^2}{2},\ \pi a^2 - \frac{1}{2}a^2.$$

Taking moments of the masses about G,

$$GG_2(\pi a^2 - \frac{1}{2}a^2) = GG_1\left(\frac{a^2}{2}\right) \quad \text{or} \quad GG_2\,(2\pi - 1) = GG_1\,\cdot$$

$$\therefore \quad GG_2(2\pi-1) = \frac{a}{2} \quad \text{or} \quad GG_2 = \frac{a}{4\pi-2}.$$

EXERCISES

1. Find the C.G. of the segment of a sphere of radius a cut off by a plane at a distance c from the centre. **(M.U.)**

[Hint: Distance from the centre $= \dfrac{\pi\rho\displaystyle\int_c^a (a^2-x^2)\,x\,dx}{\pi\rho\displaystyle\int_c^a (a^2-x^2)\,dx} = \dfrac{3}{4}\dfrac{(a+c)^2}{2a+c}$]

2. Show that the distance of the C.G. of the surface of a sphere of radius a included between parallel planes at distances b and c from the centre is $\tfrac{1}{2}(b+c)$. **(M.U.)**

3. A circular lamina of radius a is cut into two portions along a chord which subtends an angle 2α at the centre. Show that the centres of mass of the two parts from the centre are at distances

$$\frac{4a\sin^3\alpha}{3(2\alpha - \sin 2\alpha)},\ \frac{4a\sin^3\alpha}{3(2\pi - 2\alpha + \sin 2\alpha)}.$$

(M.U., M.K.U.)

[Hint: For the smaller area the distance $= \dfrac{\int_{a\cos\alpha}^{a} x(2y)\,dx}{\int_{a\cos\alpha}^{a} 2y\,dx} = \dfrac{\int_{a\cos\alpha}^{a} x\sqrt{a^2-x^2}\,dx}{\int_{a\cos\alpha}^{a} \sqrt{a^2-x^2}\,dx}$.

Use $\sin^{-1}(\cos\alpha) = \sin^{-1}[\sin(\pi/2 - \pi)] = \pi/2 - \alpha$.]

4. A hemispherical solid of radius a is such that its density varies as the distance from the axis of symmetry. Show that the distance of its C.G. from the centre is $\dfrac{16a}{5\pi}$. **(M.U.)**

5. A solid circular cylinder is attached to a solid hemisphere of equal base, with bases together. Show that, if the centre of mass of the solid lies in the common base, the ratio of the height of the cylinder to the radius of the base is $1:\sqrt{2}$. **(M.U., A.U., K.U.)**

[Hint: Ht. and base radius of the cylinder : h, a. Taking moments about the mass centre,

$$\frac{h}{2}\left(\pi a^2 h\rho\right) = \frac{3a}{8}\left(\frac{2}{3}\pi a^3\rho\right) \text{ gives } \frac{h^2}{a^2} = \frac{1}{2}]$$

6. A homogeneous solid is formed by a cone of height a standing on a cylinder of height b, the base of the cone coinciding with one plane end of the cylinder. If the C.G. of the whole solid lies at the base of the cone, show that $a = b\sqrt{6}$. **(M.U.)**

[Hint: If r is the base radius, taking moments about the C.G,

$$\frac{a}{4}\left(\frac{1}{3}\pi r^2 a\rho\right) = \frac{b}{2}\left(\pi r^2 b\rho\right) \quad \text{or} \quad \frac{a^2}{6} = b^2]$$

7. A uniform solid is in the shape of a hemisphere surmounted by a cone. If the C.G. is at the centre of the hemisphere, compare the height h of the cone with the radius a of the hemisphere. **(M.K.U.)**

[Hint: Taking moments about the C.G.,

$$\frac{h}{4}\left(\frac{1}{3}\pi a^2 h\rho\right) = \frac{3a}{8}\left(\frac{2}{3}\pi a^3\rho\right) \quad \text{or} \quad \frac{h^2}{a^2} = \frac{3}{1}.]$$

8. A solid cone is attached to a solid hemisphere of equal base, with bases together. If the height of the cone equals its base radius a, show that the mass centre of the combined body is at a distance $7a/6$ from the vertex of the cone. **(M.U.)**

[Hint: Vertex : O; central radius of the sphere : AB;

$$OG\,(m_1 + m_2) = \left(\frac{3}{4}OA\right)m_1 + \left(OA + \frac{3}{8}AB\right)m_2,$$

where $m_1 = \frac{1}{3}\pi a^3\rho$, $m_2 = \frac{2}{3}\pi a^3\rho$, $OA = a, AB = a$]

9. A uniform rod is bent into the arc of a circle whose radius is equal to the length of the rod. Show that its mass centre lies on the middle radius at a distance $2a\sin\frac{1}{2}$ from the centre.

10. A piece of wire of given length l is bent into the form of a circular quadrant and its two bounding radii. Find the centre of gravity of the whole. **(M.U.)**

[Hint: Centre : O; Radius : a; C.G's of two radii, the arc and the whole wire : G_1, G_2, G; Masses at G_1, G_2 : $2a$, $\pi a/2$;

$$OG_1 = \frac{a}{2\sqrt{2}},\ OG_2 = \frac{4a}{\sqrt{2}\pi}.\ \text{So } OG = \frac{3\sqrt{2}}{\pi+4}a,$$

where $2a + \dfrac{\pi a}{2} = l$. Thus $OG = \dfrac{6\sqrt{2}}{(\pi+4)^2}l$.**]**

Note. In the hints in the following sums, unless otherwise specified, G_1, G_2 are the C.G's of the components of a body and G is the C.G. of the body.

11. From a solid sphere of radius R is removed a sphere of radius r, the distance between their centres being d. Show that the distance of the mass centre of the remainder from the centre of the sphere is

$$\frac{d\,r^3}{R^3 - r^3}.$$ **(M.U.)**

[Hint: $GG_2\left(\tfrac{4}{3}\pi R^3 - \tfrac{4}{3}\pi r^3\right) = GG_1\left(\tfrac{4}{3}\pi r^3\right)$, where $GG_1 = d$.**]**

12. Two spheres of radii a and b $(a > b)$ touch internally. Find the C.G. of the solid included between them. **(M.K.U.)**

[Hint: $G_2G\left(\tfrac{4}{3}\pi a^3 - \tfrac{4}{3}\pi b^3\right) = GG_1\left(\tfrac{4}{3}\pi b^3\right)$, $GG_1 = a - b$. Find G_2G.**]**

13. If a cone of height h is cut off by a plane bisecting its axis at right angles, show that the C.G. of the frustum is at a distance $\dfrac{45h}{56}$ from the vertex. **(M.U.)**

[Hint: $GG_2\left(\dfrac{1}{3}\pi a^2 h - \dfrac{1}{3}\pi\dfrac{a^2}{4}\dfrac{h}{2}\right) = GG_1\left(\dfrac{1}{3}\pi\dfrac{a^2}{4}\dfrac{h}{2}\right)$, where $GG_1 = \dfrac{h}{4} + \dfrac{1}{4}\left(\dfrac{h}{2}\right) = \dfrac{3}{8}h$.**]**

14. The radii of the faces of a frustum of a right circular cone, are 2 m. and 3 m. and the thickness of the frustum is 4 m. Show that the distance of the mass centre from the larger face is $33/19$ m.

15. Prove that, if the radius of one plane end-face of a frustum of a right circular cone is n times the radius of the other end-face, the C.G. divides the axis of the frustum in the ratio $3n^2 + 2n + 1 : n^2 + 2n + 3$. **(M.U., M.K.U.)**

16. The length and width of a rectangular lamina are $2a$, $2b$. A portion of it, in the form of a semicircle on the width as diameter, is cut off. Find the C.G. of the remainder. **(M.K.U.)**

[Hint: $GG_2\ (4ab - \tfrac{1}{2}\pi b^2) = GG_1\left(\tfrac{1}{2}\pi b^2\right)$, where $GG_1 = a - 4b/3\pi$.**]**

17. From a triangular lamina ABC, one quarter of its area is cut off by a line parallel to its base BC. Find the C.G. of the remainder. **(M.U.)**

[Hint: Let the line cut AB, AC and the median AD at B', C', D'. Then $\dfrac{b'}{b} = \dfrac{c'}{c} = \dfrac{AD'}{AD} = k$, say. Considering the areas

$$\frac{1}{2}b'c'\sin A = \frac{3}{4}\left(\frac{1}{2}bc\sin A\right) \text{ or } \frac{b'c'}{b\,c} = \frac{3}{4} \text{ or } k^2 = \frac{3}{4}.$$

So $AG' = \frac{2}{3}AD' = \frac{2}{3}k\,AD = \frac{AD}{\sqrt{3}}$, where G' is the C.G. of the triangle $AB'C'$.]

18. AD, BE, CF are the medians of a triangle ABC and G is their point of concurrence.

(*i*) If the portion $AFGE$ is removed, show that the C.G. of the remainder is on GD at a distance $\frac{7}{12}GD$ from D. **(M.U.)**

(*ii*) Show that the centroid of the quadrilateral $AFGE$ divides AD in the ratio 7 : 11. **(M.U.)**

[Hint: Let area $ABC = 4\Delta$, $AD = 6x$. Then it follows

Figure	*C.G.*	*Dist. from D*	*Area*
ΔABC	G	$DG = 2x$	4Δ
ΔAEF	G_1	$DG_1 = 4x$	Δ
ΔGEF	G_2	$DG_2 = 2x + 2x/3$	$\Delta/3$
$GFBDCEG$	G_3	$DG_3 = ?$	$8\Delta/3$

$$\therefore\ 2x\cdot 4\Delta = 4x\cdot\Delta + \frac{8x}{3}\cdot\frac{\Delta}{3} + DG_3\cdot\frac{8\Delta}{3};\ DG_3 = \frac{7}{12}(2x) = \frac{7}{12}GD\,]$$

19. One corner of a square lamina of side $2a$ is cut off along the line joining the midpoints of its adjacent sides. Show that the distance of the C.G. of the remainder from the opposite corner is

$$\frac{19\sqrt{2}}{21}a.$$ **(M.U.)**

20. A solid right cone has its base scooped out so that the hollow part is a right cone on the same base. Find the height of the scooped out portion if the C.G. of the remainder coincides with the vertex of the hollow cone. **(M.U.)**

[Hint: h, x : Heights of original and scooped out cones.

$$GG_2\left(\tfrac{1}{3}\pi a^2 h - \tfrac{1}{3}\pi a^2 x\right) = GG_1\left(\tfrac{1}{3}\pi\, a^2 x\right),$$

where $GG_1 = h/4 - x/4$. $GG_2 = x - h/4$.]

21. From a circular disc of radius a, a circular portion of radius $a/2$ is cut off. Find the distance between the centres of the disc and the hole, if the centre of mass of the remainder is on the circumference of the hole. **(M.U.)**

[Hint: Let $GG_1 = x$. Then $\left(\frac{a}{2} - x\right)\left(\frac{3\pi}{4}a^2\right) = x\left(\frac{\pi a^2}{4}\right)$. Find x.]

22. A circular hole of radius a is cut off from a circular disc of radius $3a$. If the C.G. of the remaining area is at a distance $a/6$ from the centre of the disc, find where the hole has been cut. **(M.U.)**

[Hint: $GG_1 = x;\ x\left(\pi a^2\right) = a/6\left(8\pi a^2\right)$ or $x = 4a/3$]

23. A quadrant is removed from a circular lamina of radii a. Find the position of the C.G. of the remainder. **(M.U.)**

[**Hint:** $3\cdot GG_2 = 1\cdot GG_1 = \frac{4\sqrt{2}}{3\pi}a. \therefore GG_2 = \frac{4\sqrt{2}}{9\pi}a.$]

24. A wire is bent in the form of a circular arc and its bounding radii, the arc being greater than a semicircle. If the C.G. of the whole wire is at the centre of the circle, show that the angle 2α between the bounding radii is given by

$\tan 2\alpha = 4/3$. **(M.U.)**

[**Hint:** The C.G. of the bigger arc and the radii and the C.G. of the bigger arc and smaller arc are the same point, namely, the centre O. So the moment of the mass of the radii about O equals the moment of the smaller arc. Thus

$$\frac{a}{2}\cos\alpha\cdot 2a = \frac{a\sin\alpha}{\alpha}\cdot 2\alpha a \text{ or } \tan\alpha = \frac{1}{2};\ \tan 2\alpha = \frac{2\cdot 1/2}{1-1/4}.]$$

6.3 A HANGING BODY IN EQUILIBRIUM

Let A be a point from which a body is hung and G, the mass centre of the body. Then there are just two forces acting on the body, namely,

(*i*) Earth's gravitation acting at G vertically downwards.

(*ii*) Reaction acting at A.

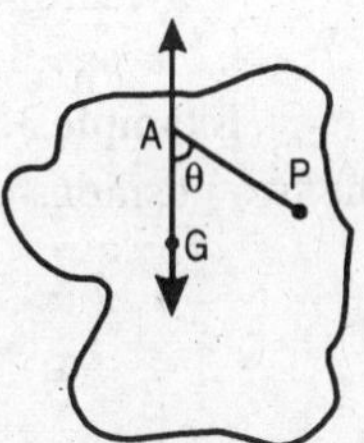

If the body is to be in equilibrium, then necessarily these two forces should act along the same line. This requires that A and G are in the same vertical line and G is below A. Thus, if AP is a line fixed in the rigid body, then, in the equilibrium position, the inclination of AP to the vertical can be obtained by finding the angle θ it makes with the vertical. This θ may be obtained using the formula

$$\tan\theta = \frac{|\bar{a}\times\bar{b}|}{\bar{a}\cdot\bar{b}} \quad \text{or} \quad \cos\theta = \frac{\bar{a}\cdot\bar{b}}{|\bar{a}||\bar{b}|},$$

where $\bar{a}, \bar{b}$ are vectors parallel to $\overline{AP}$, $\overline{AG}$ respectively.

EXAMPLES

Example 1. A triangular lamina ABC right angled at A is suspended from A and $AB = 3\,AC$. Show that, if the hypotenuse is inclined to the vertical at an angle θ, then $\sin\theta = 3/5$.

(M.U., M.K.U.)

The C.G. lies on the median AD. So AD is vertical. The triangle is actually half of the rectangle $ABPC$ as shown in the figure and θ is the angle between the diagonals.

If M is the mid point of AC

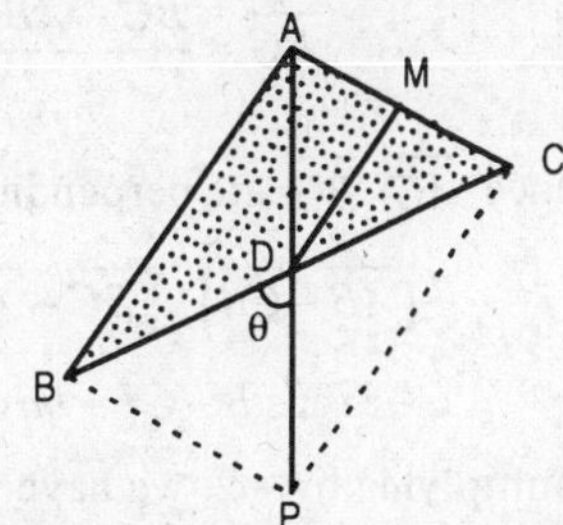

$DM : MA : AD = 3 : 1 : \sqrt{10}$.

$$\therefore \quad \sin\frac{\theta}{2} = \frac{1}{\sqrt{10}},\ \cos\frac{\theta}{2} = \frac{3}{\sqrt{10}}.$$

$$\sin\theta = 2\sin\frac{\theta}{2}\cos\frac{\theta}{2}$$

$$= 2\cdot\frac{1}{\sqrt{10}}\cdot\frac{3}{\sqrt{10}} = \frac{3}{5}.$$

Example 2. Two uniform rods OA, OB of lengths $2a$, $2b$ rigidly jointed at O so that angle AOB is a right angle. When the system hangs from A, it is in equilibrium. Find the angle θ made by OA with the vertical.

Let $\bar{i}, \bar{j}$ be the unit vectors parallel to $\overline{AO}$, $\overline{OB}$ and M, N the midpoints of OA, OB. Let G be the mass centre of the system, then

$$\overline{AM} = a\bar{i},$$

$$\overline{AN} = \overline{AO} + \overline{ON} = 2a\bar{i} + b\bar{j}$$

and masses of the rods are proportional to their lengths $2a$, $2b$.

$$\therefore \quad \overline{AG} = \frac{(2a)\overline{AM} + (2b)\overline{AN}}{2a+2b} = \frac{2a(a\bar{i}) + 2b(2a\bar{i} + b\bar{j})}{2a+2b}$$

$$= \frac{(a^2 + 2ab)\,\bar{i} + b^2\,\bar{j}}{a+b}.$$

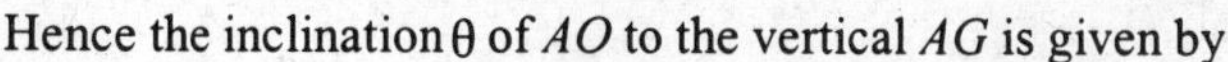

Hence the inclination θ of AO to the vertical AG is given by

$$\tan\theta = \frac{\bar{j} \text{ component of } \overline{AG}}{\bar{i} \text{ component of } \overline{AG}} = \frac{b^2}{a^2 + 2ab}.$$

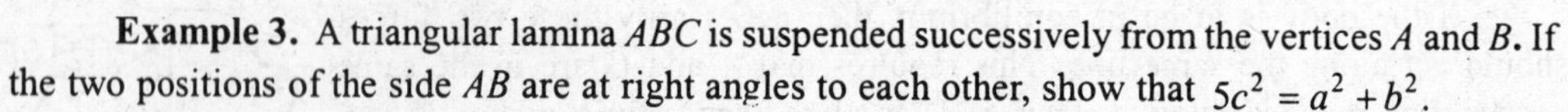

Example 3. A triangular lamina ABC is suspended successively from the vertices A and B. If the two positions of the side AB are at right angles to each other, show that $5c^2 = a^2 + b^2$.

(M.U.)

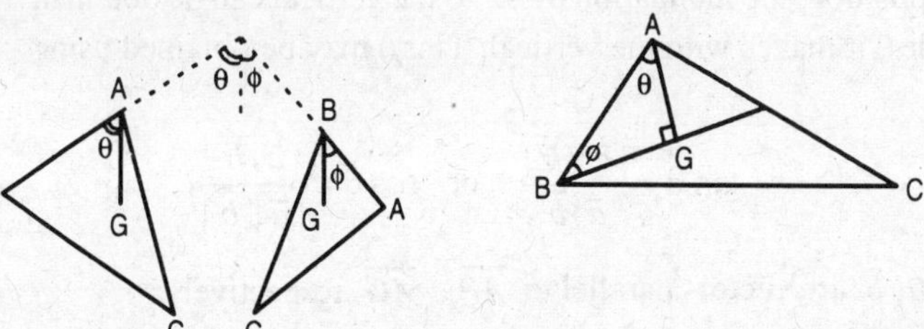

Let G be the mass centre of the lamina and $\angle GAB = \theta$, $\angle GBA = \phi$. When the lamina is hung from A, AG is vertical and when the lamina is hung from B, BG is vertical. The positions of the side AB in these two cases are given to be perpendicular. So, from the figure, it can be seen that $\theta + \phi = 90^\circ$. But

$$\overline{AG} = \frac{2}{3}\overline{AD} = \frac{2}{3}\cdot\frac{1}{2}\left(\overline{AB} + \overline{AC}\right) = \frac{\overline{AB} + \overline{AC}}{3} = \frac{\overline{AB} - \overline{CA}}{3}.$$

$$\overline{BG} = \frac{\overline{BC} - \overline{AB}}{3}.$$

Since $\overline{AG}$, $\overline{BG}$ are perpendicular, $\overline{AG}\cdot\overline{BG} = 0$. So

$$\left(\overline{AB} - \overline{CA}\right)\cdot\left(\overline{BC} - \overline{AB}\right) = 0$$

$$-ca\cos B - C^2 + ba\cos C - bc\cos A = 0.$$

Multiplying by -2, we have

$$2ca\cos B + 2c^2 - 2ab\cos C + 2bc\cos A = 0.$$

$$\therefore \quad \left(a^2+c^2-b^2\right)+2c^2-\left(a^2+b^2-c^2\right)+\left(b^2+c^2-a^2\right)=0$$

$$5c^2-a^2-b^2=0 \quad \text{or} \quad 5c^2=a^2+b^2.$$

Example 4. *AB*, *BC*, *CD* are three equal rods firmly jointed so as to form the three successive sides of a regular hexagon. The system is suspended from *A*. Show that

(*i*) *AC* is vertical. **(M.U., A.U.)**

(*ii*) *CD* is horizontal. **(M.U., K.U.)**

(*i*) Let $\bar{i}$, $\bar{j}$ be the unit vectors parallel and perpendicular to *AB*. Let the mass and length of each rod be $2m$, a. Each rod is equivalent to particles of masses m, m at their ends. Thus the system is equivalent to

$$m,\ m+m,\ m+m,\ m$$

at the vertices *A*, *B*, *C*, *D*. Now we have

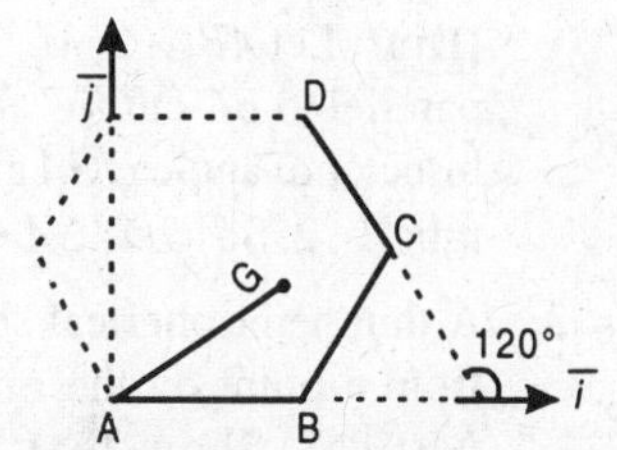

$$\overline{AB} = a\bar{i}$$

$$\overline{AC} = a\bar{i} + a\left(\cos 60^\circ\,\bar{i} + \sin 60^\circ\,\bar{j}\right) = \frac{3a}{2}\left(\bar{i} + \frac{1}{\sqrt{3}}\bar{j}\right)$$

$$\overline{AD} = 2a\left(\cos 60^\circ\,\bar{i} + \sin 60^\circ\,\bar{j}\right) = a\left(\bar{i} + \sqrt{3}\bar{j}\right)$$

If *G* is the C.G. of the system,

$$\overline{AG} = \frac{m\bar{0} + 2m\,\overline{AB} + 2m\,\overline{AC} + m\,\overline{AD}}{m+2m+2m+m} = a\left(\bar{i} + \frac{1}{\sqrt{3}}\bar{j}\right)$$

It is evident that $\overline{AG}$ and $\overline{AC}$ are parallel. But *AG* is vertical. So *AC* is vertical.

(*ii*) $\overline{CD} = 2a\left(\cos 120^\circ\,\bar{i} + \sin 120^\circ\,\bar{j}\right) = a\left(-\bar{i} + \sqrt{3}\bar{j}\right)$

$$\therefore \quad \overline{AG}\cdot\overline{CD} = a\left(\bar{i} + \frac{1}{\sqrt{3}}\bar{j}\right)\cdot a\left(-\bar{i} + \sqrt{3}\bar{j}\right) = a^2(-1+1) = 0$$

Therefore *AG* and *CD* are perpendicular. But *AG* is vertical. So *CD* is horizontal.

Example 5. A pack of cards is laid on a table and each card projects in the direction of the length of the pack beyond the one below it. If each projects as far as possible, show that the distances between the extremities of successive cards will form a harmonic progression.

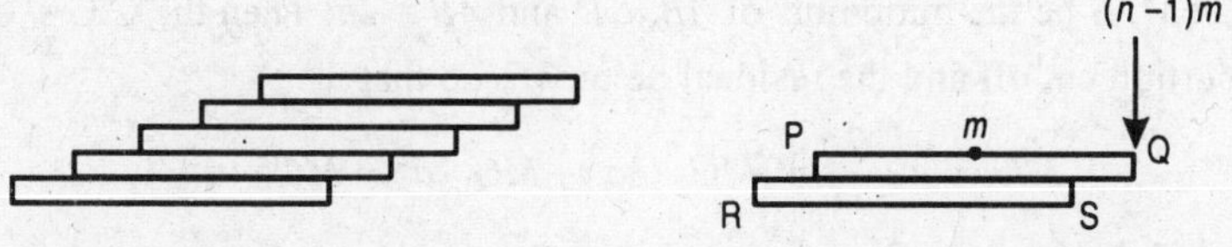

Let *PQ* and *RS* be the n_{th} and $(n+1)_{\text{th}}$ cards, counted from the top, and *M*, the midpoint of *PQ*. Now $n - 1$ cards rest on *PQ*. Unless the mass centre of this lot lies above *PQ*, this lot will topple. So, in the limiting equilibrium position, this mass centre should be just above *Q*. Similarly, for the n cards to be in the limiting equilibrium on *RS*, the mass centre of these n cards should be above *S*. In such a situation *S* should be the mass centre of the mass m and $(n - 1)m$ situated at *M* and *Q*, where m is the mass of each card. In this situation S divides MQ in the ratio $n-1:1$ and consequently $SQ = a/n$, where a is half the length of the card. Here SQ is the distance between the extremities of the n_{th} and $(n+1)_{th}$ cards. So such distances considered from the topmost card are obtained by setting 1, 2, 3, ... for n in a/n as $a/1, a/2, a/3, ...$ These are in H.P.

EXERCISES

1. A cone whose height is equal to four times the radius of its base is hung from a point in the circumference of its base. Show that the base and the axis of the cone are equally inclined to the vertical. **(M.U.)**

[**Hint:** If A is the point of suspension, G the centre of gravity and C the centre of the base, then $AC = GC$ and so angle GAC = angle AGC, where AG is vertical.]

2. Find the vertical angle of a solid cone in order that, when suspended from the midpoint of a generator, the base and the axis may be equally inclined to the vertical. **(M.K.U.)**

[**Hint:** Let AB, AC, M, G be the axis, a generator, its midpoint and C.G. Let the line through G parallel to BC cut AC at D. It is given that GD, GA are equally inclined to GM. So GM is the bisector of angle DGA and divides AD in the ratio of the sides GA, GD. But M divides DA in the ratio 1 : 2. So $GD : GA = 1:2$; $\tan GAD = 1/2$]

3. A thin hemispherical shell closed by a plane base is filled with water and when suspended from a point on the rim of the base, it hangs with the base, inclined at an angle α to the vertical. Show that the ratio of the weight of the water to that of the shell is $\tan\alpha - 1/3 : 3/8 - \tan\alpha$. **(M.U.)**

[**Hint:** Let AO be the middle radius $(O$: centre, $AO = a)$. Let G_1, G_2, G be the C.G's of the shell with the lid, the water, and the shell and water. Then

$$OG_1 = a/3, \quad OG_2 = 3a/8, \quad OG = a\tan\alpha.$$

If w_1, w_2 are the weights of the shell and the water taking moments about G,

$$GG_2 \cdot w_2 = GG_1 \cdot w_1 \quad \text{or} \quad \frac{w_2}{w_1} = \frac{GG_1}{GG_2} = \frac{OG - OG_1}{OG_2 - OG}]$$

4. A square lamina $ABCD$ whose diagonals meet at G. The triangle CGD is cut off and the remaining part is hung at A. Prove that, in the position of equilibrium, AB makes an angle θ with the vertical such that

$$\tan\theta = 7/9.$$ **(M.U., M.K.U.)**

[**Hint:** Let M, N be the midpoints of AB, CD and $AB = 2a$. Then the C.G's G, G_1, G_2 of the square, portion cut off and the residual lie on MN so that

$$MG_1 = a + \frac{2a}{3}; \quad MG_2 \cdot 3a^2 + MG_1 \cdot a^2 = MG \cdot 4a^2.$$

$$\therefore MG_2 = \frac{7a}{9} \text{ or } \tan\theta = \frac{7}{9}]$$

5. From a square lamina $ABCE$ a triangle ADE is cut away, where D is the middle point of CE. If the lamina $ABCD$ is suspended from A and if θ is the angle between AD and the vertical, show that

$$\tan\theta = \frac{14}{27}.$$ **(M.U.)**

[Hint: Let $\bar{i}$, $\bar{j}$ be the unit vectors along AB, AE and $AB = 2a$. If G, G_1, G_2 are the C.G's of the square, portion cut off and the residual (with masses $4a^2$, a^2, $3a^2$). Then

$$\overline{AG} = a(\bar{i} + \bar{j}),\ \ \overline{AG_1} = a/3(\bar{i} + 4\bar{j});\ 4\overline{AG} = \overline{AG_1} + 3\overline{AG_2}.$$

So $\overline{AG_2} = a/9 \cdot (11\bar{i} + 8\bar{j}) \cdot$ But $\overline{AD} = a(\bar{i} + 2\bar{j})$.

$$\therefore \qquad \tan\theta = \frac{|\overline{AG_2} \times \overline{AD}|}{\overline{AG_2} \cdot \overline{AD}} = \frac{14}{27}.]$$

6. A lamina is in the form of an isosceles right angled triangle ABC with a semicircle described on its hypotenuse BC. It is hung from C. Show that, if θ is the angle made by CB with the vertical,

$$\tan\theta = \frac{2}{6 + 3\pi}.$$

(M.U., M.K.U., K.U.)

[Hint: Let O be the midpoint of BC and $AO = a$. Then $BO = CO = a$. Let G, G_1, G_2 be the C.G.'s of the lamina, triangular portion, semicircular portion. Then

$$OG_1 = \frac{a}{3},\ \ OG_2 = \frac{4a}{3\pi};\ \ OG \cdot \left(1 + \frac{\pi}{2}\right)a^2 = \frac{4a}{3\pi} \cdot \frac{\pi a^2}{2} - \frac{a}{3} \cdot a^2.$$

So $OG = \dfrac{2a}{6 + 3\pi}$ and $\tan\theta = \dfrac{OG}{a} = \dfrac{2}{6 + 3\pi}$.]

7 STABILITY OF EQUILIBRIUM

7.1 STABILITY OF EQUILIBRIUM

A body in equilibrium is slightly disturbed. If the body tends to regain the original position of equilibrium, then the equilibrium is said to be stable; otherwise, it is said to be unstable. If, however, the body remains in equilibrium, in the new position also, then the equilibrium is said to be neutral.

7.1.1 Stability of spherical bodies

Now we consider the stability of equilibrium of a body on another assuming that the surfaces of the bodies in the neighbourhood of the point of contact are spherical.

Bookwork 7.1. A body is in equilibrium resting on another fixed body. The portions of the surfaces of the bodies around the points of contact are spherical and rough enough to prevent sliding. To find the condition for stability of equilibrium.

Let us have the following assumptions for the lower sphere and the upper sphere.

O	:	Centre of lower sphere
R	:	Radius of lower sphere

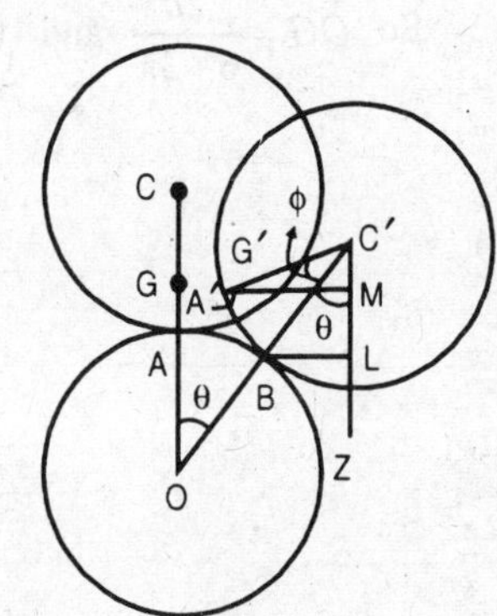

Equilibrium position.

C	:	Centre of upper sphere
r	:	Radius of upper sphere
A	:	Pt. of contact of upper sphere
G	:	C.G. of upper sphere

Displaced position.

C'	:	Centre of upper sphere
G'	:	C.G. of upper sphere
A'	:	Position of A
h	:	AG and $A'G'$

Let $C'Z$ be the vertical through C' and B, the point of contact in the displaced position. Let

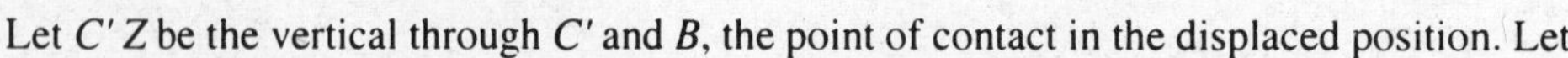

$$\underline{|COC'} = \underline{|OC'Z} = \theta,\ A'B.\ \underline{|BC'A'} = \phi.$$

Rolling condition. Now arc AB = arc $A'B$. That is,

$$R\theta = r\phi \qquad \text{or} \qquad \phi = \frac{R}{r}\theta.$$

In the displaced position, there are only two forces on the upper sphere, namely,

(*i*) Weight at G'

(*ii*) Reaction at B.

So, if G' lies on the left of the vertical through B, then the upper sphere rolls backward and hence the equilibrium is stable. Thus, if

$$G'M > BL \quad \text{or} \quad G'C' \sin(\theta+\phi) > BC' \sin\theta \qquad ...(1)$$

where L, M are the feet of the perpendiculars drawn from G', B to $C'Z$. We know that, when θ is small, $\sin\theta=\theta$ nearly. Now the displacement is small and hence θ is small. Thus (1) becomes

$$G'C'(\theta+\phi) > BC'\theta \quad \text{or} \quad (r-h)(\theta+\phi) > r\theta$$

i.e.,
$$r\phi-h\theta-h\phi > 0 \quad \text{or} \quad R\theta-h\theta-\frac{hR}{r}\theta > 0$$

i.e.,
$$rR-rh-hR > 0 \quad \text{or} \quad \frac{1}{h} > \frac{1}{r}+\frac{1}{R}.$$

So the equilibrium is

Stable if $\frac{1}{h} > \frac{1}{r}+\frac{1}{R}$,

Unstable if $\frac{1}{h} < \frac{1}{r}+\frac{1}{R}$.

Note 1. Stability requires a low height for the C.G. of the upper body so that $1/h$ is large enough to exceed $1/r + 1/R$.

Note 2. Flat surfaces are surfaces of infinite spheres of radii ∞.

Remark. Suppose that the outer sphere contains the upper sphere within it as in the figure. Then it can be shown that the equilibrium of the upper sphere is stable if

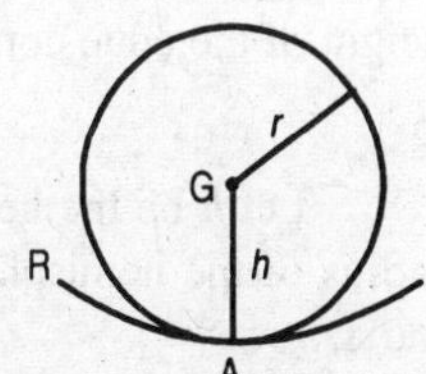

$$\frac{1}{h} > \frac{1}{r}-\frac{1}{R},$$

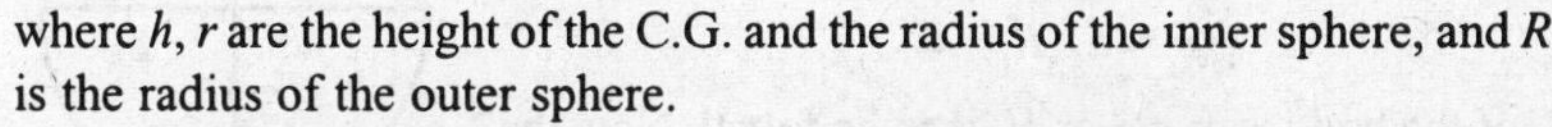

where h, r are the height of the C.G. and the radius of the inner sphere, and R is the radius of the outer sphere.

EXAMPLES

Example 1. A rough solid hemisphere rests on a fixed rough sphere of equal radius. Show that the equilibrium is

(*i*) Stable if the flat surface of the hemisphere rests on the sphere **(M.U.)**

(*ii*) Unstable if the curved surface of the hemisphere rests on the sphere. **(M.U., M.K.U., C.U.)**

(*i*) Let the radii of the spheres be a, a so that, in the formula,

$$r=\infty, \quad R=a, \quad h=3a/8.$$

In this $r=\infty$, since the radius of curvature of a plane is infinite. Thus we have

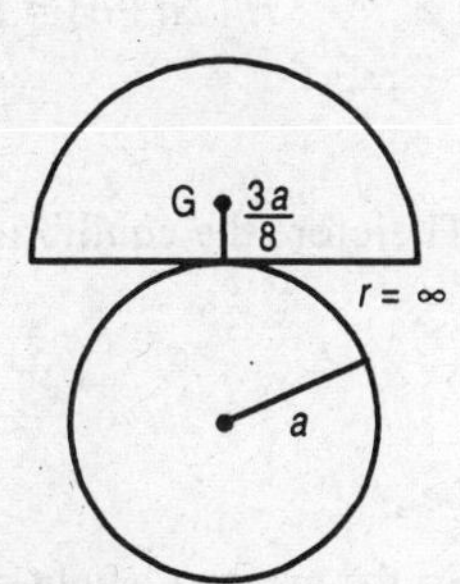

$$\frac{1}{h}=\frac{8}{3a}.$$

Also we have

$$\frac{1}{r}+\frac{1}{R}=\frac{1}{\infty}+\frac{1}{a}=\frac{1}{a}$$

$$\therefore \qquad \frac{1}{h} > \frac{1}{r} + \frac{1}{R}.$$

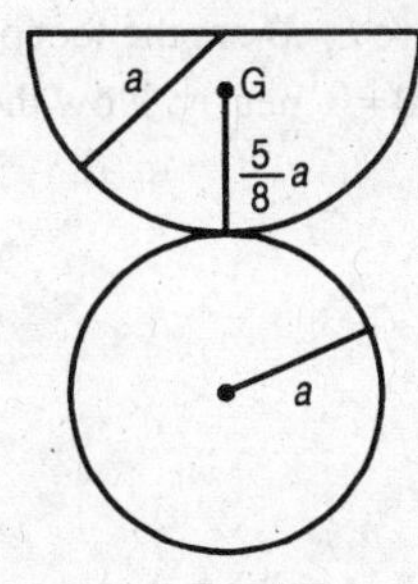

Therefore the equilibrium is stable.

(*ii*) In this case we have

$$r = a,\ R = a,\ h = {}^{5a}\!/_{8}.$$

Therefore

$$\frac{1}{h} = \frac{8}{5a},$$

$$\frac{1}{r} + \frac{1}{R} = \frac{1}{a} + \frac{1}{a} = \frac{2}{a}.$$

$$\therefore \qquad \frac{1}{h} < \frac{1}{r} + \frac{1}{R}.$$

Therefore the equilibrium is unstable.

Example 2. A solid consisting of a right circular cone and a hemisphere on the same base rests on a rough horizontal plane, the hemisphere being in contact with the plane. Show that the greatest height of the cone consistent with stability is $\sqrt{3}$ times the radius of the hemisphere.

(M.U., A.U., C.U.)

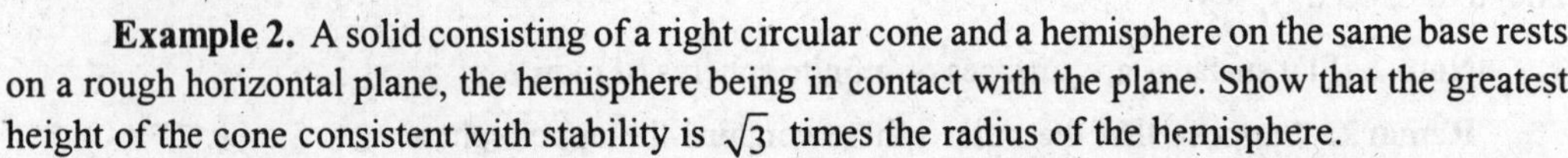

Let h be the height and a, the base radius of the cone. Then a is the radius of the hemisphere which is in contact with the plane. So, in the formula,

$$r = a,\ R = \infty$$

and the height of the C. G. of the body, say AG or H, is to be found. Now the masses of the hemisphere and the cone are proportional to

$$\frac{1}{2}\frac{4\pi a^3}{3},\ \frac{1}{3}\pi a^2 h \quad \text{or} \quad 2a,\ h.$$

The distances of their C.G's from A are

$$\frac{5a}{8},\ a + \frac{h}{4}.$$

Therefore, taking moments of the masses about A,

$$H(2a+h) = \frac{5a}{8}\cdot 2a + \left(a + \frac{h}{4}\right)h$$

i.e., $\quad 8H(2a+h) = 10a^2 + 8ah + 2h^2$

$$\therefore \qquad \frac{1}{H} = \frac{4(2a+h)}{5a^2+4ah+h^2}.$$

Therefore the equilibrium is stable if

$$\frac{4(2a+h)}{5a^2+4ah+h^2} > \frac{1}{a} + \frac{1}{\infty} \quad \text{or} \quad 8a^2 > 5a^2 + h^2$$

i.e., $$3a^2 > h^2 \quad \text{or} \quad \sqrt{3}a > h.$$

So the greatest height of the cone for stability is $\sqrt{3}\,a$.

EXERCISES

1. A right circular solid cone of height h rests on a fixed rough sphere of radius a. Show that the equilibrium is stable if $h < 4a$. **(M.U., K.U.)**

   [Hint: $r = \infty$, $R = a$, $H = h/4$ where H is the height of the C.G. from the point of contact. So equilibrium is stable if

$$\frac{1}{h/4} > \frac{1}{\infty} + \frac{1}{a} \text{ or } \frac{4}{h} > \frac{1}{a} \text{ or } 4a > h]$$

2. A right circular solid cylinder of height h rests on a fixed rough sphere of radius a. Show that the equilibrium is stable if $h < 2a$.

3. A uniform closed cubical box of edge a and made of a thin sheet is placed on the top of a fixed sphere, the centre of a face of the cube being in contact with the highest point of the sphere. Show that the least radius of the sphere for which the equilibrium is stable, is $a/2$. **(M.U., M.K.U)**

   [Hint: $\frac{1}{a/2} > \frac{1}{\infty} + \frac{1}{R}$, where R is the radius of the sphere]

4. A solid consisting of a right circular cylinder and a hemisphere on the same base rests on a rough horizontal plane with the hemisphere in contact with the plane. Show that the greatest height of the cylinder consistent with stability is $1/\sqrt{2}$ times the radius of the hemisphere. **(M.U., C.U., M.K.U.)**

   [Hint: Let h be the height and a the base radius of the cylinder. Then $R = \infty$, $r = a$ and the height of the mass centre above the horizontal plane $= \dfrac{5a^2 + 12ah + 6h^2}{8a + 12h}$]

5. A sphere of negligible mass and of radius a carries a mass m at the highest point. Show that the greatest possible radius of a rough hemispherical bowl inside which the sphere can rest in stable equilibrium, is $2a$.

   [Hint: Stable if $\frac{1}{h} > \frac{1}{r} - \frac{1}{R}$. Let R be the radius of the bowl. Then $h = 2a$, $r = a$, $R = R$]

6. A sphere of negligible weight and of radius a rests inside a fixed rough hemispherical bowl of radius less than $2a$. Show that, however large a weight is attached to the highest point of the sphere, the equilibrium is stable.

7.2 STABILITY USING DIFFERENTIATION

When a body is in equilibrium, the height z of the C.G. of the body may be expressed as a function of a single variable, say x. In this case

$$\frac{dz}{dx} = 0$$

gives the value of x, say x_0, for which the body is in equilibrium. If the corresponding

$$\frac{d^2z}{dx^2} < 0,$$

then z is a maximum at $x = x_0$ and a small disturbance will cause a decrease in z and so the body falls and hence the equilibrium is unstable.

EXERCISES

1. A uniform beam of length l rests with its ends on two smooth planes which intersect in a horizontal line. If the inclinations of the planes to the horizontal are α and $\beta, (\beta > \alpha)$, show that in the equilibrium position, the inclination θ of the beam to the horizontal is given by $\tan\theta = \frac{1}{2}(\cot\alpha - \cot\beta)$ and that the equilibrium is unstable.

[**Hint:** Beam : AB; CG: G, midpoint of AB. So

$$\text{Ht. of } G = \tfrac{1}{2}(\text{ht. of } A + \text{ht. of } B) = \tfrac{1}{2}(OA\sin\beta + OB\sin\alpha),$$

where O is the meet of the planes. By sine formula,

$$\frac{OA}{\sin(\theta+\alpha)} = \frac{OB}{\sin(\beta-\theta)} = \frac{AB}{\sin[180^\circ-(\alpha+\beta)]}.$$

$$OG = z = \frac{1}{2}\left[\frac{l\sin(\theta+\alpha)}{\sin(\alpha+\beta)}\sin\beta + \frac{l\sin(\beta-\theta)}{\sin(\alpha+\beta)}\sin\alpha\right]$$

$\frac{dz}{d\theta} = 0$ gives $2\tan\theta = \cot\alpha - \cot\beta$; $\frac{d^2z}{d\theta^2} < 0$.]

2. Two uniform rods each of length $2a$ are freely joined and rest in a symmetrical position on a smooth sphere of radius r. Show that

$$a\sin^3\theta = r\cos\theta$$

and that the equilibrium is stable.

[**Hint:** In the equilibrium position, if 2θ is the angle between the rods, the height z of the mass centre above the centre of the sphere is

$z = r\operatorname{cosec}\theta - a\cos\theta$; $\frac{dz}{d\theta} = 0$ gives $a\sin^3\theta = r\cos\theta$ and $\frac{d^2z}{d\theta^2} > 0$ and so equilibrium is stable]

VIRTUAL WORK

8.1 VIRTUAL WORK

When bodies were in equilibrium, we obtained earlier some or other results pertaining to the configuration of the bodies, using resolved components and moments of the forces. We now obtain some of those results by the principle of virtual work.

Work. A force is said to do work when its point of application moves. Let $\overline{F}$ be a force acting on a particle. When the particle moves from a point whose position vector is $\overline{r}$ to a neighbouring point whose position vector is $\overline{r}+\Delta\overline{r}$, the work done by the force in this displacement of $\Delta\overline{r}$ is defined to be the scalar quantity

$$\overline{F}\cdot\Delta\overline{r}.$$

Consider a dynamical system, made up of several rigid bodies. Now we define an imaginary possible displacement called virtual displacement and the corresponding virtual work.

Definition. Virtual displacement. A change in the configuration of a dynamical system, as a result of any arbitrary infinitesimal change in the coordinates of the system, is called a virtual displacement of the system.

Definition. Virtual work. The work done by the forces in a virtual displacement, is called the *virtual work* done by the forces.

8.1.1 Principle of Virtual work.

The following result is called the *principle of virtual work.*

Bookwork 8.1. If a dynamical system is in equilibrium, then the work done by the applied forces in a virtual displacement, is zero, provided the virtual displacement is such that the forces, due to the constraints imposed on the system, do no work.

Let the system be constituted by n particles of masses m_1, m_2, ...,m_n and their position vectors with reference to a fixed point O, be $\overline{r}_1,\overline{r}_2,.....,\overline{r}_n$. The forces, acting on each particle may be classified as

(*i*) Applied forces

(*ii*) Internal forces due to its contact with other particles

(*iii*) Forces due to the external constraints imposed on the system (*i.e.,* the reactions due to the contact with the external bodies on which the particle is constrained to move).

Let the forces on a general particle of mass m_i be

(*i*) $\overline{F}_{ii}$, the applied force

(*ii*) $\overline{F}_{ij}$, $i \neq j$, the reaction exerted by m_j on m_i due to mutual contacts

(*iii*) $\overline{F}_i$, the force due to the external constraints.

Of these forces, $\overline{F}_{ij}$ and $\overline{F}_{ji}$ are equal in magnitude but opposite in direction. So

$$\overline{F}_{ij}+\overline{F}_{ji}=\overline{0}, \quad i \neq j. \qquad ...(1)$$

Let $\Delta\bar{r}_1, \Delta\bar{r}_2, ..., \Delta\bar{r}_n$ be the infinitesimal displacements of $m_1, m_2, ..., m_n$ in a virtual displacement in which the forces due to the constraints imposed on the system do no work. If m_i and m_j are particles having contact with each other, then $\Delta\bar{r}_i = \Delta\bar{r}_j$ and consequently

$$\begin{aligned} \bar{F}_{ij}\cdot\Delta\,\bar{r}_i + \bar{F}_{ji}\cdot\Delta\,\bar{r}_j &= \bar{F}_{ij}\cdot\Delta\,\bar{r}_i + \bar{F}_{ji}\cdot\Delta\,\bar{r}_i \\ &= (\bar{F}_{ij} + \bar{F}_{ji})\cdot\Delta\,\bar{r}_i \\ &= (\bar{0})\cdot\Delta\,\bar{r}_i \qquad \text{by (1)} \\ &= 0. \end{aligned} \qquad ...(2)$$

The equation of motion of m_i is

$$m_i\,\ddot{\bar{r}}_i = \bar{F}_{ii} + (\bar{F}_{i1} + ... + \bar{F}_{i(i-1)} + \bar{F}_{i(i+1)} + ... + \bar{F}_{in}) + \bar{F}_i.$$

Multiplying this scalarly by $\Delta\bar{r}_i$, we get

$$m_i\,\ddot{\bar{r}}_i\cdot\Delta\bar{r}_i = \bar{F}_{ii}\cdot\Delta\bar{r}_i + (\Sigma\,\bar{F}_{ij},\, i \neq j)\cdot\Delta\bar{r}_i + \bar{F}_i\,.\Delta\bar{r}_i.$$

Adding such equations for all of $m_1, m_2, ..., m_n$,

$$\begin{aligned} &m_1\,\ddot{\bar{r}}_1\cdot\Delta\bar{r}_1 + m_2\,\ddot{\bar{r}}_2\cdot\Delta\bar{r}_2 + ... + m_n\,\ddot{\bar{r}}_n\cdot\Delta\bar{r}_n \\ &\qquad = \bar{F}_{11}\cdot\Delta\bar{r}_1 + \bar{F}_{22}\cdot\Delta\bar{r}_2 + ... + \bar{F}_{nn}\cdot\Delta\bar{r}_n + W_1 + W_2, \text{ say,} \end{aligned}$$

of which W_1 vanishes by (2) and W_2 vanishes by the imposed condition that the virtual displacement is such that the forces due to the constraints do no work. Therefore

$$\begin{aligned} m_1\,\ddot{\bar{r}}_1\cdot\Delta\bar{r}_1 + m_2\,\ddot{\bar{r}}_2\cdot\Delta\bar{r}_2 + ... &= \bar{F}_{11}\cdot\Delta\bar{r}_1 + \bar{F}_{22}\cdot\Delta\bar{r}_2 + ... \\ &= \text{Virtual work done by the applied forces.} \end{aligned}$$

But the system is in equilibrium. So the accelerations $\ddot{\bar{r}}_1, \ddot{\bar{r}}_2, ..., \ddot{\bar{r}}_n$ are zero. Therefore

Virtual work done by the applied forces = 0.

Remark 1. Conversely, if the virtual work done by the applied forces is zero, then

$$m_1\,\ddot{\bar{r}}_1\cdot\Delta\bar{r}_1 + m_2\ddot{\bar{r}}_2\cdot\Delta\bar{r}_2 + ... + m_n\,\ddot{\bar{r}}_n\cdot\Delta\bar{r}_n = 0.$$

But the virtual displacements $\Delta\bar{r}_1, \Delta\bar{r}_2, ..., \Delta\bar{r}_n$ are arbitrary. This implies that

$$\ddot{\bar{r}}_1 = 0,\ \ddot{\bar{r}}_2 = 0, ...,\ \ddot{\bar{r}}_n = 0.$$

Since the accelerations of the particles are zero, the dynamical system is in equilibrium if initially the system is in equilibrium.

Remark 2. If a particle of the system is constrained to move on a surface, then the forces on the particle due to this constraint are (*i*) the normal reaction and (*ii*) the frictional force. In this case, in applying the principle of virtual work, we must see that the virtual displacement is such that this particular particle does not undergo any displacement at all. If, however, the surface is smooth, then the virtual displacement may be such that the particle slides on the surface, so that the normal reaction does no work. However, for a body which rolls on a fixed rough surface without slipping, the point of application of the total reaction is the instantaneous centre of rotation and therefore it undergoes no displacement.

If the dynamical system consists of rigid bodies connected by joints, then the joints should be smooth, if not, the virtual displacement should be such that no frictional force is called into play. If the displacement is such that frictional forces are called into play, then the work done by them will all be positive and their sum cannot vanish.

If two component bodies of the system are tied to the ends of an inelastic string of length, say l, and the string is taught in the equilibrium position, then the tensions of the string acting on the bodies can be thought of as applied forces acting at different points of the system. In this case, to effect an arbitrary infinitesimal displacement, it can be assumed that the string is elastic.

EXAMPLES

Example 1. Four equal uniform rods are hinged together to form a rhombus $ABCD$ and the frame is suspended from A. The corners A and C are connected by an inelastic string to prevent the frame from collapsing. Show that the tension in the string is $2w$, where w is the weight of each rod. **(M.U., C.U.)**

We shall use the principle of virtual work. Let us have the following assumptions:

P, Q, R, S	:	Midpoints of AB, BC, CD, DA.
$2a$	:	Length of each rod.
θ	:	Inclination of each rod to the vertical.
$\bar{i}$	:	Horizontal unit vector from D to B.
$\bar{j}$	:	Downward vertical unit vector.

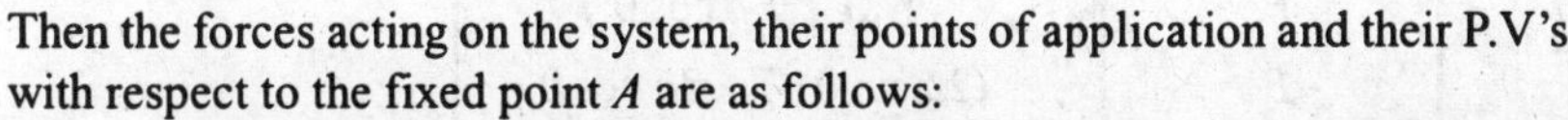

Then the forces acting on the system, their points of application and their P.V's with respect to the fixed point A are as follows:

Force	*Point*	*Position Vector*
$w\bar{j}$	P	$\bar{r}_P = a\sin\theta\,\bar{i} + a\cos\theta\,\bar{j}$
$w\bar{j}$	Q	$\bar{r}_Q = a\sin\theta\,\bar{i} + (3a)\cos\theta\,\bar{j}$
$T(-\bar{j})$	C	$\bar{r}_C = (0)\bar{i} + (4a)\cos\theta\,\bar{j}$
$w\bar{j}$	R	$\bar{r}_R = -a\sin\theta\,\bar{i} + (3a)\cos\theta\,\bar{j}$
$w\bar{j}$	S	$\bar{r}_S = -a\sin\theta\,\bar{i} + a\cos\theta\,\bar{j}$
$(T - R_1)\bar{j}$	A	$\bar{r}_A = \bar{0}.$

So
$$\begin{aligned}\Delta W &= w\bar{j}.\Delta\bar{r}_p + w\bar{j}.\Delta\bar{r}_Q + \ldots..\\ &= w\bar{j}\cdot(a\cos\theta\,\bar{i} - a\sin\theta\,\bar{j})\Delta\theta\\ &\quad + w\bar{j}\cdot(a\cos\theta\,\bar{i} - 3a\sin\theta\,\bar{j})\Delta\theta\\ &\quad + \mathrm{T}(-\bar{j})\cdot(-4a\sin\theta\,\bar{j})\Delta\theta\\ &\quad + w\bar{j}\cdot(-a\cos\theta\,\bar{i} - 3a\sin\theta\,\bar{j})\Delta\theta\\ &\quad + w\bar{j}\cdot(-a\cos\theta\,\bar{i} - a\sin\theta\,\bar{j})\Delta\theta\\ &= wa\sin\theta\,(-1-3-3-1)\Delta\theta + 4aT\sin\theta\,\Delta\theta.\end{aligned}$$

By the principle of virtual work, $\Delta W = 0$. Hence,

$$4aT\sin\theta\,\Delta\theta - 8aw\sin\theta\,\Delta\theta = 0. \qquad \therefore\ T = 2w.$$

Remark 1. The tension is independent of θ.

Remark 2. All the forces involved in the system are only in the $\bar{j}$ direction. So, in the calculation of ΔW, that is, in the dot product, only the $\bar{j}$ components and not the $\bar{i}$ components of the position vectors play a part. As such, the calculation of $\bar{i}$ components may be ignored.

Example 2. A square framework formed by four rods of equal weights w joined together, is hung up by one corner. A weight w is suspended from each of the three lower corners. If the shape of the square is preserved by a light rod along the horizontal diagonal, show that its thrust T on the frame is $4w$. **(M.U., K.U., C.U., Bn.U.)**

It is given that the frame is a square. However, we have to consider first only a general case, namely a rhombus. Let the inclination of the rods to the vertical be θ. Thrusts of the light rod act on the frame at B and D as shown in the figure. Let us have the following assumptions:

P, Q, R, S	:	Midpoints of AB, BC, CD, DA.
$2a$	:	Length of each rod.
$\bar{i}$	:	Horizontal unit vector from D to B.
$\bar{j}$	:	Downward vertical unit vector.

Force	***Point***	***Position Vector* w.r.t. *A***
$w\bar{j}$	P	$(...)\ \bar{i} + a\cos\theta\ \bar{j}$
$T\bar{i} + w\bar{j}$	B	$(2a\sin\theta)\ \bar{i} + 2a\cos\theta\ \bar{j}$
$w\bar{j}$	Q	$(...)\ \bar{i} + 3a\cos\theta\ \bar{j}$
$w\bar{j}$	C	$(...)\ \bar{i} + 4a\cos\theta\ \bar{j}$
$w\bar{j}$	R	$(...)\ \bar{i} + 3a\cos\theta\ \bar{j}$
$-T\bar{i} + w\bar{j}$	D	$(-2a\sin\theta)\ \bar{i} + 2a\cos\theta\ \bar{j}$
$w\bar{j}$	S	$(...)\ \bar{i} + a\cos\theta\ \bar{j}$
$R_1\ \bar{j}$	A	$\bar{0}$

$$\therefore \quad \Delta W = \Sigma \bar{F}\cdot\Delta\bar{r} = T(2a\cos\theta\,\Delta\theta) + (-T)(-2a\cos\theta)\Delta\theta - wa\sin\theta\,\Delta\theta(1+2+3+4+3+2+1)$$
$$= [(4a\cos\theta)T - (16a\sin\theta)w]\Delta\theta$$

Thus, from the principle of virtual work, we get

$$(4a\cos\theta)T - (16a\sin\theta)w = 0 \quad \text{or} \quad T = 4w\tan\theta.$$

So, when $\theta = \pi/4$, $T = 4w\tan \pi/4 = 4w$.

Example 3. A ladder of weight w rests at an angle θ to the horizon, with its ends resting on a smooth floor and against a smooth vertical wall, the lower end being attached by a string to the junction O of the wall and the floor. Find the tension of the string when a man whose weight is one-half of the ladder, has ascended the ladder two-thirds of its length. **(C.U.)**

Let us have the following assumptions:

$2a, G$	:	Length and mass centre of the ladder AB.
M	:	Position of the man.
$\bar{i}, \bar{j}$	:	Unit vectors in the directions of $\overline{OA}, \overline{OB}$.
T	:	Tension in the string.

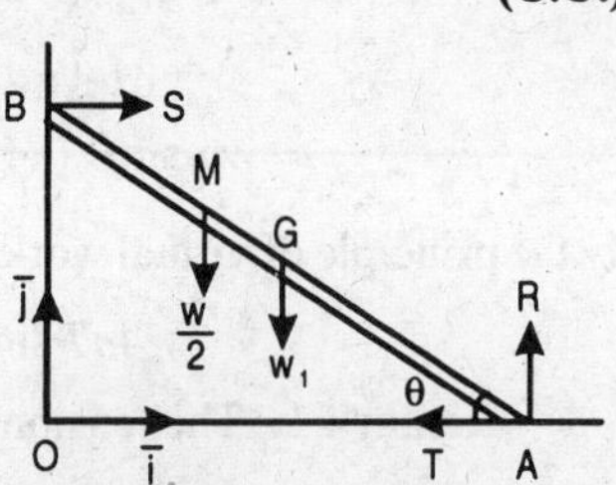

Five forces act on the ladder, namely, the weights of the ladder and the man, the tension and the normal two reactions. In a displacement due to a small change in θ, the normal reactions R and S do no work. The forces which do work, their points of application and their position vectors with respect to the fixed point O are as follows:

Force	*Point*	*Position Vector*	$\Delta\bar{r}$
$-w\bar{j}$	G	$(...)\ \bar{i}\ + a\sin\ \theta\bar{j}$	$(...)\bar{i} + a\cos\theta\ \Delta\theta\bar{j}$
$-\frac{1}{2}w\bar{j}$	M	$(...)\bar{i} + \frac{4}{3}a\sin\theta\bar{j}$	$(...)\bar{i} + \frac{4}{3}a\cos\theta\Delta\theta\bar{j}$
$-T\bar{i} + R\bar{j}$	A	$(2a\cos\theta)\bar{i}$	$(-2a\sin\theta)\ \Delta\theta\bar{i}$

$\therefore \qquad \Delta W = -w(a\cos\theta)\Delta\theta - \frac{1}{2}w\left(\frac{4}{3}a\cos\theta\right)\Delta\theta + T.(2a\sin\theta)\Delta\theta = 0.$

i.e., $\qquad (2a\sin\theta)T = \left(\frac{5}{3}a\cos\theta\right)w$ or $T = \frac{5}{6}w\cot\theta.$

Example 4. A uniform beam of length $2a$, rests in equilibrium against a smooth vertical wall and upon a smooth peg O at a distance d from the wall. Show that in the position of equilibrium, the beam is inclined to the wall at an angle θ given by

$$\sin^3\theta = d/a. \qquad \textbf{(M.U.)}$$

In a displacement due to a small change in θ, the normal reactions S, R of the peg and the wall do no work. The only force which does work is the weight of the rod, namely,

$$-w\bar{j},$$

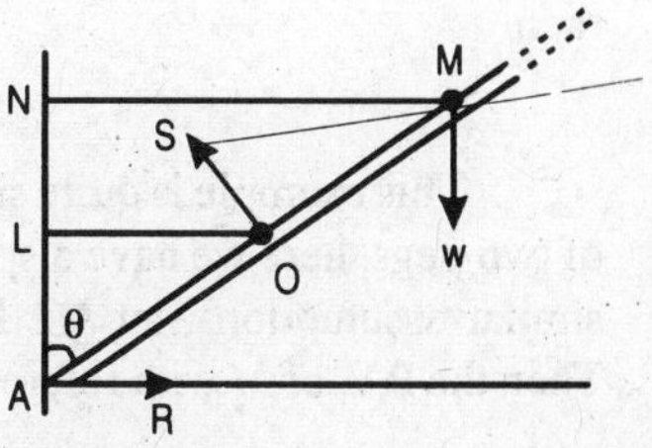

where $\bar{j}$ is the unit vector vertically upward. Let OL, MN be the perpendiculars drawn from O, M to the wall. Then the $P.V.$ of M with reference to the fixed point O, the peg, is

$$\bar{r}_M = (...)\bar{i} + LN\bar{j} = (...)\bar{i} + (AN - AL)\bar{j}$$

$$= (...)\bar{i} + (a\cos\theta - d\cot\theta)\bar{j}.$$

$$\therefore \qquad \Delta W = (-W\bar{j})\cdot\Delta\bar{r}_M = -w\bar{j}\cdot(-a\sin\theta + d\operatorname{cosec}^2\theta)\Delta\theta\bar{j}$$

$$= w(a\sin\theta - d\operatorname{cosec}^2\theta)\Delta\theta$$

Thus $\Delta W = 0$ gives $\sin^3\theta = d/a.$

Example 5. Two uniform heavy rods, each of length $2a$, jointed together, at their ends, by a smooth hinge, are placed symmetrically over two smooth pegs at a distance $2d$ apart in the same horizontal line. Show that in the position of equilibrium the inclination θ to the horizon of each of the rod is given by

$$\cos^3\theta = \frac{d}{a}. \qquad \textbf{(M.U., Bn.U.)}$$

Assumptions made are

AB, AC : Rods

P, Q : Pegs

M, N, L : Mid points of AB, AC, PQ

$\bar{i}, \bar{j}$: Unit vectors (horizontal and upward vertical)

We shall obtain first the work done in the virtual displacement of AB alone. The normal reaction R and the reaction at A do not do any work and the only force which does work is $-w\bar{j}$, the weight of the rod. The P.V. of M with reference to the fixed point P is

$$\bar{r}_M = \overline{PM} = (...)\bar{i} - PM\sin\theta\ \bar{j} = (...)\bar{i} - (AM - AP)\sin\theta\,\bar{j}$$

$$= (...)\bar{i} - (a - d\sec\theta)\sin\theta\,\bar{j} = (...)\ \bar{i} - (a\sin\theta - d\tan\theta)\,\bar{j}$$

$$\therefore \quad \Delta\bar{r}_M = (...)\bar{i} - (a\cos\theta - d\sec^2\theta)\Delta\theta\,\bar{j}$$

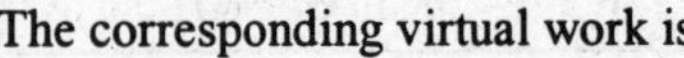

The corresponding virtual work is

$$(-w\bar{j})\cdot\Delta\bar{r}_M = w(a\cos\theta - d\sec^2\theta)\Delta\theta$$

By symmetry, the total virtual work done is

$$2w(a\cos\theta - d\sec^2\theta)\Delta\theta.$$

Thus $\Delta W = 0$ gives $\cos^3\theta = d/a$.

Example 6. Two uniform rods AB and AC, each of length $2a$, are freely jointed at A and rest in a symmetrical position on a smooth sphere of radius r. Show that, if 2θ is the angle between them, then

$$a\sin^3\theta = r\cos\theta. \qquad \textbf{(M. U., Bn. U.)}$$

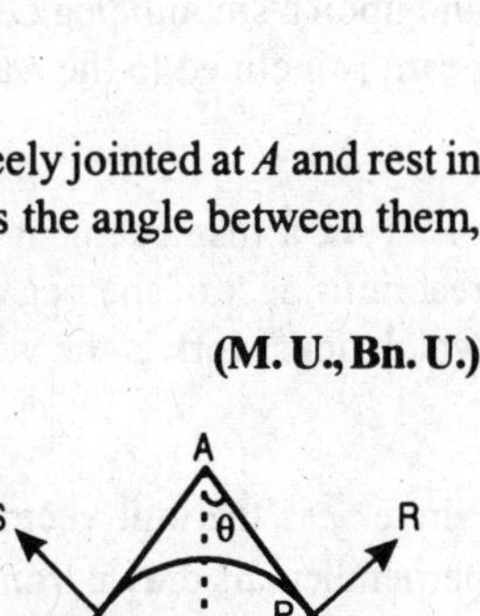

This example is quite similar to the previous one; but instead of two pegs, here we have a sphere whose centre is O. With a set of similar assumptions, let ML be the perpendicular drawn from M. Then the P.V. of M with reference to the fixed point O is

$$\bar{r}_M = \overline{OM} = (...)\bar{i} + OL\,\bar{j} = (....)\bar{i} + (OA - LA)\bar{j}$$

$$= (...)\bar{i} + (OP\,\mathrm{cosec}\,\theta - AM\cos\theta)\,\bar{j}$$

$$= (...)\bar{i} + (r\,\mathrm{cosec}\,\theta - a\cos\theta)\,\bar{j}$$

$$\therefore \quad \Delta\bar{r}_M = (...)\bar{i} + (-r\,\mathrm{cosec}\,\theta\cot\theta + a\sin\theta)\Delta\theta\,\bar{j}.$$

Therefore, by symmetry, the total virtual work ΔW done in the displacement due to the change in θ, is

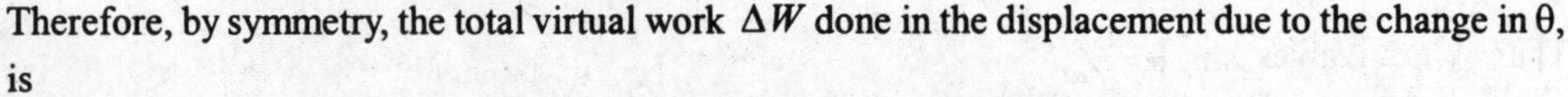

$$2[(-w\bar{j})\cdot(-r\,\mathrm{cosec}\,\theta\cot\theta + a\sin\theta)\Delta\theta\,\bar{j}].$$

Thus, $\Delta W = 0$, gives

$$r\frac{1}{\sin\theta}\frac{\cos\theta}{\sin\theta} = a\sin\theta \text{ or } r\cos\theta = a\sin^3\theta.$$

Example 7. A solid hemisphere is supported by a string fixed to a point A on its rim and to a point O on a smooth vertical wall with which the curved surface of the sphere is in contact at P. If θ and ϕ are the inclinations of the string and the plane base of the hemisphere to the vertical, prove that

$$\tan\phi = 3/8 + \tan\theta. \qquad \textbf{(M.U.)}$$

Let us make the following assumptions:

l : Length of string OA

a : Radius of sphere

C : Centre of sphere

CM : Middle radius

G : Mass centre

D : Pt. of intersection of PC with the vertical through G

The forces acting on the solid are

(*i*) Tension T

(*ii*) Weight W

(*iii*) Normal reaction R of the wall.

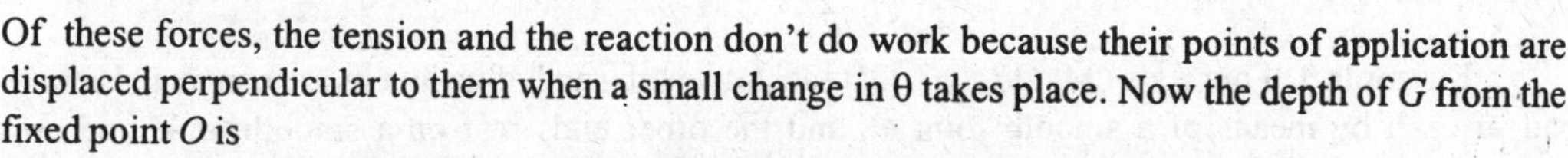

Of these forces, the tension and the reaction don't do work because their points of application are displaced perpendicular to them when a small change in θ takes place. Now the depth of G from the fixed point O is

$$OP + DG = \text{Proj. } OA + \text{Proj. } AC + \text{Proj. } CG, \text{ all on } OP$$

$$= l\cos\theta + a\cos\phi + \frac{3}{8}a\sin\phi, \text{ since } CG = \frac{3a}{8}.$$

$\therefore$ $\Delta(\text{depth of } G) = (-l\sin\theta)\Delta\theta + (-a\sin\phi + \frac{3}{8}a\cos\phi)\Delta\phi.$

So the principle of virtual work gives

$$w\{(-l\sin\theta)\Delta\theta + (-a\sin\phi + \frac{3}{8}a\cos\phi)\Delta\phi\} = 0.$$

$$\therefore \quad l\sin\theta\,\Delta\theta = a(-\sin\phi + \frac{3}{8}\cos\phi)\Delta\phi. \qquad ...(1)$$

But the Proj. OA on CP + Proj. AC on $CP = a$. Therefore

$$l\sin\theta + a\sin\phi = a.$$

$$\therefore \quad l\cos\theta\,\Delta\theta + a\cos\phi\,\Delta\phi = 0$$

or

$$l\cos\theta\,\Delta\theta = -a\cos\phi\,\Delta\phi. \qquad ...(2)$$

Dividing (1) by (2), we get

$$\tan\theta = \tan\phi - 3/8 \text{ or } \tan\phi = \tan\theta + 3/8.$$

Example 8. A heavy elastic string, whose natural length is $2\pi a$, is placed round a smooth cone whose axis is vertical and whose semi-vertical angle is α. If w is the weight and λ the modulus of elasticity of the string, prove that it will be in equilibrium in the form of a circle of radius

$$a\left(1 + \frac{w}{2\pi\lambda}\cot\alpha\right). \qquad \text{(M.U.)}$$

Let B be the centre of the string when its length equals its natural length

$$2\pi a.$$

In its equilibrium position, let C be the centre and

$$2\pi x,$$

its length. We shall first find the work W done by the weight and tension from the natural length position to the equilibrium position.

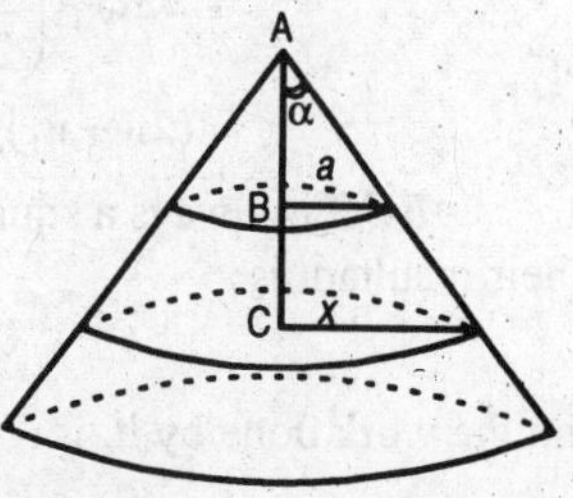

$$W = (\text{String's weight}) \times (\text{Downward distance } BC) + (\text{Extension}) \times \tfrac{1}{2}(\text{Initial} + \text{Final tensions})$$

$$= w(AC - AB) + (2\pi x - 2\pi a).\frac{1}{2}\left[0 + \lambda\frac{2\pi x - 2\pi a}{2\pi a}\right]$$

$$= w(x\cot\alpha - a\cot\alpha) - \frac{\pi\lambda}{a}(x-a)^2.$$

$$\therefore \qquad dW = w(1\cdot\cot\alpha - 0) - \frac{2\pi\lambda}{a}(x-a).$$

Thus $dW = 0$ gives the required radius x as

$$a\left(1 + \frac{w}{2\pi\lambda}\cot\alpha\right).$$

Example 9. Four rods OA, OB, OC, OD each of length l and of weight w, are connected at one end of each by means of a smooth joint O, and the other ends rest on a smooth table and are connected by equal strings of length d. A weight w_1, is suspended from the joint. Show that the tension of the string is

$$\frac{d\,(w_1 + 2w)}{4\sqrt{4l^2 - 2d^2}}. \qquad \textbf{(M.U)}$$

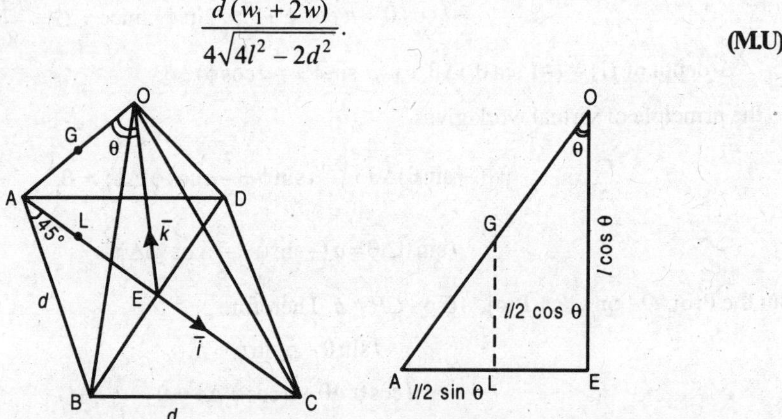

Let AC, BD intersect at E. Then E is a fixed point being independent of θ, the inclination of the rods to the vertical. Let $\bar{i}, \bar{k}$ be the unit vectors in the directions of $\overline{EC}$ and $\overline{EO}$. Let G, L be the midpoints of OA, AE. We shall consider the virtual displacement corresponding to a change $\Delta\theta$ in θ. In this displacement, the sum ΔW of the virtual works done by the weights of the rods and the weight of the suspended particle alone is

$$4(-w\bar{k})\cdot\Delta(\overline{LG}) + (-w_1\bar{k})\cdot\Delta(\overline{EO})$$

$$= 4(-w\bar{k})\cdot\Delta(-EL\,\bar{i} + LG\,\bar{k}) + (-w_1\bar{k})\cdot\Delta(EO\,\bar{k})$$

$$= -4w\,\Delta(LG) - w_1\,\Delta(EO)$$

$$= -4w\,\Delta\left(\frac{1}{2}l\cos\theta\right) - w_1\,\Delta(l\cos\theta)$$

$$= (2w + w_1)\,l\sin\theta\,\Delta\theta.$$

$ABCD$ is always a square. The point A is subjected to the tensions T, T acting along AB, AD. Their resultant is

$$2T\cos 45^\circ\,\bar{i} \;\text{ or }\; \sqrt{2}\,T\,\bar{i}$$

and the work done by it, is

$$(\sqrt{2}T\bar{i})\cdot\Delta(\overline{EA})=(\sqrt{2}T\bar{i})\cdot\Delta(-EA\bar{i})=-\sqrt{2}T(\Delta\text{EA})$$
$$=-\sqrt{2}T\Delta(l\sin\theta)=-\sqrt{2}Tl\cos\theta\Delta\theta.$$

So the work done by all the tensions is

$$-4\sqrt{2}T\,l\cos\theta\Delta\theta.$$

Hence, from the principle of virtual work,

$$(2w+w_1)l\sin\theta\Delta\theta-4\sqrt{2}T\,l\cos\theta\Delta\theta=0$$

$$\therefore\quad T=\frac{2w+w_1}{4\sqrt{2}}\tan\theta=\frac{2w+w_1}{4\sqrt{2}}\frac{AE}{OE}$$

$$=\frac{2w+w_1}{4\sqrt{2}}\frac{AE}{\sqrt{OA^2-AE^2}},\text{ when }AE=\frac{d}{\sqrt{2}}$$

$$=\frac{(2w+w_1)d}{4\sqrt{4l^2-2d^2}}.$$

EXERCISES

1. Four rods, each of the length a and weight w, are smoothly joined together to form a rhombus $ABCD$ which is kept in shape by a light rod BD. The angle BAD is 60° and the rhombus is suspended in a vertical plane from A. Find the thrust of BD. **(M.U.)**

   [Ans. $^{2w}/_{\sqrt{3}}$ **]**

2. Four uniform rods are freely jointed so as to form a rhombus which is freely suspended by one angular point and the midpoints of the two upper rods are connected by a light rod, so that the rhombus cannot collapse. Prove that the thrust of this light rod is $4w\tan\alpha$, where w is the weight of each rod and 2α is the angle of the rhombus at the point of suspension.

3. Four uniform heavy rods are smoothly jointed, so as to form a square $PQRS$ with a light rod connecting the middle points of PQ and PS. In this shape, the frame is hung vertically from P and a weight is attached to R equal to that of the square. Find the thrust of the light rod. **(M.U.)**

   [Ans. 12 times the weight of a rod**]**

4. A rhombus $ABCD$, formed of four rods, each of length l and weight w, jointed by smooth hinges, rests in a vertical plane on two smooth pegs in the same horizontal line distance $2d$ apart; a weight W is attached to the lowest hinge C, and B, D are joined by a light string. If angle at A is 2α, show that the tension in the string is

$$\left\{\frac{d}{2l}(W+4w)\operatorname{cosec}^3\alpha-(W+2w)\right\}\tan\alpha.$$ **(M.U.)**

5. A frame of 5 weightless bars forms the sides of a rhombus $ABCD$ and the diagonal AC. If four equal forces P act inwards at the middle points of the sides at right angles to them, and if angle BAC is θ, show that the thrust on AC, is

$$\frac{P\cos2\theta}{\sin\theta}.$$ **(M.U.)**

6. A string of length a forms the shorter diagonal of a rhombus formed of four uniform rods, each of length b and weight w, which are hinged together. If one of the rods is supported in a horizontal position, show that the tension of the string is

$$\frac{2w(2b^2-a^2)}{4\sqrt{4b^2-a^2)}}.$$ **(M.U.)**

7. A ladder of length $2l$ and weight w rests at an angle θ to the horizon with its ends resting on a smooth floor and against a smooth vertical wall, the lower end being attached by a string to the junction of the wall and the floor. A weight n times the weight of the ladder is placed on a rung at a distance x from the bottom. Show that the tension of the string is

$$\frac{w(l+nx\cot\theta)}{2l}.$$ **(M.U.)**

8. Six rods, each of weight w, are freely jointed at their extremities, so as to form a regular hexagon $ABCDEF$; the rod AB is fixed in a horizontal position and the middle points of AB and DE are joined by a string. Show that the tension of the string is $3w$. **(C.U., Bn.U.)**

[**Hint:** Let L, M, N, O, P, Q be the midpoints of AB, BC, CD, DE, EF, FA and θ, the angle of inclination of BC, CD, EF, FA with the vertical. Then, with A as the origin and $\bar{j}$ downward, we have the following:

Force	***Point***	***P.V. of the point***
$w\bar{j}$	M	$(...)\,\bar{i}+(a\cos\theta)\,\bar{j}$
$w\bar{j}$	N	$(...)\,\bar{i}+(3a\cos\theta)\,\bar{j}$
$-T\bar{j}+w\bar{j}$	O	$(...)\,\bar{i}+(4a\cos\theta)\,\bar{j}$
$w\bar{j}$	P	$(...)\,\bar{i}+(3a\cos\theta)\,\bar{j}$
$w\bar{j}$	Q	$(...)\,\bar{i}+(a\cos\theta)\,j$

where $AB = 2a$. AB does not undergo any displacement.]

9. A regular hexagon $ABCDEF$ consists of six equal rods which are of weight w each and are freely jointed together. The hexagon rests in a vertical plane and AB is in contact with a horizontal table. If C and F are connected by a light string, show that its tension is $w\sqrt{3}$. **(M.U.)**

10. Six beams are freely jointed at their ends to form a hexagon and are placed in a vertical plane with one beam resting on a horizontal plane; the midpoints of the two upper slant beams which are inclined at an angle θ to the horizon, are connected by a light cord. Show that its tension is $6w\cot\theta$, where w is the weight of each beam. **(M.U., C.U.)**

11. A regular hexagon is composed of six equal heavy rods freely jointed together, and two opposite angular points are connected by a horizontal string, the lowermost rod being in contact with a horizontal plane. At the middle point of the uppermost rod is placed a weight w_1. If w is the weight of each rod, show that the tension of the string is

$$\frac{3w+w_1}{\sqrt{3}}.$$ **(M.U.)**

12. A smooth paraboloid of revolution is fixed with its axis vertical and vertex upwards; on it is placed a heavy elastic string of unstretched length $2\pi c$; when the string is in equilibrium, show that it rests in the form of a circle of radius $4\pi ac\lambda/(4\pi a\lambda - cw)$, where w is the weight of the string, λ the modulus of elasticity and $4a$ the latus rectum of the generating parabola.

13. A tripod consists of three equal bars each of length $2a$ and weight w, which are freely jointed at one extremity, their middle points being joined by a string of length b. The tripod is placed with its free ends in contact with a smooth horizontal plane and a weight w_1 is attached to the common point. Prove that the tension in the string is

$$\frac{b(3w+2w_1)}{3\sqrt{9a^2-3b^2}}.$$

14. Two equal beams, each of weight w, connected by a smooth hinge at A, are placed with their ends B, C resting on a smooth horizontal plane. The end B is connected by a string to the midpoint of AC and in the equilibrium position ABC is equilateral. Show that the tension in the string is $w/2$. **(M.U.)**

[Hint: M, N: Midpoints of AB, AC (AB being on the left of AC); $AB = 2a$, 2θ : Angle BAC. With reference to the midpoint of BC, the P.V. and the force there are

$$\bar{r}_M = -a \sin\theta\, \bar{i} + a \cos\theta\, \bar{j}; \qquad -w\bar{j}$$

$$\bar{r}_N = a \sin\theta\, \bar{i} + a \cos\theta\, \bar{j}; \qquad -w\bar{j} - T\,\widehat{BN}$$

$$\bar{r}_B = -2a \sin\theta\, \bar{i}; \qquad T\,\widehat{BN},$$

where $\overline{BN} = \overline{BO} + \bar{r}_N = 3a\sin\theta\,\bar{i} + a\cos\theta\,\bar{j}$ and hence

$$\widehat{BN} = \frac{3a\sin\theta\,\bar{i} + a\cos\theta\,\bar{j}}{\sqrt{(3a\sin\theta)^2 + (a\cos\theta)^2}}.$$

Use $dW = 0$ and set in it $\theta = 30°$.]

HANGING STRINGS

9.1 EQUILIBRIUM OF A UNIFORM HOMOGENEOUS STRING

In this section we consider the equilibrium of an inextensible, uniform, homogeneous string hanging freely under gravity with its ends tied to two points.

Bookwork 9.1. To show that the shape of a uniform string hanging under gravity is a catenary.

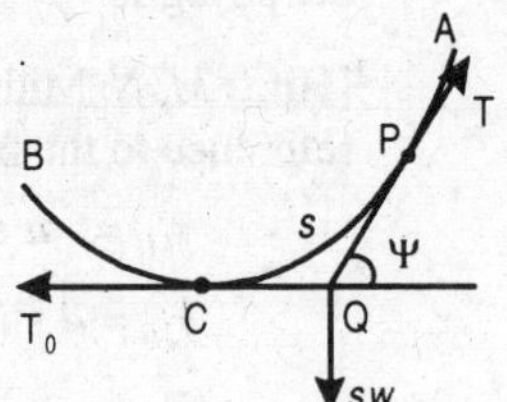

Let A, B be the points of suspension not lying in the same vertical line, C the lowest point of the string, Q the point of intersection of the tangents at C and P and ψ the angle between these tangents. Let s be the length of the arc CP. Then the applied forces acting on the portion CP of the string are

(*i*) The tension T at P along the tangent

(*ii*) The tension T_0 at C along the tangent

(*iii*) The weight sw acting through Q,

where w is the weight per unit length of the string. Let the length of the string whose weight equals T_0 be c. Then $T_0 = cw$. Now the portion CP is in equilibrium. So the sum of the horizontal components of the applied forces on CP is zero. Also the sum of the vertical components of the applied forces is zero.

$\therefore \quad T\cos\psi - T_0 = 0, \quad T\sin\psi - sw = 0.$

i.e., $\quad T\cos\psi = cw, \quad T\sin\psi = sw.$

Dividing the second by the first, we get

$$s = c\tan\psi.$$

This is the intrinsic equation of the shape of the string. But this equation represents a catenary. So the shape of the string is a catenary.

Remark 1. $T\cos\psi = cw$ gives that the tension at any point "ψ" on the string is

$$T = wc\sec\psi.$$

Vertex and directrix. C is the vertex of the catenary and the horizontal line at a depth c below C is the directrix of the catenary.

Span and sag. If A, B are the points of suspension in the same horizontal line, AB is called span and the depth of C below AB is called sag.

Bookwork 9.2. To obtain the equation of the curve formed by the string in the previous bookwork in the parametric form as

$$x = c\log(\sec\psi + \tan\psi),$$

$$y = c\sec\psi$$

and in the cartesian form as

$$y = c\cosh {x}/{c}.$$

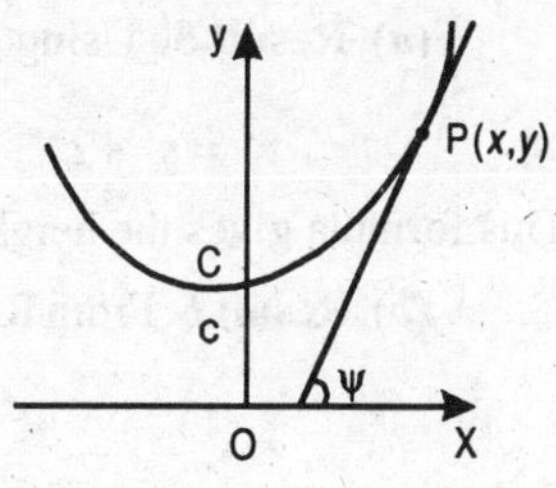

(*i*) Let O be the point vertically below C at a distance c. Let Ox and Oy, the horizontal and vertical lines in the plane of the string, be the x and y axes. Note that Ox is the directrix of the catenary.

The parametric equations of the string may be obtained from the Calculus results

$$\frac{dx}{ds} = \cos\psi, \frac{dy}{ds} = \sin\psi$$

as follows:

$\frac{dx}{ds} = \cos\psi$	$\frac{dy}{ds} = \sin\psi$
$\frac{dx}{d\psi}.\frac{d\psi}{ds} = \cos\psi$	$\frac{dy}{d\psi}.\frac{d\psi}{ds} = \sin\psi$
$\frac{dx}{d\psi} = \cos\psi\,\frac{ds}{d\psi} = \cos\psi(c\sec^2\psi)$	$\frac{dy}{d\psi} = \sin\psi\,\frac{ds}{d\psi} = \sin\psi(c\sec^2\psi)$
$\int dx = c\int \sec\psi\, d\psi$	$\int dy = c\int \tan\psi\sec\psi\, d\psi$
$x = c\log(\sec\psi + \tan\psi) + A$	$y = c\sec\psi + B.$

But, when $x = 0, y = c$ and $\psi = 0$. So $A = 0$ and $B = 0$. Thus

$$x = c\log(\sec\psi + \tan\psi), \quad y = c\sec\psi.$$

(*ii*) Now $x = c\log(\sec\psi + \tan\psi)$. Therefore

$$e^{x/c} = \sec\psi + \tan\psi. \qquad ...(1)$$

Considering its reciprocal,

$$e^{-x/c} = \frac{1}{\sec\psi + \tan\psi} = \frac{\sec\psi - \tan\psi}{\sec^2\psi - \tan^2\psi}$$

$$\therefore \quad e^{-x/c} = \sec\psi - \tan\psi. \qquad ...(2)$$

Adding (1) and (2) and dividing by 2,

$$\frac{e^{x/c} + e^{-x/c}}{2} = \sec\psi \quad \text{or} \quad \cosh x/c = \sec\psi.$$

But $y = c\sec\psi$. Thus we have the cartesian equation $y = c\cosh x/c$.

List of results. We shall derive some more results from the following four results already obtained :

Result 1. $s = c\tan\psi$.

Result 2. $x = c\log(\sec\psi + \tan\psi)$.

Result 3. $y = c\sec\psi$.

Result 4. $y = c\cosh x/c$.

(a) Result 5. Using $\sec^2\psi - \tan^2\psi$, $R.1$ and $R.3$, we get $y^2 - s^2 = c^2$

or $$y^2 = s^2 + c^2.$$

This formula gives the height of the point on the string whose arcual distance from C is s.

(b) Result 6. From R.4 and R.5, we get

$$\cosh^{-1} y/c = x/c \quad \text{or} \quad x = c\cosh^{-1} y/c.$$

$$\therefore \quad x = c\log\frac{y+\sqrt{y^2-c^2}}{c} = c\log\frac{y+s}{c}.$$

(c) Result 7. From R.5 and R.4, we get

$$s^2 = y^2 - c^2 = c^2\cosh^2 x/c - c^2 = c^2\sinh^2 x/c$$

or $$s = c\sinh x/c.$$

(d) Result 8. From R.7, we get

$$\sinh^{-1} s/c = x/c \text{ or } x = c\sinh^{-1} s/c.$$

$$\therefore \quad x = c\log\frac{s+\sqrt{s^2+c^2}}{c}.$$

Results pertaining to tension

(e) Result 9. From bookwork 9.1,

$$T = wc\sec\psi.$$

(f) Result 10. From R.3 and R.9

$$T = wy.$$

That is, the tension T at any point (x, y) on the catenary is

$$T = (\text{weight per unit length}) \times y,$$

where y is the height of the point from the x axis.

Result 11. Since $T = wy$, $T_0 = wc$, we have

$$\frac{T}{T_0} = \frac{y}{c}.$$

Result 12. Multiplying $y^2 = s^2 + c^2$ by w^2, $(wy)^2 = (ws)^2 + (wc)^2$

or $$T^2 = (ws)^2 + T_0^{\,2}.$$

A mnemonic. As a mnemonic to remember some of the above results we can imagine a right-angled triangle with y as its hypotenuse as in the figure. As an example, we have

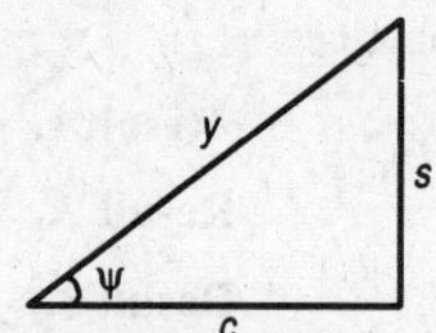

Result 13. $\sin\psi = \dfrac{s}{y}$.

Note. Solving sums in this chapter is a simple application of the above formulae.

EXAMPLES

Example 1. A uniform string of length l is freely suspended between two fixed points A and B, not in the same level. The inclinations to the horizontal of the string at A and B are found to be $60°$ and $30°$. Obtain the value of the parameter c of the catenary formed by the string and show that the tension at A is equal to the weight of the string of length

$$\frac{\sqrt{3}}{2}l.$$

(M.U.,M.K.U.)

Let C be the lowest point and s_1, s_2 the arcual distances of A, B from C. Then the intrinsic coordinates of A, B are

$$A: \quad s_1, 60°,$$
$$B: -s_2, 150°,$$

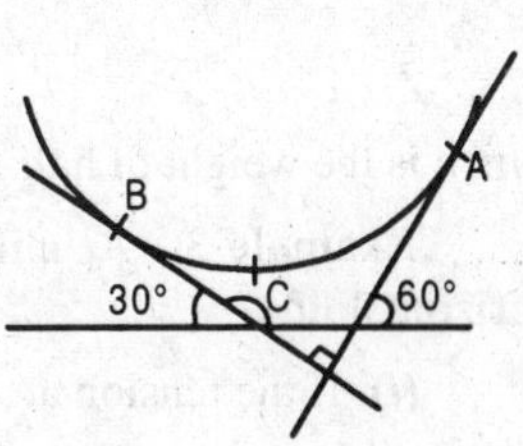

They satisfy the equation of the catenary $s = c \tan \psi$. So

$$s_1 = c \tan 60° = c\sqrt{3},$$

$$-s_2 = c \tan 150° = -\frac{c}{\sqrt{3}} \text{ or } s_2 = \frac{c}{\sqrt{3}}.$$

$$\therefore \quad l = s_1 + s_2 = c\left(\sqrt{3} + \frac{1}{\sqrt{3}}\right) \text{ or } c = \frac{\sqrt{3}}{4}l.$$

If w is the weight per unit length, then, by R. 9,

$$T_A = w\,c \sec 60° = w.\frac{\sqrt{3}\,l}{4}.2 = \frac{\sqrt{3}}{2}wl.$$

Example 2. If the tangents at the points A and B of a hanging string are at right angles, show that the tension at the middle point M of the arc AB is equal to half of the weight of the string AB.

(M.U., M.K.U., Bn.U.)

Choose the x, y axes in the usual manner. Let the tangent at A make an angle θ with the x axis. Let s_1, s_2 be the lengths of arcs CA, CB. Then half of length of arc AB is

$$\tfrac{1}{2}(s_1 + s_2).$$

The intrinsic coordinates of A, B are

$$A: \quad s_1, \theta$$
$$B: -s_2, 90° + \theta.$$

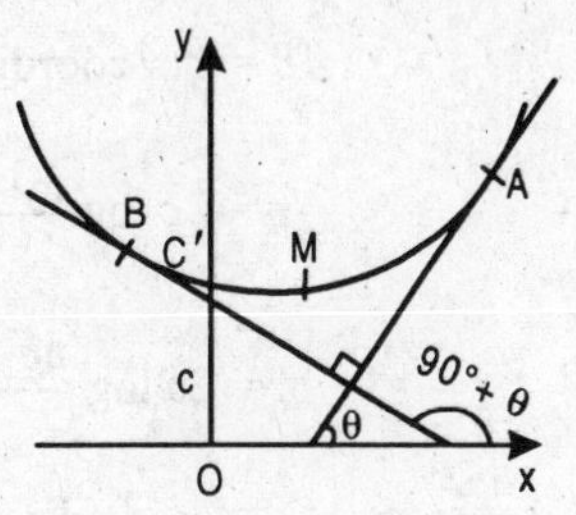

They satisfy the equation $s = c \tan \psi$. So

$$s_1 = c \tan \theta,$$

$$-s_2 = c \tan (90° + \theta)$$

$$= -c \cot \theta$$

or $$s_2 = c \cot \theta.$$

$$\therefore \quad s_1\, s_2 = c^2. \qquad \text{...(1)}$$

If M is the middle point of AB and if s is its arcual distance from C, then

$$s = \widehat{CM} = \widehat{CA} - \widehat{MA} = s_1 - \frac{s_1+s_2}{2} = \frac{s_1-s_2}{2}$$

and, by $y^2 = s^2 + c^2$, For M,

$$y^2 = \left(\frac{s_1-s_2}{2}\right)^2 + s_1 s_2 = \left(\frac{s_1+s_2}{2}\right)^2 \text{ by (1)}$$

$$\therefore \quad y = \frac{s_1+s_2}{2}.$$

So, by R. 10, the tension at M is

$$T = wy = w.\tfrac{1}{2}(s_1+s_2)$$

which is the weight of half the length of the arc AB.

Example 3. A uniform string of length l is suspended from the points A, B in the same horizontal line.

(i) If the tension at A is n times the tension at the lowest point C, then show that the span is

$$\frac{l}{\sqrt{n^2-1}} \log\left(n+\sqrt{n^2-1}\right).$$ **(M.U., M.K.U., Bn.U., Br.U)**

(ii) If the tension at A is twice that at the lowest point C, then show that the span is

$$\frac{l}{\sqrt{3}} \log\left(2+\sqrt{3}\right).$$ **(M.K.U.)**

Choose the x, y axes in the usual manner. Let T, T_0 be the tensions at A, C. Then it is given that

$$T = nT_0.$$

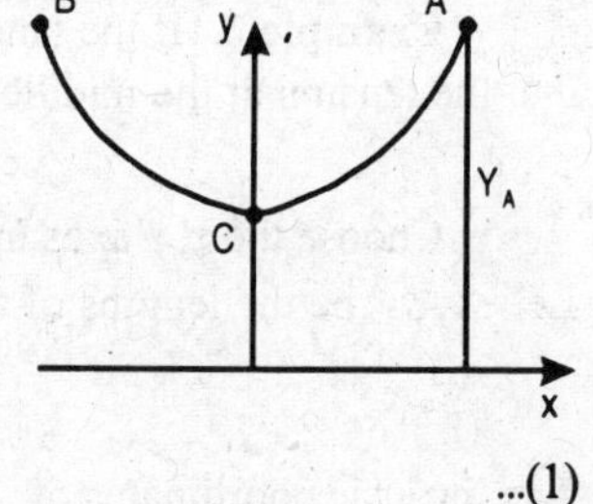

But, from R. 11, if y_A is the y coordinate of A,

$$\frac{T}{T_0} = \frac{y_A}{c}.$$

$$\therefore \quad n = \frac{y_A}{c}.$$

or $$y_A = nc. \qquad \text{...(1)}$$

Now the span is AB and

$$AB = 2\,(x \text{ coordinate of } A)$$

$$= 2c \log \frac{y_A + \sqrt{y_A^2 - c^2}}{c} \text{ by R.6}$$

$$= 2c \log \frac{nc + \sqrt{n^2c^2 - c^2}}{c} \text{ by (1)}$$

$$= 2c \log\left(n + \sqrt{n^2-1}\right). \qquad \text{...(2)}$$

To get c. Since l is the length of the string, for the point A,

$$s = \tfrac{l}{2},\ y = y_A = nc$$

and by $y^2 = s^2 + c^2$,

$$(nc)^2 = (l/2)^2 + c^2 \quad \text{or} \quad c = \frac{l}{2\sqrt{n^2-1}}.$$

Substituting in (2), we get the first result. $n = 2$ gives the second result.

Example 4. Show that the length of a chain whose ends are tied together and which is hanging over a circular pulley of radius a, so as to be in contact with two-thirds of the circumference of the pulley, is

$$a\left[\frac{3}{\log(2+\sqrt{3})} + \frac{4\pi}{3}\right].$$ **(M.U., M.K.U., Bn.U.)**

Let O be the centre of the circle. Let ACB be the hanging portion of the chain in the form of a catenary. Choose the x, y axes in the usual manner. Now it is evident that angle $AOB = 120°$ and the tangent at A makes an angle 60° with the x axis. Let the length of arc CA be l. Then for A, we have

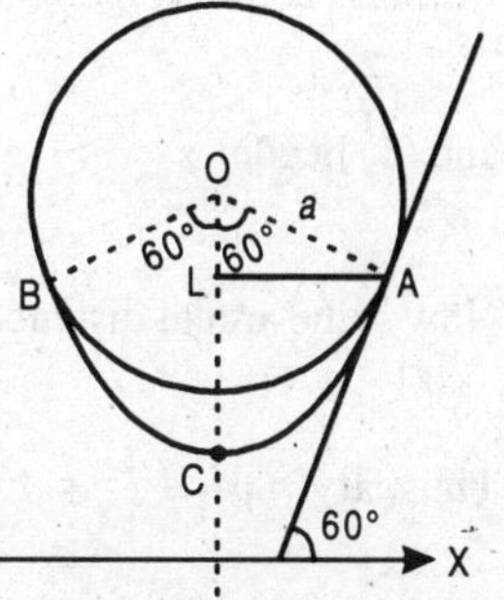

$$s = l, \psi = 60°.$$

They satisfy

$$s = c \tan \psi$$

$$\therefore \quad l = c \tan 60°.$$

$$\therefore \quad c = \frac{l}{\sqrt{3}}. \qquad \text{...(1)}$$

If A is the point (x, y), then, by R. 2,

$$x = c \log(\sec \psi + \tan \psi)$$

$$= \frac{l}{\sqrt{3}} \log(\sec 60° + \tan 60°)$$

$$= \frac{l}{\sqrt{3}} \log\left(2+\sqrt{3}\right). \qquad \text{...(2)}$$

If AL is the distance of A from the y axis,

$$x = AL = a \sin 60° = \frac{\sqrt{3}}{2}a \qquad \text{...(3)}$$

Equating (2) and (3) we get

$$\frac{l}{\sqrt{3}} \log\left(2+\sqrt{3}\right) = \frac{\sqrt{3}}{2}a \quad \text{or} \quad l = \frac{3a}{2\log\left(2+\sqrt{3}\right)}.$$

Thus the total length of the string is

$$2l + \frac{2}{3}(2\pi a) \quad \text{or} \quad \frac{3a}{\log\left(2+\sqrt{3}\right)} + \frac{4\pi a}{3}.$$

Example 5. A string of length $2l$ hangs over two small smooth pegs in the same horizontal level. Show that, if h is the sag in the middle, the length of either part of the string that hangs vertically is $h+l-\sqrt{2hl}$. **(M.U., M.K.U., Bn.U.)**

Let A and B be the pegs and C, the vertex of the catenary formed by the string. Let O be the point below C at a distance c and Ox, Oy be the x, y axes. Then the height of A from the x axis is $c+h$. Let a be the length of the string hanging on either side.

Now, at A, we have

$$\begin{Bmatrix}\text{Tension at } A\\ \text{on the left}\end{Bmatrix} = \begin{Bmatrix}\text{Weight of the}\\ \text{string hanging}\end{Bmatrix} \quad \text{...(1)}$$

But, if w is the weight per unit length of the string, then by "$T = yw$"

$$\text{Tension at } A = (c+h)\,w.$$

and (1) becomes

$$(c+h)\,w = aw \quad \text{or} \quad c+h = a. \quad \text{...(2)}$$

Now s, the arcual distance of A from C, is $l-a$. So, for A, the values of y and s are

$$y = c+h, \quad s = l-a.$$

Thus, at A, $y^2 = s^2 + c^2$ becomes

$$(c+h)^2 = (l-a)^2 + c^2$$

and eliminating c, by (2), we get

$$a^2 = (l-a)^2 + (a-h)^2$$

or

$$a^2 - 2(l+h)a + (h^2 + l^2) = 0.$$

Solving for a and taking the admissible value,

$$a = l + h - \sqrt{2lh}.$$

Example 6. If a chain is suspended from two points A, B on the same level and the depth of the middle point below AB is l/n, where $2l$ is the length of the chain, show that the horizontal span AB is equal to

$$l\frac{n^2-1}{n}\log\frac{n+1}{n-1}. \quad \textbf{(M.U., M.K.U.)}$$

Choose the x, y axis in the usual manner. Let $AB = 2a$. Then, for A,

$$x = a,$$

$$y = c + l/n,$$

$$s = l.$$

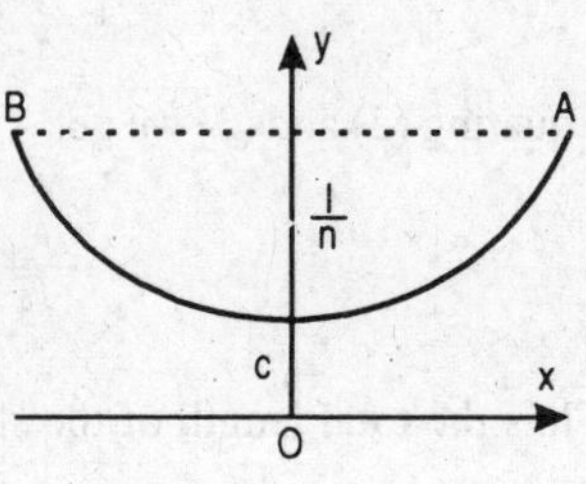

So, from $y^2 = s^2 + c^2$,

$$\left(c+\frac{l}{n}\right)^2 = l^2 + c^2$$

or

$$2c = l\left(n - \frac{1}{n}\right)$$

and, from $\quad x = c \log \dfrac{s+\sqrt{s^2+c^2}}{c},$

$$a = c \log \frac{l+\sqrt{l^2+c^2}}{c}.$$

$$\therefore \qquad 2c = l\left(n - \frac{1}{n}\right), \quad a = c \log \frac{l+\sqrt{l^2+c^2}}{c}.$$

Elimination of c leads to the result.

Example 7. A string of weight W is suspended from two points A and B at the same horizontal level and a weight P is attached at the lowest point M. If α and β are the inclinations to the horizontal of the tangents at A and M, show that

$$\frac{\tan\alpha}{\tan\beta} = 1 + \frac{W}{P}. \qquad \textbf{(M.U.)}$$

Let T_1 be the tension of both the parts of the string at M. Since these two tensions and P keep M in equilibrium, resolving them vertically, we get

$$P = T_1 \sin\beta + T_1 \sin\beta = 2T_1 \sin\beta. \qquad \text{...(1)}$$

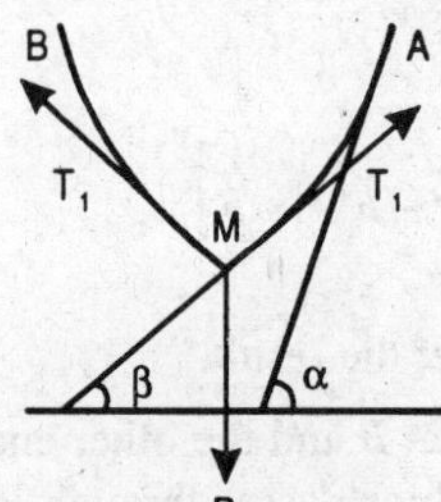

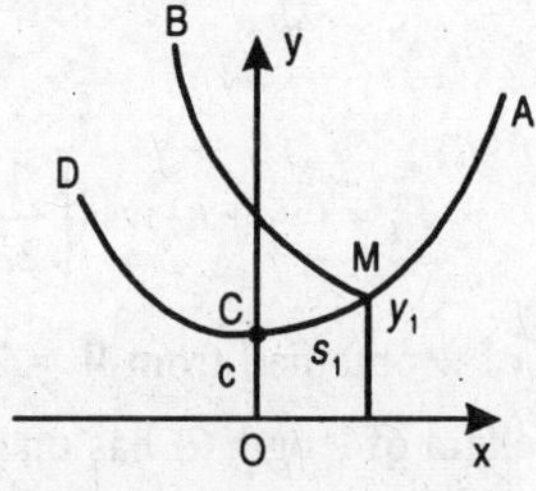

Let $AMCD$ be the full catenary of which arc AM forms a part, where C is the vertex of this catenary. Choose the x, y axes as usual through O below C at a distance c.

Then the equation of the catenary is

$$s = c \tan\psi. \qquad \text{...(2)}$$

Let the total length of the string be $2l$. Then arc $MA = l$. If the length of the arc $CM = s_1$, then

$$M \text{ is } (s_1, \beta), \quad A \text{ is } (s_1 + l, \alpha).$$

They satisfy (2). Therefore

$$s_1 = c \tan\beta, \; s_1 + l = c \tan\alpha.$$

$$\therefore \qquad \frac{\tan\alpha}{\tan\beta} = \frac{s_1 + l}{s_1} = 1 + \frac{l}{s_1} = 1 + \frac{2lw}{2s_1 w}$$

$$= 1 + \frac{W}{2s_1 w}, \qquad \text{...(3)}$$

where w is the mass per unit length of the string. Let M be (s_1, y_1), then (1) becomes

$$P = 2T_1 \sin\beta = 2T_1 \frac{s_1}{y_1} \quad \text{by R.13}$$

$$= 2(y_1 w)\frac{s_1}{y_1} = 2s_1 w \quad \text{by R.10}$$

Thus (3) becomes

$$\frac{\tan\alpha}{\tan\beta} = 1 + \frac{W}{P}.$$

Example 8. A chain of length $2l$ and weight W is suspended from two points A and B in the same horizontal line. A weight P is attached to the middle point M of the chain. When the system is in equilibrium, the depth of P below AB is h. Show that the tension at A is

$$\frac{1}{2}\left\{\frac{lP}{h} + \frac{(h^2+l^2)W}{2hl}\right\}.$$ **(M.U., Bn.U.)**

In continuation of the previous sum, using $y^2 = s^2 + c^2$, for A and M, we get

$$(y_1 + h)^2 = (s_1 + l)^2 + c^2, \quad {y_1}^2 = {s_1}^2 + c^2.$$

Subtracting and using $P = 2s_1 w$, we have

$$y_1 = \frac{1}{2h}(2s_1 l + l^2 - h^2) = \frac{1}{2h}\cdot\left(\frac{Pl}{w} + l^2 - h^2\right).$$

But tension T_A at A is

$$T_A = (y_1 + h)w = \left[\frac{1}{2h}\left(\frac{Pl}{w} + l^2 - h^2\right) + h\right] w.$$

Substituting the value of w obtained from $W = 2lw$, we get the result.

Example 9. A chain of length $2l$ has one end tied at B and the other end attached to a small heavy ring A which can slide on a rough horizontal rod which passes through B. If the weight of the ring is n times that of the chain and if μ is the coefficient of friction, show that, for the system to be in equilibrium, the greatest possible distance $2a$ of the ring from B is

$$\frac{2l}{\lambda}\log\left(\lambda + \sqrt{\lambda^2 + 1}\right), \text{ where } \frac{1}{\lambda} = \mu\,(2n+1).$$ **(M.U.)**

Four forces act on the ring at A as shown in the figure. Since the system is in equilibrium, equating the horizontal and vertical forces to zero, we get

$$\mu R = T\cos\psi, \qquad R = T\sin\psi + n(2lw).$$

But $T = cw\sec\psi$. Therefore

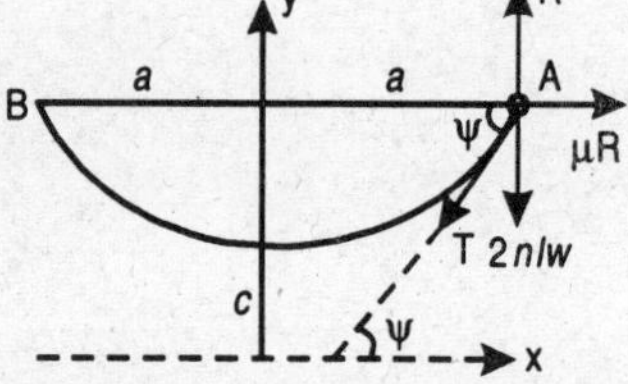

$$\mu R = cw, \qquad R = cw\tan\psi + 2nlw.$$

Also, $s = c\tan\psi$. Therefore

$$\mu R = cw, \quad R = sw + 2nlw.$$

Now, for A, $s = l$, $x = a$. Therefore

$$\mu R = cw, \qquad R = lw + 2nlw.$$

Eliminating R and using $1/\lambda = \mu(2n+1)$, we have

$$c = \mu l\,(1+2n) \quad \text{or} \quad c = \frac{l}{\lambda}.$$

Now, in $x = c \log \dfrac{s+\sqrt{s^2+c^2}}{c}$, setting $x = a,\ s = l$,

$$a = c \log \frac{l+\sqrt{l^2+c^2}}{c}.$$

Substitution of l/λ for c and multiplication by 2 give

$$2a = \frac{2l}{\lambda} \log\left(\lambda + \sqrt{\lambda^2+1}\right).$$

EXERCISES

1. If T is the tension at any point P of a uniform string which hangs under gravity with its ends tied to two points and T_0 is the tension at the lowest point C, show that $T^2 - T_0{}^2 = W^2$, where W is the weight of the portion CP of the string. **(M.U., M.K.U., Bn.U.)**

   [Hint: $y^2 = s^2 + c^2 \Rightarrow (wy)^2 = (ws)^2 + (wc)^2 \Rightarrow T^2 = W^2 + T_0{}^2$]

2. A string of length l is suspended from a fixed point A and its other end B is pulled horizontally by a force equal to the weight of a length a of the string. Show that the horizontal and the vertical distances between A and B are $a \sinh^{-1} l/a$ and $\sqrt{l^2+a^2} - a$. **(M.U., M.K.U.)**

   [Hint: B is the vertex of the catenary and, with usual notations, $T_0 = cw$. But now $T_0 = aw$. So $c = a$. If the sag is h, then for A, $y = a+h$, $s = l$. Get the horizontal distance x from $s = c \sinh x/c$ or $l = a \sinh x/c$. Using $y^2 = s^2 + c^2$, get the vertical distance h

3. A kite is flying at a height h with a length l of the string paid out and with the vertex of the catenary on the ground. Show that, at the kite, the inclination of the string is $2 \tan^{-1} h/l$. If w is the weight per unit length of the string, show that the tensions at the ground and at the kite are

$$\frac{w\,(l^2-h^2)}{2h},\ \frac{w\,(l^2+h^2)}{2h}.$$ **(M.U.)**

   [Hint: For the kite, $s = l,\ y = c+h,\ \psi = \theta$, say. Then

   (i) $y^2 = s^2 + c^2$ gives $(c+h)^2 = l^2 + c^2$ or $c = \dfrac{l^2-h^2}{2h}$;

   $s = c \tan\psi$ gives $l = c\tan\theta$ or $\tan\theta = \dfrac{2hl}{l^2-h^2}$.

$$\therefore \quad \tan\theta = \frac{2\,h/l}{1-(h/l)^2} = \frac{2\tan\alpha}{1-\tan^2\alpha} = \tan 2\alpha, \text{ where } \tan\alpha = h/l. \text{ So } \theta = 2\alpha.$$

(*ii*) $T_0 = cw = \dfrac{l^2 - h^2}{2h} w$; $T = yw = (h+c)\, w$. Substitute for *c*.]

4. A string of length *l* hangs with its ends tied to two points *A* and *B*, makes angles α, β with the vertical at *A* and *B*. Show that, if *h* is the height of one point above the other and the vertex of the catenary does not lie between them, then

$$h \cos \tfrac{1}{2}(\alpha - \beta) = l \cos \tfrac{1}{2}(\alpha + \beta).$$

(M.U.)

[**Hint:** Let, for the lower point *B*, $\psi = 90° - \beta,\ s = s_1,\ y = y_1$. Then for *A*, $\psi = 90° - \alpha, s = s_1 + l, y = y_1 + h$; Use $y = c \sec \psi,\ s = c \tan \psi$.

$$\frac{h}{l} = \frac{(y_1 + h) - y_1}{(s_1 + l) - s_1} = \frac{c \sec (90° - \alpha) - c \sec (90° - \beta)}{c \tan (90° - \alpha) - c \tan (90° - \beta)} = \frac{\sin \beta - \sin \alpha}{\sin (\beta - \alpha)}.]$$

5. A string hangs with its ends tied at two points. α, β are the inclinations to the horizon of the tangents at the extremities of a portion of the string and *l*, the length of the portion. If the extremities lie on one side of the vertex, show that the height of one extremity above the other is

$$\frac{\sin \tfrac{1}{2}(\alpha + \beta)}{\cos \tfrac{1}{2}(\alpha - \beta)}.$$

(M.K.U., Bn.U.)

6. An endless chain rests in equilibrium over a smooth pulley of radius *r* and is in contact with it on three quarters of the circumference. Show that the length of the free portion is

$$\frac{\sqrt{2}}{\log\left(\sqrt{2} + 1\right)} r.$$

(M.U.)

7. A chain of length *l* which can just bear a tension of *n* times its weight, is stretched between two points in the same horizontal line. Show that the least sag is

$$\tfrac{1}{2} l \left(2n - \sqrt{4n^2 - 1}\right).$$

(M.U., M.K.U., Bn.U.)

[**Hint:** With the usual notations, if *h* is the sag,

$y_{max} = h + c$ and $T_{max} = (h + c)\, w$. But $T_{max} \le n\,(lw)$.

So $(h + c)\, w = nlw$ or $c = nl - h$. From $y^2 = s^2 + c^2$, we get

$(c + h)^2 = (\tfrac{l}{2})^2 + c^2$. Eliminate *c* and get *h*]

8. A chain of length 2*l* hangs between two points *A* and *B* on the same level. The tension at *A* is five times the tension at the lowest point. Show that the horizontal distance between *A* and *B* is

$$\frac{\log\left(5 + 2\sqrt{6}\right)}{\sqrt{6}} l.$$

(M.U., Bn.U.)

9. A chain of length 2*l* is to be suspended from two points *A* and *B* at the same level and the tension in the chain should not exceed the weight of the chain of length λ. Show that the greatest span possible is

$$\sqrt{\lambda^2 - l^2} \log \frac{\lambda + l}{\lambda - l}.$$

(M.U.)

[Hint: If w is the weight per unit length, $T_A = \lambda w$. If h is the height of A from the directrix, $T_A = hw$. So $h = \lambda$. Thus, from $y^2 = s^2 + c^2$, we get $h^2 = l^2 + c^2$ and $c = \sqrt{\lambda^2 - l^2}$. By R. 6, the span is

$$2x = 2\left[c \log \frac{s+y}{c}\right] = c \log\left(\frac{s+y}{c}\right)^2 .]$$

10. A chain of length $2l$ is suspended by its ends which are on the same horizontal level. The distance between the ends is $2a$ and the sag is a. Show that, if c is the parameter of the catenary

$$\frac{2a^2}{l^2 - a^2} = \log\frac{l+a}{l-a}, \quad \tanh\frac{a}{c} = \frac{2al}{l^2 + a^2}.$$

(M.U., M.K.U.)

11. The ends of a string are attached to two small rings of negligible weight, which slide along a fixed rough horizontal rod, whose coefficient of friction is μ. Show that, to have equilibrium, the ratio of the maximum span to the length of the chain is

$$\mu \log \frac{1+\sqrt{1+\mu^2}}{\mu}.$$

(M.U.)

[Hint: See Example 9. Consider now one ring and set $n = 0$ and get $\frac{2a}{2l}$ from $c = \mu l$ and

$$a = c \log \frac{l + \sqrt{l^2 + c^2}}{c}]$$

9.1.1 Sag

If A, B are the points of suspension of the string in the same horizontal line. We shall find the sag that is the depth of the lowest point C of the string below the line AB. We know that C is the vertex of the catenary.

Bookwork 9.3. To calculate approximately the sag of a telephone wire in terms of its length and span when the wire is tightly pulled and tied and to find the tension if w is the weight of the wire per unit length.

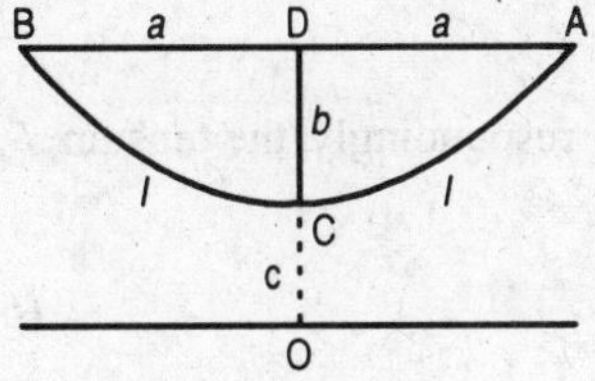

Let the length of the wire be $2l$, its span $AB = 2a$ and its sag $CD = b$. Let the tension at C be denoted by cw, where w is the weight of the wire per unit length. Then take O below C at a depth c and choose the horizontal and vertical lines through O as the x, y axes. Then, for the point A, we have

$$x = a,\ y = c + b,\ s = l,$$

where c is such that $T_0 = c.\ w$, T_0 being the tension at C. But the tension in the string is large. So c is large and a/c is small.

Parameter c. First we shall find c in terms of a and l. From $s = c \sinh x/c$, we get

$$l = c \sinh\frac{a}{c} = c\left(\frac{a}{c} + \frac{1}{3!}\frac{a^3}{c^3} + \ldots\right)$$

$$= a + \frac{1}{6}\frac{a^3}{c^2} + \ldots\ldots = a + \frac{1}{6}\frac{a^3}{c^2}.$$

$$\therefore \qquad 6c^2 l = 6c^2 a + a^3 \text{ or } c = \sqrt{\frac{a^3}{6(l-a)}}. \qquad ...(1)$$

Sag *b*. From $y = c \cosh x/c$, corresponding to A, we get

$$c + b = c \cosh \frac{a}{c} = c\left(1 + \frac{1}{2!}\frac{a^2}{c^2} + \frac{1}{4!}\frac{a^4}{c^4} + ...\right)$$

$$= c + \frac{1}{2!}\frac{a^2}{c} + \frac{1}{4!}\frac{a^4}{c^3} + ... = c + \frac{1}{2}\frac{a^2}{c}$$

or
$$b \simeq \frac{a^2}{2c} = \frac{a^2}{2}\sqrt{\frac{6(l-a)}{a^3}} \text{ by } (1)$$

$$= \tfrac{1}{2}\sqrt{6(l-a)\,a}. \qquad ...(2)$$

Result (2) can be expressed as

$$\begin{pmatrix}\text{Length of} \\ \text{the string}\end{pmatrix} - (\text{span}) = \frac{8}{3}\frac{(\text{sag})^2}{\text{span}} \qquad ...(3)$$

because, squaring (2),

$$b^2 = \frac{1}{4} 6(l-a)\,a \quad \text{or} \quad l - a = \frac{4b^2}{3(2a)}$$

or
$$2(l-a) = \frac{8b^2}{3(2a)}.$$

Tensions. The tension at the lowest point C is

$$T_0 = cw = \sqrt{\frac{a^3}{6(l-a)}}\, w, \text{ nearly.}$$

Correspondingly, the tension T_A at A is

$$(b+c)\,w \quad \text{or} \quad \frac{1}{2}\sqrt{6(l-a)\,a}\; w + \sqrt{\frac{a^3}{6(l-a)}}\; w.$$

Remark. $y = c \cosh x/c \simeq c\left(1 + \frac{1}{2!}\frac{x^2}{c^2}\right)$ when c is large. So

$$y = c + \frac{x^2}{2c} \quad \text{or} \quad x^2 - 2c(y - c) = 0$$

which represents a parabola. Thus, when c is large, the shape of the string is nearly a parabola. Also, when x is small, the same conclusion follows whatever may c be. In other words, in the neighbourhood of the lowest point, a hanging string is nearly parabolic.

EXAMPLES

Example 1. The sag of a telegraph wire tightly stretched between two poles distant a apart, is b. Show that, if the weight per unit length is w, the terminal tension is approximately

$$\left(\frac{a^2}{8b}+\frac{7b}{6}\right)w. \qquad \textbf{(M.U., M.K.U., Bn.U.)}$$

If c is the parameter, using $y = c\cosh{}^{x}\!/_{c}$, for the terminal $({}^{a}\!/_{2},\, c+b)$, we get

$$c+b = c\cosh\frac{a}{2c} = c\left[1+\frac{1}{2!}\frac{a^2}{4c^2}+\ldots\ldots\right].$$

$$\therefore \qquad b \simeq \frac{1}{2!}\frac{a^2}{4c} \quad \text{or} \quad b \simeq \frac{a^2}{8c} \qquad \text{...(1)}$$

to the first approximation. But, to the second approximation,

$$c+b \simeq c\left[1+\frac{1}{2!}\frac{a^2}{4c^2}+\frac{1}{4!}\frac{a^4}{16\,c^4}\right]$$

$$\therefore \qquad b \simeq \frac{a^2}{8c}+\frac{1}{384}\frac{a^4}{c^3} = \frac{a^2}{8c}+\frac{1}{6c}\left(\frac{a^2}{8c}\right)^2$$

$$= \frac{a^2}{8c}+\frac{1}{6c}b^2 \text{ by (1).}$$

Multiplying by c and dividing by b,

$$c = \frac{a^2}{8b}+\frac{b}{6}.$$

Adding b to both sides, we get

$$c+b = \frac{a^2}{8b}+\frac{7b}{6}.$$

$$\therefore \text{ Terminal tension} = (c+b)w = \left(\frac{a^2}{8b}+\frac{7b}{6}\right)w.$$

EXERCISES

1. A heavy string of length $2l$ is hung from two points on the same horizontal level distant $2a$ apart. Show that if c is large, the sag b is approximately equal to $\frac{a^2}{2c}$. Also show that $l = a+\frac{2b^2}{3a}$ approximately. **(M.U.)**

   [Hint: Square (2) of the bookwork 9.3. find $l-a$ and then l.**]**

2. A uniform chain of length l when tightly stretched between two points at the same level has a sag b in the middle. Prove that the length of the chain exceeds the distance between the two points by $\frac{8b^2}{3l}$ approximately. **(M.U.)**

   [Hint: See Bookwork 9.3. In $\frac{8b^2}{3(2a)}$, replace $2a$ by l**]**

9.2 SUSPENSION BRIDGE

A suspension bridge is a bridge hung horizontally from two parallelly hanging cables by means of vertical strings at equal horizontal distances. In the figure,

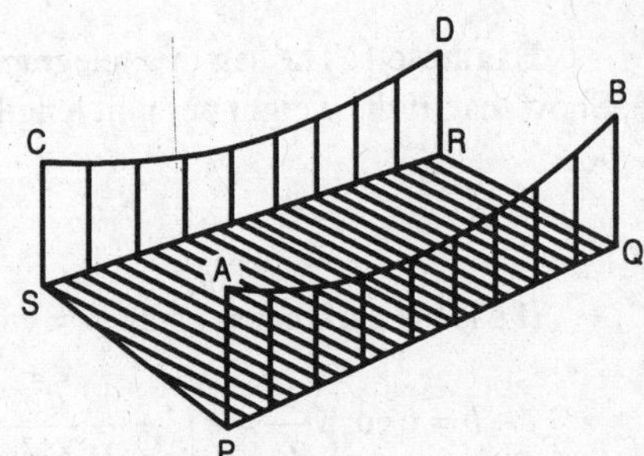

AB, CD are the cables and $PQRS$ is the horizontal bridge. From the following book work it can be seen that the shape of the cables AB, CD is parabolic.

Bookwork 9.4. A heterogeneous string, the weight of any portion of which varies as its projection on the horizontal, hangs under gravity. To show that the curve formed by the string is a parabola.

Let A, B be points of suspension and C, the lowest point of the string. Choose the horizontal and vertical lines through C in the plane of the string as the x, y axes. Let $p\ (x, y)$ be any point on the string. Let the weight of the string vertically above a unit horizontal length be w. Then the weight of the portion CP of the string is wx. The other forces acting on the portion CP are the tension T at P and the tension T_0 say wc, at C. Since the portion CP is in equilibrium, from the horizontal and vertical components of the forces, we get

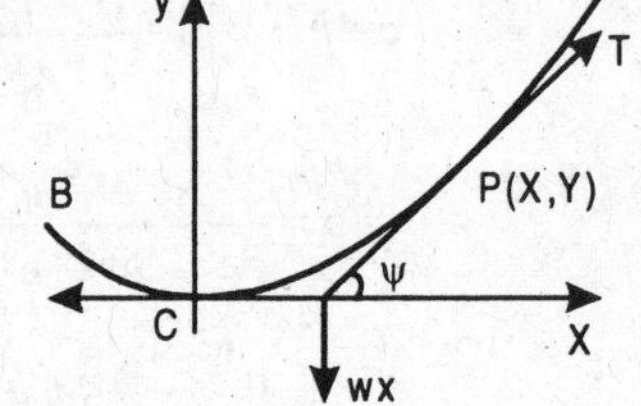

$$\therefore \qquad T\cos\psi - T_0 = 0, \quad T\sin\psi - wx = 0.$$

i.e., $$T\cos\psi - wc, \qquad T\sin\psi = wx.$$

Dividing the second by the first,we get

$$c\tan\psi = x \text{ or } c\frac{dy}{dx} = x.$$

Integration in its turn gives

$$cy = \frac{1}{2}x^2 + A.$$

But when $x = 0$, $y = 0$. So $A=0$ and $x^2 = 2cy$. This represents a parabola. Hence the result.

Tension at (x, y). Since $T\cos\psi = wc$, and $T\sin\psi = wx$, it follows that

$$T^2 = w^2(x^2 + c^2) \text{ or } T = w\sqrt{x^2 + c^2}.$$

EXAMPLES

Example 1. The span of a suspension bridge is 100 m. and the sag at the middle of each cable is 10 m. If the total load on each cable is 750 quintals, find the greatest tension in each cable and the tension at the lowest point. **(M.U., Bn.U.)**

Let ACB be one cable with C as its middle point. Its form is parabolic. Choosing the horizontal and vertical lines Cx and Cy as the x, y axis, the equation of the parabola is of the form

$$x^2 = 2cy.$$

Now the terminal A is

$$(50, 10).$$

This satisfies $x^2 = 2cy$. So

$$2500 = 20c \text{ or } c = 125.$$

The weight w per unit length along the bridge is

$$\frac{750}{100} \text{ or } 7.5 \text{ quintal wt.}$$

So the tension at A is

$$T_A = \sqrt{x^2 + c^2}\; w = \sqrt{50^2 + 125^2} \times 7\cdot 5$$

$$= (187\cdot 5)\sqrt{29} \text{ quintal wt.}$$

The tension at C is

$$T_0 = cw = 125 \times 7\cdot 5 = 937\cdot 5 \text{ quintal wt.}$$

EXERCISES

1. The span of a suspension bridge is 150 feet and the sag at the middle of each cable is 20 feet. If the total load on each cable is 200 quintals, find the greatest tension in each cable and the tension at the lowest point of it. **(M.U., M.K.U., Bn.U.)**

[Ans. 212·5 quintal wt., 187·5 quintal wt.**]**

2. In a suspension bridge, 200 m. of span and 20 m. of dip, the whole weight supported is 1 kg per horizontal meter. Find the greatest tension. **(M.K.U.)**

[Ans. $50\sqrt{29}$ kg.wt. **]**

RECTILINEAR MOTION UNDER CONSTANT FORCES

10.1 ACCELERATION AND RETARDATION

In this section we consider situations in which a force causes constant acceleration or retardation. Retardation is caused by frictional and resisting forces.

Since the acceleration (or retardation) is constant, we can use the formulae

$$v = u + at,$$

$$s = ut + \tfrac{1}{2}at^2,$$

$$v^2 = u^2 + 2as.$$

EXAMPLES

Example 1. A force acting on a body of mass 1 kilogram for 5 seconds produces a velocity of 1m./sec. Find the magnitude of the force. **(M.K.U.)**

Let the force be F newtons and let it produce an acceleration of a m./sec^2., then

$$F = \text{mass} \times \text{acceleration}. \qquad \therefore F = 1 \cdot a = a. \qquad ...(1)$$

Now the velocity is developed from zero to 1m./sec in 5 seconds. So $v = u + at$ gives

$$1 = 0 + a \times 5 \text{ or } a = \tfrac{1}{5}.$$

So, by (1), the required force is $\tfrac{1}{5}$ newtons.

Example 2. A shot of mass m_1 penetrates a thickness s of a fixed uniform block of wood of mass m_2. If the block is free to move, show that the thickness penetrated will be

$$\frac{m_2 s}{m_1 + m_2}. \qquad \textbf{(M.U., M.K.U., C.U.)}$$

Case (*i*) Block is fixed. Let R be the resistance of the block and the corresponding retardation of the shot be a. Then

$$\text{Force} = \text{mass} \times \text{retardation} \quad \text{or} \quad R = m_1 a. \qquad ...(1)$$

If u is the velocity of the shot in the beginning of penetration and s is the distance penetrated, then

$$\text{“}v^2 = u^2 - 2as\text{”} \quad \text{or} \quad 0 = u^2 - 2as. \qquad ...(2)$$

Eliminating a from (1) and (2), we get

$$R = \frac{m_1 u^2}{2s}. \qquad ...(3)$$

Case (*ii*) Block is free to move. Now the force acting on the block is R. So acceleration of the block is

$$\frac{R}{m_2}$$

So the acceleration of the shot relative to the block, in the direction of motion of the shot, is

$$(-a)-\frac{R}{m_2} \quad \text{or} \quad -\left(\frac{1}{m_1}+\frac{1}{m_2}\right)R \text{ by (1)}$$

But the initial relative velocity of the shot is $u - 0$. So, if the penetration in the block is through a distance s', that is, if the shot comes to relative rest after moving a relative distance s', from $v^2 = u^2 + 2as$,

$$\therefore \quad 0=u^2-2\left(\frac{1}{m_1}+\frac{1}{m_2}\right)Rs' \quad \text{or} \quad u^2=2\left(\frac{1}{m_1}+\frac{1}{m_2}\right)\frac{m_1u^2}{2s}s' \text{ by (3)}$$

$$\therefore \quad 1=\frac{m_1+m_2}{m_2}\,\frac{s'}{s} \quad \text{or} \quad s'=\frac{m_2}{m_1+m_2}s.$$

EXERCISES

1. An automobile weighs 1570 kg. What force is required to make it reach 90 km./h. in 10 seconds, starting from rest. **(M.U.)**

[Hint: $v = 90$ km./h. $= 90\times\frac{5}{18} = 25$ m./sec. If the required force is F newtons and if the acceleration produced is a m./sec^2., then

$$F = 1570 \times a, \text{ where } 25 = 0 + a \times 10 \text{ or } F = 3925.]$$

2. A car is moving at 72 km./h. and, when the driver applies the brakes to stop it, it moves further in the same direction. The car weighs 2400 kg and the coefficient of friction between the tyres and the road is 0·50. How far will the car move before stopping? **(M.U.)**

[Hint: Friction $= \mu R = (0.5)\,2400g\ n$. If a m/sec. is the retardation, $2400\,a = 1200\,g$; where $g = 9{\cdot}8$. Now 72 km./h $= 20$ m/sec. So $0 = u^2 - 2as$ gives $s = \frac{u^2}{2a} = \frac{400}{g}$ m.]

3. A train weighing W kg. is to reach a station which is at the top of an incline of 1 in 100. At a distance of l m. from the station, the brakes are applied and the train is then running at a speed of v m./sec. up the incline. If the frictional resistance is w kg. wt, show that the additional brake resistance necessary to stop the train at the station is equal to

$$\frac{Wv^2}{2gl}-\frac{W}{100}-w \text{ kg. wt.}$$ **(M.U.)**

[Hint: Retarding forces: (*i*) $W\sin\alpha$ or $W/_{100}$ (*ii*) w (*iii*) Brake resistance R, say. Let a be the retardation and M, the mass of the train. Then $Mg = W$. Find R from $Ma = W/_{100} + w + R$, $0 = v^2 - 2al$.]

4. A particle is projected directly up a plane inclined at an angle α to the horizon, with an initial velocity u given by $u^2 = 2gh\,(\sin\alpha + \mu\cos\alpha)$, where μ is the coefficient of friction. Show that it travels a distance h, and comes to rest at the highest point if $\tan\alpha < \mu$. **(M.U.)**

[Hint: If m is the mass, a the retardation, and s the distance travelled, show that $s = h$ from $ma = mg\sin\alpha + \mu\,(mg\cos\alpha)$ and $0 = u^2 - 2as$]

5. A shot weighing 4 kg. is fired through a stack of asbestos sheets 2 metres thick. If the shot strikes the stack with a velocity of 540 m./sec. and leaves with a velocity of 270 m./sec., determine the average penetration resistance offered by the stack. **(M.U.)**

   [Hint: Let the resistance be R N. Then $Ma = R$ and $v^2 = u^2 - 2as$ become $4a = R$, and $270^2 = 540^2 - 2a\,(2)$. So $R = 218700$.]

6. The muzzle velocity of a bullet is 500 m/sec. If the length of the barrel is $\frac{1}{2}$ m. and if the force on the bullet due to the charge is uniform, find the acceleration produced by the charge. What should be the length of the barrel if the muzzle velocity should be 600 m./sec.?

   [Hint: If a m./sec^2. is the acceleration, from $v^2 = u^2 + 2as$, we get $500 \times 500 = 2 \times a \times \frac{1}{2}$. If l m. is the required length $600 \times 600 = 2 \times a \times l$; $l = 0{\cdot}72$.]

10.2 THRUST ON A PLANE

We know that the rate of change of momentum produced on a body equals the applied force on it. If the change of momentum is uniform, then the applied force equals the change in momentum in unit time.

When a system of particles impinge uniformly on a plane and get their velocities reduced to zero, then the thrust on the plane is the change of momentum of the particles in unit time.

EXAMPLES

Example 1. Water issued from a circular pipe of 5 cm. diameter with a speed of 8m./sec. impinges directly upon a plane and its momentum is thereby wholly destroyed. What is the thrust of the jet upon the plane? (Mass of 1 c.c. of water is 1 gm.)

Now 8 m. = 800 cm. Area of the circular section of the pipe is $\pi(\frac{5}{2})(\frac{5}{2})$ sq. cm. Thus

$$\left.\begin{array}{l}\text{Volume of water}\\ \text{delivered in 1 sec.}\end{array}\right\} = \pi \times \frac{5}{2} \times \frac{5}{2} \times 800 \text{ c.c.}$$

$$= 5000\pi \text{ c.c.}$$

$$\left.\begin{array}{l}\text{Mass of water}\\ \text{delivered in 1 sec.}\end{array}\right\} = 5000\pi \text{ gm.} = 5\pi \text{ kg.}$$

$$\left.\begin{array}{l}\text{Momentum of the water}\\ \text{delivered in 1 sec.}\end{array}\right\} = 5\pi \times 8 \text{ M.K.S. units}$$

$$\left.\begin{array}{l}\text{Momentum of the water}\\ \text{destroyed in 1 sec.}\end{array}\right\} = 5\pi \times 8 \text{ M.K.S. units}$$

Thrust on the plane = Change in momentum in 1 sec.

$$= 40\pi \text{ newtons.}$$

Example 2. 3·5 cm of rain falls in 20 minutes. Assuming that the fall is steady and uniform and that the velocity of the rain drops on striking the ground is 21 m./sec., find, in tonne wt., the pressure on the ground per square kilometre due to the shower.

For one second the relevant physical quantities are

$$\text{Volume} = \text{Area} \times \text{Height} = 10^{10} \times \frac{3{\cdot}5}{20 \times 60} = \frac{35 \times 10^7}{12} \text{ c.c.}$$

$$\text{Mass} = \frac{35\times10^7}{12}\text{gm.} = \frac{35\times10^4}{12}\text{kg.}$$

$$\left.\begin{matrix}\text{Momentum}\\ \text{destroyed}\end{matrix}\right\} = \frac{35\times10^4}{12}\times 21 \text{ M.K.S. units}$$

$$\text{Thrust} = \frac{35\times10^4}{12}\times 21\,\text{n} = \frac{35\times10^4\times21}{12\times1000\times g}\text{tonne wt.,}$$

where $g = 9{\cdot}8$.

EXERCISES

1. A jet of water issued from a circular nozzle of diameter 2 cm. with a velocity of 70 cm./sec. impinges normally on a wall and thereby gets its velocity destroyed. Show that the total pressure on the wall is 0·154 n, $(\pi = 22/7)$.

[Hint: Thrust $= \left(\frac{22}{7}\times1\times1\times70\times\frac{1}{1000}\right)\frac{70}{100} = 0{\cdot}154\,\text{N.}$ **]**

10.3 MOTION ALONG A VERTICAL LINE UNDER GRAVITY

When a particle moves in a vertical line either upwardly or downwardly, its acceleration in the downward direction is g if the air resistance is neglected. Further, if the motion is close to the surface of the earth, then g may be taken to be a constant.

EXAMPLES

Example 1. A particle is projected vertically upwards with a velocity u cm./sec. and, after t seconds, another particle is projected upwards from the same point with the same velocity. Prove that the particles will meet at a height $\frac{u^2}{2g} - \frac{gt^2}{8}$ cm. at a time $\frac{t}{2} + \frac{u}{g}$ secs. after the first particle is projected. **(M.K.U.)**

Let the particles meet after a time t_1 sec. after the second particle is projected. Then, for their motion upto their meeting, we have

		First particle	***Second particle***
Initial velocity	:	u	u
Acceleration	:	$-g$	$-g$
Time	:	$t + t_1$	t_1
Final velocity	:	$u - g(t + t_1)$	$u - gt_1$

In this, the final velocity of the first one is downward and that of the second one is upward. Therefore they are equal in magnitude but opposite in sign. Thus

$$u - gt_1 = -\left[u - g\left(t + t_1\right)\right] \text{ or } t_1 = \frac{u}{g} - \frac{t}{2}.$$

If h is the height of the meeting point, finding the height of the second particle when $t = t_1$,

$$h = ut_1 - \frac{1}{2}gt_1^2 = u\left(\frac{u}{g} - \frac{t}{2}\right) - \frac{g}{2}\left(\frac{u}{g} - \frac{t}{2}\right)^2$$

$$= \frac{u^2}{2g} - \frac{gt^2}{8} \text{ cm.}$$

Also the time taken for the meeting after the first particle is projected is

$$t + t_1 = t + \frac{u}{g} - \frac{t}{2} = \frac{u}{g} + \frac{t}{2} \text{ secs.}$$

EXERCISES

1. A man can throw a stone up to a height of h. With what velocity does he throw it and how long will it be in the air? **(M.U.)**

[Ans : $\sqrt{2gh}$, $\sqrt{8h/g}$. **]**

2. A body is let fall from a point on the top of the tower 60 m. high and another is simultaneously projected from the ground vertically below the point at the top, with the velocity of 30 m./sec. Find the time and the height when they meet. **(M.U.)**

[Hint: $60 = \{(0)t + \frac{1}{2}gt^2\} + \{(30)t - \frac{1}{2}gt^2\}$; $t = 2$, height is $40 \cdot 4$ m. **]**

3. A ball is projected vertically upwards with a velocity of 49 m./sec. If another ball is projected in the same manner after 2 sec., show that the balls will meet 4 sec. after the projection of the second ball. **(M.U.)**

[Hint: Let the balls meet t sec. after the projection of the second ball. Then, comparing the velocities at the meet and using $g = 9{\cdot}8$,

$$49 - gt = -[49 - g(t+2)] \text{ or } t = 4]$$

4. A particle is dropped to the ground from the top of a tower and during the last second of its fall, it describes $\frac{9}{25}$ of the height of the tower. Find the height of the tower. **(M.U.)**

[Hint: Let h be the height of the tower and t sec. be the total time for the fall. Then

(*i*) $h = \frac{1}{2}gt^2$, considering the distance travelled in t sec.

(*ii*) $h - \frac{9}{25}h = \frac{1}{2}g(t-1)^2$, distance travelled in $t - 1$ sec.

Dividing (*i*) by (*ii*), $\left(\frac{t}{t-1}\right)^2 = \frac{25}{16}$ or $t = 5$; $h = \frac{25g}{2}$. **]**

5. A particle is dropped to the ground from the top of a tower and during the last second of its fall, it describes $\frac{104}{225}$ of the height of the tower. Find the height of the tower. **(M.U.)**

[Ans. $t = \frac{15}{4}$, $h = \frac{225}{32}g$. **]**

6. A rocket is launched from rest and it moves with a constant vertical acceleration of magnitude g. A second rocket is launched 10 sec. later with a constant vertical acceleration of $2g$. Determine the altitude h at which the second overtakes the first. **(M.U.)**

[Hint: Let the rockets attain the same vertical heights t sec. after the second is launched. Then

$$\tfrac{1}{2}g(t+10)^2=\tfrac{1}{2}(2g)t^2 \text{ or } t=10\left(\sqrt{2}+1\right);\ h=100\left(\sqrt{2}+1\right)^2 g.]$$

7. If a particle takes n seconds less and acquires a velocity m cm./sec. more at one place than at another, in falling through the same distance, show that m/n equals the geometrical mean between the numerical values of gravity at the two places. **(M.U.)**

[Hint: Time taken, velocity, distance, gravity in the places be $(t-n, v+m, h, g_1)$, (t, v, h, g_2). Then

(*i*) $(v+m)^2=2g_1h$, and $v^2=2g_2h$ give $m=\sqrt{2g_1h}-\sqrt{2g_2h}$.

(*ii*) $h=\dfrac{1}{2}g_1(t-n)^2,\ h=\dfrac{1}{2}g_2t^2$ give $\sqrt{\dfrac{2h}{g_2}}-\sqrt{\dfrac{2h}{g_1}}=n.$

Show that $m/n=\sqrt{g_1g_2}$.]

8. A stone is dropped into a well and the sound of the splash is heard in $7\frac{7}{10}$ seconds. If the velocity of the sound is 1120 ft./sec., prove that the depth of the well is 784 ft. **(M.K.U., C.U.)**

[Hint: If h is the depth and time taken for the fall of the stone and travel of the sound are t_1, t_2, then

$$t_1+t_2=\sqrt{\frac{2h}{g}}+\frac{h}{1120}=\frac{77}{10},\ g=32;\ h=28^2.]$$

10.4 LINE OF QUICKEST DECENT

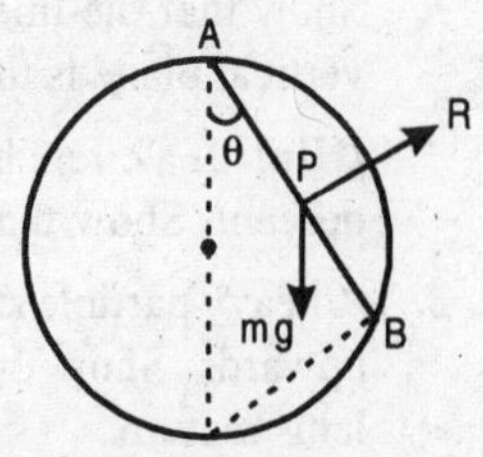

Suppose a particle P of mass m slides down from rest at the highest point A of a vertical circle along the chord AB which is smooth. The forces acting on the particle are its weight mg vertically downwards and the normal reaction R of the chord, perpendicular to the chord in the upward sense. If the chord is inclined to the vertical at an angle θ, then the components of these forces in the direction of $\overline{AB}$, are

$$mg\cos\theta,\ 0.$$

If x is the distance of the particle from A at time t, then the equation of motion, $ma = F$, is

$$m\ddot{x}=mg\cos\theta+0$$

or

$$\ddot{x}=g\cos\theta.$$

Hence the acceleration $g\cos\theta$ of the particle is a constant. Now $AB = d\cos\theta$, where d is the diameter of the circle. So the time T of descent of the particle from A to B is obtained, from $s = ut + \frac{1}{2}at^2$, as

$$d\cos\theta=0+\tfrac{1}{2}g\cos\theta\, T^2 \text{ or } T=\sqrt{2d/g}.$$

Remark 1. It is evident that this time is independent of θ and

$$\left.\begin{array}{l}\text{the time of descent from } A\text{, the highest point of}\\ \text{a vertical circle, to any point } B \text{ on the circle}\\ \text{along a smooth chord } AB \text{ is constant.}\end{array}\right\} \quad ...(1)$$

Remark 2. It can be shown that the time of descent from any point B on a vertical circle to the bottommost point A on the circle, along the chord BA, is constant.

10.4.1 Quickest descent to a curve

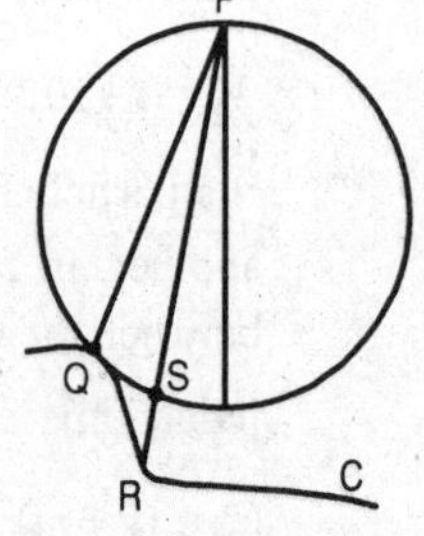

Using (1) we shall now obtain the line of quickest descent from a given point to a given curve, both lying in the same vertical plane. Let P be the point and C, the curve. Draw a circle through P, having P as its topmost point and touching the curve C, say at Q.

Suppose R is any other point on C and S is the point of intersection of PR and the circle. Let the symbol $t\,(PR)$ denote time for the travel from P to R, then, using (1) of the previous section,

$$t(PR) = t(PS) + t(SR) = t(PQ) + t(SR)$$

i.e., $\quad t\,(PR) > t\,(PQ)$

for all positions of R except at Q. So PQ is the line of quickest descent.

A particular case. We now find the line of quickest descent from a point P to a straight line l. Draw the circle through P having its centre on the downward drawn vertical through P and touching the line l. If Q is the point of contact, then PQ is the line of quickest descent. If the horizontal line through P meets l at T, then $TP = TQ$. So, in this particular case, we need not draw the circle to obtain the line of quickest descent but we should draw the horizontal line through P to meet l at T. Then Q should be taken on l below T such that $PT = TQ$. Thus PQ is the line of quickest descent.

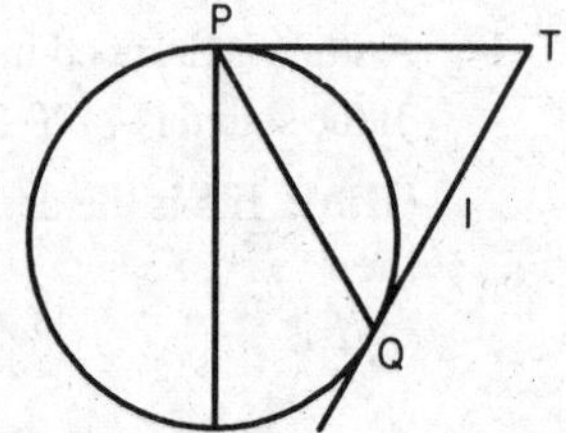

EXERCISES

1. Show that the line of quickest descent from a given point P to a given circle C in the same vertical plane is the line joining P to the bottommost point A of C.

   [Hint: If a circle having P as the topmost point touches C at Q, then PQ is the line of quickest descent. Show that PQ passes through A by using similar triangles**]**

2. A heavy particle starts from rest from the focus of a parabola having its axis vertical and vertex upwards. Show that the length of the line of quickest descent to the parabola is equal to the latus rectum. **(M.U.)**

   [Hint: Let the parabola be $y^2 = 4ax$ with S as the focus and x axis vertically downward. Let a circle having S as its topmost point touch the parabola at $P(at^2, 2at)$. The normal at P is $y + xt = at^3 + 2at$ and it intersects the x axis at $N(at^2 + 2a, 0)$. Now $SN = PN$ gives $t = \sqrt{3}$ and $SP = 4a$.**]**

10.5 MOTION ALONG AN INCLINED PLANE

Now we have two cases, one is that the inclined plane is smooth and the other is that the inclined plane is rough.

10.5.1 Motion along a smooth inclined plane

Consider a particle of mass m sliding along a line of greatest slope of a smooth plane inclined at an angle α to the horizontal. The forces acting on the particle are its weight mg vertically downwards and the reaction R perpendicular to the plane in the upward sense.

The sum of the components of these forces, along the line of greatest slope down the plane, is

$mg \sin \alpha + 0$. So, if the acceleration down the plane is a, then the equation of motion, in this direction is

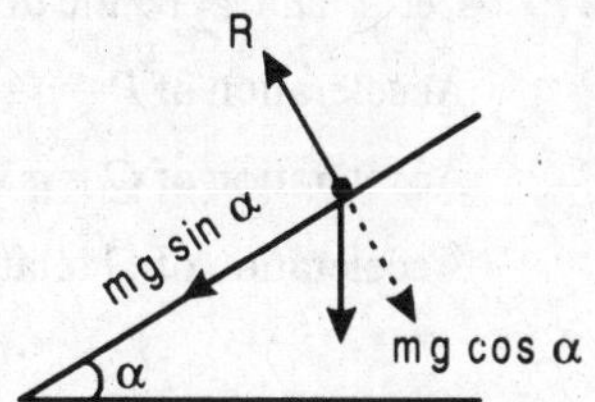

$$ma = mg \sin \alpha .$$

So $a = g \sin \alpha$. Hence the particle possesses a downward constant acceleration $g \sin \alpha$. Thus in its downward motion its velocity steadily increases while in its upward motion it steadily decreases.

10.5.2 Motion along a rough inclined plane

We consider now a particle of mass m sliding on a rough plane inclined at an angle α to the horizontal, along a line of greatest slope.

Case (*i*). Let the particle slide downwards. Then the forces acting on the particle are its own weight mg vertically downwards, the normal reaction R of the plane perpendicular to the plane in the upward sense and the limiting friction μR along the plane opposite to the direction of the motion of the particle, that is, up the plane, where μ is the coefficient of friction. Now the components of these forces along the plane downwards and perpendicular to the plane in the upward sense, are respectively

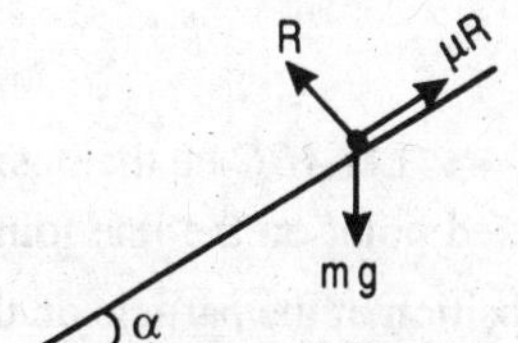

$$mg \sin \alpha - \mu R, \; R - mg \cos \alpha.$$

So, if a is the acceleration of the particle along the plane in the downward sense, then the equations of motion are

$$ma = mg \sin \alpha - \mu R, \; R = mg \cos \alpha$$

of which the second follows from N.3. Now the elimination of R from these equations gives

$$a = g(\sin \alpha - \mu \cos \alpha).$$

It is evident that, if the particle is projected down the plane, then the particle slides down the plane with its motion accelerated or retarded according as

$$\sin \alpha > \mu \cos \alpha \text{ or } \sin \alpha < \mu \cos \alpha$$

i.e., $\tan \alpha > \mu$ or $\tan \alpha < \mu$

i.e., $\tan \alpha > \tan \lambda$ or $\tan \alpha < \tan \lambda$

i.e., $\alpha > \lambda$ or $\alpha < \lambda$,

where λ is the angle of friction.

Remark. If the angle of inclination is equal to the angle of friction, then the acceleration is zero. So, in this case, the particle slides down with a uniform speed.

Case (*ii*) When the particle slides upwards, the frictional force acts down the plane. In this case it can be shown that the acceleration of the particle is down the plane and its magnitude is

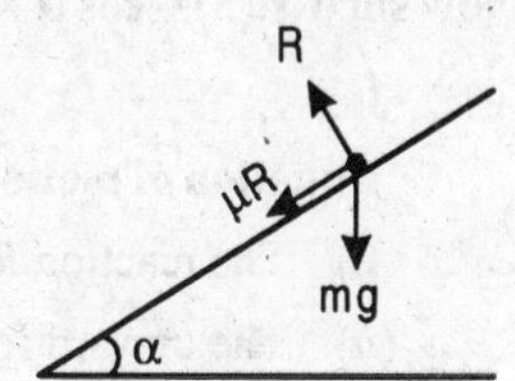

$$g(\sin \alpha + \mu \cos \alpha).$$

EXAMPLES

Example 1. Two particles P and Q start simultaneously from a point A, P sliding down a smooth plane AB inclined at an angle α to the horizon and Q, falling freely (vertically). Show that their relative acceleration is $g \cos \alpha$ and it is always perpendicular to AB. **(M.U.)**

Let $\hat{e}_1$ and $\hat{e}_2$ be the unit vectors along and perpendicular to AB in the downward sense. Then

Acceleration of $P = g \sin\alpha\ \hat{e}_1$

Acceleration of $Q = g \sin\alpha\ \hat{e}_1 + g\cos\ \alpha\ \hat{e}_2$

Acceleration of Q relative to $P = \{g \sin\alpha\ \hat{e}_1 + g\cos\alpha\ \hat{e}_2\} - g\sin\alpha\ \hat{e}_1$

$$= g\cos\alpha\ \hat{e}_2$$

which is perpendicular to AB.

Example 2. A smooth wedge of mass M is placed on a smooth horizontal plane and a particle of mass m slides down on its slant surface which is inclined at an angle α to the horizontal. Show that the acceleration of the wedge is

$$\frac{mg\sin\alpha\cos\alpha}{M + m\sin^2\alpha}. \qquad \textbf{(M.U.)}$$

Let ABC be the position of the wedge at time t. Let O be a fixed point on the line joining A and B and $OA = x$. Let P be the position of the particle on the wedge at time t and $AP = y$. Let $\bar{i}, \bar{j}$ be the unit vectors along OA and in the upward vertical direction. Let $\bar{r}$ be the P.V. of the particle with reference to O. Then

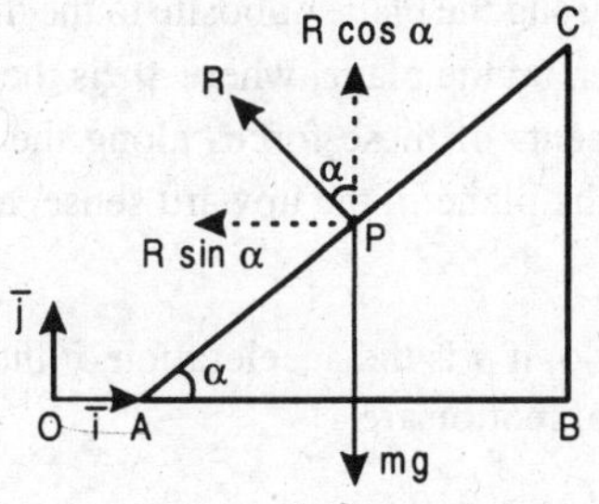

$$\bar{r} = \overline{OP} = \overline{OA} + \overline{AP} = x\bar{i} + \left(y\cos\alpha\bar{i} + y\sin\alpha\bar{j}\right)$$

$$\therefore \qquad \ddot{\bar{r}} = (\ddot{x} + \ddot{y}\cos\alpha)\bar{i} + (\ddot{y}\sin\alpha)\bar{j}. \qquad ...(1)$$

Equation of motion of the particle. The forces acting on m are the normal reaction of the wedge and the weight mg. In vectors, their resultant is,

$$-R\sin\alpha\ \bar{i} + (R\cos\alpha - mg)\ \bar{j}. \qquad ...(2)$$

From (1) and (2) we get the equation of motion of m as

$$m\left[\left(\ddot{X} + \ddot{Y}\cos\alpha\right)\bar{i} + \ddot{Y}\sin\alpha\bar{j}\right] = -R\sin\alpha\bar{i} + (R\cos\alpha - mg)\bar{j}.$$

Considering the $\bar{i}$ and $\bar{j}$ components, we get the equations

$$m\left(\ddot{x} + \ddot{y}\cos\alpha\right) = -R\sin\alpha, \qquad ...(3)$$

$$m\left(\ddot{y}\sin\alpha\right) = R\cos\alpha - mg. \qquad ...(4)$$

Now $\sin\alpha \times (3) - \cos\alpha \times (4)$ gives

$$m\sin\alpha\ \ddot{x} = -R + mg\cos\alpha. \qquad ...(5)$$

Equation of motion of the wedge. The forces on the wedge are

(*i*) The reaction R of the particle

(*ii*) The upward reaction S of the plane

(*iii*) The weight Mg.

But the wedge moves horizontally. So we shall consider only the horizontal component of the forces which is

$$R\sin\alpha.$$

So the equation of motion of the wedge is

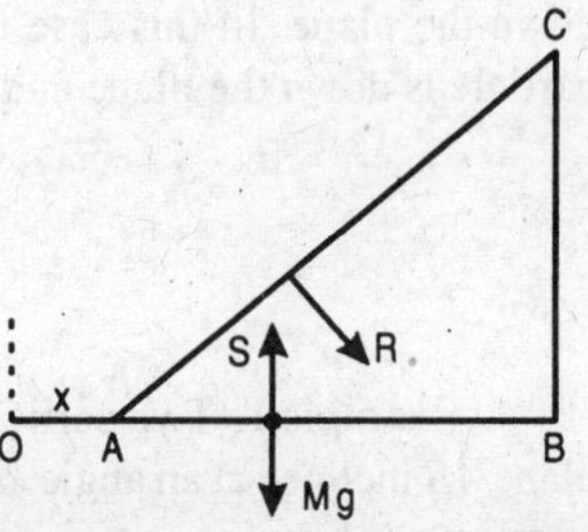

$$M\ddot{x} = R\sin\alpha. \qquad ...(6)$$

Substituting the value of R in (5), we get

$$m \sin\alpha\, \ddot{x} = -\frac{M\ddot{x}}{\sin\alpha} + mg\cos\alpha$$

or
$$\ddot{x} = \frac{mg\sin\alpha\cos\alpha}{M + m\sin^2\alpha}.$$

This is the acceleration of the wedge.

EXERCISES

1. Two particles start together from a point O and slide down straight smooth wires inclined at angles 30°, 60° to the vertical, and in the same vertical plane and on the same side of the vertical through O. Show that the relative acceleration of the second particle with respect to the first is vertical and equal to $g/2$. **(M.U.)**

[Hint: If $\bar{i}$, $\bar{j}$ are the horizontal and the downward vertical unit vectors, then the accelerations of the particles are

(*i*) $[g\sin 60°](\sin 30°\,\bar{i} + \cos 30°\,\bar{j}) = g/4\left[\sqrt{3}\,\bar{i} + 3\bar{j}\right]$

(*ii*) $[g\sin 30°](\sin 60°\,\bar{i} + \cos 60°\,\bar{j}) = g/4\left[\sqrt{3}\,\bar{i} + \bar{j}\right]$

Relative acceleration $= \frac{g}{4}\left[\left(\sqrt{3}\,\bar{i} + \bar{j}\right) - \left(\sqrt{3}\,\bar{i} + 3\bar{j}\right)\right] = -\frac{g}{2}\bar{j}$.]

10.6 MOTION OF CONNECTED PARTICLES

In this section we study the motion of a system of heavy particles connected by light inelastic strings which are taut and pass over pegs or pulleys. When the pegs or the pulleys are smooth, the tensions in the string on both sides of a peg or pulley are the same.

We consider the cases wherein the particles move along straight lines. In these cases we have to choose a direction (called positive direction) to measure the distance of a particle from a fixed point. In this direction the distance x of a particle increases. In this direction the velocity and acceleration of the particle are x and $\ddot{x}$.

Bookwork 10.1. Particles of masses m_1, m_2 $(m_1 > m_2)$ are tied to the ends of a light, inextensible string. The string is hung over a smooth peg. Find the acceleration of the particles and the tension in the string in the ensuing motion. What is the pressure on the peg? **(M.U.)**

If the system moves from rest, find the distances travelled by the masses in t sec.

Let the tension in the string be T. Since $m_1 > m_2$, the particle m_1 descends. Let x be the distance, of m_1, at time t, measured vertically downward. Now the forces on m_1 in the vertically downward direction are

$$m_1 g,\ -T$$

$$\therefore \quad m_1\ddot{x} = m_1 g - T. \qquad \text{...(1)}$$

Let, at time t, the distance of m_2 measured vertically upward be x. The forces on m_2 in the vertically upward direction are

$$T,\ -m_2 g$$

$$\therefore \quad m_2 x = T - m_2 g \qquad \text{...(2)}$$

Solving (1) and (2) for $\ddot{x}$ and T, we get

$$\ddot{x}=\frac{m_1-m_2}{m_1+m_2}g, \qquad T=\frac{2m_1m_2}{m_1+m_2}g.$$

The pressure on the peg is $T+T$ or $2T$. From $s=ut+\frac{1}{2}at^2$ we get the distance travelled by m_1 as

$$0+\frac{1}{2}\frac{m_1-m_2}{m_1+m_2}gt^2 \quad \text{or} \quad \frac{1}{2}\frac{m_1-m_2}{m_1+m_2}gt^2.$$

Bookwork 10.2. Bodies of masses m_1, m_2 are tied to the ends of a light inextensible string. The mass m_2 lies on a smooth horizontal table and the string passes over a smooth pulley A at an edge of the table and m_1 hangs. Find the acceleration of the particles and the tension in the string in the ensuing motion.

Show that the tension is the same when m_1 and m_2 are interchanged. **(M.U., M.K.U.)**

(i) Let the tension in the string be T. Let x be the distance of m_1, at time t, measured vertically downward. Now the forces on m_1 in the vertically downward direction are

$$m_1g, \; -T.$$

$$\therefore \quad m_1\ddot{x}=m_1g-T. \qquad \text{...(1)}$$

In time t, m_2 would move horizontally towards right through a distance x. The force on m_2 horizontally towards right is T only.

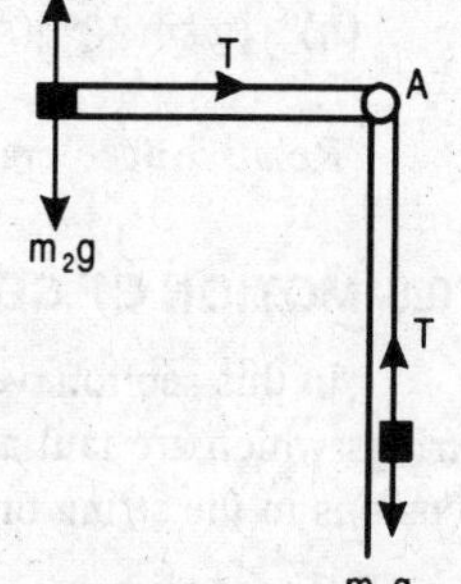

$$\therefore \quad m_2\ddot{x}=T \qquad \text{...(2)}$$

Solving (1) and (2) for $\ddot{x}$ and T, we get

$$\ddot{x}=\frac{m_1}{m_1+m_2}g, \qquad T=\frac{m_1m_2}{m_1+m_2}g.$$

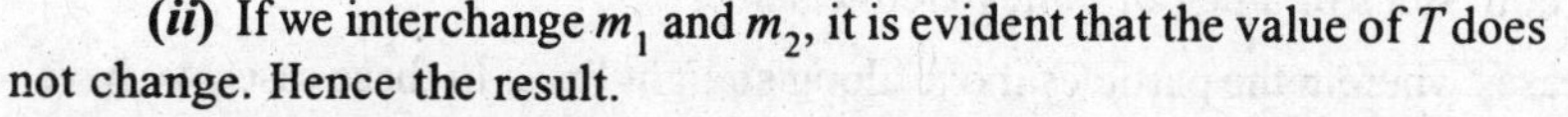

(ii) If we interchange m_1 and m_2, it is evident that the value of T does not change. Hence the result.

Case where the table is rough. Let the coefficient of friction be μ. Then, from

$$m_1\ddot{x}=m_1g-T, \quad m_2\ddot{x}=T-\mu m_2g,$$

we get the acceleration and tension as

$$\ddot{x}=\frac{m_1-\mu m_2}{m_1+m_2}g, \qquad T=\frac{m_1m_2(1+\mu)}{m_1+m_2}g.$$

Bookwork 10.3. Two of masses m_1, m_2 are tied to the ends of a light inextensible string. The mass m_2 lies on a smooth inclined plane, inclined to the horizontal at an angle α, and the string passes over a smooth pulley at the top of the inclined plane and m_1 hangs. Find the acceleration of the ensuring motion and the tension in the string.

Let the tension in the string be T. Let x be the distance of m_1, at time t, measured vertically downward. Now the forces on m_1 in the vertically downward direction are

$$m_1g, \; -T.$$

$$\therefore \quad m_1\ddot{x}=m_1g-T. \qquad \text{...(1)}$$

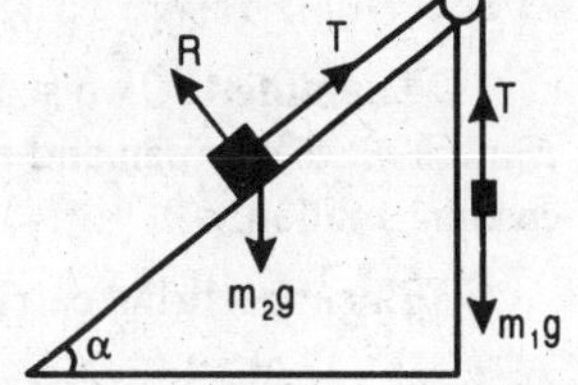

In time t, m_2 would move, up the plane, through a distance x. The forces on m_2 along the plane in the upward sense are

$$T, \quad -m_2 g \sin\alpha.$$

$\therefore$ $$m_2\ddot{x} = T - m_2 g\sin\alpha. \qquad \text{...(2)}$$

Solving for $\ddot{x}$ and T, we get

$$\ddot{x} = \frac{m_1 - m_2\sin\alpha}{m_1 + m_2}g, \quad T = \frac{m_1 m_2(1+\sin\alpha)}{m_1 + m_2}g.$$

Bookwork 10.4. A mass M rests on a smooth horizontal table and is connected by two light inelastic strings to masses m_1, m_2 $(m_1 > m_2)$ which hang over two smooth pulleys at opposite edges of the table. Find the ensuing motion and the tensions in the strings.

Let the tension between m_1 and M be T_1 and that between M and m_2 be T_2. Let us choose the positive directions for measuring the distances of the masses as follows:

m_1 : Vertically downward.

M : Horizontally to the right.

m_2 : Vertically upward.

Let, at time t, the distances of the masses in the respective directions be x.

(*i*) The forces on m_1 vertically downward are

$$m_1 g, \; -T_1.$$

$\therefore$ $$m_1\ddot{x} = m_1 g - T_1. \qquad \text{...(1)}$$

(*ii*) The forces on M horizontally to the right are

$$T_1, \; -T_2.$$

$\therefore$ $$M\ddot{x} = T_1 - T_2. \qquad \text{...(2)}$$

(*iii*) The forces on m_2 vertically upward are

$$T, \; -m_2 g.$$

$\therefore$ $$m_2\ddot{x} = T_2 - m_2 g. \qquad \text{...(3)}$$

Adding (1), (2), (3), we get $\ddot{x}$ and by substitution T_1 and T_2 as

$$\ddot{x} = \frac{m_1 - m_2}{m_1 + m_2 + M}g, \qquad T_1 = \frac{m_1(2m_2 + M)}{m_1 + m_2 + M}g, \qquad T_2 = \frac{m_2(2m_1 + M)}{m_1 + m_2 + M}g.$$

Case where the table is rough. When the table is rough with the coefficient of friction μ, only the equation of M differs. It is now

$$M\ddot{x} = T_1 - T_2 - \mu R, \; R = Mg. \qquad \text{...(4)}$$

Thus, when the table is rough, (1) + (2) + (4) gives

$$\ddot{x} = \frac{m_1 - m_2 - \mu M}{m_1 + m_2 + M}g.$$

EXAMPLES

Example 1. Two scale pans each of mass m are connected by a string and hung a smooth peg. A mass m_1 is one pan and a mass m_2 $(m_1 > m_2)$ in the other. Find the pressure on m_1 and m_2 in the ensuing motion.

Since the string carries on either side masses

$$m_1 + m, m_2 + m.$$

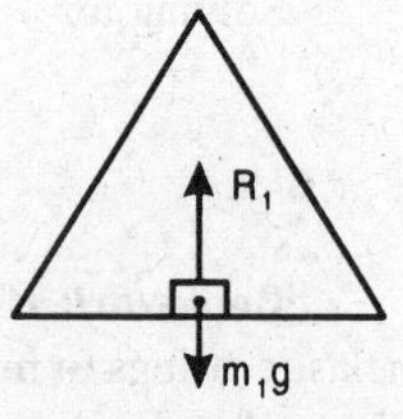

as in Bookwork 10.1, the acceleration of $m_1 + m$ is downward with the value

$$\frac{(m_1+m)-(m_2+m)}{(m_1+m)+(m_2+m)}g$$

or

$$\frac{m_1-m_2}{m_1+m_2+2m}g.$$

Now m_1 is in contact with the pan. So the forces on m_1 vertically downward are the weight m_1g and the normal reaction of the pan, say R_1, vertically upward. Hence the equation of motion of m_1 is

$$m_1\left(\frac{m_1-m_2}{m_1+m_2+2m}g\right)=m_1g-R_1$$

$$\therefore \quad R_1=\frac{2m_1(m_2+m)}{m_1+m_2+2m}g.$$

Similarly the equation of motion of m_2 is

$$m_2\left(\frac{m_1-m_2}{m_1+m_2+2m}g\right)=R_2.-m_2g.$$

$$\therefore \quad R_2=\frac{2m_2(m_1+m)}{m_1+m_2+2m}g.$$

Example 2. A given mass is split into two masses m_1 and m_2 and is used in an Atwood's machine. If the string can bear weights upto that of $\frac{1}{8}(m_1+m_2)$, show that the least possible acceleration so that the string will not break is $\frac{1}{2}g\sqrt{3}$. **(M.K.U.)**

The tension and acceleration are

$$T=\frac{2m_1m_2}{m_1+m_2}g, \quad a=\frac{m_1-m_2}{m_1+m_2}g.$$

Let $m_1 + m_2 = k$. Then, from the identity,

$$(m_1-m_2)^2 + 4m_1m_2 = (m_1+m_2)^2,$$

we see that, as the acceleration decreases, the tension increases since $m_1 + m_2$ is a constant.

Denote the maximum bearable tension $\frac{1}{8}(m_1+m_2)g$ by T_0. Then in the limiting situation of breaking

$$T = T_0 \quad \text{or} \quad \frac{2m_1m_2}{(m_1+m_2)}g=\frac{1}{8}(m_1+m_2)g$$

or

$$(m_1+m_2)^2 = 16\, m_1m_2.$$

Subtracting $4\,m_1m_2$ from both sides,

$$(m_1-m_2)^2 = 12m_1m_2.$$

$$\therefore \quad \left(\frac{m_1 - m_2}{m_1 + m_2}\right)^2 = \frac{3}{4} \quad \text{or} \quad \frac{m_1 - m_2}{m_1 + m_2} = \frac{\sqrt{3}}{2}$$

$$\therefore \quad a = \frac{\sqrt{3}}{2} g.$$

But, as acceleration decreases, tension increases. So the acceleration cannot be less than $(\frac{1}{2})\sqrt{3}\, g$.

Example 3. Two bodies A and B of masses p and q gm. ($p > q$, $p - q$: is even) are attached to the ends of a string which passes over a smooth weightless pulley. At the end of each second after motion begins, 1 gm. is taken from A and simultaneously 1 gm. is added to B without jerking. Show that the motion will be reversed after $p - q + 1$ seconds and find the maximum tension of the string during the motion. **(A.U)**

The acceleration during the successive seconds are

$$\frac{p-q}{p+q} g, \quad \frac{(p-1)-(q+1)}{p+q} g, \quad \frac{(p-2)-(q+2)}{p+q} g, \ldots.$$

Denoting $g/(p + q)$ by λ, the accelerations are

$$\lambda\,(p-q),\ \lambda\,(p-q-1\times 2),\ \lambda\,(p-q-2\times 2), \ldots..$$

which are in a decreasing A.P. Thus, in the nth second, where $n = \frac{1}{2}(p-q)+1$, the acceleration is zero and the velocity is a constant. Subsequently, retardation takes place. That is, during the first $n - 1$ sec. the velocity increases and during the nth sec. it remains constant and in the following $n - 1$ sec. it decreases to zero in the same manner as it was developed and thereafter the motion is reversed. Thus after $(n - 1) + 1 + (n - 1)$ sec. the motion is reversed. But

$$(n-1) + 1 + (n-1) = 2n - 1 = p - q + 1.$$

The tension is a maximum when the acceleration is a minimum. The minimum value of acceleration is zero. When the acceleration is zero, the masses are equal and the tension is obtained by substituting $\frac{1}{2}$ $(p + q)$ for both m_1 and m_2 in $\dfrac{2m_1 m_2}{m_1 + m_2} g$ as $\dfrac{p+q}{2} g$.

Example 4. Two masses m_1, m_2 are tied to the ends of a light inextensible string. Mass m_2 lies on a smooth table and the string passes over a smooth pulley B at the edge of the table and over another fixed pulley A as in the figure and m_1 hangs. A pulley of mass M is placed over the string between A and B and the system is set in motion. Show that the tension in the string is

$$\frac{3}{m_1^{-1} + 4M^{-1} + m_2^{-1}} g.$$

The tension in the string is uniform. Let it be T. Let, at time t,

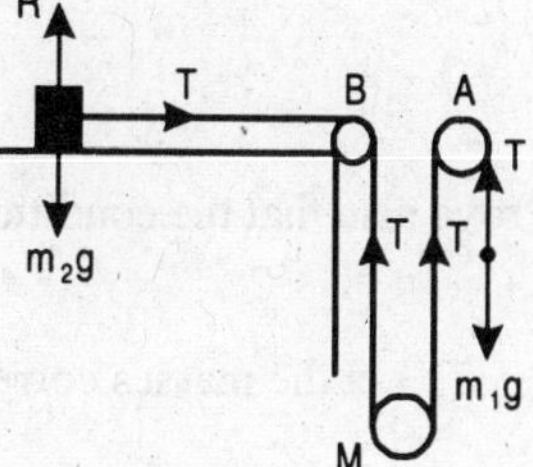

(*i*) The distance of m_1 from A measured vertically downward be x.

(*ii*) The distance of M from A (and B) measured vertically downward be y.

(*iii*) The distance of m_2 from B, measured horizontally to the left, be z.

Then, if l is the length of the string,

$$x + 2y + z = l.$$

So, differentiating twice w.r.t t, we get

$$\ddot{x}+2\ddot{y}+\ddot{z}=0. \quad ...(1)$$

Now the equations of motion of the masses are

$$m_1\ddot{x}=m_1 g-T, \quad ...(2)$$

$$M\ddot{y}=Mg-2T, \quad ...(3)$$

$$m_2\ddot{z}=-T \text{ since tension to the left is } -T. \quad ...(4)$$

Substituting in (1) the values of $\ddot{x}, \ddot{y}, \ddot{z}$ obtained from (2), (3), (4) we get

$$T=\frac{3}{m_1^{-1}+4M^{-1}+m_2^{-1}}g.$$

Example 5. Two particles of masses m_1 and m_2 lie together on a smooth horizontal table. A string which joins them hangs over the edge in the form of a loop and supports a smooth heavy pulley of mass M. Show that the pulley descends with an acceleration

$$\frac{M(m_1+m_2)g}{M(m_1+m_2)+4m_1m_2}. \quad \textbf{(M.U.)}$$

The tension is uniform. Let it be T. Let, at time t,

(*i*) the distance of M from the edge measured vertically downwards be y.

(*ii*) the distances of m_1, m_2 from the edge measured horizontally to the left be x, z.

If l is length of the string, then we have

$$x+2y+z=l. \quad \therefore \ddot{x}+2\ddot{y}+\ddot{z}=0.$$

The equations of motions of m_1, M, m_2 are

$$m_1\ddot{x}=-T, \quad M\ddot{y}=Mg-2T, \quad m_2\ddot{z}=-T.$$

$$\therefore \quad T=\frac{2g}{m_1^{-1}+4M^{-1}+m_2^{-1}}, \quad \ddot{y}=\frac{M(m_1+m_2)g}{M(m_1+m_2)+4m_1m_2}.$$

Example 6. A and B are two fixed smooth pulleys in the same horizontal line. A light string is placed over A and B and the string carries weights w_1, w_2 at the free ends. Another pulley of weight W is placed over the string between A, B. If the portions of the string, not on the pulleys, are vertical, show that the tension in the string is

$$\frac{4}{w_1^{-1}+4W^{-1}+w_2^{-1}}.$$

Prove also that the condition for w to remain at rest is

$$4w_1w_2=W(w_1+w_2). \quad \textbf{(M.K.U.)}$$

Let the masses corresponding to the weights w_1, W, w_2 be m_1, M, m_2 so that

$$w_1=m_1g, \ W=Mg, \ w_2=m_2g. \quad ...(1)$$

The tension in the string is uniform. Let it be T. Let, at time t, the distances of the masses

$$m_1, M, m_2$$

measured vertically downward from the line AB be

$$x,\ y,\ z.$$

Thus, if l is the length of the string, then

$$x+2y+z=l.$$

$$\ddot{x}+2\ddot{y}+\ddot{z}=0 \qquad ...(2)$$

But the equations of motion of m_1, M, m_2 are

$$m_1\ddot{x}=m_1g-T, \qquad ...(3)$$

$$M\ddot{y}=Mg-2T, \qquad ...(4)$$

$$m_2\ddot{z}=m_2g-T. \qquad ...(5)$$

Substituting in (2) the values of $\ddot{x}, \ddot{y}\,\ddot{z}$ obtained from (3), (4), (5), we get

$$T=\frac{4}{m_1^{-1}+4M^{-1}+m_2^{-1}}g=\frac{4}{w_1^{-1}+4W^{-1}+w_2^{-1}} \text{ by (1).}$$

When W remains at rest, $\ddot{y}=0$ and the two equations (2) and (4) become

$$\ddot{x}+\ddot{z}=0, \qquad 0=Mg-2T.$$

Eliminate $\ddot{x}, \ddot{z}, T$ from the four equations to get

$$\frac{4}{M}=\frac{1}{m_1}+\frac{1}{m_2} \text{ or } \frac{4}{W}=\frac{1}{w_1}+\frac{1}{w_2}.$$

EXERCISES

1. Two equal masses, attached by an inextensible light string which passes over a pulley, hang in equilibrium. Show that the tension of the string is unaltered when $(1/n)^{\text{th}}$ of the mass is added to one and $\dfrac{1}{n+2}$ th of the mass removed from the other. **(M.U.)**

   [Hint: In the first case $T=mg$. In the second case

   $$T_1=\frac{2m_1m_2}{m_1+m_2}g, \text{ where } m_1=\left(1+\frac{1}{n}\right)m,\ m_2=\left(1-\frac{1}{n+2}\right)m\text{]}$$

2. Two scale pans each of mass 3 kg. are connected by a string passing over a smooth pulley. Show how to divide a mass of 12 kg to be placed in the pans so that the heavier may descend a distance of 50 m. in 5 seconds starting from rest. **(M.U.)**

   [Hint: $s=\frac{1}{2}at^2$ gives $50=\frac{1}{2}a\cdot 25$ or $a=4$. If the mass is divided into x kg. and $12-x$ kg, find x from

   $$4=\frac{(3+x)-(3+12-x)}{(3+x)+(3+12-x)}9\cdot 8\text{]}$$

3. Masses P and Q $(P>Q)$ in an Atwood's machine move from rest. Show that the mass which must be removed from P at the end of a distance x so that the motion in the same direction may continue to a further distance nx is

$$\frac{(n+1)\left(P^2-Q^2\right)}{(n+1)P+(n-1)Q}.$$ **(M.U.)**

[**Hint:** Let the final velocity in the first motion be v and m be the mass removed. Find m from

$$v^2=2\frac{P-Q}{P+Q}gx;\quad 0=v^2+2\frac{(P-m)-Q}{(P-m)+Q}g(nx).]$$

4. A mass of 10 kg. placed on a rough horizontal table is connected by a string, over a smooth pulley at the edge of the table, to a mass m kg. hanging vertically downwards. If the two masses move with an acceleration $\frac{1}{2}g$, find the value of m, the coefficient of friction of the table being $0\cdot3$. **(M.U.)**

[**Hint:** $\ddot{x}=\dfrac{m_1-\mu m_2}{m_1+m_2}g$ gives $\dfrac{g}{2}=\dfrac{m-(\cdot3)10}{m+10}g$ or $m=16.$]

5. Two particles P and Q are attached to the ends of a light string. The particle P is placed on a smooth horizontal table while Q hangs over the edge, and the system moves freely under gravity. The mass of Q is 1 kg. If P starts from rest and moves ·7 m. in the first second, find the mass of P. **(M.U.)**

[**Hint:** If m is the mass of P, $a=\dfrac{m_1}{m_1+m_2}g=\dfrac{g}{m+1}$; $s=ut+\dfrac{1}{2}at^2$ gives $\cdot7=\dfrac{1}{2}\dfrac{1}{m+1}g$ or $m=6$]

6. A mass m slides down a smooth inclined plane of inclination α and draws another mass from rest through a distance d in time t along a smooth horizontal table which is in level with the top of the plane over which the string passes. Prove that the mass on the table is

$$m\frac{gt^2\sin\alpha-2d}{2d}$$ **(M.U.)**

[**Hint:** $d=\frac{1}{2}at^2$ (*i*) $ma=mg\sin\alpha-T$ (*ii*) $Ma=T$. Find M]

7. A particle of mass m is drawn up a smooth inclined plane which makes an angle α with the horizontal by a light inextensible string which passes over a smooth pulley at the top of the plane and has a mass $3m$ hanging freely at the other end. The system starts from rest and, after time t, the string breaks. Find through what distance the particle of mass m will move further up before coming to rest. **(M.U.)**

[**Hint:** Let v be the velocity of m at the time t. If s is the distance moved further, then

$$v=\frac{3m-m\sin\alpha}{4m}gt;\quad 0=v^2-2(g\sin\alpha)s.\text{ Find } s]$$

8. A mass m is to be drawn up an inclined plane, of height h and length l from the bottom, by means of a string passing over the top of the plane. The other end of the string hangs carrying a mass m'. Show that in order that m may just reach the top of the plane, m' must be detached after m has moved through a distance

$$\frac{m+m'}{m'}\cdot\frac{hl}{h+l}.$$ **(M.U.)**

[**Hint:** Let the detachment be made when m is drawn up the plane through a distance x. If v is the velocity of m then,

$$v^2=2\frac{m'-m\sin\alpha}{m+m'}gx,\text{ where }\sin\alpha=\frac{h}{l}.$$

For the free motion, $0=v^2-2(g\sin\alpha)(l-x)$. Find x.]

9. Two masses m and m' are connected by a light inelastic string and m hangs vertically and draws m' up a rough plane of inclination α and coefficient of friction μ. Prove that the acceleration is less than what it would be, if the plane were smooth, by an amount

$$\frac{\mu m' \cos\alpha}{m+m'}g. \qquad \textbf{(M.K.U.)}$$

[**Hint:**

(*i*) $m'a = T - m'g\sin\alpha - \mu\,(m'g\cos\alpha)$; $ma = mg - T$.

(*ii*) $m'a' = T_1 - m'g\sin\alpha$; $ma' = mg - T_1$. Find $a' - a$.]

10. A mass W rests on a rough horizontal table and is connected by two light inelastic strings to masses $w_1, w_2\ (w_1 > w_2)$ which hang over two smooth pulleys at opposite edges of the table. Find the acceleration of W. **(M.U.,M.K.U.)**

[**Ans :** $\dfrac{w_1 - w_2 - \mu W}{w_1 + w_2 + W} g$]

11. A block and tackle consists of two light smooth pulleys A and B. A is suspended from a fixed beam and a mass m is attached to B. A string with one end fixed (near A) passes under B and over A and carries at its free end a mass M. If M descends, show that the tension of the string is

$$\frac{3Mmg}{4M+m}. \qquad \textbf{(M.U.)}$$

[**Hint:** If x, y are the distances of M, m from A, $x + 2y = l$. So $\ddot{x}+2\ddot{y}=0$ and $M\ddot{x} = Mg - T$, $m\ddot{y} = mg - 2T$.]

WORK, ENERGY AND POWER

11.1 WORK

A force is said to do work when its point of application moves. Let $\bar{F}$ be a force acting on a particle. When the particle moves, from a point whose position vector is $\bar{r}$, to a neighbouring point, whose position vector is $\bar{r}+\Delta\bar{r}$ the work done in this displacement of $\Delta\bar{r}$ is defined to be the scalar product

$$\bar{F}\cdot\Delta\bar{r}$$

This scalar quantity is positive or negative according as the angle between $\bar{F}$ and $\Delta\bar{r}$ is acute or obtuse. The work done by a variable force $\bar{F}$, when the particle describes an arc C, is the line integral

$$\int_C \bar{F}\cdot d\bar{r},$$

where $\bar{r}$ is the position vector of the particle.

Suppose that a constant force $F\hat{e}$ of magnitude F acts on a particle. When the particle moves from a point A whose position vector is $\bar{r}_1$, to a point B whose position vector is $\bar{r}_2$, the work done by the force is

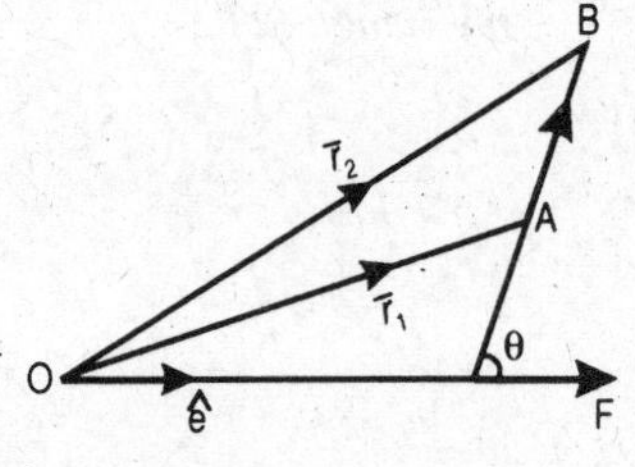

$$\int_{\bar{r}_1}^{\bar{r}_2} \bar{F}\cdot d\bar{r} = \bar{F}\cdot\int_{\bar{r}_1}^{\bar{r}_2} d\bar{r}$$

$$= \bar{F}\cdot\left[\bar{r}\right]_{\bar{r}_1}^{\bar{r}_2}$$

$$= \bar{F}\cdot\left(\bar{r}_2-\bar{r}_1\right)$$

$$= \bar{F}\cdot\overline{AB}.$$

$$= F\,AB\cos\theta$$

$$=(\text{Mag. of const. force})\times(\text{Dist. moved in the direction of the force}),$$

where θ is the angle between $\hat{e}$ and $\overline{AB}$.

11.1.1 Units of work

The units of work in the different systems are given below.

SYSTEM	*UNIT*
M.K.S	Joule
C.G.S	Erg
F.P.S.	Foot-poundal

Joule. A joule is the work done by 1 newton in moving the particle through 1 metre.

Erg. An erg is the work done by 1 dyne in moving the particle through 1 cm. (1 joule = 10^7 ergs).

Foot-Poundal. A foot-poundal is the work done by 1 poundal in moving the particle through 1 foot.

11.1.2 Work done in stretching an elastic string

Suppose OA is the natural length of a string. If the end O is fixed and the other end is pulled to B, we shall term

OB as the stretched length of the string and

AB as the extension due to pulling.

Bookwork 11.1. To show that the work done in stretching a string is

$$(\text{Extension}) \times \frac{\text{Initial tension} + \text{Final tension}}{2}.$$

Consider an elastic string of natural length a whose coefficient of elasticity is λ. When the stretched length of the string is x, let the tension be T. Then, by Hooke's law,

$$T = \lambda \frac{\text{Extension}}{\text{Natural length}} = \lambda \frac{x-a}{a}.$$

If the string is stretched further through an elementary distance dx, then the work done in this stretching is

$$T\,dx.$$

Therefore the work W done in stretching the string from its stretched length b to the stretched length c is given by

$$W = \int_b^c T\,dx = \int_b^c \lambda \frac{x-a}{a} dx$$

$$= \frac{\lambda}{2a}\left[(x-a)^2\right]_b^c = \frac{\lambda}{2a}\left[(c-a)^2 - (b-a)^2\right]$$

$$= \frac{\lambda}{2a}[(c-a)-(b-a)][(c-a)+(b-a)]$$

$$= \frac{\lambda}{2a}(c-b)[(c-a)+(b-a)]$$

$$= \frac{C-b}{2}\left[\frac{\lambda(b-a)}{a} + \frac{\lambda(c-a)}{a}\right] = (c-b)\frac{T_1+T_2}{2}$$

$$= \text{Extension} \times \frac{\text{Initial tension} + \text{Final tension}}{2}.$$

11.2 CONSERVATIVE FIELD OF FORCE

Conservative forces. Certain forces have the property that the work done by them in a displacement of the particle from one point to another depends only upon the initial and final positions of the particle and not on the nature of the paths pursued by them. Forces of this type are called *conservative forces.*

Conservative field of force. Let a force $\overline{F}$ be a vector point function of x, y, z. Then $\overline{F}(x, y, z)$ is said to define a force field. If $\overline{F}$ is conservative, then the force field is said to be conservative.

Bookwork 11.2. To show that in a conservative field of force, the force is the gradient of a scalar point function.

Suppose the symbol (AP) denotes an arc of a curve joining A and P. On it If E is a conservative force and $p(x, y, z)$ is a variable point and A, a fixed point (a, b, c), then the line integral

$$\int_{(AP)} \overline{F}\cdot d\overline{r} \qquad \text{...(1)}$$

depends on $P(x, y, z)$ and not on the curve (AP). Hence the integral defines a scalar point function, say $\phi(x, y, z)$ such that

$$\phi(x,y,z) = \int_{(AP)} \overline{F}\cdot d\overline{r} = \int_{(a,b,c)}^{(x,y,z)} \overline{F}\cdot d\overline{r}.$$

Z A P P_1 y x

Further, let $P_1(x+\Delta x, y, z)$ be a point in the neighbourhood of P. Then

$$\phi(x+\Delta x, y, z) = \int_{(AP_1)} \overline{F}\cdot d\overline{r} = \int_{(AP)} \overline{F}\cdot d\overline{r} + \int_{(PP_1)} \overline{F}\cdot d\overline{r}$$

$$= \phi(x,y,z) + \int_{(PP_1)} \overline{F}\cdot d\overline{r}.$$

$$\therefore \qquad \phi(x+\Delta x, y, z) - \phi(x,y,z) = \int_{(PP_1)} \overline{F}\cdot d\overline{r} \qquad \text{...(2)}$$

If (PP_1) is chosen as the straight line joining P and P_1, then (PP_1) is parallel to the x axis and along it $dy = 0$, $dz = 0$, So, if $\overline{F} = F_1\overline{i} + F_2\overline{j} + F_3\overline{k}$, then (2) becomes

$$\phi(x+\Delta x, y, z) - \phi(x,y,z) = \int_{P}^{P_1} \left(F_1\overline{i} + F_2\overline{j} + F_3\overline{k}\right)\cdot dx\overline{i}$$

$$= \int_{P}^{P_1} F_1\, dx = \int_{(x,y,z)}^{(x+\Delta x, y, z)} F_1\, dx.$$

$$\frac{\phi(x+\Delta x, y, z) - \phi(x,y,z)}{\Delta x} = \frac{1}{\Delta x}\int_{(x,y,z)}^{(x+\Delta x, y, z)} F_1\, dx$$

Taking limit as $P_1 \to P$, that is, as $\Delta x \to 0$, we get

$$\frac{\partial\phi}{\partial x} = F_1 \text{ and similarly } \frac{\partial\phi}{\partial y} = F_2,\ \frac{\partial\phi}{\partial z} = F_3.$$

Thus $\overline{F} = \frac{\partial\phi}{\partial x}\overline{i} + \frac{\partial\phi}{\partial y}\overline{j} + \frac{\partial\phi}{\partial z}\overline{k} = \nabla\phi.$

Remark 1. For a force field $\overline{F}$, if there exists a scalar function $\phi(x, y, z)$ such that $\overline{F} = \nabla\phi$, then $\overline{F}$ is conservative because

$$\int_C \overline{F}.d\overline{r} = \int_C \nabla\phi\cdot d\overline{r}$$

$$= \int_C \left(\overline{i}\frac{\partial\phi}{\partial x} + \overline{j}\frac{\partial\phi}{\partial y} + \overline{k}\frac{\partial\phi}{\partial z}\right).\left(\overline{i}\,dx + \overline{j}\,dy + \overline{k}\,dz\right)$$

$$= \int_C \left(\frac{\partial\phi}{\partial x}dx + \frac{\partial\phi}{\partial y}dy + \frac{\partial\phi}{\partial z}dz\right) = \int_C d\phi$$

$$= \left[\phi\right]_{(a,b,c)}^{(x,y,z)} = \phi(x,y,z) - \phi(a,b,c)$$

which is independent of the configuration of C, where C is any curve joining A and P.

Remark 2. In a conservative field of force $\overline{F}$, if C is any simple closed curve, then

$$\int_C \overline{F}\cdot d\overline{r}=0.$$

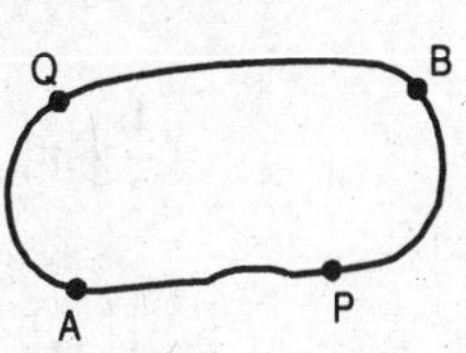

For, if A, P, B, Q are points on C, then

$$\int_C = \int_{APB} + \int_{BQA} = \int_{APB} - \int_{AQB} = \int_{APB} - \int_{APB} = 0.$$

Conversely, a force field $\overline{F}$ may be also defined to be conservative if the line integral of $\overline{F}$ along any simple closed curve vanishes.

In the cases of friction and resistance, the above line integral will always be negative and cannot vanish. So these forces are not conservative.

Remark 3. In a conservative field of force $\overline{F}$, $\nabla\times\overline{F}=\overline{0}$ because

$$\nabla\times\overline{F}=\nabla\times(\nabla\phi)=\overline{0}.$$

11.2.1 Energy

Mechanical energy is of two kinds, namely,

(*i*) Kinetic energy

(*ii*) Potential energy.

Kinetic energy. The kinetic energy T of a particle of mass m and p.v. $\overline{r}$ at any moment is defined to be

$$T=\frac{1}{2}m\,\dot{\overline{r}}\cdot\dot{\overline{r}}=\frac{1}{2}m\overline{v}\cdot\overline{v}=\frac{1}{2}mv^2.$$

Potential energy. When a particle is subject to the action of a conservative force, the work that will be done by the force in the displacement of the particle from any point P to an arbitrarily chosen fixed point A is called the *potential energy* of the particle at P. Thus the potential energy V of the particle at P is

$$V=\int_P^A \overline{F}\cdot d\overline{r}.$$

Units of energy. Kinetic energy and postential energy have the same units as work.

11.2.2 Conservation of Energy

In the following bookwork, the first result is called principle of energy and the second result is called principle of conservation of energy.

Bookwork 11.2. To show that, when a particle is subject to the action of conservative forces,

(*i*) the increase in K.E. in an interval is equal to the work done in that interval and

(*ii*) the sum of the K.E. and P.E. is a constant with respect to time.

(*i*) Let $\overline{r}_1$, T_1 and V_1 be respectively the position vector, *K.E.* and *P. E.* of a particle of mass m at time t_1. Let $\overline{r}_2$, T_2, V_2 be the corresponding quantities at time t_2. Then

$$T_2 - T_1 = \left[T\right]_{T_1}^{T_2} = \int_{T_1}^{T_2} dT = \int_{t_1}^{t_2} \frac{dT}{dt} dt = \int_{t_1}^{t_2} \frac{d}{dt}\left(\frac{1}{2} m \dot{r} \cdot \dot{r}\right) dt$$

$$= \frac{1}{2}\int_{t_1}^{t_2} m\left(\ddot{r} \cdot \dot{r} + \dot{r} \cdot \ddot{r}\right) dt = \frac{1}{2}\int_{t_1}^{t_2} m\left(2\ddot{r} \cdot \dot{r}\right) dt = \int_{t_1}^{t_2} m\ddot{r} \cdot \left(\frac{d\bar{r}}{dt} dt\right)$$

$$= \int_{\bar{r}_1}^{\bar{r}_2} \left(m\ddot{r}\right) \cdot d\bar{r} = \int_{\bar{r}_1}^{\bar{r}_2} \bar{F} \cdot d\bar{r}$$

= Workdone in the interval $t_2 - t_1$.

(ii) Choosing the position vector of the standard point for the calculation of the P.E. as $\bar{r}_0$,

$$V_2 - V_1 = \int_{\bar{r}_2}^{\bar{r}_0} \bar{F} \cdot d\bar{r} - \int_{\bar{r}_1}^{\bar{r}_0} \bar{F} \cdot d\bar{r} = \int_{\bar{r}_2}^{\bar{r}_0} \bar{F} \cdot d\bar{r} + \int_{\bar{r}_0}^{\bar{r}_1} \bar{F} \cdot d\bar{r} = \int_{\bar{r}_2}^{\bar{r}_1} \bar{F} \cdot d\bar{r}$$

$$= -\int_{\bar{r}_1}^{\bar{r}_2} \bar{F} \cdot d\bar{r} = -\left(T_2 - T_1\right) = T_1 - T_2.$$

$$\therefore \quad T_1 + V_1 = T_2 + V_2.$$

Thus K.E. + P.E at $\bar{r}_1$ is equal to K.E + P.E. at $\bar{r}_2$ and consequently K.E. + P.E is a constant.

Illustration 1. Verify the principle of conservation of energy in the case of a particle of mass m falling freely under gravity.

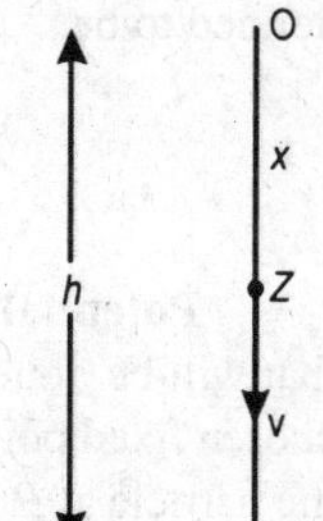

Consider a particle which starts from rest at O and hits the surface of the earth at A. Let $OA = h$. We shall choose A as the standard point for the calculation of the potential energy.

Let P be the position of the particle at time t and $OP = x$. Let the kinetic and potential energies of the particle at P be T, V. Then, by $v^2 = u^2 + 2as$,

$$T = \tfrac{1}{2} mv^2 = \tfrac{1}{2} m\left(2gx\right) = mgx$$

$$V = mg\left(AP\right) = mg\left(h - x\right).$$

$$\therefore \quad T + V = mgx + mg\left(h - x\right) = mgh \qquad \text{...(2)}$$

which shows that the mechanical energy of the particle is conserved.

Illustration 2. Verify the principle of conservation of energy sliding down on a smooth inclined plane freely under gravity.

Suppose a particle starts from rest at O on a smooth inclined plane OA. Let A be the standard position for the calculation of potential energy. If x is the distance travelled in time t and v, the velocity then,

$$T + V = \tfrac{1}{2} mv^2 + (mg)(OA - x)\sin\alpha$$

$$= \tfrac{1}{2} m(2g\sin\alpha\, x) + mg\sin\alpha\,(OA - x)$$

$$= mg\, OA\sin\alpha,$$

which is a constant. Therefore the mechanical energy of the particle is conserved.

EXAMPLES

Example 1. A body is projected along a rough inclined plane straight up with kinetic energy E. Show that the work done against friction before the body comes to rest is

$$\frac{E\mu\cos\alpha}{\sin\alpha+\mu\cos\alpha},$$

where μ is the coefficient of friction and α, the inclination of the plane to the horizontal. **(M.U.)**

Let the velocity of projection be u. Then

$$\tfrac{1}{2}mu^2=E$$

or

$$u^2=\frac{2E}{m}.$$

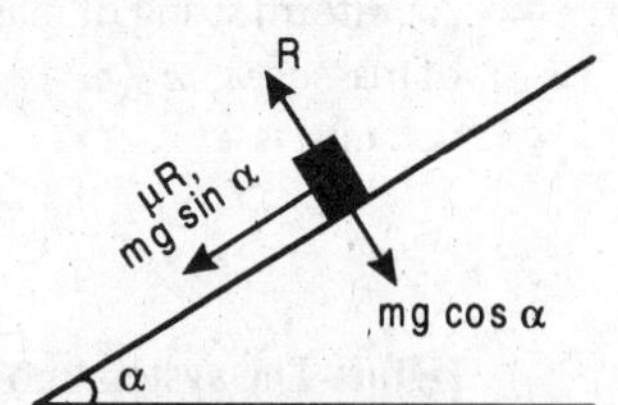

Let the body move through a distance s before it comes to rest. Now the forces on the body up the plane are

(*i*) Component $-mg\sin\alpha$ of the weight

(*ii*) Frictional force $-\mu R$ or $-\mu\, mg\cos\alpha$.

So the acceleration of the body up the plane is

$$-(\sin\alpha+\mu\cos\alpha)g.$$

Therefore, by $v^2=u^2+2as$,

$$0=\frac{2E}{m}-2(\sin\alpha+\mu\cos\alpha)gs.$$

$$\therefore \qquad s=\frac{E}{m(\sin\alpha+\mu\cos\alpha)g}$$

Thus the work W done against the frictional force is

$$W=(\text{Friction})\times(\text{distance})$$

$$=\mu mg\cos\alpha\times\frac{E}{m(\sin\alpha+\mu\cos\alpha)g}=\frac{E\mu\cos\alpha}{\sin\alpha+\mu\cos\alpha}.$$

EXERCISES

1. Show that the force field $2x\bar{i}+6y\bar{j}$ is conservative while $6y\bar{i}+2x\bar{j}$ is not.

   [Hint: $\nabla\times(2x\bar{i}+6y\bar{j})=\bar{0}$ but $\nabla\times(6y\bar{i}+2x\bar{j})\neq\bar{0}$ **]**

2. Two masses m and n are moving in the same straight line. If V is the velocity of their mass centre and v is their relative velocity, prove that their kinetic energy is

$$\frac{1}{2}(m+n)V^2+\frac{mn}{m+n}v^2$$ **(M.U.)**

   [Hint: If the velocities of m, n are u, w, then

$$V=\frac{mu+nw}{m+n}, \qquad v=u-w$$

and $\frac{1}{2}(m+n)V^2+\frac{1}{2}\frac{mn}{m+n}v^2=\frac{1}{2}mu^2+\frac{1}{2}nw^2]$

3. A particle moves in a straight line under the action of a constant force along the line. Show that, at any moment, the rate of change of the K.E. with respect to distance x is equal to the magnitude of the force. **(M.U.)**

[Hint: With usual notations, from "$v^2 = u^2 + 2as$", $T=\frac{1}{2}mv^2=\frac{1}{2}m\left(u^2+2ax\right)$. So $\frac{dT}{dx}=0+\frac{1}{2}m(2a)=ma=F]$

4. A uniform string of mass M and length $2a$ is placed symmetrically over a smooth peg. Particles of masses m, m' ($m > m'$) are attached to its ends. Show that when the string suns of the peg the velocity is

$$\sqrt{ag\frac{M+2(m-m')}{M+m+m'}}.$$ **(M.U.)**

[Hint: The system moves under earth's gravity. If v is the final velocity of the system,

$$\text{Increase in } K.E.=\tfrac{1}{2}\left(m+M+m'\right)v^2-0. \quad ...(1)$$

The $C.G$'s of m, M, m' have descended through distances a, $a/2$, $-a$. So work done by gravity is

$$(a)mg+(a/2)Mg+(-a)m'g. \quad ...(2)$$

Equate (1) and (2) and find v]

11.3 POWER

Power is the time rate of doing work. The defining equation of power P is

$$P=\frac{dW}{dt},$$

where W is the work done in time t. The units of power are watt and horse-power.

1 watt is 1 joule per second (1 kilowatt = 1000 watts)

1 horse power is 550 foot-pounds per second, that is, 550 g foot-poundals per second.

When the driving force F of an agent is a constant, the power developed then by the agent is obtained from "$W = Fs$" as

$$\frac{dW}{dt}=F\frac{ds}{dt}=Fv.$$

In other words, when the driving force F is a constant, the power developed at a moment is the force multiplied by the velocity at that moment.

EXAMPLES

Example 1. Find the power of the pump which lifts 3000 litres of water per minute from a well 10 metres deep and projects it with a velocity of 16 m/sec. (1 litre water is of mass 1 kg.) **(M.U.)**

The pump does work in two different ways, one in just carrying the water vertically upwards through 10 m and the other, in imparting to it a velocity of 16 m/sec. when projected. Let the work done in 1 sec. in these two ways be W_1 and W_2 joules. Now the mass of the water lifted in 1 sec. is

$$\frac{3000}{60}\text{kg.} \quad \text{or} \quad 50\,\text{kg.}$$

Since the earth's attraction acting on this water is 50 × 9·8 newtons (= 490) newtons) vertically downwards, the work done by gravitation in just lifting this water through 10 metres is

$$-490 \times 10 \text{ joules} \quad \text{or} \quad -4900 \text{ joules.}$$

But the work done by the pump is the negative of this . So

$$W_1 = 4{,}900.$$

The work done by the pump in 1 sec. in imparting a velocity to the water, is the increase in K.E. in 1 sec. which is

$$\tfrac{1}{2} \times 50 \times 16^2 - 0 \text{ joules or } W_2 = 6{,}400 \text{ joules.}$$

Thus the total work done by the pump in 1 sec. is $W_1 + W_2$ joules = 11,300 joules and hence the power of the pump is 11,300 watts or 11·3 kilowatts.

Example 2. The total mass of a train is 500 tonnes. When it moves with a uniform speed of 72 km. p.h. on the level, the resistance due to friction is 16 kg-wt. per tonne. Find the power developed then. **(M.U.)**

The train moves with a constant velocity. So its acceleration is zero. So the drawing force of the engine just overcomes the resistance. Thus

$$\text{Driving force} = \text{Resistance} = 500 \times 16 \times 9.8 \text{ n.}$$

$$\text{Const. velocity} = \frac{72 \times 1000}{60 \times 60} = 72 \times \frac{5}{18} = 20 \text{ m./sec.}$$

$$\therefore \quad \text{Power} = (\text{Constant driving force}) \times (\text{Velocity})$$

$$= (500 \times 16 \times 9 \cdot 8) \times 20 = 15{,}68{,}000 \text{ watts}$$

$$= 1{,}568 \text{ kilowatts.}$$

Example 3. A lift of mass 300 kg rises from rest with uniform acceleration through a height of 15 m in 5 seconds. Find the power developed at the end of the fourth second and the average power during the period of the five seconds. **(M.U.)**

Let the acceleration of the lift be a m/sec². during the first five seconds. Since the initial velocity in this period is zero and the distance travelled is 15 m., from $s = ut + \frac{1}{2}at^2$, we get

$$15 = \tfrac{1}{2} \cdot a \cdot 5^2 \quad \text{or} \quad a = 1 \cdot 2.$$

Let the force exerted on the lift by the engine be F newtons. But the earth's attraction on the lift is 300 × 9.8 newtons. So the resultant force acting on it is

$$F - 300 \times 9 \cdot 8 \text{ newtons.}$$

So the equation of its motion $ma = F$ gives

$$300 \times 1 \cdot 2 = F - 300 \times 9 \cdot 8 \text{ or } F = 3{,}300.$$

Since the velocity at the end of the fourth second is 4·8 m./sec., from "Power = constant driving force × velocity", the rate of doing work at this moment is

$$3{,}300 \times 4 \cdot 8 \text{ joules / sec. or } 15{,}840 \text{ watts.}$$

Also the average power, namely, force × average velocity, is

$$F \times \frac{\text{distance}}{\text{time}} = \frac{3{,}300}{5} \text{ joule/sec.} = 9{,}900 \text{ watts.}$$

Example 4. A car of mass 1 tonne attains a maximum speed of 45 km. p.h. when freely running down an incline of 1 in 10. What power must its engine develop to take it up an incline of 1 in 20 with the same speed if in both the cases the resistance is the same? **(M.U.)**

In the first case, the car moves freely with a constant velocity down the plane. So its acceleration is zero. So the gravitational force down the plane just overcomes the resistance. Thus

$$\left.\begin{array}{l}\text{Component of weight}\\ \text{down the plane}\end{array}\right\}=\text{Resistance R newtons}$$

$$\therefore \qquad 1000g\times\frac{1}{10}=R \quad \text{or} \quad R=100g=980.$$

In the second case, the car moves up the second plane with a constant velocity. So its accelaration is zero. So the driving force, *h* say *F* newtons, of the engine just overcomes

(*i*) The gravitational force down the plane and

(*ii*) The resistance *R*.

$$\therefore \qquad F=100g\times\frac{1}{20}+R=490+980=1470.$$

$$\therefore \qquad \text{Power}=(\text{Constant driving force})\times(\text{velocity})$$

$$=1470\times\frac{45\times1000}{60\times60}=18,375 \text{ watts.}$$

$$=18\cdot375 \text{ kilowatts.}$$

Example 5. A train of mass 400 tonnes is ascending an incline of 1 in 200 with an acceleration of $\frac{1}{5}$ m./sec^2. Find the frictional resistance of motion per tonne of the train when the speed is 20 km. p. h. if the power developed then is 700 kilowatts. **(M.U.)**

The forces acting along the inclined plane are

(*i*) The driving force *F* newtons up the plane

(*ii*) The resistance *R* newtons down the plane

(*iii*) The component, along the plane, in the downward direction, of the weight of the train namely,

$$400\times1000\times9\cdot8\times\frac{1}{200} \quad \text{or} \quad 19600n$$

Hence the resultant force up the plane is

$$F-R-19600 \text{ n.}$$

Thus, from $ma=F$

$$400\times1000\times\frac{1}{5}=F-R-19600$$

or

$$F=R+80000+19600=R+99600.$$

But we know that "Power = driving force × velocity." Hence the power developed is 700000 watts.

$$\therefore \qquad 700000=(R+99600)\frac{20\times1000}{60\times60} \quad \text{or} \quad R=26400.$$

Therefore the resistance per tonne is

$$\frac{26400}{400} \text{ or } 66 \text{ n.}$$

EXERCISES

1. An engine pumps 20 litres of water per second from a well through an average height of 8 m. If the water is ejected out of nozzle with a speed of 10 m/sec., show that its power is 2568 watts.

2. Show that the power of a pump which lifts 1,100 gallons of water per minute from a well 20 feet deep and projects it with a velocity of 192 ft./sec. from the nozzle, is $596/3$ H.P. (1 gallon of water is of mass 10 lb.)

3. The total mass of a train is 500 tonnes. If its maximum speed on the level is 90 km p.h., the resistance due to friction being 8 kg. wt. per tonne, find the power of the engine. **(M.U.)**
[Ans. 980 kilowatts]

4. The mass of a train is 300 tons. If it can just move at a maximum speed of 45 ml. p.h. on the level, the resistance due to friction being 25 lb. wt. per ton, find the H.P. of the engine.

   [Ans. 900]

5. A train of mass 250 tonnes is ascending an incline of 1 in 100 with a uniform speed of 36 km. p.h., the resistance being 15 kg. wt. per tonne. Find the power fo the engine developed.

   [Ans. 612·5 kilowatts]

6. A train of mass 100 tons is running up an incline of 1 in 112 with a uniform velocity of 30 ml. p.h. If the resistance due to friction, air, etc., is 10 lbs. wt. per ton, find the H.P. developed.

   [Ans. 240]

7. The mass of a train is 400 tonnes. The power of the engine is 1225 kilowatts. If the maximum speed of the train up an incline of 1 in 200 is 75 km.p.h., find the resistance per tonne.

   [Ans. 10 kg. wt.]

8. The power of a train of mass 400 tonnes is 1,568 kilo-watts. What is the maximum speed with which it can ascend an incline of 1 in 125 if the frictional resistance is 12 kg. wt. per tonne?

   [Ans. 72 km. p.h.]

9. If a car of mass 3,000 kg. can travel on the level at a maximum speed of 48 km. p.h., at what maximum speed will it move up an incline of 1 in 100, the total frictional resistance being the weight of 50 kg. in both the cases?

   [Ans. 30 km. p.h.]

10. A car whose weight is M kg. wt. runs freely down a slope of 1 in p with a constant speed. Show that, when it travels up an incline of 1 in q with a constant speed v m./sec., the power developed is $Mgv\left[\frac{1}{p}+\frac{1}{q}\right]$ watts, if the speed in both the cases are the same.

11. What is the power developed when a train of mass 300 tonnes is moving on the level rails with a speed of 18 km. p. h. and an acceleration of $\frac{1}{2}$ m./sec^2. if the friction is 15 kg. wt. per tonne?

    [Ans. 720·5 kilowatts]

12. At an instant a car whose mass is 3 tonnes, is moving with a speed of 20 km. p. h. and with an acceleration of $\frac{1}{2}$ m./sec.^{2} down an incline of 1 in 50. What is the power developed then if the total resistance due to friction is 30 kg. wt.?

    [Ans. 6·7 kilowatts]

13. A train of mass 450 tonnes is ascending an incline of 1 in 200. What is its acceleration when its velocity is 48 km. p.h. if the power of the engine then developed is 1,788 kilowatts and the resistance to motion is 5 kg. wt. per tonne.

[Ans. $\frac{1}{5}$ m./sec^2.]

14. A train of mass 360 tonnes is running down an incline of 1 in 200, the resistance to the motion being 10 kg.wt. per tonne. When its speed has reached 30 km. ph., what is its acceleration if the power developed is 897 kilowatts?

[Ans. $\frac{1}{4}$ m./sec^2.]

15. A locomotive starting from rest gets up a velocity of 45 km. p.h. on a level line in a train of 240 tonnes in $2\frac{1}{2}$ minute. If the force exerted by the engine is a constant and the frictional resistance is a constant being $6\frac{1}{4}$ kg. wt. per tonne, find the power of the engine developed at the end of the second minute.

[Ans. 347 kilowatts]

RECTILINEAR MOTION UNDER VARYING FORCE

12.1 SIMPLE HARMONIC MOTION

The motion of a particle moving along a straight line with an acceleration which is always towards a fixed point on the straight line and whose magnitude, is proportional to the distance of the particle from the fixed point is called a *simple harmonic motion.* First we shall find the equation of a simple harmonic motion.

Equation of motion. Let O be the fixed point, P the position of the particle at any time t and $OP = x$. Let $\bar{i}$ be the unit vector in the direction as shown in the figure and the position vector of the particle with reference to O at time t be $\bar{r}$. Then

$$\bar{r} = x\bar{i}. \qquad \therefore \ \ddot{\bar{r}} = \ddot{x}\bar{i}.$$

The acceleration is proportional to the distance from O. So its magnitude can be taken as n^2x, where n^2 is a positive constant. Further the acceleration is towards O. Hence it is

$$n^2x(-\bar{i}).$$

Equating the above two quantities, we get

$$\ddot{x}\bar{i} = n^2x(-\bar{i}).$$

This is the equation of motion of the particle. The scalar form of this equation is

$$\ddot{x} = -n^2x.$$

Harmonic motion. The term *harmonic motion* without the qualifier "simple" denotes a general motion in which the variable x is not a displacement along a straight line but an angle θ or an arcual distances, etc. such that

$$\ddot{\theta} = -n^2\theta, \ \ddot{s} = -n^2s.$$

Bookwork 12.1 In the S.H.M. whose equation is

$$\ddot{x} = -n^2x$$

to express *(i)* x in t *(ii)* $\dot{x}$ in t *(iii)* $\dot{x}$ in x.

Let O be the fixed point towards which the acceleration is and let the particle be at rest initially at A, where $OA = a$. The equation of motion may be rewritten as

$$(D^2 + n^2)x = 0.$$

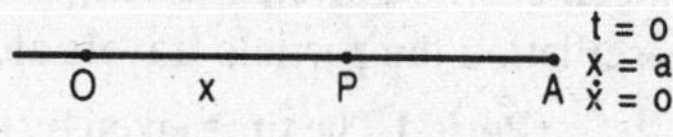

Its auxiliary equation is $m^2 + n^2 = 0$ and its roots are in and $-in$. So the general solution of the equation of motion is

$$x = A\cos nt + B\sin nt. \qquad \text{...(1)}$$

From the initial conditions, when $t = 0, x = a$. So

$$a = A\cos n(0) + B\sin n(0) \quad \text{or} \quad A = a.$$

Thus (1) becomes

$$x = a \cos nt + B \sin nt. \quad \text{...(2)}$$

$$\therefore \quad \dot{x} = -an \sin nt + Bn \cos nt. \quad \text{...(3)}$$

But, when $t = 0$, $v = \dot{x} = 0$. Therefore

$$0 = -an \sin n(0) + Bn \cos n(0) \text{ or } B = 0.$$

Thus (2) and (3) become

$$x = a \cos nt, \quad \text{...(4)}$$

$$\dot{x} = -an \sin nt \text{ or } v = -an \sin nt. \quad \text{...(5)}$$

Eliminating t from (4), (5), we get

$$\frac{x^2}{a^2} + \frac{v^2}{a^2 n^2} = 1 \text{ or } v^2 = n^2\left(a^2 - x^2\right). \quad \text{...(6)}$$

Now (4), (5), (6) are the required results.

Maximum speed. It is clear that, as t increases from zero, x decreases from a and the speed increases from zero. The speed is maximum when $x = 0$. This maximum speed is na.

Nature of motion. The particle has same speed at points equidistant from O. So the motion is an oscillatory motion between A and A', with O as the mean position, where $OA' = OA$.

Other defining equations of S. H. M. If the velocity $\dot{x}$ of a particle moving in a straight line is given by $\dot{x}^2 = n^2(a^2 - x^2)$, then its motion is simple harmonic because differentiation of this with respect to t gives

$$2\dot{x}\ddot{x} = -2n^2 x\dot{x} \quad \text{or} \quad \ddot{x} = -n^2 x.$$

Also, if the displacement of the particle is given by $x = a \cos (nt + \epsilon)$, then also the motion is simple harmonic. In this case

$$\dot{x} = -na \sin (nt + \epsilon), \quad \ddot{x} = -n^2 a \cos (nt + \epsilon) = -n^2 x.$$

Also the equations

$$x = a \sin (nt + \epsilon), \quad x = A \cos nt + B \sin nt$$

define S.H.M's.

Now we furnish a set of definitions pertaining to a simple harmonic motion.

Oscillation. One complete motion of the particle from a point on its path to one extremity of its path, then to the other extremity and back to the point, is called an oscillation.

Vibration. The motion of the particle from one extremity to the other extremity of its path, is called a vibration.

Amplitude. The maximum distance through which the particle moves on either side of the mean position of the motion, is called the amplitude of the motion ($OA = a$ is the amplitude). In an oscillation the particle travels along a distance equal to 4 times amplitude.

Period. The time taken by the particle to make one oscillation is called the period of the motion.

In the above working, let the time taken by the particle to move from A to O, be t_0. Then, from (4),

$$0 = a \cos nt_0 \quad \text{or} \quad nt_0 = \frac{\pi}{2} \quad \text{or} \quad t_0 = \frac{\pi}{2n}.$$

But the period T is four times t_0. Therefore

$$T = 4.\frac{\pi}{2n} = \frac{2\pi}{n}.$$

It is important to note that the period of a simple harmonic motion is independent of its amplitude.

Frequency. The number of oscillations per second is called the frequency of the motion; that is, the frequency is the reciprocal of the period. So it is

$$\frac{1}{T} \text{ or } \frac{n}{2\pi}.$$

Phase and epoch. The general form of the displacement x of the particle is

$$x = a\cos(nt + \in).$$

Here $nt + \in$ is called the *phase* at time t. The initial phase, that is, the phase when $t = 0$, is called *epoch*. So $\in$ is the epoch.

Bookwork 12.2. To show that, in a simple harmonic motion, the sum of the K.E. and P.E. is a constant.

$$\text{K.E. at } P = \tfrac{1}{2} m(vel.)^2 = \tfrac{1}{2} m\left[n^2\left(a^2 - x^2\right)\right]$$

Taking O as the standard point for the calculation of P.E.,

$$\text{P.E. at } P = \int_P^O (force)\,dx = \int_P^O (m\ddot{x})\,dx$$

$$= \int_x^0 m\left(-n^2 x\right)dx = \frac{1}{2} mn^2 x^2.$$

$$\therefore \quad \text{K.E.} + \text{P.E.} = \frac{1}{2} mn^2\left(a^2 - x^2\right) + \frac{1}{2} mn^2 x^2 = \frac{1}{2} mn^2 a^2$$

which is a constant.

Bookwork 12.3. If initially the particle is projected from A with a velocity V away from O ($OA = a$), then to find the S.H.M.

Now the initial conditions are when

t = 0 | O a A V

$$t = 0,\ x = a,\ v = \dot{x} = V.$$

So in $x = C\cos nt + D\sin nt$, $C = a$, $D = \dfrac{V}{n}$.

$$\therefore \quad x = a\cos nt + \frac{V}{n}\sin nt,\quad \frac{\dot{x}}{n} = -a\sin nt + \frac{V}{n}\cos nt.$$

Squaring and adding these two, we get

$$x^2 + \frac{v^2}{n^2} = a^2 + \frac{V^2}{n^2}.$$

or

$$v^2 = n^2(a^2 - x^2) + V^2.$$

Amplitude. The amplitude of this motion is the value of x when $\dot{x} = 0$. So it is

$$\sqrt{a^2 + \frac{V^2}{n^2}}.$$

12.1.1. Projection of a particle having a uniform circular motion. In this section we consider a circular motion whose projection on a diameter illustrates a simple harmonic motion.

Bookwork 12.4. A particle moves along a circle with a uniform speed. To show that the motion of its projection on a fixed diameter is simple harmonic.

Let us have the following assumptions:

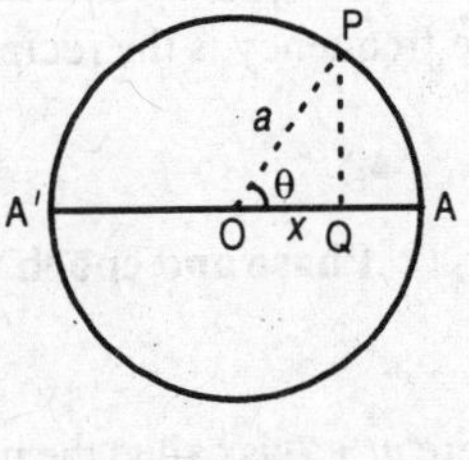

O : Centre of the circle

a : Radius of the circle

AA' : A diameter of the circle

P : Position of the particle at time t

Q : Projection of P on AA'

θ : Angle AOP

ω : Angular velocity $\dot{\theta}$ of P about O which is a constant

Let the distance of Q, the projection of P, from O be x. Then

$$x = OQ = a\cos\theta.$$

$$\dot{x} = -a\sin\theta\,\dot{\theta} = -a\omega\sin\theta,$$

$$\ddot{x} = -a\omega\cos\theta\,\dot{\theta} = -a\omega^2\cos\theta$$

$$= -\omega^2 x.$$

So the motion of Q along the diameter is simple harmonic whose amplitude and period of oscillation are

$$a, \quad \frac{2\pi}{\omega}.$$

Remark. Suppose initially P commences its uniform motion when $\theta = \epsilon$. Then, at time t,

$$\theta = \omega t + \epsilon.$$

Therefore, at time t,

$$x = a\cos(\omega t + \epsilon).$$

Thus, in this case, at time t, the phase is the angle $\omega t + \epsilon$ and the epoch is ϵ.

12.1.2 Composition of two simple harmonic motions of same period.

In this section we study the superposition of two simple harmonic motions.

Bookwork 12.5. To show that the resultant of two simple harmonic motions of *same period* along the same straight line is also simple harmonic with the same period.

Let the displacements in the two given motions be

$$x_1 = a_1\cos(nt + \epsilon_1), \quad x_2 = a_2\cos(nt + \epsilon_2).$$

Then the resultant displacement x is given by

$$x = x_1 + x_2 = a_1\cos(nt + \epsilon_1) + a_2\cos(nt + \epsilon_2).$$

$$= a_1(\cos nt\cos\epsilon_1 - \sin nt\sin\epsilon_1) + a_2(\cos nt\cos\epsilon_2 - \sin nt\sin\epsilon_2)$$

$$= (a_1\cos\epsilon_1 + a_2\cos\epsilon_2)\cos nt - (a_1\sin\epsilon_1 + a_2\sin\epsilon_2)\sin nt$$

$$= (a\cos\epsilon)\cos nt - (a\sin\epsilon)\sin nt$$

$$= a\cos(nt + \epsilon),$$

where

$$a \cos \epsilon = a_1 \cos \epsilon_1 + a_2 \cos \epsilon_2, \quad a \sin \epsilon = a_1 \sin \epsilon_1 + a_2 \sin \epsilon_2$$

$$a = \sqrt{(a_1 \cos \epsilon_1 + a_2 \cos \epsilon_2)^2 + (a_1 \sin \epsilon_1 + a_2 \sin \epsilon_2)^2}$$

$$= \sqrt{a_1^2 + a_2^2 + 2a_1 a_2 \cos(\epsilon_1 - \epsilon_2)}$$

and $$\epsilon = \tan^{-1} \frac{a_1 \sin \epsilon_1 + a_2 \sin \epsilon_2}{a_1 \cos \epsilon_1 + a_2 \cos \epsilon_2}.$$

So the resultant motion is also simple harmonic with the same period as the component motions. Its amplitude and epochs are a and ϵ.

Bookwork 12.6. To show that the resultant motion of two simple harmonic motions of same period along two perpendicular lines, is along an ellipse.

Choose the lines of motion as the x, y axes. Let us count the time from the moment when the first particle is at one extreme of its path so that at time t its displacement is

$$x = a \cos nt.$$

Let the displacement of the second particle, at that time t, be

$$y = b \cos(nt + \epsilon)$$

$$= b(\cos nt \cos \epsilon - \sin nt \sin \epsilon).$$

Elimination of t from these two equations gives the equation of the path, corresponding to the resultant motion, as

$$y = b\left(\frac{x}{a}\cos \epsilon \pm \sqrt{1 - \frac{x^2}{a^2}} \sin \epsilon\right)$$

or $$\left(\frac{y}{b} - \frac{x}{a}\cos \epsilon\right)^2 = \left(1 - \frac{x^2}{a^2}\right)\sin^2 \epsilon$$

or $$\frac{x^2}{a^2} - 2\cos \epsilon \frac{xy}{ab} + \frac{y^2}{b^2} = \sin^2 \epsilon$$

which is an ellipse, since the equation satisfies "$h^2 - ab < 0$".

EXAMPLES

Example 1. The displacement x of a particle moving along a straight line is given by $x = A \cos nt + B \sin nt$, where A, B, n are constants. Show that its motion is S.H. If $A = 3$, $B = 4$, $n = 2$, find its period, amplitude, maximum velocity and maximum acceleration. **(M.U.)**

Differentiating $x = A \cos nt + B \sin nt$, twice w.r.t. t, we get

$$\ddot{x} = -n^2 x,$$

so the motion is simple harmonic.

When $A = 3,\ B = 4,\ n = 2,$

$$x = 3\cos 2t + 4\sin 2t$$

$$v = \dot{x} = 2(-3\sin 2t + 4\cos 2t).$$

$$\therefore \qquad x^2+\left(\frac{v}{2}\right)^2=3^2+4^2.$$

When $v=0,\ x=$ amplitude $a=\sqrt{3^2+4^2}=5.$

Max. velocity $=na=2\times 5=10,$

Max. acceleration $=n^2a=4\times 5=20.$

Example 2. A particle is moving with S.H.M. and while moving from the mean position to one extreme position its distances at three consecutive seconds are x_1, x_2, x_3. Show that its period is

$$\frac{2\pi}{\cos^{-1}\{(x_1+x_3)/2x_2\}}.$$

(M.U., A.U., C.U.)

Let the three consecutive seconds be $t-1, t, t+1$. Then, from "$x=a\cos nt$",

$$x_1=a\cos n(t-1),\quad x_2=a\cos nt,\quad x_3=a\cos n(t+1).$$

$$\therefore \qquad x_1+x_3=a\{\cos(nt-n)+\cos(nt+n)\}$$

$$=a\{2\cos nt\cos n\}=2x_2\cos n.$$

$$\therefore \qquad \frac{x_1+x_3}{2x_2}=\cos n \quad\text{or}\quad n=\cos^{-1}\frac{x_1+x_3}{2x_2}.$$

But the period is $2\pi/n$. So the result, as stated.

Example 3. A particle is executing a S.H.M. with O as the mean position and a as the amplitude. When it is at a distance $a/2$ from O, its velocity is quadrupled by a blow. Show that its new amplitude is $7a/2$.

Let v and $4v$ be the velocities immediately before and after the blow and a_1, the new amplitude. Then from "$\dot{x}^2=n^2(a^2-x^2)$"

$$v^2=n^2\left[a^2-\frac{a^2}{4}\right], \qquad ...(1)$$

$$16v^2=n^2\left[a_1^{\,2}-\frac{a^2}{4}\right], \qquad ...(2)$$

Eliminating v^2 from (1), (2),

$$16n^2\left[\frac{3a^2}{4}\right]=n^2\left[a_1^{\,2}-\frac{a^2}{4}\right] \quad\text{or}\quad 12a^2=a_1^{\,2}-\frac{a^2}{4}.$$

$$\therefore \qquad \frac{49a^2}{4}=a_1^{\,2} \quad\text{or}\quad a_1=\frac{7a}{2}.$$

Example 4. A particle is executing a S.H.M. of period T with O as the mean position. The particle passes through a point P with velocity V in the direction of OP. Show that the time which lapses before its return to P is

$$\frac{T}{\pi}\tan^{-1}\frac{VT}{2\pi\, OP}.$$

(M.U., M.K.U.)

Let the particle take a time t_1 to reach the end A from P. Then the time it takes to reach P from A is also t_1. Now the required time is $2t_1$. Let $OP = b$ and $OA = a$. Then, considering the motion from A to P, from $x = a\cos nt$ and $v^2 = n^2(a^2 - x^2)$,

$$b = a\cos nt_1, \quad V^2 = n^2(a^2 - b^2).$$

$$\therefore \qquad \cos nt_1 = \frac{b}{a} \text{ or } \tan nt_1 = \frac{\sqrt{a^2-b^2}}{b} = \frac{V}{nb}.$$

But $\quad T = \dfrac{2\pi}{n}$ or $n = \dfrac{2\pi}{T}$. Therefore

$$\tan\frac{2\pi}{T}t_1 = \frac{VT}{2\pi b} \quad \text{or} \quad \frac{2\pi t_1}{T} = \tan^{-1}\frac{VT}{2\pi b}.$$

$$\therefore \qquad 2t_1 = \frac{T}{\pi}\tan^{-1}\frac{VT}{2\pi\, OP}.$$

Example 5. A particle P of mass m moves in a straight line OB under the force $mn^2 \times$(distance from A) directed towards A, where A moves along OB with constant acceleration α. Show that the motion of P is simple harmonic, of period $2\pi/n$, about a moving centre which is always at a distance α/n^2 behind A. **(M.U., M.K.U.)**

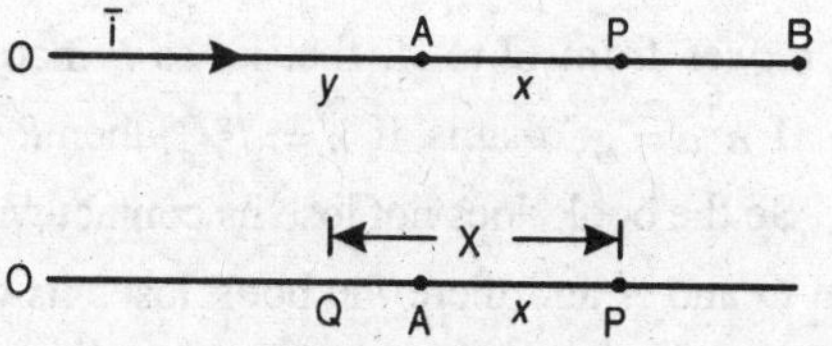

Let $\bar{i}$ be the unit vector along the line, $OA = y$ and $AP = x$. Then the position vector of P with respect to the fixed point O, is

$$\bar{r} = (x+y)\,\bar{i}.$$

The force acting on the particle is

$$\bar{F} = mn^2 AP\,(-\bar{i}) = -mn^2 x\bar{i}.$$

So, the equation of motion, $m\ddot{\bar{r}} = \bar{F}$, is

$$m(\ddot{x}+\ddot{y})\,\bar{i} = -mn^2 x\,\bar{i} \quad \text{or} \quad \ddot{x}+\ddot{y} = -n^2 x.$$

But $\ddot{y} = \alpha$. Hence

$$\ddot{x}+\alpha = -n^2 x \quad \text{or} \quad \ddot{x} = -n^2(x + \alpha/n^2).$$

Set $x + \alpha/n^2 = X$. Then X is the distance of P from a point Q behind A at a distance α/n^2 and

$$\ddot{X} = -n^2 X$$

which shows that the motion of P is S.H. with period $2\pi/n$ and with mean position Q.

Example 6. A horizontal shelf oscillates vertically with a S.H.M. of period $2\pi/n$ and amplitude a. Show that a book of mass m resting on the shelf, will not leave it provided $n^2 \le g/a$. In the case where it leaves, obtain its velocity then.

Let us make the following assumptions:

O : Mean position of S.H.M.

A, A' : Highest and lowest points on the path

$\overline{j}$: Unit vector in the vertically upward direction

P : Position of the book at time t

x : OP

$\overline{r}$: Position vector $x\overline{d}$ of P with reference to O.

The forces acting on the book are earth's gravitation $-mg\,\overline{j}$ and reaction of the shelf $R\,\overline{j}$. So the equation $m\ddot{\overline{r}} = \overline{F}$ of motion of the book is

$$m\ddot{x}\,\overline{j} = -mg\,\overline{j} + R\overline{j}$$

or

$$m\ddot{x} = R - mg \qquad ...(1)$$

The period of the S.H.M. of the shelf is $2\pi/n$. So its equation is

$$\ddot{x} = -n^2 x. \qquad ...(2)$$

Thus, eliminating $\ddot{x}$ from (1) and (2),

$$R = m(g - n^2 x).$$

This shows that as the shelf moves from O to A, that is, as x increases from zero, R decreases gradually. But, at A, $x = a$. So, if $n^2 a = g$, that is, if $n = \sqrt{g/a}$, then R vanishes at A but immediately it becomes positive thereafter . So the book does not lose its contact with the shelf. If $n > \sqrt{g/a}$, then R vanishes at a point between O and A and there the book loses its contact with the shelf. At this moment the value of x is given by

$$g - n^2 x = 0 \quad \text{as} \quad x = g/n^2.$$

The velocity v of the book then is obtained from $\dot{x}^2 = n^2(a^2 - x^2)$ as follows:

$$v^2 = n^2\left(a^2 - \frac{g^2}{n^4}\right) = \frac{n^4a^2 - g^2}{n^2} \quad \text{or} \quad v = \frac{1}{n}\sqrt{n^4a^2 - g^2}.$$

R does not vanish at all when the shelf moves from A' to O because, in this motion x is negative and hence R is positive.

EXERCISES

1. A particle moves in a straight line. If v is its velocity, when at a distance x from a fixed point in the line and if $v^2 = \alpha - \beta x^2$, where α and β are constants, show that the motion is simple harmonic and determine its period and amplitude. **(M.U.,M.K.U.)**

   [**Hint:** Differentiating $\dot{x}^2 = \alpha - \beta x^2$ with respect to time, $\ddot{x} = -\beta x$. So S. H.M., with the fixed point as the mean position and $2\pi/\sqrt{\beta}$ as period. Amplitude= the value of x when $\dot{x} = 0$. So it is $\sqrt{\alpha/\beta}$.]

2. If the distance x of a point moving on a straight line measured from a fixed point on it and its velocity v are connected by the relation $4v^2 = 25 - x^2$, show that the motion is simple harmonic. Find the period and amplitude of the motion. **(M.U.)**

[Hint: $4\dot{x}^2 = 25 - x^2 . 4(2\dot{x}\ddot{x}) = -2x\dot{x}$ or $\ddot{x} = -x/4; \ddot{x}$ $n = 1/2$. Period $= 2\pi/n = 4\pi$ and $0 = 25 - a^2$ or $a = 5$]

3. The velocity of a particle moving in a straight line, at a distance x from a fixed point on the line, is given by $v = k\sqrt{a^2 - x^2}$ where k and a are constants. Show that the motion is simple harmonic and find the amplitude and periodic time. **(M.U.)**

[Ans. Amplitude $= a$, period $= 2\pi/k$]

4. A rod AB is in motion so that the end B moves with uniform speed u in a circle whose centre is C, while the end A moves in a straight line passing through C. If $AB = BC = a$ and $AC = x$, show that the velocity of A is $\dfrac{u\sqrt{4a^2 - x^2}}{a}$ and that the motion is simple harmonic **(M.U.)**

[Hint: If θ is the angle made by CB with the line, then $\dot{\theta} = u/a$; $x = 2a\cos\theta$]

5. The displacement x of a particle moving along a straight line is given by $x = a\cos nt + b\sin nt$. Show that the motion is simple harmonic with amplitude $\sqrt{a^2 + b^2}$ and period $2\pi/n$. **(M.K.U.)**

[Hint: Find $\dot{x}\ (= v)$ and then $x^2 + (v/n)^2 = a^2 + b^2$. When $v = 0$, x is the amplitude.]

6. A particle, moving in a S.H.M. has amplitude 8 cm. If its maximum acceleration is $2\ \text{cm/sec}^2$, find **(i)** its period **(ii)** maximum velocity and **(iii)** its velocity when it is 3 cm. from the extreme position. **(M.U.)**

[Hint: $a = 8, n^2 a = 2$ give **(i)** $T = 2\pi/n = 4\pi$. **(ii)** $na = 4$. **(iii)** $v^2 = n^2(a^2 - x^2) = n^2(a^2 - 5^2) = 39/4$]

7. A particle is moving with a S.H.M. in a straight line. When the distance of the particle from the equilibrium position has the values x_1 and x_2, the corresponding values of the velocity are u_1 and u_2. Show that the period is

$$2\pi\sqrt{\frac{x_1^2 - x_2^2}{u_2^2 - u_1^2}}.$$ **(M.U., M.K.U., Bn.U., C.U.)**

[Hint: $u_1^2 = n^2(a^2 - x_1^2)$, $u_2^2 = n^2(a^2 - x_2^2)$. Subtract to get n. $T = 2\pi/n$]

8. A particle moving with a S.H.M. has speeds v_1 and v_2 $(v_1 > v_2)$ and accelerations with magnitude α_1 and α_2 at the points A and B which lie on the same side of the mean position O. Show that

$$AB = \frac{v_1^2 - v_2^2}{\alpha_1 + \alpha_2}.$$ **(M.U., M.K.U., K.U.)**

Show also that the amplitude of the motion is

$$\frac{[(v_1^2 - v_2^2)(\alpha_2^2 v_1^2 - \alpha_1^2 v_2^2)]^{1/2}}{\alpha_2^2 - \alpha_1^2}.$$ **(M.U.)**

[Hint: If x_1, x_2 be the respective displacements, $x_2 > x_1$, and

$\alpha_1 = n^2 x_1$, $\alpha_2 = n^2 x_2$; $v_1^2 = n^2(a^2 - x_1^2)$, $v_2^2 = n^2(a^2 - x_2^2)$

$\therefore\ v_1^2 - v_2^2 = -n^2(x_1^2 - x_2^2)$ or $\dfrac{v_1^2 - v_2^2}{x_1 + x_2} = n^2(x_2 - x_1) = n^2 AB$]

9. A particle executing a S.H.M. has velocities v_1 and v_2 when its distances from the mean position O are d_1 and d_2. Find the amplitude, period and the velocity V when its distance from O is $\frac{1}{2}(d_1+d_2)$. **(M.U,M.K.U.)**

[Hint: $v_1^2 = n^2(a^2-d_1^2)$, $v_2^2 = n^2(a^2-d_2^2)$, $V^2 = n^2\{a^2 - \frac{1}{4}(d_1+d_2)^2\}$. Solving the first two, we get a, n. We get V by eliminating n^2a^2 and n^2 as

$$\begin{vmatrix} v_1^2 & 1 & d_1^2 \\ v_2^2 & 1 & d_2^2 \\ V^2 & 1 & \frac{1}{4}(d_1+d_2)^2 \end{vmatrix} = 0\ ]$$

10. A particle describes a S.H.M. along a straight line on which A is fixed point. If P, Q, R are points on this straight line lying on the same side of A such that $AP=p, AQ=q, AR=r$ and if u, v, w are the speeds of the particle at these points, show that the periodic time T of the motion is given by

$$4\pi^2(q-r)(r-p)(p-q) \div T^2 = u^2(q-r) + v^2(r-p) + w^2(p-q).$$

[Hint: If the distance between A and the mean position is y,

$$u^2 = n^2[a^2-(p-y)^2],\ v^2 = n^2[a^2-(q-y)^2],\ w^2 = n^2[a^2-(r-y)^2].$$

Eliminate a and y by using determinant or by finding $\sum u^2(q-r)$]

11. Prove that in a S.H.M. if f is the acceleration v, the velocity at any moment and T, the periodic time, then $f^2T^2 + 4\pi^2v^2$ is a constant. **(M.K.U., Bn.U.)**

[Hint: $f = n^2x,\ T = 2\pi/n,\ v^2 = n^2(a^2-x^2)$.]

12. A body moving with a simple harmonic motion has an amplitude a and period T. Show that the velocity v at a distance x from the mean position is given by $v^2T^2 = 4\pi^2(a^2-x^2)$. **(M.U.)**

13. *(i)* Show that a particle executing a S.H.M. requires one-sixth of its period to move from the position of maximum displacement to one in which the displacement is one-half the amplitude. **(M.U.)**

(ii) A particle performs simple harmonic motion along a straight line between the points A, A'. P is a point in AA' such that $AP : PA' = 1:3$. Show that the time from A to P is half the time taken from P to A'. **(M.U.)**

[Hint: *(i)* When $x=a$, let $t=0$ and when $x=\frac{a}{2}$, let $t=t_1$. Then $\frac{a}{2} = a\cos nt_1$. So $nt_1 = \frac{\pi}{3}$ or

$$t_1 = \frac{\pi}{3n} = \frac{1}{6}\left(\frac{2\pi}{n}\right) = \frac{T}{6}.$$

(ii) $T_{AP} = \frac{T}{6}$; $T_{PA'} = T_{AA'} - T_{AP} = \frac{T}{2} - \frac{T}{6} = \frac{2T}{6}$]

14. A mass of 1 gm vibrates through a millimetre on each side of the midpoint of its path 256 times per sec. If the motion is simple harmonic, find the maximum velocity. **(A.U.)**

[Hint: 1 oscillation = 2 vibrations. So time for 1 oscillation

$$= \frac{1}{128}\text{ sec. Thus } \frac{2\pi}{n} = \frac{1}{128} \text{ or } n = 256\pi.$$

Max. vel $= na = 256\pi \times 1$ mm./sec.]

15. A particle is moving in a straight line with a simple harmonic motion of amplitude a. At a distance s from the centre of motion, the particle receives a blow in the direction of motion which instantaneously doubles the velocity. Find the new amplitude.

[Hint: $v^2 = n^2[a^2 - s^2]$, $4v^2 = n^2[a_1^2 - s^2]$ gives $a_1 = \sqrt{4a^2 - 3s^2}$]

16. A particle is executing a S.H.M. with O as the mean position, $2\pi/n$ as the period and a as the amplitude. When it is at a distance $(a/2)\sqrt{3}$ from O, it receives a blow which increases its velocity by na. Show that the new amplitude is $a\sqrt{3}$. **(M.U.)**

17. A mass lies on a shelf which makes vertical simple harmonic oscillations of amplitude 1 m. and period 1 sec. Show that the mass leaves the shelf at a height $\dfrac{g}{4\pi^2}$ m. above the mean position and that it then rises above the mean position to a height $\dfrac{2\pi^2}{g} + \dfrac{g}{8\pi^2}$ m. **(M.U.)**

[Hint: $a = 1$, $n = 2\pi$; $R = m(g - n^2x) = m(g - 4\pi^2 x)$. When R vanishes

$x = \dfrac{9}{4\pi^2}$, $V^2 = 4\pi^2\left[1 - \dfrac{g^2}{16\pi^4}\right]$ which lifts to a further height $\dfrac{V^2}{2g}$]

12.2 S.H.M. ALONG A HORIZONTAL LINE

In this section we consider simple harmonic motions along a horizontal line, the forces being tensions of light elastic strings or light spiral springs. Here, by Hooke's law,

$$\text{Tension} = \lambda \frac{\text{Extension or compression}}{\text{Natural length}}.$$

Bookwork 12.7. One end of a light spiral spring of length l is fixed to a fixed point O on a smooth horizontal table and a heavy particle of mass m is attached to the other end. If the particle is pulled through a distance a, $(a < l)$, and then let go, to find its motion.

Let $OA = l$ and $AB = a$. Let P be the position of the particle at time t after the particle is let go. Let the direction OA be the positive direction to measure the distance and $AP = x$. Then the acceleration of the particle in this horizontal direction is $\ddot{x}$ and the tension on it is in the opposite direction with a magnitude

O —— l —— A —— x —— P —— B

$$\lambda \frac{x}{l}.$$

So the corresponding equation of motion is

$$m\ddot{x} = -\lambda \frac{x}{l}.$$

If we denote the positive constant $\dfrac{\lambda}{lm}$ by n^2, then

$$\ddot{x} = -n^2 x.$$

This shows that the particle executes a S.H.M. such that

(i) $x = a\cos nt = a\cos\sqrt{\frac{\lambda}{lm}}\,t$

(ii) $v^2 = n^2\,(a^2 - x^2) = \frac{\lambda}{lm}(a^2 - x^2)$

(iii) $T = 2\pi/_n = 2\pi\sqrt{\frac{lm}{\lambda}}.$

Remark. If the spring is replaced with an elastic string and A', B', are points such that

B′ A′ O A B

$OA' = OA$, $OB' = OB$, then the motion of the particle will be S.H. so long as the tension acts; otherwise, it will be a free motion under no force. Thus the motions from

$$B \text{ to } A,\ A' \text{ to } B',\ B' \text{ to } A',\ A \text{ to } B$$

Form a complete oscillation of the S.H.M. and the motions from A to A' and A' to A are free motions with a constant speed. As such the time taken for one full to-and-fro motion, from B to B' and back to B is the period of the S.H.M. plus twice the time for the motion from A to A'. So it is

$$\frac{2\pi}{n} + 2\frac{AA'}{\text{maximum velocity}} = \frac{2\pi}{n} + 2.\frac{2l}{na} = \frac{1}{n}\left(2\pi + \frac{4l}{a}\right)$$

$$= 2\sqrt{\frac{lm}{\lambda}}\left(\pi + \frac{2l}{a}\right).$$

EXAMPLES

Example 1. The ends of an elastic string of natural length a are fixed at points A and B, distance $2a$ apart, on a smooth horizontal table. A particle of mass m is attached to the middle point of the string and slightly displaced along the direction perpendicular to AB. Show that the period of small oscillation is

$$\pi\sqrt{\frac{2am}{\lambda}}.$$ **(M.U., A.U.)**

Let O be the midpoint of AB, P the position of the particle at time t and $OP = x$. The force acting on m along PO and towards O is

$$2T\cos APO.$$

$$\therefore \quad m\ddot{x} = -2T\cos APO = -2\lambda\frac{\text{Extension}}{\text{nat. length}}\frac{x}{AP}$$

P T T x A a O a B

$$= -2\left(\lambda\frac{2AP - a}{a}\right)\frac{x}{AP} = -\frac{2\lambda x}{a}\left(2 - \frac{a}{AP}\right)$$

$$= -\frac{2\lambda x}{a}\left(2 - \frac{a}{\sqrt{a^2 + x^2}}\right).$$

For a small oscillation, x is small. So

$$2-\frac{a}{\sqrt{a^2+x^2}}=2-1=1.$$

$$\therefore \quad m\ddot{x}=-\frac{2\lambda x}{a} \text{ or } \ddot{x}=-\frac{2\lambda}{am}x.$$

$$\therefore \quad \text{Period}=2\pi\sqrt{\frac{am}{2\lambda}}=\pi\sqrt{\frac{2am}{\lambda}}.$$

EXERCISES

1. One end of an elastic string whose modulus of elasticity is λ and natural length a, is fixed to a point on a smooth horizontal plane and the other end is attached to a particle of mass m lying on the table. The particle is pulled from the fixed point to a distance $2a$ and then let go. Show that the time of a complete oscillation is $2\sqrt{\frac{am}{\lambda}}(\pi+2)$. **(M.U.)**

[Hint: $m\ddot{x}=-\frac{\lambda}{a}x;\ n^2=\frac{\lambda}{am}$. Time $=\frac{2\pi}{n}+2\cdot\frac{2a}{\text{maximum velocity}}=\frac{2\pi}{n}+\frac{4a}{na}$**]**

2. A particle of mass m resting on a smooth horizontal plane, is attached to two points A and B on the plane by two equal strings each of natural length a and modulus of elasticity λ, the points A and B being $2a$ apart. The particle is held at A and then released. Show that the particle will oscillate with the periodic time $2\pi\sqrt{\frac{am}{\lambda}}$. **(M.U.)**

[Hint: In the motion, one string is slack and the other is in elongation whose tension acts on the particle. Equation: $\ddot{x}=-\frac{\lambda}{am}x$**]**

3. A light elastic string of natural length $2a$ is stretched and is tied to two fixed points on a smooth horizontal table, distance $4a$ apart. A particle of mass m is attached to its middle point and is displaced in the line of the string through the distance a and released. Find the period of oscillation and the maximum velocity acquired in the motion. **(M.U.)**

[Hint: If O is the midpoint, P the particle and $OP=x$,

$$m\ddot{x}=-T_1+T_2,\ T_1=\frac{\lambda}{a}(2a+x-a),\ T_2=\frac{\lambda}{a}(2a-x-a)$$

$$\ddot{x}=-\frac{2\lambda}{am}x,\ n^2=\frac{2\lambda}{am}.\ \text{Period}=\frac{2\pi}{n};\ \text{Max. vel}=na]$$

4. Two particles of equal mass lying on a smooth horizontal plane are connected by a light spring of natural length a and modulus of elasticity λ. They are pulled apart so that the spring is elongated and then released. Show that the particles execute S.H.M. of same period and find it. **M.U.)**

[Hint: Due to symmetry, the midpoint is always at rest. say at O. If the distance of one particle from O is $\frac{a}{2}+x$, then $m\ddot{x}=-\lambda\frac{2x}{a}$ **]**

12.3 S.H.M. ALONG A VERTICAL LINE

In this section we consider simple harmonic motions along a vertical line, the forces being tensions of light elastic strings or light spiral springs and earth's gravitation.

Bookwork 12.8. A light spiral spring of length l hangs vertically in the position OA where O is the point of suspension. Let OB be its equilibrium position when a mass m is attached to its lower end and $AB = a$. If m is pulled vertically downward from B to C, through a distance b, and let go, to find its motion. **(M.U., A.U.)**

The forces on the particle in the equilibrium position are

(*i*) Weight mg vertically downward

(*ii*) Tension T of the string upwards

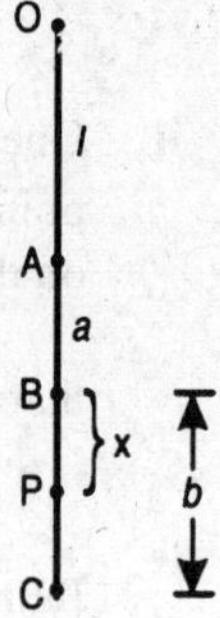

with their magnitudes equal. Therefore

$$mg = \lambda \frac{a}{l}. \qquad \text{...(1)}$$

Let us choose the downward vertical direction as the positive direction to measure the distance. Let P be the position of the particle at time t. Let its distance from the equilibrium position B be x. Then the acceleration in the positive direction is $\ddot{x}$ and the forces in this direction are

(*i*) The weight mg

(*ii*) The tension $-\lambda \dfrac{a+x}{l}$.

$$\therefore \quad m\ddot{x} = mg - \lambda \frac{a+x}{l} = mg - \lambda \frac{a}{l} - \frac{\lambda}{l} x$$

$$= -\frac{\lambda}{l} x \text{ by (1)}$$

$$\therefore \quad \ddot{x} = -\frac{\lambda}{lm} x = -n^2 x, \text{ say.}$$

So the motion is simple harmonic with B as its mean position. Its amplitude is b because at C ($BC = b$) its velocity is zero. Its period and maximum speed are

$$\frac{2\pi}{n}, \; nb.$$

Remark. Suppose that the spring is replaced with an elastic string. Then the motion of the string from C to A will be S.H. and the motion above A will be a free motion under earth's gravity till the string becomes slack.

EXAMPLES

Example 1. Two bodies of masses m and m' are attached to the lower end of an elastic string whose upper end is fixed and hang at rest. m', falls off. Show that the distance of m from the upper end of the string at time t is

$$a + b + c\cos\sqrt{\frac{g}{b}}\, t.$$

where a is the unstretched length of the string and b and c are the distances by which it would be stretched when supporting m and m'.

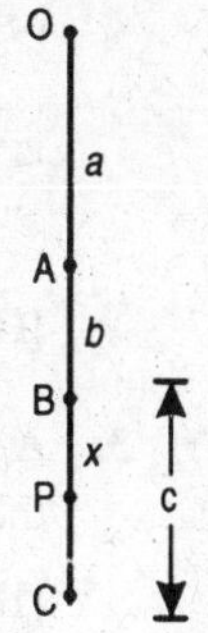

Let OA denote the natural length a of the string and B the equilibrium position of m so that $AB = b$. When m is in equilibrium the forces on it in the downward direction are

$$mg, -\lambda\frac{b}{a}.$$

Their magnitudes are equal.

$$\therefore \quad mg = \lambda\frac{b}{a}. \quad ...(1)$$

Similarly, for m',

$$m'g = \lambda\frac{c}{a}. \quad ...(2)$$

Therefore, from (1) and (2),

$$(m+m')\,g = \lambda\frac{b+c}{a}.$$

That is, if C is the equilibrium position of $m+m'$, then

$$AC = b+c, \ BC = c.$$

Let P be the position of m at time t after m' falls off from C and $BP = x$. Then

$$m\,\ddot{x} = mg - \lambda\frac{b+x}{a} = mg - \frac{\lambda b}{a} - \frac{\lambda x}{a}.$$

$$\therefore \quad m\ddot{x} = -\frac{\lambda x}{a} \quad \text{by (1)}$$

$$\therefore \quad \ddot{x} = \frac{-\lambda}{am}x.$$

Thus the motion of m is S.H. with B as the mean position. The amplitude is $BC = c$ because the velocity at C is zero. Therefore

$$x = c\cos\sqrt{\frac{\lambda}{am}}\,t = c\cos\sqrt{\frac{g}{b}}\,t \text{ by (1).}$$

$$\therefore \quad OP = OA + AB + x = a + b + c\cos\sqrt{\frac{g}{b}}\,t.$$

EXERCISES

1. An elastic string of natural length l and modulus of elasticity λ hangs vertically from one extremity and at the other end a particle of mass m is suspended. The particle is held with the string just unstretched and then let go. Show that it performs a simple harmonic oscillation and find the period and amplitude. **(C.U.)**

   [Hint: As in the Bookwork the motion is S.H. with B as the mean position. Here AB is the amplitude since the velocity at A is zero.**]**

2. A vertical spring extends through a distance a when a given weight is attached to its lowest point. The weight is pulled down a further distance b, where $b < a$, and let go. Find the period

of the simple harmonic motion that ensues and show that the maximum velocity of the weight is $b\sqrt{\frac{g}{a}}$. **(M.U.)**

[Hint: See the Bookwork. Max. vel $= b\sqrt{\frac{\lambda}{lm}}$. Use $mg = \lambda\frac{a}{l}$ to eliminate λ]

3. A mass m is suspended from a spring causing an extension a. If a mass m' is added to m, find the periodic time of the ensuing motion and the amplitude of the oscillation. **(M.U.)**

[Hint: Let $OA = l$ be the natural length and B, C be the equilibrium positions for m, $m+m'$ and $AC = a+b$. Then

$$mg = \lambda\frac{a}{l}, \qquad (m+m')g = \lambda\frac{a+b}{l}.$$

If x is the distance of $m+m'$ below C,

$$(m+m')\,\ddot{x} = (m+m')\,g - \lambda\frac{a+b+x}{l} = -\frac{\lambda x}{l}$$

which is S.H. with amplitude $b = \frac{ma}{m'}$]

4. If T_1 and T_2 are the periods corresponding to two different masses when attached to a vertical elastic string and if a_1 and a_2 are the statical extensions due to these masses, show that

$$g = \frac{4\pi^2\,(a_1 - a_2)}{T_1^2 - T_2^2}.$$ **(M.U.)**

[Hint: $m_1 g = \lambda\frac{a_1}{l}$, $m_2 g = \lambda\frac{a_2}{l}$; $n_1^2 = \frac{\lambda}{m_1 l}$, $n_2^2 = \frac{\lambda}{m_2 l}$; $T_1 = \frac{2\pi}{n_1}$, $T_2 = \frac{2\pi}{n_2}$]

5. An elastic string of natural length l has one extremity fixed at a point O and the other attached to a heavy particle of mass m. When m is in equilibrium, the total length of the string is l_1. Show that, if the particle is dropped from rest at O, it will come to instantaneous rest at a depth $\sqrt{l_1^2 - l^2}$ below the equilibrium position. **(M.U.)**

[Hint: $mg = \lambda\frac{l_1 - l}{l}$; $\ddot{x} = -\frac{\lambda}{ml}$, where x is the distance of m from the equilibrium position at time t. The velocity acquired by a free fall through a distance l is $\sqrt{2gl}$. This is the velocity when $x = l_1 - l$. Thus, if a is the amplitude, from $v^2 = n^2\,(a^2 - x^2)$,

$$\left(\sqrt{2gl}\right)^2 = \frac{\lambda}{ml}[a^2 - (l_1 - l)^2] \text{ or } a = \sqrt{l_1^2 - l^2}\text{]}$$

6. A heavy particle of mass m is attached to one end of an elastic string of length l and coefficient of elasticity $\frac{mg}{k}$. The other end of the string is fixed at O. If the particle is allowed to fall from rest at O, show that the greatest speed of the particle is $\sqrt{gl\,(2+k)}$. **(M.U.)**

[Hint: With the usual notations, if amplitude $= b$,

$$\lambda = \frac{mg}{k}, \quad mg = \lambda\frac{a}{l}, \quad n^2 = \frac{\lambda}{ml}, \quad v_A{}^2 = 2gl = n^2\,(b^2 - a^2).$$

Find nb or $\sqrt{2gl + n^2a^2}$, eliminating n, a, λ in succession]

7. A heavy particle of mass m is attached to one point of a uniform light elastic string. The ends of the string are attached to two points in a vertical line. If λ is the coefficient of elasticity of the string and h is the harmonic mean between the unstretched lengths of the two parts of the string, show that the period of a vertical oscillation with the string remaining taut is $2\pi\sqrt{\frac{mh}{2\lambda}}$. **(M.U.)**

[**Hint:** If the natural lengths are a_1 (upper), a_2 (lower),

$$\frac{2}{h} = \frac{1}{a_1} + \frac{1}{a_2}.$$

If l_1, l_2 are the lengths in equilibrium position, say at A,

$$\lambda\frac{l_1 - a_1}{a_1} = \lambda\frac{l_2 - a_2}{a_2} + mg.$$

If x is the distance of m below A at time t,

$$m\,\ddot{x} = mg + \lambda\frac{l_2 - x - a_2}{a_2} - \lambda\frac{l_1 + x - a_1}{a_1} = -\frac{2\lambda x}{h}\ ]$$

12.4 MOTION UNDER GRAVITY IN A RESISTING MEDIUM

In this section, we discuss a few practical problems in which the air resistance is taken into account besides gravity. The air resistance is assumed to be proportional to the speed of the particle or its square.

The resistance is opposite to the direction of motion of the particle.

12.4.1 Resistance proportional to square of velocity

Bookwork 12.9. To obtain the motion of a particle let fall from rest in a medium whose resistance varies as the square of the speed.

Let us choose the vertically downward direction as the positive direction to measure the distance of the particle. Let us make the following assumptions:

O	:	Point from which the particle falls.
P	:	Position of the particle at time t.
x	:	Distance of P from O.
v	:	Velocity of the particle at time t downward.
μv^2	:	Resistance per unit mass.
m	:	Mass of the particle

The forces on the particle are

(*i*) The weight mg downward

(*ii*) The resistance $m\mu v^2$ upward

But the acceleration of the particle in the vertically downward direction is $\ddot{x}$. So the equation of motion is

$$m\frac{d^2x}{dt^2} = mg - m\mu v^2 \quad\text{or}\quad \frac{d^2x}{dt^2} = g - \mu v^2.$$

Limiting velocity. It is evident that the acceleration of the particle decreases as its velocity increases. Suppose it vanishes when $v = V$. Then

$$0 = g - \mu V^2 \text{ or } V = \sqrt{\frac{g}{\mu}}.$$

This velocity is called limiting velocity or terminal velocity of the particle in the medium in question.

Expressing the equation of motion in V and getting rid of μ,

$$\frac{d^2x}{dt^2} = g - \frac{g}{V^2}v^2 \text{ or } \frac{d^2x}{dt^2} = \frac{g}{V^2}(V^2 - v^2).$$

Now we shall obtain the following results:

(*i*) Velocity at a distance x

(*ii*) Velocity at time t

(*iii*) Distance at time t

(*i*) To obtain v in x. Now we have to express the differential equation in v and x. For this, we shall use

$$\frac{d^2x}{dt^2} = \frac{dv}{dt} = \frac{dv}{dx}.\frac{dx}{dt} = \frac{dv}{dx}v = v\frac{dv}{dx}.$$

Using this and rewriting the equation,

$$v\frac{dv}{dx} = \frac{g}{V^2}(V^2 - v^2) \text{ or } \frac{v}{V^2 - v^2}dv = \frac{g}{V^2}dx.$$

On integration,

$$-\frac{1}{2}\log(V^2 - v^2) = \frac{g}{V^2}x + A.$$

But initially $x = 0$ and $v = 0$. So

$$-\tfrac{1}{2}\log(V^2 - 0^2) = 0 + A.$$

So, eliminating A by subtraction,

$$-\frac{1}{2}\left[\log(V^2 - v^2) - \log V^2\right] = \frac{g}{V^2}x$$

i.e., $$\log V^2 - \log(V^2 - v^2) = \frac{2g}{V^2}x$$

i.e., $$\log\frac{V^2}{V^2 - v^2} = \frac{2g}{V^2}x \quad ...(1)$$

i.e., $$\frac{V^2}{V^2 - v^2} = e^{2gx/V^2}$$

i.e., $$v^2 = V^2(1 - e^{-2gx/V^2}) \quad ...(2)$$

Remark. From (1), we see that, when $v = V$, $x = \infty$. So the particle attains the limiting velocity only after travelling an infinite distance. That is, practically the particle does not attain the limiting velocity in the medium.

***(ii)* To obtain *v* in *t*.** The equation of motion is

$$\frac{dv}{dt}=\frac{g}{V^2}(V^2-v^2) \quad \text{or} \quad \frac{1}{V^2-v^2}dv=\frac{g}{V^2}dt.$$

Its solution is

$$\frac{1}{V}\tanh^{-1}\frac{v}{V}=\frac{g}{V^2}t+B.$$

But, when $t=0$, $v=0$. So $\tanh^{-1}0=0+B$ or $B=0$. Thus

$$\frac{1}{V}\tanh^{-1}\frac{v}{V}=\frac{gt}{V^2} \quad \text{or} \quad \tanh^{-1}\frac{v}{V}=\frac{gt}{V}.$$

Hence we get

$$v=V\tanh\frac{gt}{V}. \qquad ...(3)$$

***(iii)* To obtain *x* in *t*.** Elimination of v from (2) and (3) gives

$$V^2\tanh^2\frac{gt}{V}=V^2(1-e^{-2gx/V^2})$$

or

$$\tanh^2\frac{gt}{V}=1-e^{-2gx/V^2}$$

i.e.,

$$e^{-2gx/V^2}=1-\tanh^2\frac{gt}{V}=\operatorname{sech}^2\frac{gt}{V}$$

i.e.,

$$e^{2gx/V^2}=\cosh^2\frac{gt}{V} \quad \text{or} \quad e^{gx/V^2}=\cosh\frac{gt}{V}.$$

Hence $\dfrac{gx}{V^2}=\log\cosh\dfrac{gt}{V}$ or $x=\dfrac{V^2}{g}\log\cosh\dfrac{gt}{V}$. ...(4)

Bookwork 12.10. To obtain the motion of a particle projected vertically upwards with a velocity u in a medium whose resistance varies as the square of the speed.

Let us choose the vertically upward direction as the positive direction to measure the distance of the paricle. Let us make the following assumptions:

O	:	Point from which the particle is projected
P	:	Position of the particle at time t
x	:	Distance of P from O
v	:	Velocity of the particle at time t upward
μv^2	:	Resistance per unit mass
m	:	Mass of the particle.

The forces on the particle are

(*i*) The weight mg downward

(*ii*) The resistance $m\mu v^2$ downward.

But the acceleration of the particle in the vertically upward direction is $\ddot{x}$. So the equation of motion is

$$m\ddot{x}=-mg-m\mu v^2 \quad \text{or} \quad \ddot{x}=-(g+\mu v^2).$$

Expressing this in terms of the limiting velocity $V\left(=\frac{\sqrt{g}}{\mu}\right)$, we get

$$\frac{d^2x}{dt^2}=\ddot{x}=-\left(g+\frac{g}{V^2}v^2\right) \text{ or } \frac{d^2x}{dt^2}=-\frac{g}{v^2}(V^2+v^2).$$

***(i)* To obtain *v* in *x*.** Since $\frac{d^2x}{dt^2}=v\frac{dv}{dx}$,

$$v\frac{dv}{dx}=-\frac{g}{V^2}(V^2+v^2) \text{ or } \frac{v}{V^2+v^2}dv=-\frac{g}{V^2}dx.$$

On integration we get

$$\frac{1}{2}\log(V^2+v^2)=-\frac{g}{V^2}x+C.$$

But, when $x=0$, $v=u$. So

$$\frac{1}{2}\log\left(V^2+u^2\right)=0+C.$$

Subtracting the first from the second,

$$\log\frac{V^2+u^2}{V^2+v^2}=\frac{2g}{V^2}x. \quad ...(5)$$

***(ii)* To obtain *v* in *t*.** The equation of motion may be written as

$$\frac{dv}{dt}=-\frac{g}{V^2}(V^2+v^2) \text{ or } \frac{1}{V^2+v^2}dv=-\frac{g}{V^2}dt.$$

Its solution is

$$\frac{1}{V}\tan^{-1}\frac{v}{V}=-\frac{g}{V^2}t+D.$$

But, when $t=0$, $v=u$. Therefore

$$\frac{1}{V}\tan^{-1}\frac{u}{V}=0+D.$$

Subtraction of the first from the second leads to

$$\tan^{-1}\frac{u}{V}-\tan^{-1}\frac{v}{V}=\frac{g}{V}t. \quad ...(6)$$

Remark. The particle moves upward with a retardation

$$\frac{g}{V^2}(V^2+v^2).$$

The velocity decreases gradually and becomes zero at time $t=t_0$ given by

$$\tan^{-1}\frac{u}{V}=\frac{g}{V}t_0.$$

Thereafter the case of falling, discussed in the previous Bookwork, follows with an acceleration

$$\frac{g}{V^2}(V^2-v^2).$$

It should be noted that the equations of motion for the downward and upward motions are entirely different and so a result derived for one motion should not be used for the other motion.

EXAMPLES

Example 1 (*i*) A particle of mass m is projected vertically upwards with a velocity u in a medium whose resistance is $m\mu v^2$ when the speed is v and whose limiting velocity is V. Show that, if the particle returns to the point of projection with a velocity u', then

$$\frac{1}{u'^2}=\frac{1}{u^2}+\frac{1}{V^2}.$$ **(M.U., A.U.)**

(*ii*) In the above sum, if E is the K.E. with which the particle is projected and E' is the limiting K.E., show that, when the particle comes back to the point of projection, the loss in K.E. is

$$\frac{E^2}{E+E'}.$$ **(M.U.)**

Let the maximum height attained by the particle be h. At that moment its velocity is zero. We know that, in the upward motion, the relation between velocity v and distance x is

$$\log\frac{V^2+u^2}{V^2+v^2}=\frac{2g}{V^2}x.$$

But, when $x=h,\ v=0$. Therefore

$$\log\frac{V^2+u^2}{V^2}=\frac{2g}{V^2}h. \quad ...(1)$$

Also in the downward motion the relation between velocity v and distance x is

$$\log\frac{V^2}{V^2-v^2}=\frac{2g}{V^2}x.$$

Here, when $x=h,\ v=u'$. Therefore

$$\log\frac{V^2}{V^2-u'^2}=\frac{2g}{V^2}h. \quad ...(2)$$

Thus, from (1) and (2) we get

$$\frac{V^2+u^2}{V^2}=\frac{V^2}{V^2-u'^2} \quad \text{or} \quad V^4-V^2u'^2+u^2V^2-u^2u'^2=V^4.$$

$$\therefore \qquad V^2u'^2+u^2u'^2=u^2V^2 \quad ...(3)$$

Dividing both sides by $V^2\,u^2\,u'^2$, we get

$$\frac{1}{u^2}+\frac{1}{V^2}=\frac{1}{u'^2}.$$

(*ii*) Also, from (3), we get

$$u'^2=\frac{u^2\,V^2}{u^2+V^2}.$$

So, if L is the loss in K.E., then

$$L=\frac{1}{2}mu^2-\frac{1}{2}mu'^2=\frac{1}{2}mu^2-\frac{1}{2}m\frac{u^2\,V^2}{u^2+V^2}$$

$$= \frac{1}{2}mu^2 - \frac{(\frac{1}{2}m)u^2 . (\frac{1}{2}m)V^2}{(\frac{1}{2}m)u^2 + (\frac{1}{2}m)V^2} = E - \frac{EE'}{E+E'}$$

$$= \frac{E^2}{E+E'}.$$

EXERCISES

1. **A particle of mass *m* is projected vertically upwards with a velocity *u*. If the resistance of the medium is $m\mu v^2$, where *v* is the speed of the particle, show that the particle attains its greatest height in time *t* given by**

$$\sqrt{g}\tan(t\sqrt{\mu g}) = u\sqrt{\mu}.$$

(ii) Deduce that, however large *u* may be, *t* cannot exceed $\frac{1}{2}\pi(\mu g)^{-\frac{1}{2}}$. **(M.U., M.K.U.)**

[**Hint:** Relation in *v* and *t* : $\tan^{-1}\frac{u}{V} - \tan^{-1}\frac{v}{V} = \frac{g}{V}t$, where $V = \sqrt{\frac{g}{\mu}}$. **(i)** Set $v = 0$. **(ii)** $u\sqrt{\mu} < \infty$.

$\therefore\ t\sqrt{\mu g} < \pi/2$.]

12.4.2 Resistance proportional to velocity

Bookwork 12.11. To obtain the motion of a particle let fall from rest in a medium where resistance varies as the speed.

Let us choose the vertically downward direction as the positive direction to measure the distance of the particle. Let us make the following assumptions.

O	:	Point from which the particle falls.
P	:	Position of the particle at time t.
x	:	Distance of P from O.
v	:	Velocity of the particle at time t downward
μv	:	Resistance per unit mass.
m	:	Mass of the particle.

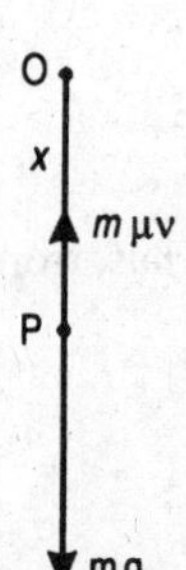

The forces on the particle are

(*i*) The weight mg downward

(*ii*) The resistance $m\mu v$ upward

But the acceleration of the particle in the vertically downward direction is $\ddot{x}$. So the equation of motion is

$$m\frac{d^2x}{dt^2} = mg - m\mu v \quad \text{or} \quad \frac{d^2x}{dt^2} = g - \mu v. \qquad ...(1)$$

Limiting velocity. It is evident that the acceleration of the particle decreases as its velocity increases. Suppose it vanishes when $v = V$. Then

$$0 = g - \mu V \quad \text{or} \quad V = \frac{g}{\mu}.$$

This velocity is called limiting velocity or terminal velocity of the particle in the medium.

***(i)* To obtain x in t.** Using the notation $D=\dfrac{d}{dt}$, the equation of motion (1) may be written as

$$(D^2+\mu D)\,x=g.$$

The auxiliary equation is $m^2+\mu m=0$. Hence $m=0,-\mu$ and so

$$C.F=A+Be^{-\mu t}.$$

$$P.I=\frac{1}{D\,(D+\mu)}\,g=\frac{1}{D}\left[\frac{1}{0+\mu}\right]g=\frac{gt}{\mu}.$$

$$\therefore\qquad x=A+Be^{-\mu t}+\frac{gt}{\mu}.$$

But, $x=0$ and $\dfrac{dx}{dt}=0$, when $t=0$.

$$\therefore\qquad A+B=0,\ -\mu B+\frac{g}{\mu}=0.$$

$$\therefore\qquad x=-\frac{g}{\mu^2}(1-e^{-\mu t})+\frac{gt}{\mu}. \qquad ...(2)$$

Differentiating this w.r.t. t, we get the velocity as

$$v=\frac{dx}{dt}=-\frac{g}{\mu}e^{-\mu t}+\frac{g}{\mu}. \qquad ...(3)$$

Remark 1. From (3) it is evident that the particle attains the limiting velocity only after an infinite time.

***(ii)* To obtain v in x.** Elimination of t from (2) and (3) yields the relation between v and x. This relation can be obtained otherwise as given below. Since $\ddot{x}=v\dfrac{dv}{dx}$, (1) becomes

$$v\frac{dv}{dx}=g-\mu v \quad\text{or}\quad \frac{v}{g-\mu v}dv=dx$$

or

$$\left(-1+\frac{g}{g-\mu v}\right)dv=\mu\,dx.$$

Integration gives

$$-v-\frac{g}{\mu}\log(g-\mu v)=\mu x+A.$$

But, when $x=0,\ v=0$. Therefore

$$0-\frac{g}{\mu}\log g=0+A.$$

Elimination of A gives

$$-v-\frac{g}{\mu}\log\frac{g-\mu v}{g}=\mu x \quad\text{or}\quad -v+\frac{g}{\mu}\log\frac{g}{g-\mu v}=\mu x$$

i.e.,

$$x=\frac{g}{\mu^2}\log\frac{g}{g-\mu v}-\frac{v}{\mu}. \qquad ...(4)$$

Bookwork 12.12. To find the motion of a particle projected vertically upwards with a velocity u in a medium whose resistance varies as the speed of the particle.

Let us choose the vertically upward direction as the positive direction to measure the distance of the particle. Let us make the following assumptions:

O : Point from which the particle is projected.

P : Position of the particle at time t.

x : Distance of P from O.

v : Velocity of the particle at time t upward

μv : Resistance per unit mass

m : Mass of the particle.

P
mμv
mg
O

The forces on the particle are

(*i*) The weight mg downward

(*ii*) The resistance $m\mu v$ downward.

But the acceleration of the particle in the vertically upward direction is $\ddot{x}$. So the equation of motion is

$$m\ddot{x} = -mg - m\mu v \text{ or } \ddot{x} = -(g + \mu v). \quad ...(1)$$

(*i*) **To obtain *x* in *t*.** Using the notation $D = \frac{d}{dt}$, the equation of motion (1) may be written as

$$(D^2 + \mu D)\,x = -g.$$

The general solution is

$$x = A + B\,e^{-\mu t} - \frac{gt}{\mu}.$$

But $x = 0$ and $\frac{dx}{dt} = u$, when $t = 0$.

$$\therefore \quad A + B = 0, \; -B\mu - \frac{g}{\mu} = u.$$

$$\therefore \quad x = \left(\frac{u}{\mu} + \frac{g}{\mu^2}\right)\left[1 - e^{-\mu t}\right] - \frac{gt}{\mu}. \quad ...(2)$$

(*ii*) **To obtain *v* in *t*.** Differentiating (2),

$$v = \left(\frac{u}{\mu} + \frac{g}{\mu^2}\right)\left[\mu e^{-\mu t}\right] - \frac{g}{\mu}. \quad ...(3)$$

(*iii*) **To obtain *x* in *v*.** Since $\ddot{x} = v\frac{dv}{dx}$, (1) becomes

$$v\frac{dv}{dx} = -(g + \mu v) \text{ or } \frac{v}{g + \mu v}\,dv = -dx.$$

or

$$\frac{1}{\mu}\left(1 - \frac{g}{\mu v + g}\right)dv = -dx.$$

Now integration yields,

$$v-\frac{g}{\mu}\log(\mu v+g)=-\mu x+A.$$

But, when $x=0, v=u$. Therefore

$$u-\frac{g}{\mu}\log(\mu u+g)=A.$$

Thus, eliminating A,

$$x=\frac{1}{\mu}(u-v)+\frac{g}{\mu^2}\log\frac{\mu v+g}{\mu u+g}. \qquad \text{...(4)}$$

Maximum height. Maximum height h is obtained by setting $v=0$ in (4) as

$$h=\frac{u}{\mu}+\frac{g}{\mu^2}\log\frac{g}{\mu u+g}. \qquad \text{...(5)}$$

The corresponding time t is obtained by setting $v=0$ in (3) as follows:

$$\left(\frac{u}{\mu}+\frac{g}{\mu^2}\right)\mu e^{-\mu t}=\frac{g}{\mu} \quad \text{or} \quad (\mu u+g)\,e^{-\mu t}=g.$$

Taking logarithm,

$$\log(\mu u+g)-\mu t=\log g \quad \text{or} \quad \mu t=\log\frac{\mu u+g}{g}.$$

EXERCISES

1. A particle of mass m, is falling under the influence of gravity through a medium whose resistance equals μ times the velocity. If the particle be released from rest, show that the distance fallen through in time t is

$$\frac{gm^2}{\mu^2}\left[e^{-\mu t/m}-1+\frac{\mu t}{m}\right]. \qquad \text{(M.K.U.)}$$

[**Hint:** Eqn. of motion : $m\frac{d^2x}{dt^2}=mg-\mu v$]

2. A particle of mass m is projected vertically upwards. If the resistance of air is $m\mu v$, where v is the speed of the particle, show that the greatest height attained by the particle is

$$\frac{V^2}{g}\left[\frac{u}{V}-\log\left(1+\frac{u}{V}\right)\right],$$

where V is the limiting speed in the medium and u is the velocity of projection.

[**Hint:** Maximum height: $\frac{u}{\mu}+\frac{g}{\mu^2}\log\frac{g}{\mu u+g}$, where $V=\frac{g}{\mu}$.]

PROJECTILES

13.1 FORCES ON A PROJECTILE

In this chapter we study coplanar motions of particles under gravity only, neglecting the air resistance and assuming that the motion is so close to the surface of the earth so that g is a constant.

Projectile. A particle or body projected is called a projectile.

Trajectory. The path pursued by a projectile is called the trajectory of the projectile.

Horizontal range. If O is the point of projection and if A is the point at which the projectile hits the horizontal plane through O, then OA is called the horizontal range.

Range on an inclined plane. Suppose OA is a line of greatest slope on an inclined plane. If a particle projected from O hits on OA at B, then OB is the range on the inclined plane.

13.1.1 Displacement as a combination of vertical and horizontal displacements

The only force acting on a projectile is the earth's gravity which is always vertically downward. So the projectile has an acceleration g always in the vertically downward direction. Now we shall consider the displacement of the projectile as a resultant of the displacements in two perpendicular directions, namely,

(*i*) Horizontal direction

(*ii*) Vertical direction

***(i)* Horizontal displacement.** In the horizontal direction there is no force on the projectile. So the acceleration of the projectile in this direction is zero and hence the projectile moves in the horizontal direction with a constant velocity which is the component of the velocity of projection in this direction.

If the projectile is projected with a velocity u in a direction which is inclined to the horizontal at an angle α, then its horizontal component of velocity is

$$u \cos \alpha.$$

So the horizontal displacement of the projectile in time t is

$$(\text{velocity}) \times (\text{time})$$

or

$$(u \cos \alpha)\, t.$$

***(ii)* Vertical displacement.** To study the vertical displacement we shall choose the upward direction as the positive direction for measuring the distance of the particle. In this direction the acceleration of the particle is $-g$. So the vertical displacement can be studied with the equations meant for constant accelerations a, namely,

$$v = u + at,$$

$$s = ut + \tfrac{1}{2}at^2,$$

$$v^2 = u^2 + 2as.$$

Now $a = -g$ and the initial velocity in the positive direction is

$$u \sin \alpha.$$

13.1.2 Nature of trajectory

Bookwork 13.1. To show that the path of a projectile is a parabola.

Suppose a particle of mass m is projected from a point O with a speed u in a direction which makes an angle α with the horizontal. Let the particle hit the horizontal plane through O, at A. Choose OA as the x axis and the upward vertical line through O as the y axis. Let

$$P(x, y)$$

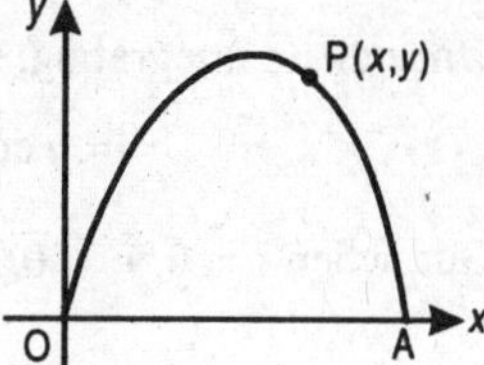

be the position of the particle at time t. Then the horizontal and vertical displacements of the particle at time t are

$$x, y.$$

Since earth's gravity is the only force on the projectile the horizontal and upward vertical components of the acceleration are

$$0, -g.$$

Therefore the horizontal component of the velocity is always a constant which is the initial component $u \cos \alpha$. Therefore the horizontal displacement in time t is

$$x = (\text{velocity}) \times (\text{time}) = (u \cos \alpha)\, t. \qquad \text{...(1)}$$

For the upward displacement during the motion of the particle from O to P, we have

Initial velocity	:	$u \sin \alpha$	Formula : $s = ut + \frac{1}{2}at^2$
Acceleration	:	$-g$	$\therefore\ y = u \sin \alpha\, t - \frac{1}{2}gt^2.$ ...(2)
Time	:	t	
Distance travelled	:	y	

Now (1) and (2) are the parametric equations of the trajectory. Its xy equation is obtained by eliminating the parameter t as

$$y = u \sin \alpha \left\{ \frac{x}{u \cos \alpha} \right\} - \frac{g}{2} \left\{ \frac{x}{u \cos \alpha} \right\}^2$$

or
$$y = x \tan \alpha - \frac{gx^2}{2u^2 \cos^2 \alpha}.$$

This is a second degree equation satisfying the relation "$h^2 - ab = 0$". So it represents a parabola. Hence the trajectory is a parabola.

Second method (Vector method). Choose the x, y axes as in the first method and $P(x, y)$ as the position of the particle (of mass m) at time t.

If $\bar{i}$ and $\bar{j}$ are the unit vectors in the Ox and Oy directions, then the position vector of P is

$$\bar{r} = x\bar{i} + y\bar{j}.$$

The only force acting on the particle is its own weight $mg(-\bar{j})$. So the equation of motion, $m\ddot{\bar{r}} = \bar{F}$, of the particle is

$$m\ddot{\bar{r}} = -mg\,\bar{j} \quad \text{or} \quad \ddot{\bar{r}} = -g\,\bar{j}.$$

Integration of this with respect to t, gives

$$\dot{\bar{r}} = -gt\,\bar{j} + \bar{A},$$

where $\overline{A}$ is a constant vector. But, when $t = 0$, $\dot{\overline{r}} = u\cos\alpha\,\overline{i} + u\sin\alpha\,\overline{j}$, because the components of the initial velocity u in the $\overline{i}$ and $\overline{j}$ directions are respectively $u\cos\alpha$ and $u\sin\alpha$. So

$$u\cos\alpha\overline{i} + u\sin\alpha\overline{j} = -g(0)\overline{j} + \overline{A} \quad \text{or} \quad \overline{A} = u\cos\alpha\overline{i} + u\sin\alpha\overline{j}.$$

$$\therefore \quad \dot{\overline{r}} = -gt\overline{j} + (u\cos\alpha\overline{i} + u\sin\alpha\overline{j})$$

$$= u\cos\alpha\overline{i} + (u\sin\alpha - gt)\overline{j}.$$

Once again integrating, we get

$$\overline{r} = u\cos\alpha t\overline{i} + \left(u\sin\alpha t - \tfrac{1}{2}gt^2\right)\overline{j} + \overline{B}.$$

But, when $t = 0$, $\overline{r} = \overline{0}$. So

$$\overline{0} = u\cos\alpha(0)\overline{i} + \left\{u\sin\alpha(0) - \tfrac{1}{2}g(0)^2\right\}\overline{j} + \overline{B}.$$

That is, $\overline{B} = \overline{0}$. Thus we get

$$\overline{r} = u\cos\alpha\, t\overline{i} + \left(u\sin\alpha\, t - \tfrac{1}{2}gt^2\right)\overline{j}.$$

$$\therefore \quad x = u\cos\alpha\, t$$

$$y = u\sin\alpha\, t - \tfrac{1}{2}gt^2.$$

Eliminating t from these two equations, we obtain the equation of the trajectory to be

$$y = x\tan\alpha - \frac{gx^2}{2u^2\cos^2\alpha}$$

This is a second degree equation satisfying the relation "$h^2 - ab = 0$". So it represents a parabola. Hence the trajectory is a parabola.

Remark. The above equation can be rewritten as

$$\left(x - \frac{u^2\sin\alpha\cos\alpha}{g}\right)^2 = -\frac{2u^2\cos^2\alpha}{g}\left(y - \frac{u^2\sin^2\alpha}{2g}\right)$$

which shows that the parabola has a downward vertical as its axis

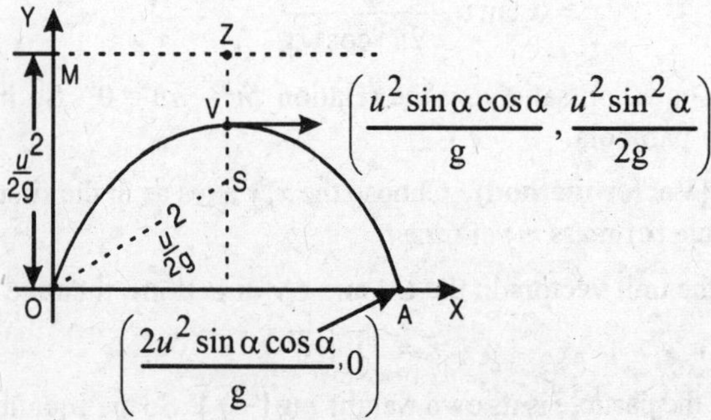

Its latus-rectum $(2u^2\cos^2\alpha)/g$ and its vertex V is

$$\left(\frac{u^2\sin\alpha\cos\alpha}{g}, \frac{u^2\sin^2\alpha}{2g}\right).$$

Height of the directrix. Let Z be the point on the directrix vertically above V and M, the point on the directrix vertically above O. Then the height of the directrix above O is

$$OM = y \text{ coordinate of } V + VZ$$

$$= y \text{ coordinate of } V + \tfrac{1}{4} \text{ (latus rectum)}$$

$$= \frac{u^2 \sin^2\alpha}{2g} + \frac{1}{4}\left(\frac{2u^2\cos^2\alpha}{g}\right) = \frac{u^2}{2g}.$$

Since $u^2/2g$ is independent of the angle of projection α, we achieve that,

if several particles are projected from a point with the same speed u but in different directions (in the same vertical plane), their trajectories have the same horizontal line as their directrices which is at a height $u^2/2g$ from the point of projection.

Distance of focus from the point of projection. If S is the focus of the trajectory, then from the focus-directrix property of the parabola, that is, from $SO = OM$, we get that $OS = u^2/2g$. From this we achieve that,

if several particles are projected from a point with the same speed u but in different directions (in the same vertical plane), then their trajectories have their foci on a circle whose centre is the point of projection and radius is $u^2/2g$.

Bookwork 13.2. The speed of a projectile at any point on its path equals the speed of a particle acquired by it in falling from the directrix to the point.

Let the projectile be projected from a point O with a speed u and with an angle of projection α. Let M be the point on the directrix of its path vertically above O. Then we know that the height of the directrix above the point of projection is

$$OM = \frac{u^2}{2g}.$$

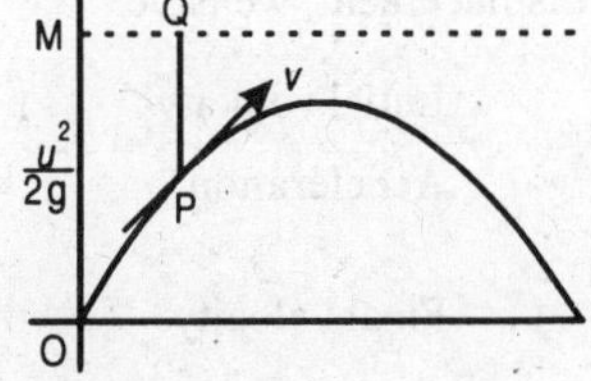

So also, if P is the position of the projectile at an arbitrarily chosen moment and if v is its speed then,

$$PQ = \frac{v^2}{2g}.$$

where Q is the point on the directrix vertically above P because, when the projectile is moving at P with speed v, it can be assumed that the projectile is then projected, from there with a speed v along the tangent at P.

When the other particle falls through the distance QP, starting from rest at Q, its velocity at P, say V, is obtained, from the formula $v^2 = u^2 + 2as$, as

$$V^2 = 0 + 2g\,PQ = 2g\frac{v^2}{2g} = v^2 \quad \text{or} \quad V = v.$$

This completes the proof.

Maximum height. From the equation of the trajectory we see that the maximum height attained by the particle is the y coordinate of the vertex, namely,

$$\frac{u^2\sin^2\alpha}{2g}.$$

Horizontal range. If the horizontal range is R, then $(R, 0)$ is a point on the parabola and hence substituting in the equation of the parabola,

$$0 = R\tan\alpha - \frac{gR^2}{2u^2\cos^2\alpha} \quad \text{or} \quad R\left(\tan\alpha - \frac{gR}{2u^2\cos^2\alpha}\right) = 0.$$

$R = 0$ corresponds to initial position and the range is

$$R = \frac{2u^2 \cos^2 \alpha}{g} . \tan \alpha = \frac{2u^2 \sin \alpha \cos \alpha}{g} .$$

$$\therefore \quad R = \frac{u^2 \sin 2\alpha}{g} .$$

We obtain such results differently in the following bookwork.

13.1.3 Results pertaining to the motion of a projectile.

Bookwork 13.3. A particle is projected from a point O on the ground with a velocity u inclined to the horizontal at an angle α. It hits the ground at A. To find

(*i*) Maximum height H attained by the particle

(*ii*) Time taken to attain the maximum height

(*iii*) Time of flight (from O to A)

(*iv*) Horizontal range R (Range on the ground).

(*v*) Velocity at time t.

Choose the vertically upward direction as the positive direction to measure the distance of the particle.

(*i*) Maximum height H. Let V be the topmost point of the trajectory. Then, for the motion from O to V, considering the vertical displacement, we have

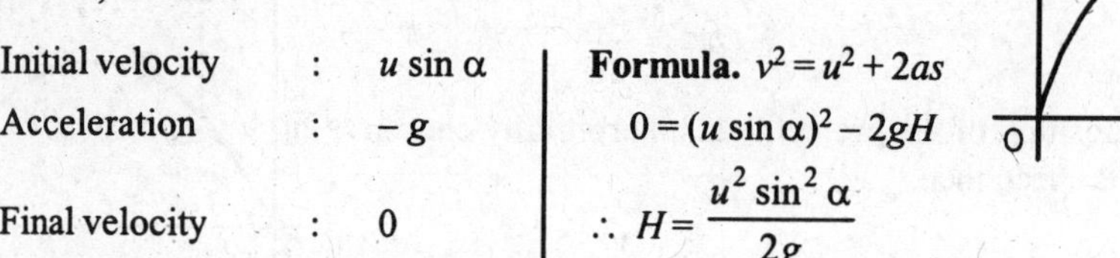

Initial velocity	:	$u \sin \alpha$	**Formula.** $v^2 = u^2 + 2as$
Acceleration	:	$-g$	$0 = (u \sin \alpha)^2 - 2gH$
Final velocity	:	0	$\therefore H = \frac{u^2 \sin^2 \alpha}{2g}$
Distance	:	H	

(*ii*) Time taken to reach the topmost point. For the motion from O to V, considering the vertical displacement, we have

Initial velocity	:	$u \sin \alpha$	**Formula.** $v = u + at$
Acceleration	:	$-g$	$0 = u \sin \alpha - gt$
Final velocity	:	0	$\therefore t = \frac{u \sin \alpha}{g}$.
Time	:	t, say	

(*iii*) Time of flight. For the motion from O to A, considering the vertical displacement, we have

Initial velocity	:	$u \sin \alpha$	**Formula.** $s = ut + \frac{1}{2} at^2$
Acceleration	:	$-g$	$0 = u \sin \alpha \, T - \frac{g}{2} T^2$
Distance	:	0	
Time	:	T, say	$\therefore T = \frac{2u \sin \alpha}{g}$ or 0.

$T = 0$ corresponds to the initial position.

(iv) Horizontal range R.

Horizontal velocity (a constant) : $u \cos \alpha$

Time of flight T : $\dfrac{2u \sin \alpha}{g}$

$$R = (\text{Horl. vel.}) \times (\text{time}) = u \cos \alpha \times \frac{2u \sin \alpha}{g}$$

$$= \frac{u^2 \sin 2\alpha}{g}.$$

Note: $R = \dfrac{2}{g}$ (Initial horizontal velocity) × (Initial vertical velocity)

(v) Velocity at time t. Let the particle be at P at time t. Let its velocity there be V and its horizontal and upward vertical components be v_1, v_2. Since the horizontal component is always $u \cos \alpha$,

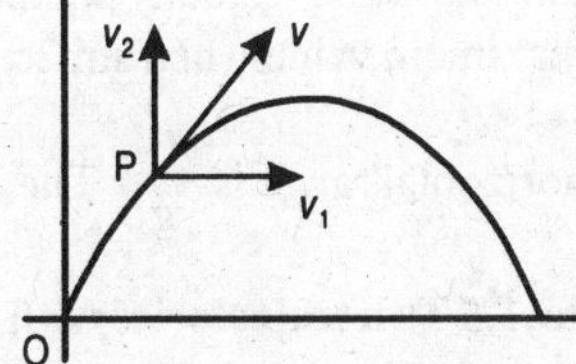

$$v_1 = u \cos \alpha.$$

Considering the vertical displacement, for the motion from O to P, we have

Initial velocity	:	$u \sin \alpha$	**Formula.** $v = u + at$
Acceleration	:	$-g$	$v_2 = u \sin \alpha - gt.$
Time	:	t	
Final velocity	:	v_2	

$$\therefore \quad V = \sqrt{v_1^2 + v_2^2} = \sqrt{(u \cos \alpha)^2 + (u \sin \alpha - gt)^2}$$

$$= \sqrt{u^2 - 2u\, g \sin \alpha\, t + g^2 t^2}.$$

The angle made by this velocity with the horizontal is

$$\tan^{-1} \frac{v_2}{v_1} = \tan^{-1} \frac{u \sin \alpha - gt}{u \cos \alpha}.$$

Bookwork 13.4. To verify, in the case of a projectile,

K.E + P.E = a constant.

Let m be the mass of the projectile. Then, with usual meanings, at time t,

$$\text{K.E} = \tfrac{1}{2} mv^2 = \tfrac{1}{2} m\left(u^2 - 2ug \sin \alpha t + g^2 t^2\right). \quad \text{...(1)}$$

At time t, let the vertical height of the particle be h. Then, considering the vertical displacement, we have

Initial velocity	:	$u \sin \alpha$	
Acceleration	:	$-g$	
Time	:	t	$\therefore \quad h = u \sin \alpha \; t - \frac{1}{2} gt^2$
Distance	:	h	

Thus, choosing the point of projection O as the standard point, P.E at t,

$$\text{P.E} = mg \times h = mg\left(u \sin \alpha t - \tfrac{1}{2} g t^2\right) \quad \text{...(2)}$$

$\therefore$

$$\text{K.E} + \text{P.E} = \tfrac{1}{2} m u^2$$

which is a constant.

13.1.4 Maximum horizontal range for a given velocity

Suppose a particle is projected with a velocity u and with the angle of projection α. Then we know that its horizontal range is

$$\frac{u^2 \sin 2\alpha}{g}.$$

For the same velocity u, this range assumes different values for different α's and it attains the maximum value when $\sin 2\alpha$ is a maximum. But the maximum value of $\sin 2\alpha$ is 1. So the maximum horizontal range is $\frac{u^2}{g}$. The corresponding angle of projection is given by $2\alpha = 90^\circ$. So it is 45°.

13.1.5 Two trajectories with a given speed and range

If the given speed is u and the given horizontal range is R, $\left(R < u^2/g\right)$, then the corresponding angle of projection α is given by

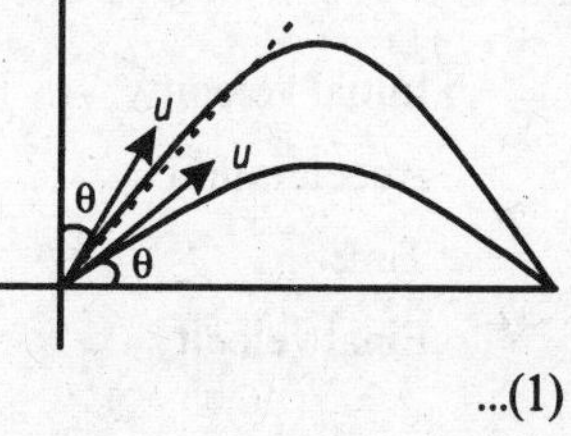

$$\frac{u^2 \sin 2\alpha}{g} = R$$

or

$$\sin 2\alpha = \frac{gR}{u^2}. \quad \text{...(1)}$$

So, from trigonometry, we see that there are two values for 2α satisfying (1). The sum of these values is 180°. In other words, there are two values for α whose sum is 90°. Hence, for a given speed, there are two trajectories giving the same horizontal range. If the two values of α are θ and $90^\circ - \theta$, it can be seen that the directions corresponding to these two values are equally inclined to the direction which gives the maximum horizontal range because

$$(45^\circ) - (\theta) = (90^\circ - \theta) - (45^\circ).$$

EXAMPLES

Example 1. A ball is projected so as to just clear two parallel walls, the first of height a at a distance b from the point of projection and the second of height b at a distance a from the point of projection. Supposing the path of the ball to lie in a plane perpendicular to the walls, find the range on the horizontal plane and show that the angle of projection exceeds $\tan^{-1} 3$.

(M.U., C.U., K.U., M.K.U.)

With the usual notations the equation of the trajectory is

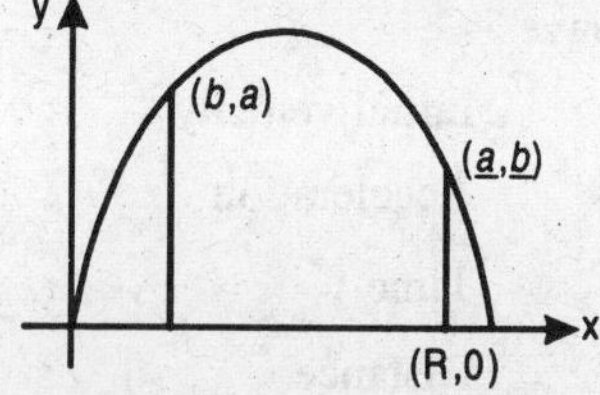

$$y = x \tan \alpha - \frac{g x^2}{2u^2 \cos^2 \alpha}$$

Range. The trajectory passes through the points

$$(b, a),\ (a, b),\ (R, 0),$$

where R is the horizontal range. So

$$a = b\tan\alpha - \frac{gb^2}{2u^2\cos^2\alpha} \quad ...(1)$$

$$b = a\tan\alpha - \frac{ga^2}{2u^2\cos^2\alpha} \quad ...(2)$$

$$0 = R\tan\alpha - \frac{gR^2}{2u^2\cos^2\alpha} \quad ...(3)$$

Now, eliminating $\tan\alpha$ and $-\dfrac{g}{2u^2\cos^2\alpha}$ from (1), (2), (3), we get the eliminant as

$$\begin{vmatrix} a & b & b^2 \\ b & a & a^2 \\ 0 & R & R^2 \end{vmatrix} = 0 \text{ or } \begin{vmatrix} a & b & b^2 \\ b & a & a^2 \\ 0 & 1 & R \end{vmatrix} = 0$$

i.e., $\quad a\left(aR - a^2\right) - b\left(bR\right) + b^2\left(b\right) = 0$ or $R\left(a^2 - b^2\right) = a^3 - b^3$

$$\therefore \qquad R = \frac{a^3 - b^3}{a^2 - b^2} = \frac{a^2 + ab + b^2}{a + b}.$$

Angle of projection. To get $\tan\alpha$ consider $a^2 \times (1) - b^2 \times (2)$. Then

$$(ba^2 - ab^2)\tan\alpha = a^3 - b^3.$$

$$\therefore \qquad \tan\alpha = \frac{a^3 - b^3}{ab(a - b)} = \frac{a^2 + ab + b^2}{ab}.$$

$$\therefore \qquad \alpha = \tan^{-1}\frac{a^2 + ab + b^2}{ab}.$$

Restriction on α. The angle α is such that

$$\tan\alpha = \frac{a^2 + ab + b^2}{ab} = \frac{(a - b)^2 + 3ab}{ab}$$

$$= \frac{(a - b)^2}{ab} + 3.$$

But $\dfrac{(a - b)^2}{ab}$ is positive and 0 when $a = b$.

$$\therefore \qquad \tan\alpha > 3 \text{ or } \alpha > \tan^{-1} 3.$$

Example 2. A particle projected from the top O of a wall AO, 50 m. high, at an angle of 30° above the horizon, strikes the level ground through A at B at an angle of 45°. Show that the angle of depression of B from O is

$$\tan^{-1}\frac{\sqrt{3} - 1}{2\sqrt{3}}. \qquad \textbf{(M.U., C.U.)}$$

With O as the origin, etc., the equation of the trajectory is

$$y = x\tan\alpha - \frac{gx^2}{2u^2\cos^2\alpha}. \quad ...(1)$$

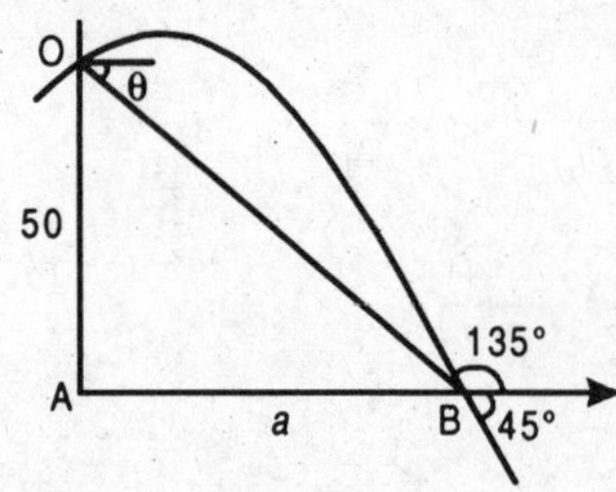

If $AB = a$, then B is

$$(a, -50)$$

which satisfy (1). So

$$-50 = a\tan\alpha - \frac{ga^2}{2u^2\cos^2\alpha}. \quad ...(2)$$

But the slope of the curve at A is tan 135° or −1. Finding the slope by differentiation,

$$\left(\frac{dy}{dx}\right)_{(a,-50)} = \left[\tan\alpha - \frac{gx}{u^2\cos^2\alpha}\right]_{x=a} = \tan\alpha - \frac{ga}{u^2\cos^2\alpha}$$

$$\therefore \quad -1 = \tan\alpha - \frac{ga}{u^2\cos^2\alpha}. \quad ...(3)$$

Thus (2) $-a/2\times(3)$ and $\alpha = 30°$ give

$$-50 = a\left(-\frac{1}{2}+\frac{1}{2}\tan\alpha\right); \quad a = \frac{100\sqrt{3}}{\sqrt{3}-1}.$$

If θ is the angle of depression at O,

$$\tan\theta = \frac{OA}{AB} = 50\frac{\sqrt{3}-1}{100\sqrt{3}} = \frac{\sqrt{3}-1}{2\sqrt{3}}.$$

Example 3. (*i*) A particle is projected over a triangle from one end of its horizontal base to graze the vertex and fall at the other end of the base. If B and C are the base angles and α, the angle of projection, show that $\tan\alpha = \tan B + \tan C$. **(M.U.,M.K.U.)**

(*ii*) A particle is projected from a point P at an angle of 30° to the horizontal. If PQ is its horizontal range and if angles of elevation of the particle at P and Q at any instant of its flight are A and B respectively, show that, $\tan A + \tan B = \frac{1}{\sqrt{3}}$. **(M.U.)**

(*i*) Let the projectile be projected from B with a velocity u. Let AL be the altitude through A and

$$AL = h, \; BL = a, \; LC = b.$$

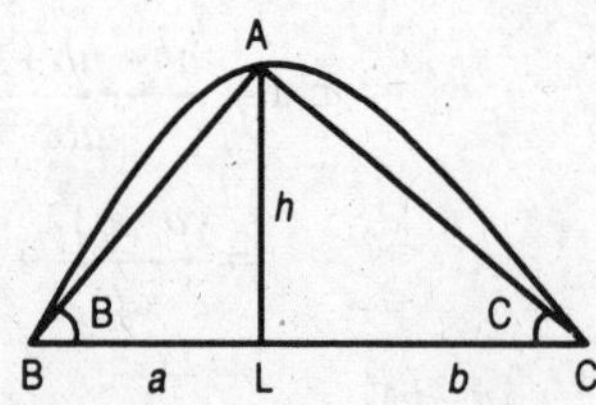

If B is the origin and BC, the x axis, then A and C are

$$(a, h), \; (a+b, 0)$$

and the equation of the trajectory is

$$y = x\tan\alpha - \frac{gx^2}{2u^2\cos^2\alpha}.$$

This is satisfied by A and C. Therefore

$$h = a\tan\alpha - \frac{ga^2}{2u^2\cos^2\alpha}, \quad 0 = \tan\alpha - \frac{g(a+b)}{2u^2\cos^2\alpha}.$$

Eliminating u, by multiplying the first by $a + b$ and the second by a^2 and then subtracting,

$$(a+b)h = ab\tan\alpha.$$

$$\therefore \qquad \tan\alpha = \frac{h}{a} + \frac{h}{b} = \tan B + \tan C.$$

(*ii*) $\tan\alpha = \tan A + \tan B \Rightarrow \tan 30^\circ = \tan A + \tan B.$

Example 4. A particle is projected with a velocity whose horizontal and vertical components are U and V. If P_1 and P_2 are the points on its trajectory at the same height h above the point of projection, show that

$$P_1P_2 = \frac{2U}{g}\sqrt{V^2 - 2gh}.$$

With usual notations, we have

$$U = u\cos\alpha,$$

$$V = u\sin\alpha.$$

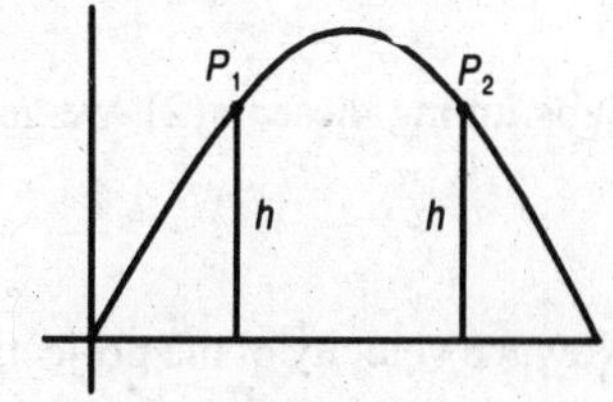

Let the particle attain a height h at time t. Then

$$h = u\sin\alpha\ t - \tfrac{1}{2}gt^2$$

or $$h = Vt - \tfrac{1}{2}gt^2.$$

or $$gt^2 - 2Vt + 2h = 0.$$

The roots of this quadratic are the two values of t at which the particle is at the height h. Let them be t_1, t_2. Then

$$t_1 + t_2 = \frac{2V}{g}, \quad t_1 t_2 = \frac{2h}{g}.$$

$$\therefore \qquad (t_2 - t_1)^2 = (t_1 + t_2)^2 - 4t_1 t_2 = \frac{4V^2}{g^2} - \frac{8h}{g} = 4\left(\frac{V^2 - 2gh}{g^2}\right)$$

$$\therefore \qquad t_2 - t_1 = \frac{2}{g}\sqrt{V^2 - 2gh}.$$

So the time interval for the particle to move from P_1 to P_2 is $t_2 - t_1$.

$$\therefore \qquad P_1P_2 = (t_1 - t_2)U = \frac{2U}{g}\sqrt{V^2 - 2gh}.$$

Example 5. If v_1 and v_2 are the velocities of a projectile at the ends of a focal chord of its path and v, the horizontal component of its velocity, show that

$$\frac{1}{v_1^2} + \frac{1}{v_2^2} = \frac{1}{v^2}. \qquad \textbf{(M.U.)}$$

Let P_1SP_2 be the focal chord and l, the semilatus rectum of the parabola. Then we know, from geometry, that

$$\frac{1}{SP_1} + \frac{1}{SP_2} = \frac{2}{l}. \qquad ...(1)$$

If Q_1, Z, Q_2 are the points on the directrix vertically above P_1, V, P_2. Then

$$SP_1 = P_1Q_1,\ SP_2 = P_2Q_2,\ \tfrac{l}{2} = VZ.$$

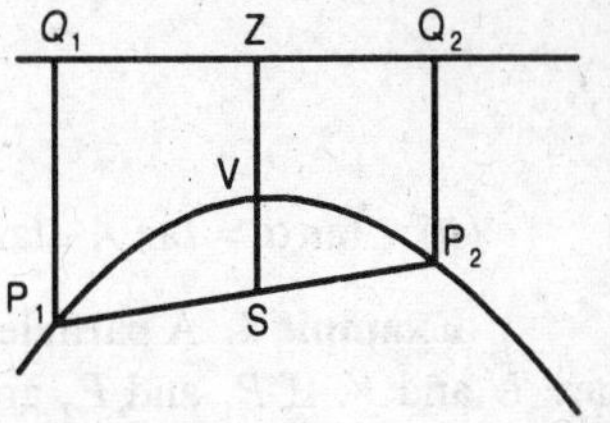

Thus, (1) becomes

$$\frac{1}{P_1Q_1}+\frac{1}{P_2Q_2}=\frac{1}{VZ}. \quad ...(2)$$

But we know that the velocity of a projectile at any point on its path is the velocity of a particle falling freely from the directrix to that point. Thus

$$v_1^2 = 2g\,P_1Q_1,\ v_2^2 = 2g\,P_2Q_2,\ v^2 = 2gVZ$$

or

$$P_1Q_1 = \frac{v_1^2}{2g},\ P_2Q_2 = \frac{v_2^2}{2g},\ VZ = \frac{v^2}{2g}.$$

Substituting these in (2), we get

$$\frac{2g}{v_1^2}+\frac{2g}{v_2^2}=\frac{2g}{v^2} \text{ or } \frac{1}{v_1^2}+\frac{1}{v_2^2}=\frac{1}{v^2}.$$

Now the velocity of the projectile at V, namely v, is the horizontal component of its velocity.

EXERCISES

1. Prove the relation $gT^2 = 2R\tan\alpha$, where T is the time of flight, R, the horizontal range and α, the angle of projection of a particle projected from the ground. **(M.U.)**

   [Hint: $\frac{T^2}{R}=\left(\frac{2u\sin\alpha}{g}\right)^2\left(\frac{g}{2u^2\sin\alpha\cos\alpha}\right)$]

2. If the greatest height attained by a projectile is one quarter of its range on the horizontal plane, show that the angle of projection is 45°. **(M.U.)**

   [Hint: $4\frac{u^2\sin^2\alpha}{2g}=\frac{2u^2\sin\alpha\cos\alpha}{g} \Rightarrow \tan\alpha = 1$]

3. If the range on the horizontal plane of a projectile is equal to the height due to the velocity of projection, show that the angle of projection is either 15° or 75°. **(M.U.)**

   [Hint: $\frac{u^2\sin 2\alpha}{g}=\frac{u^2}{2g}$ or $\sin 2\alpha = \frac{1}{2}$]

4. If the range on the horizontal plane of a projectile and the greatest height above the point of projection are R and H respectively, show that the velocity of projection is

   $$\sqrt{2gH+\frac{gR^2}{8H}}. \quad \textbf{(Bn.U., M.U.)}$$

   [Hint: $R=\frac{u^2\sin 2\alpha}{g}$, $H=\frac{u^2\sin^2\alpha}{2g}=\frac{u^2}{2g}\frac{1-\cos 2\alpha}{2}$. Eliminate α using $\sin^2 2\alpha+\cos^2 2\alpha=$ 1 and find u]

5. A particle is projected in a vertical plane with a velocity u at an angle α to the horizontal. If the range on the horizontal is R and the greatest height attained is h, show that

   $$\frac{u^2}{2g}=h+\frac{R^2}{16h},\ \tan\alpha=\frac{4h}{R}. \quad \textbf{(Bn.U.)}$$

[**Hint:** See previous sum. $\frac{4h}{R} = \frac{4u^2 \sin^2 \alpha}{2g} \cdot \frac{g}{2u^2 \sin\alpha \cos\alpha}$]

6. Two particles are projected from the same point O with the same velocity at angles α and β aimed at a target on the horizontal plane through O. One falls a m. too short and the other b m. too far from the target. If θ is the correct angle of projection so as to hit the target, show that

$$(a+b)\sin 2\theta = a \sin 2\beta + b \sin 2\alpha. \qquad \textbf{(M.U.)}$$

[**Hint:** $R = \frac{u^2 \sin 2\theta}{g}$, $R - a = \frac{u^2 \sin 2\alpha}{g}$, $R + b = \frac{u^2 \sin 2\beta}{g}$.

Eliminating R and u^2/g, we get

$$\begin{vmatrix} 1 & \sin 2\theta & 0 \\ 1 & \sin 2\alpha & a \\ 1 & \sin 2\beta & -b \end{vmatrix} = 0]$$

7. A particle projected from a given point on the ground, just clears a wall of height h at a distance a from the point of projection. If the particle moves in a vertical plane perpendicular to the wall and if the horizontal range is R, show that the elevation of projection is given by

$$\tan\alpha = \frac{Rh}{a(R-a)}. \qquad \textbf{(M.U., A.U.)}$$

[**Hint:** (a, h) and $(R, 0)$ lie on the trajectory. Therefore

$h = a\tan\alpha - \frac{ga^2}{2u^2\cos^2\alpha}$, $0 = R\tan\alpha - \frac{gR^2}{2u^2\cos^2\alpha}$. Eliminate u^2]

8. Find the velocity and the angle of projection of a stone so that it may just clear a tree 3·6 m. high and 4·8 m. distant and fall on the other side at a distance of 3·6 m. from the tree. **(M.U.)**

[**Hint:** (4·8, 3·6) and (8·4, 0) lie on the trajectory.

Ans. $\frac{\sqrt{39g}}{2}$ m./sec; $\tan^{-1}\frac{7}{4}$]

9. A projectile is fired from the base of a hill whose shape is that of a right circular cone with axis vertical. The projectile grazes the vertex and strikes the hill again at a point on the base. If α be the semi vertical angle of the cone, h its height, V the initial speed of the projectile and θ the angle of projection measured from the horizontal, show that

$$\tan\theta = 2\cot\alpha \quad \text{and} \quad V^2 = gh\left(2 + \tfrac{1}{2}\tan^2\alpha\right). \qquad \textbf{(M.U.)}$$

[**Hint:** $(h\tan\alpha, h)$, $(2h\tan\alpha, 0)$ lie on the trajectory]

10. ABC is a triangle in a vertical plane with AB horizontal and $A = 45°$, $B = 60°$. A particle projected from A passes through C and falls at B. Show that the angle of projection is given by

$$\tan\theta = \sqrt{3} + 1. \qquad \textbf{(M.K.U.)}$$

[**Hint:** See Example 3; $\tan\theta = \tan A + \tan B = 1 + \sqrt{3}$.]

11. A shot projected with a velocity V at an inclination 45° reaches a point A on the horizontal plane through the point of projection. Show that, to hit a mark at a height h above A projecting the shot at the same elevation, the velocity of projection must be increased to

$$\frac{V^2}{\sqrt{V^2-gh}}$$ **(M.U.)**

[Hint: $R = \dfrac{2V^2 \sin 45^\circ \cos 45^\circ}{g} = \dfrac{V^2}{g}$. If u is the second velocity, (R, h) lies on

$y = x \tan 45^\circ - \dfrac{gx^2}{2u^2 \cos^2 45^\circ}$**]**

12. A particle is projected with velocity u in a direction which makes an angle α with the horizontal. Find the greatest height attained and show that it is unaltered if u is increased to ku and α is decreased by λ, where cosec $\lambda = k$ (cot λ – cot α). **(M.U.,M.K.U.)**

[Hint: Since $\dfrac{1}{\sin\lambda} = k\left(\dfrac{\cos\lambda}{\sin\lambda} - \dfrac{\cos\alpha}{\sin\alpha}\right) = k\dfrac{\sin(\alpha-\lambda)}{\sin\lambda \sin\alpha}$ becomes $\sin \alpha = k \sin (\alpha - \lambda)$, the maximum heights $\dfrac{u^2 \sin^2\alpha}{2g}$ and $\dfrac{(ku)^2 \sin^2(\alpha-\lambda)}{2g}$ are equal**]**

13. Two particles are projected at an interval of time t from the same point with velocities u and u' at elevations α and α'. If the particles collide, show that

$$t = \frac{2uu' \sin(\alpha - \alpha')}{g(u\cos\alpha + u'\cos\alpha')}$$ **(M.U.)**

[Hint: Let the particles collide at (a, b). Then

$$b = a\tan\alpha - \frac{ga^2}{2u^2\cos^2\alpha}, \quad b = a\tan\alpha' - \frac{ga^2}{2u'^2\cos^2\alpha'}$$

Subtract to get a. Let the times of flight be t_0, $t_0 - t$. Then

$$t_0 = \frac{a}{u\cos\alpha}, \quad t_0 - t = \frac{a}{u'\cos\alpha'}. \text{ So } t = \frac{a}{u\cos\alpha} - \frac{a}{u'\cos\alpha'}.]$$

14. A projectile reaches a point Q of its path in time t and t' is the time it takes to travel from Q to the horizontal plane through the point of projection. Show that the height of Q above the plane is $\frac{1}{2}gtt'$. **(M.U.,M.K.U.,K.U.)**

[Hint: If h is the height of Q, $h = u\sin\alpha t - \frac{1}{2}gt^2$. Now

$$\frac{1}{2}gtt' = \frac{1}{2}gt(T-t) = \frac{1}{2}gt\left(\frac{2u\sin\alpha}{g} - t\right) = u\sin\alpha\, t - \frac{1}{2}gt^2 = h]$$

15. Two particles are projected simultaneously from a point in the same vertical plane. Show that the direction of the line joining them is unaltered throughout the motion. **(M.U.)**

[Hint: Let the particles be projected with speeds u_1 and u_2 and with angles of elevation α_1 and α_2. Then the P.V's of the particles at time t are

$$\bar{r}_1 = (u_1\cos\alpha_1 \cdot t)\bar{i} + \left(u_1\sin\alpha_1 \cdot t - \frac{1}{2}gt^2\right)\bar{j},$$

$$\bar{r}_2 = (u_2\cos\alpha_2 \cdot t)\bar{i} + \left(u_2\sin\alpha_2 \cdot t + \frac{1}{2}gt^2\right)\bar{j}.$$

$$\bar{r}_1 - \bar{r}_2 = \{(u_1\cos\alpha_1 - u_2\cos\alpha_2)\bar{i} + (u_1\sin\alpha_1 - u_2\sin\alpha_2)\bar{j}\}t = (a\bar{i} + b\bar{j})t.]$$

16. If several particles are projected from the same point with equal velocities in the same vertical plane, prove that, at any instant, the particles all lie on a circle and find the locus of the centre of this circle. **(M.U.,M.K.U.)**

[Hint: If α is the angle of projection of a particle, at a time t,

$$x = u\cos\alpha\ t,\ \ y = u\sin\alpha\ t - \tfrac{1}{2}gt^2.$$

Eliminating α, $x^2 + \left(y + \tfrac{1}{2}gt^2\right)^2 = (ut)^2$ which is a circle. The locus of the centre is the lower half of the y axis]

17. If particles are projected from the same point and in the same vertical plane to describe equal parabolas, show that the vertices of their paths lie on a parabola. **(M.U.)**

[Hint: Here u and α vary such that the latus rectum, namely $\dfrac{2u^2\cos^2\alpha}{g} = k$, a const. If (x, y) is the vertex, then

$$x = \frac{u^2\sin\alpha\cos\alpha}{g},\ \ y = \frac{u^2\sin^2\alpha}{2g},\ \ k = \frac{2u^2\cos^2\alpha}{g}.$$

Eliminate u, α and get $x^2 = ky$]

18. A car is running at a speed v. Show that no mud will be thrown off from the wheel of the car of radius a higher than a height

$$\frac{\left(v^2 + ag\right)^2}{2v^2g}$$

above the ground. **(M.U.)**

[Hint: Let P be a point on the circumference of the rear portion of the wheel such that its angular distance from the highest point of the wheel is θ. Then the upward component of the velocity of P, is $v\sin\theta$. Hence h, the height from the ground through which the mud from P will rise is

$$h = (a + a\cos\theta) + \frac{v^2\sin^2\theta}{2g};\ \ \frac{dh}{d\theta} = 0 \text{ gives } \cos\theta = \frac{ag}{v^2}]$$

19. A particle is projected from a point on a horizontal table so as to just grace the four upper corners of a regular hexagon, whose side is a and which is placed vertically with one side on the table. Show that the range on the table is $a\sqrt{7}$ and the square of the time of flight is

$$\frac{28a}{g\sqrt{3}}.$$

(M.U.)

[Hint: $ABCDEF$: Hexagon with AB on the table. Let OQ be the range and $OA = b$. The trajectory passes through

$$F(b - a\cos 60^\circ,\ a\sin 60^\circ),\ \ E(b,\ 2a\sin 60^\circ),\ \ Q(a + 2b,\ 0),$$

$$\therefore \begin{vmatrix} a\sin 60^\circ & b - a\cos 60^\circ & (b - a\cos 60^\circ)^2 \\ 2a\sin 60^\circ & b & b^2 \\ 0 & a + 2b & (a + 2b)^2 \end{vmatrix} = 0$$

or $b = \tfrac{1}{2}\left(-a + \sqrt{7}\,a\right)$. Range $= 2b + a$]

20. A particle is projected with a velocity u at an angle α to the horizontal. If after time t it is moving in a direction making an angle β to the horizontal, show that

$$gt\cos\beta = u\sin(\alpha-\beta).$$ **(M.U.)**

[Hint: $\tan\beta = \dfrac{\text{Ver. comp.of vel.}}{\text{Hor.comp.of vel.}} = \dfrac{u\sin\alpha - gt}{u\cos\alpha}$]

21. A particle is projected with a velocity of 49 m. /sec. at an angle of 60° to the horizontal. Find after what time it moves at an angle of 45° to the horizontal. **(M.K.U.)**

[Hint: $\dfrac{u\sin\alpha - gt}{u\cos\alpha} = \tan 45°$, where $\alpha = 60°$, $u = 49$, $g = 9{\cdot}8$]

22. Two seconds after its projection, a projectile is moving in a direction at 30° to the horizon. After one more second it is moving horizontally. Find the magnitude and direction of the initial velocity.

[Hint: $\tan 30° = \dfrac{u\sin\alpha - g(2)}{u\cos\alpha}$, and $\tan 0° = \dfrac{u\sin\alpha - g(3)}{u\cos\alpha}$ give $u = 2g\sqrt{3}$, $\alpha = 60°$]

23. A ball thrown from a point P with velocity v at an inclination α to the horizontal, reaches a point Q after t secs. Find the horizontal and vertical distances of Q from P and show that, if PQ is inclined at θ to the horizontal, and the direction of the ball when at Q is inclined at an angle ϕ, then

$$\tan\phi = 2\tan\theta - \tan\alpha.$$ **(M.K.U.)**

[Hint: $\tan\theta = \dfrac{y}{x} = \dfrac{u\sin\alpha\, t - \frac{1}{2}gt^2}{u\cos\alpha t}$ and $\tan\phi = \dfrac{u\sin\alpha - gt}{u\cos\alpha}$.

Consider $2\tan\theta - \tan\alpha$ which simplifies to $\tan\phi$]

24. P and Q are two points on the path of a projectile. α, β, γ are the inclinations to the horizontal of PQ and the directions of motion at P and Q respectively. Prove that

$$\tan\alpha = \tfrac{1}{2}(\tan\beta + \tan\gamma).$$ **(M.U.)**

[Hint: When P is taken as the point of projection, the sum is same as the previous one]

25. A particle is projected with a velocity u at an elevation α to the horizontal. Show that the deviation D in the direction of motion of the particle at time t is given by

$$\tan D = \frac{gt\cos\alpha}{u - gt\sin\alpha}.$$ **(M.U., M.K.U., C.U.)**

[Hint: At time t, the inclination of the velocity to the horizontal is $\alpha - D$. Therefore

$$\tan(\alpha - D) = \frac{u\sin\alpha - gt}{u\cos\alpha} = \tan\alpha - \frac{gt}{u\cos\alpha}.$$

$$\therefore\ \tan(\alpha - D) - \tan\alpha = -\frac{gt}{u\cos\alpha} \quad \text{or} \quad \frac{\tan D(1+\tan^2\alpha)}{1+\tan\alpha\tan D} = \frac{gt}{u\cos\alpha}$$]

26. If initially the velocity of a projectile is u and its direction makes an angle α to the horizontal, show that it will be moving at right angles to the initial direction after a time

$$\frac{u\,\text{cosec}\,\alpha}{g}.$$ **(M.U., M.K.U.)**

[Hint: $(u\cos\alpha\,\bar{i} + u\sin\alpha\,\bar{j}).\left[u\cos\alpha\,\bar{i} + (u\sin\alpha - gt)\bar{j}\right] = 0$]

27. A particle is projected with velocity u and angle of projection α. When it is moving at right angles to the direction of projection, prove that its velocity is $u \cot \alpha$ and its distance from the point of projection is

$$\frac{u^2}{2g \sin^2 \alpha}$$ **(A.U.)**

[**Hint:** $t = \dfrac{u}{g \sin \alpha}$; At time t, $\dot{x} = u \cos \alpha$, $\dot{y} = -\dfrac{u \cos^2 \alpha}{\sin \alpha}$, $x = \dfrac{u^2 \cot \alpha}{g}$, $y = \dfrac{u^2 \left(1 - \cot^2 \alpha\right)}{2g}$]

28. A particle is projected with a velocity u so that its range on the horizontal plane through the point of projection is a maximum. Prove that its range on a horizontal plane at a depth $h/2$ below the point of projection is

$$\frac{u\left(u + \sqrt{u^2 + 2gh}\right)}{2g}.$$ **(M.K.U.)**

[**Hint:** $\alpha = 45°$. So the trajectory is $y = x - \dfrac{gx^2}{u^2}$. This passes through $\left(a, -h/2\right)$, where a is the needed range]

29. A particle is projected from the ground with a velocity $2\sqrt{ag}$ so that it just clears two walls of equal height a which are at a distance $2a$ apart. Show that the time of passing between the walls is $2\sqrt{\dfrac{a}{g}}$. **(Bn.U., M.U., C.U.)**

[**Hint:** If U, V are the horizontal and vertical components of the initial velocity, then $U^2 + V^2 = 4ag$ (given). If $t_2 - t_1 = T$, then, as in the example sum,

$$T = \frac{2}{g}\sqrt{V^2 - 2gh}, \quad \text{where } h = a.$$

$$\therefore \quad T = \frac{2}{g}\sqrt{\left(4ag - U^2\right) - 2ga} = \frac{2}{g}\sqrt{2ag - U^2}. \qquad ...(1)$$

But $UT = 2a$ (given). Setting the value of U in (1),

$$T = \frac{2}{g}\sqrt{2ag - \frac{4a^2}{T^2}} \Rightarrow T = 2\sqrt{\frac{a}{g}}\text{]}$$

30. Show that, for a given velocity of projection u and horizontal range R, there are two different directions of projection and that the respective maximum heights and the times of flight are given by the equations

$$16\, gH^2 - 8\, u^2 H + gR^2 = 0 \text{ and } g^2T^4 - 4u^2T^2 + 4R^2 = 0.$$

[**Hint:** (*i*) $H = \dfrac{u^2 \sin^2 \alpha}{2g}$, $R = \dfrac{2u^2 \sin \alpha \cos \alpha}{g}$. Eliminate α.

(*ii*) $T = \dfrac{2u \sin \alpha}{g}$, $R = \dfrac{2u^2 \sin \alpha \cos \alpha}{g}$. Eliminate α.]

31. Two particles are projected in two different directions with same speed so that they have equal horizontal ranges R. If the greatest heights attained by them are h_1 and h_2, show that

$$R = 4\sqrt{h_1 h_2}. \quad \textbf{(M.U., A.U.)}$$

[Hint: If α is the angle of projection of one, then the angle of projection of the other is $90° - \alpha$. So

$$R = \frac{2u^2 \sin\alpha\cos\alpha}{g},\ h_1 = \frac{u^2\sin^2\alpha}{2g},\ h_2 = \frac{u^2\sin^2(90°-\alpha)}{2g}]$$

32. Two particles projected from a point with the same speed u at two different directions, have equal horizontal ranges R. If T_1, T_2 are their times of flight show that $R = \frac{1}{2}gT_1T_2$. **(M.U.)**

[Hint: $R = \dfrac{2u^2\sin\alpha\cos\alpha}{g},\ T_1 = \dfrac{2u\sin\alpha}{g},\ T_2 = \dfrac{2u\sin(90°-\alpha)}{g}$.]

33. A particle is projected from a point A so as to pass through a second point B which is at a depth of 50 m. below A and at a horizontal distance of 100 m. from A. Show that the two possible directions of projection are at right angles if the velocity of projection is that due to a fall from a height of 100 m. **(C.U.)**

[Hint: (100, – 50) satisfy $y = xt - \dfrac{gx^2(1+t^2)}{2u^2}$, where $t = \tan\alpha$, and $u^2 = 2g(100)$. Product of roots of the quadratic in t is – 1]

13.1.6 Projectile projected horizontally.

Bookwork 13.5. A particle is projected horizontally from a height. To show that the equation of its path can be put in the form

$$x^2 = \frac{2u^2}{g}y.$$

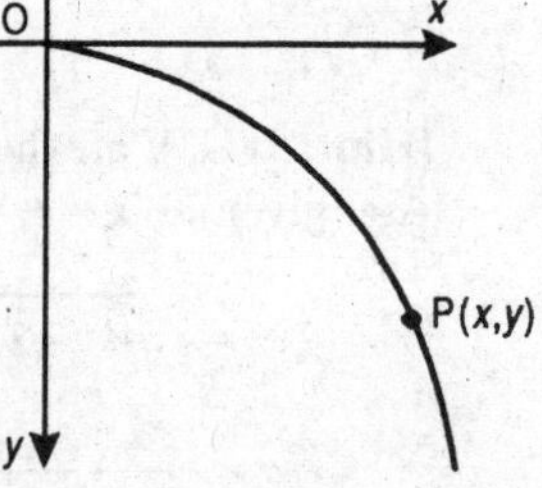

Choose the horizontal line and the vertical downward line through the point of projection, say O, as x, y axes. Let $P(x, y)$ be the position of the particle at time t. Now the horizontal component of the velocity is the constant u.

$$\therefore \quad x = ut. \quad \text{...(1)}$$

Choosing the y direction as the positive direction,

Initial vel.	:	0	
Acceleration	:	g	
time	:	t	$\therefore \quad y = \frac{1}{2}gt^2.$ ...(2)
Distance	:	y	

Eliminating t from (1) and (2), we get the equation of the trajectory as

$$x^2 = \frac{2u^2}{g}y.$$

Bookwork 13.6. A is a point on the ground. O is a point above A such that $AO = h$. A particle projected horizontally from O hits the ground at B. To find the time of flight T and the range AB.

Choosing the downward direction as the positive direction to measure the distance in the vertical displacement, we have, for the entire motion,

			Formula.
Initial velocity	:	0	$s = ut + \frac{1}{2}at^2$
Acceleration	:	g	$h = \frac{1}{2}gT^2$
Distance	:	h	$T = \sqrt{\frac{2h}{g}}.$
Time	:	T	

The horizontal component of the velocity is always u. Therefore

$$AB = (\text{Horizontal velocity}) \times (\text{Time}) = u\sqrt{\frac{2h}{g}}.$$

EXERCISES

1. A stone is projected horizontally with a velocity $\sqrt{2gh}$ from the top of a tower of height h. Find where it will strike the level ground through the foot of the tower. **(M.U., K.U.)**

   [Hint: $u\sqrt{\frac{2h}{g}} = \sqrt{2gh}\sqrt{\frac{2h}{g}} = 2h$]

2. A bomber flies horizontally at an altitude of 1960 m. with velocity 180 km./h. Find at what horizontal distance before passing over a target on the ground, a bomb should be dropped so as to hit the target. **(C.U.)**

   [Hint: $u\sqrt{\frac{2h}{g}} = \frac{180 \times 1000}{60 \times 60}\sqrt{\frac{2 \times 1960}{9 \cdot 8}} = 1000\,\text{m.}$]

3. A bomb was released from an airplane, moving horizontally with a speed of 180 km./h. when it was vertically at a height of 360 m. above a place A on the ground. Find the distance from A of the point where the bomb struck the ground. **(M.K.U.)**

   [Hint: $u\sqrt{\frac{2h}{g}} = \frac{180 \times 1000}{60 \times 60}\sqrt{\frac{2 \times 360}{9 \cdot 8}} = \frac{3000}{7}\,\text{m.}$]

13.2 Projectile projected on an inclined plane

In this section we obtain the time of flight and range of a projectile projected to travel above a line of greatest slope of an inclined plane.

Bookwork 13.7. When a particle is projected from a point O on a plane of inclination β with a velocity u making an angle α with the horizontal, to find

(*i*) T, the time of flight

(*ii*) R, the range on the plane.

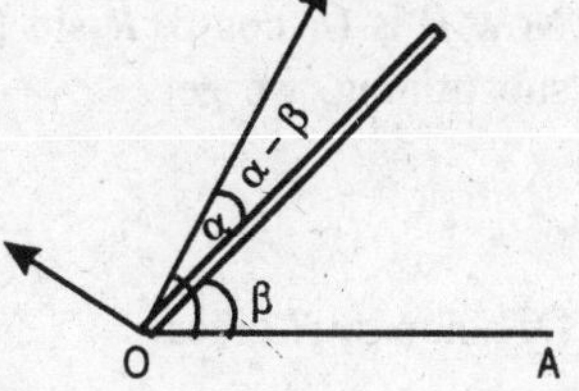

Motion perpendicular to the plane. Let us consider the direction perpendicular to the plane in the upward sense. The angle between this direction and the initial velocity is

$$90^\circ - (\alpha - \beta).$$

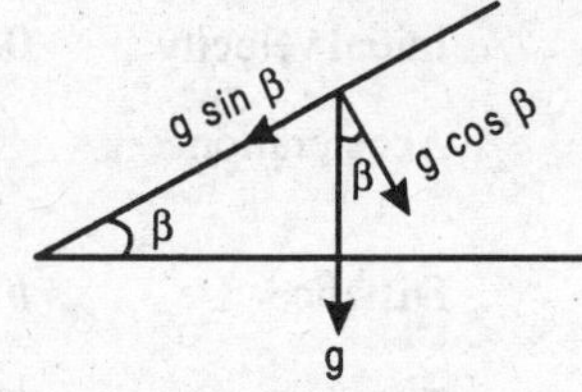

So the component of the initial velocity in this direction is

$$u \sin(\alpha - \beta).$$

Now earth's gravity is the only force acting on the particle. So the acceleration of the particle is g vertically downward. Hence the acceleration of the particle in the upward perpendicular direction is

$$-g \cos \beta.$$

Time of flight T. Let the particle hit the inclined plane at B. Then, for the motion from O to B, in the upward perpendicular direction, we have

Initial velocity	:	$u \sin(\alpha - \beta)$
Acceleration	:	$-g \cos \beta$
Time	:	T
Distance	:	0 (At B, the distance perpendicular to the plane is zero.)

Therefore, from $s = ut + \frac{1}{2}at^2$, we get

$$0 = u\sin(\alpha-\beta)T - \tfrac{1}{2}g\cos\beta T^2. \text{ So } T = \frac{2u\sin(\alpha-\beta)}{g\cos\beta}.$$

Range on the inclined plane. Let N be the foot of the perpendicular from B to the horizontal line through O. Then ON is the horizontal displacement of the projectile when it moves from O to B. So

$$ON = (\text{Horizontal velocity}) \times T$$

$$= (u\cos\alpha)\frac{2u\sin(\alpha-\beta)}{g\cos\beta}$$

$$= \frac{2u^2\cos\alpha\sin(\alpha-\beta)}{g\cos\beta}.$$

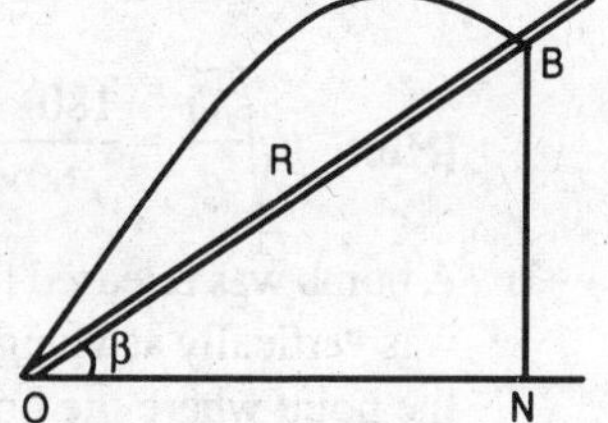

Now, from ΔONB, $\cos\beta = ON/OB = ON/R$ and so

$$R = \frac{ON}{\cos\beta} = \frac{2u^2\cos\alpha\sin(\alpha-\beta)}{g\cos^2\beta}.$$

An important note. If $\alpha > 90°$ then the algebraic value of the range is negative, that is, the actual range is down the plane.

Alternative method. The range R on the inclined plane may also be obtained from the equation of the trajectory

$$y = x\tan\alpha - \frac{gx^2}{2u^2\cos^2\alpha}.$$

Now B is $(R\cos\beta, R\sin\beta)$ and it lies on the trajectory. So it satisfies the equation. Therefore, substituting, we get

$$R\sin\beta = R\cos\beta\tan\alpha - \frac{gR^2\cos^2\beta}{2u^2\cos^2\alpha}.$$

Division by R gives

$$R\frac{g\cos^2\beta}{2u^2\cos^2\alpha} = \cos\beta\tan\alpha - \sin\beta = \cos\beta\frac{\sin\alpha}{\cos\alpha} - \sin\beta$$

$$= \frac{\cos\beta \sin\alpha - \sin\beta\cos\alpha}{\cos\alpha} = \frac{\sin(\alpha-\beta)}{\cos\alpha}.$$

$$\therefore \qquad R = \frac{2u^2 \sin(\alpha-\beta)\cos\alpha}{g\cos^2\beta}$$

13.2.1 Maximum range on an inclined plane

Since $2\sin(\alpha-\beta)\cos\alpha = \sin(2\alpha-\beta) - \sin\beta$, the range R on the inclined plane can be rewritten as

$$R = \frac{u^2}{g\cos^2\beta}[\sin(2\alpha-\beta) - \sin\beta].$$

Here β is a constant. So, for a given speed u, R is a maximum when $\sin(2\alpha-\beta)$ is a maximum, that is, when $\sin(2\alpha - \beta) = 1$. So the maximum R for a given speed u, is

$$\frac{u^2}{g\cos^2\beta}(1-\sin\beta) = \frac{u^2(1-\sin\beta)}{g(1-\sin^2\beta)} = \frac{u^2}{g(1+\sin\beta)}. \qquad \text{...(1)}$$

The value of α corresponding to the maximum range on the inclined plane is obtained from

$$2\alpha - \beta = 90^\circ$$

as

$$\alpha = 45^\circ + \tfrac{1}{2}\beta.$$

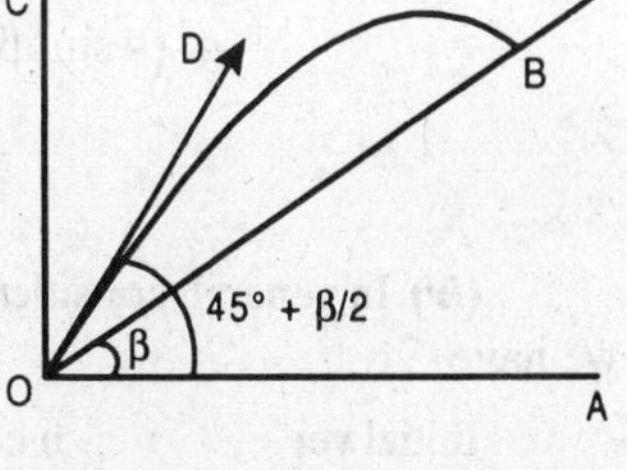

If OA is the horizontal line, OC the vertical line through O and OD the direction of projection giving the maximum range, then

$$\underline{|BOD} = \left(45^\circ + \tfrac{1}{2}\beta\right) - \beta = 45^\circ - \tfrac{1}{2}\beta,$$

$$\underline{|COD} = 90^\circ - \left(45^\circ + \tfrac{1}{2}\beta\right) = 45^\circ - \tfrac{1}{2}\beta$$

which show that OD bisects the angle between the inclined plane and the vertical line.

Maximum range down an inclined plane. For a given speed u, the maximum range down the inclined plane is obtained as

$$\frac{u^2}{g(1-\sin\beta)} \qquad \text{...(2)}$$

by replacing β with $180^\circ + \beta$ in (1).

EXAMPLES

Example 1. A particle projected with a speed u strikes at right angles a plane through the point of projection, inclined at an angle β to the horizon. If α, T and R are the angle of projection, the time of flight and the range on the inclined plane, show that

(*i*) $\cot\beta = 2\tan(\alpha-\beta)$ **(M.U., M.K.U., C.U.)**

(*ii*) $\cot\beta = \tan\alpha - 2\tan\beta$. **(M.U., C.U., A.U.)**

(*iii*) $T = \dfrac{2u}{g\sqrt{1+3\sin^2\beta}}$ **(M.U., M.K.U.)**

(*iv*) $R = \dfrac{2u^2\sin\beta}{g(1+3\sin^2\beta)}$ **(M.U., K.U.)**

***(i)* Condition for perpendicular hit.** See the Bookwork. Let OB be the range. Since the particle hits the plane perpendicularly at B, the velocity component along the plane at B is zero, that is, at $t = T$ it is zero. So, from $v = u + at$,

$$0 = u\cos(\alpha-\beta) - g\sin\beta T. \qquad ...(1)$$

But, in general,

$$T = \frac{2u\sin(\alpha-\beta)}{g\cos\beta}. \qquad ...(2)$$

Thus the condition for perpendicular hit is

$$0 = u\cos(\alpha-\beta) - g\sin\beta\frac{2u\sin(\alpha-\beta)}{g\cos\beta}$$

or

$$\cot\beta = 2\tan(\alpha-\beta). \qquad ...(3)$$

(ii) Expansion of tan $(\alpha - \beta)$ yields the results

$$\cot\beta = \tan\alpha - 2\tan\beta.$$

(iii) Finding $u\sin(\alpha-\beta)$, $u\cos(\alpha-\beta)$ from (2), (1) and squaring and adding, we get

$$u^2 = \left(\sin^2\beta + \tfrac{1}{4}\cos^2\beta\right)g^2T^2.$$

$$\therefore \quad g^2\left(4\sin^2\beta+\cos^2\beta\right)T^2 = 4u^2 \quad \text{or} \quad g^2\left(3\sin^2\beta+1\right)T^2 = 4u^2.$$

$$\therefore \quad T = \frac{2u}{g\sqrt{1+3\sin^2\beta}} \qquad ...(4)$$

(iv) In general, considering the displacement along and up the plane in the motion from O to B, we have

Initial vel	:	$u\cos(\alpha-\beta)$	Time	:	T
Acceleration	:	$-g\sin\beta$	Distance	:	R.

From "$s = ut + \tfrac{1}{2}at^2$", we get

$$R = u\cos(\alpha-\beta)T - \tfrac{1}{2}g\sin\beta T^2 \qquad ...(5)$$

$(5) - T\times(1)$ gives

$$R = T^2\left(-\tfrac{1}{2}g\sin\beta + g\sin\beta\right) = T^2\left(\tfrac{1}{2}g\sin\beta\right)$$

$$= \frac{4u^2}{g^2\left(1+3\sin^2\beta\right)}\cdot\frac{1}{2}g\sin\beta \text{ by (4)}$$

$$= \frac{2u^2\sin\beta}{g\left(1+3\sin^2\beta\right)}.$$

EXERCISES

1. A particle is projected from the top of a plane whose inclination to the horizontal is 60°. If the direction of projection is *(i)* 30° above the horizontal and *(ii)* 30° below the horizontal, show that the range down the plane in the first case is double that in the second. **(M.K.U.)**

[Hint: $R_\alpha = \dfrac{2u^2\sin(\alpha-\beta)\cos\alpha}{g\cos^2\beta}$; Now $\beta = 60°$. Prove : $R_{150°} = 2R_{210°}$**]**

2. A hill is inclined at an angle of 30° to the horizon. From a point on the hill, one projectile is projected up the hill and another down the hill, both starting with the same velocity and the same angle of projection of 45° with the horizon. Show that the range of one projectile is nearly 15⁄4 times that of the other. **(M.U.)**

[Hint: $\beta = 30°$; Prove : $\dfrac{R_{45°}}{(-R_{135°})} = \tan 15° = \dfrac{4}{15}$ nearly**]**

3. If U and V be the oblique components of the initial velocity in the vertical direction and in the direction of the line of greatest slope, show that the range on the inclined plane is

$$\frac{2UV}{g}.$$

(M.U.)

[Hint: Let $OAPB$ be the parallelogram wherein OA is up the plane, OB is vertically upward such that $OA = V$, $OB = U$. Then $OP = u$ and

$$\frac{U}{\sin(\alpha-\beta)} = \frac{V}{\sin(90°-\alpha)} = \frac{u}{\sin(90°+\beta)}.$$

Show that $\dfrac{2UV}{g} = \dfrac{2u^2\cos\alpha\sin(\alpha-\beta)}{g\cos^2\beta}$**]**

4. A particle is projected with speed u so as to strike at right angles a plane through the point of projection inclined at 30° to the horizon. Show that the range on this inclined plane is $\dfrac{4u^2}{7g}$.

(M.K.U.)

[Hint: See the example sum. $R = \dfrac{2u^2\sin\beta}{g(1+3\sin^2\beta)}$; $\beta = 30°$**]**

5. A particle is projected from a point whose perpendicular distance from a plane inclined at 60° to the horizon is d. Prove that it cannot strike the plane perpendicularly if the square of the velocity of projection is less than $\frac{1}{2}gd\left(\sqrt{13}-1\right)$. **(M.U.,M.K.U.)**

[Hint: $\beta = 60°$; For the up and perpendicular motions, upto the striking point,

$$0 = u\cos(\alpha-\beta) - g\sin\beta\, t, \quad -d = u\sin(\alpha-\beta)\,t - \tfrac{1}{2}g\cos\beta\, t^2$$

or

$$0 = u\cos(\alpha-60°) - \frac{\sqrt{3}}{2}gt, \quad -d = u\sin(\alpha-60°)t - \frac{g}{4}t^2.$$

Finding t from the first and substituting in the second,

$$-d = \frac{u^2}{\sqrt{3}\,g}\sin\theta - \frac{u^2}{3g}\left(\frac{1+\cos\theta}{2}\right), \text{ where } \theta = 2(\alpha-60°)$$

or $\left(\dfrac{6dg}{u^2}-1\right)\dfrac{1}{\sqrt{13}} = \cos(\theta+\phi)$, if $\dfrac{2\sqrt{3}}{\sqrt{13}} = \sin\phi$, $\dfrac{1}{\sqrt{13}} = \cos\phi$. Now $\cos(\theta+\phi) \le 1$**]**

6. A gun is situated on an inclined plane and the maximum ranges up and down the plane are L_1 and L_2. If L is the maximum range in a direction perpendicular to the line of greatest slope, show that

$$\frac{1}{L_1} + \frac{1}{L_2} = \frac{2}{L}.$$

(M.U.)

[**Hint:** $L_1 = \dfrac{u^2}{g(1+\sin\beta)}$, $L_2 = \dfrac{u^2}{g(1-\sin\beta)}$, $L = \dfrac{u^2}{g}$]

7. If the greatest range down an inclined plane is three times the greatest range up the plane, show that the plane is inclined at 30° to the horizon. **(M.U., Br.U.)**

[**Hint:** $\dfrac{u^2}{g(1-\sin\beta)} = \dfrac{3u^2}{g(1+\sin\beta)}$ or $4\sin\beta = 2$]

8. Show that greatest range on an inclined plane through the point of projection is equal to the distance through which the particle could fall freely during the corresponding time of flight. **(M.U.)**

[**Hint:** $R_{\max} = \dfrac{u^2}{g(1+\sin\beta)}$; $T = \dfrac{2u\sin(\alpha-\beta)}{g\cos\beta}$, where $\alpha = 45° + \dfrac{\beta}{2}$; $h = \frac{1}{2}gT^2$. Show that $R_{\max} = h$]

13.3 Enveloping parabola or bounding parabola

Suppose several particles are projected from a point O in different directions in the same vertical plane with the same speed u. The trajectories form a family of curves.

Bookwork 13.8. To find the envelope of a family of trajectories of particles projected from a fixed point O and constant velocity u.

Choose the horizontal and vertical lines through O as the x, y axes. Then the parametric equation of the family of trajectories is

$$y = x\tan\alpha - \frac{gx^2}{2u^2\cos^2\alpha} \quad \text{or} \quad y = xt - \frac{gx^2(1+t^2)}{2u^2}$$

where t is the parameter and $\sec^2\alpha = 1 + t^2$. Rewriting the equation as a quadratic in t, we get

$$gx^2(1+t^2) + 2u^2(y - xt) = 0 \quad \text{or} \quad gx^2t^2 - 2u^2xt + (gx^2 + 2u^2y) = 0,$$

To obtain the equation of the curve which envelopes all the trajectories, we have to equate the discriminant of the quadratic in t to zero. Thus we get the equation of the envelope to be

$$(-2u^2x)^2 - 4(gx^2)(gx^2 + 2u^2y) = 0$$

i.e.,
$$4u^4x^2 - 4g^2x^4 - 8gu^2x^2y = 0 \quad \text{or} \quad x^2(u^4 - g^2x^2 - 2gu^2y) = 0$$

But $x = 0$ cannot be the envelope. So the equation of the envelope is

$$u^4 - g^2x^2 - 2gu^2y = 0 \quad \text{or} \quad x^2 = -\frac{2u^2}{g}\left(y - \frac{u^2}{2g}\right).$$

This equation shows that the envelope is a parabola with its focus at O, the point of projection.

Remark 1. All the trajectories touch the enveloping parabola.

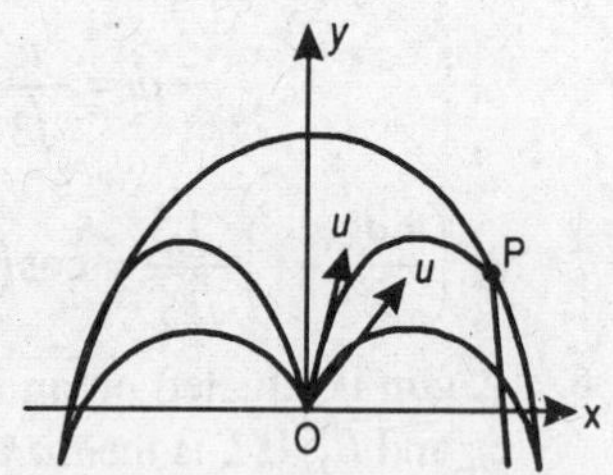

Remark 2. It is evident that, for a given velocity of projection u, all the trajectories lie inside the enveloping parabola. Each of these trajectories touches the enveloping parabola. This means that a particle can be projected with the speed u to pass through any point inside or on the enveloping parabola. That is, u is the least speed with which a particle may be projected to pass through a point on the enveloping parabola.

Remark 3. A good example of the enveloping parabola is the "flower-pot". When a flower-pot is fired, a constant pressure is created inside the pot and the fire particles are projected with constant speed but in different directions. A paraboloid can be seen to envelope all the trajectories.

EXAMPLES

Example 1. Show that, for a projectile to reach a point P at a horizontal distance a and a vertical distance b from the point of projection O, the velocity of projection u should be such that

$$u^2 \not< g\left(b+\sqrt{a^2+b^2}\right).$$ **(M.U., A.U.)**

Let O be the origin. We know that a particle can be projected from O with a speed V to pass through any point lying inside or on the enveloping parabola

$$x^2 = -\frac{2V^2}{g}\left(y-\frac{V^2}{2g}\right)$$

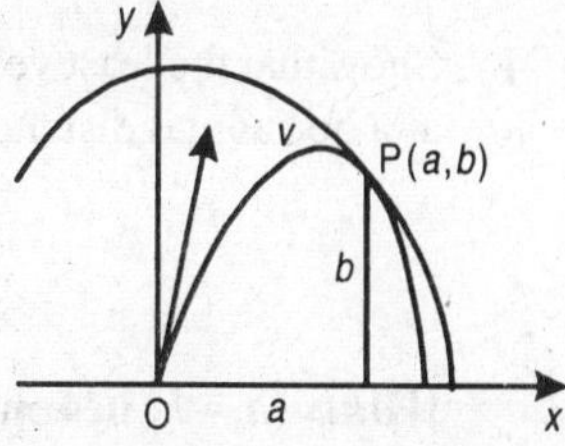

If the velocity of projection u is such that $u < V$, the particle will not reach the enveloping parabola at all. So, for the particle to pass through any point on the enveloping parabola, its velocity of projection u should be such that

$$u \not< V. \qquad ...(1)$$

Let P (a, b) be a point on the enveloping parabola, then

$$a^2 = -\frac{2V^2}{g}\left(b-\frac{V^2}{2g}\right) \text{ or } a^2 = -\frac{2V^2}{g}b+\frac{V^4}{g^2}.$$

$$\therefore \qquad V^4 - 2bg\, V^2 - a^2 g^2 = 0$$

$$\therefore \qquad V^2 = \frac{2bg \pm \sqrt{4b^2g^2+4a^2g^2}}{2} = g\left(b\pm\sqrt{a^2+b^2}\right) = g\left(b+\sqrt{a^2+b^2}\right)$$

neglecting the negative root. So (1) becomes that, if the particle is to pass through the point $P(a, b)$, a point on the enveloping parabola, its velocity of projection u should be such that

$$u^2 \not< g\left(b+\sqrt{a^2+b^2}\right).$$

EXERCISES

1. The angular elevation of an enemy's position on a fort of height h is β. Show that in order to shell it, the velocity of projection must not be less than

$$\sqrt{gh\left(1+\operatorname{cosec}\beta\right)}.$$ **(M.U.)**

[Hint: In the example sum set $b = h$ and $a = h \cot \beta$]

2. Show that the greatest height which a particle projected with a velocity u, can reach a vertical wall at a distance a from the point of projection, is

$$\frac{u^4-a^2g^2}{2gu^2}.$$ **(M.U., M.K.U., K.U.)**

[Hint: The greatest height is the height of the point at which the enveloping parabola intersects the wall. So it is the y coordinate of the point of intersection of

$$x^2 = -\frac{2u^2}{g}\left(y-\frac{u^2}{2g}\right); \quad x = a]$$

3. Show that the maximum horizontal distance of a point on the ground from the foot of a tower of height h, from which a target on the top of the tower, can be hit by a gun whose muzzle speed is u, is

$$\frac{u}{g}\sqrt{u^2-2gh}.$$ **(M.U., M.K.U.)**

[Hint: If a is the required distance, (a, h) lies on the enveloping parabola

$$x^2 = -\frac{2u^2}{g}\left(y-\frac{u^2}{2g}\right)]$$

4. Show that the least velocity u required to project a particle from a height h to fall on the ground at a horizontal distance a from the point of projection is given by

$$u^2 = g\left(\sqrt{a^2+h^2}-h\right).$$ **(M.U.)**

[Hint: $(a, -h)$ lies on $x^2 = -\frac{2u^2}{g}.\left(y-\frac{u^2}{2g}\right)$]

5. A particle is projected with a velocity $\sqrt{2ag}$ from a point at a height h above a level plane. Show that the maximum range on the plane and the corresponding angle of projection are

$$2\sqrt{a(a+h)} \text{ and } \tan^{-1}\sqrt{\frac{a}{a+h}}.$$ **(M.U., A.U.)**

[Hint: If d is the maximum range on the plane, $(d, -h)$ lies on the enveloping parabola $x^2 = -\frac{2u^2}{g}\left(y-\frac{u^2}{2g}\right)$, where $u^2 = 2ag$]

6. A particle is projected from the top of a tower of height h with a velocity $\sqrt{2ngh}$, show that the range on the horizontal plane through the foot of the tower is a maximum when the angle of projection θ is given by

$$\sec 2\theta = 2n+1.$$ **(M.K.U.)**

[Hint: $u = \sqrt{2ngh}$. So the enveloping parabola is

$$x^2 = -4nh(y-nh).$$

If the horizontal range is R, the enveloping parabola passes through $(R, -h)$. Therefore

$$R^2 = 4nh^2(n+1)$$

With $u = \sqrt{2ngh}$, if $\tan\alpha = t$, the trajectory is

$$y = xt - \frac{gx^2}{2(2ngh)}(1+t^2).$$

This passes through $(R, -h)$ and therefore we get

$$\left(t-\sqrt{\frac{n}{n+1}}\right)^2 = 0 \text{ and } \cos 2\theta = \frac{1-t^2}{1+t^2} = \frac{1}{2n+1}]$$

IMPACT

14.1 IMPULSIVE FORCE

A large force which, acting on a body for an infinitesimally small period, produces a finite change of momentum in that interval, is called an *impulsive force*. The period in which the impulsive force acts should be so short that, during this period, the change of position of the point of application and the effects of the finite forces are negligible.

Example. The force experienced by a ball due to a hit by a bat is an example for an impulsive force.

Impulse. The effect of the action of an impulsive force is measured by the change in momentum produced by the force. This change is called the *impulse* of the impulsive action. So the defining equation of an impulse imparted to a particle of mass m is

$$\bar{I} = m\,\bar{v}' - m\,\bar{v}, \qquad ...(1)$$

where $\bar{v}$ and $\bar{v}'$ are the velocities of the particle immediately before and immediately after the impulsive action. If τ is the short time during which the impulsive force acts, then

$$\bar{I} = m\,\bar{v}' - m\,\bar{v} = \left[m\,\bar{v}\right]_0^{\tau} = \int_0^{\tau} m\,d\bar{v} = \int_0^{\tau} m\frac{d\bar{v}}{dt}\,dt = \int_0^{\tau} m\,\bar{a}\,dt$$

$$= \int_0^{\tau} \bar{F}\,dt. \qquad ...(2)$$

Alternative definition. The integral (2) may also be defined to be the impulse.

Remark. Care should be taken to differentiate impulse from an impulsive force, for impulsive force is a force whereas impulse is the change in momentum. Hence impulse is measured by the unit of momentum but not by the unit of force.

14.1.1 Conservation of linear momentum

From the equation of motion of a particle of mass m,

$$m\ddot{\bar{r}} = \bar{F}.$$

We see that, if $\bar{F} = \bar{O}$, then

$$m\,\dot{\bar{r}} \text{ or } m\bar{v}$$

is a constant vector ; that is, the linear momentum is conserved. Thus we obtain the *principle of conservation of momentum for a particle that,*

if the applied force on a particle is zero, then

the linear momentum of the particle is conserved.

In the case of a rigid body or a system of particles, if the sum of the applied forces is zero, then

$$m_1\,\dot{\bar{r}}_1 + m_2\,\dot{\bar{r}}_2 + \ldots\ldots = \text{a constant vector.}$$

That is, the linear momentum of the system is conserved.

When the explosive charge in a gun forms a large amount of gas, the gun and the shot are subject to the action of a very high pressure. But this pressure is an internal force and not an external force. Therefore, when a gun is fired, the gun and the shot are not subject to any external force. So, by the principle of conservation of linear momentum, if the gun is at rest before firing, that is, if the momentum of the gun and the shot is zero before firing, then immediately after firing the sum of the momenta of the gun and the shot will also be zero. So, in firing a shot of mass m with a velocity $\bar{v}$, the gun of mass M gains a velocity $\bar{V}$ (velocity of recoiling) given by

$$m\bar{v} + M\bar{V} = \bar{0} \quad \text{as} \quad \bar{V} = -\frac{m}{M}\bar{v}.$$

It is evident that the directions of the velocities of the gun and the shot are opposite. If $|\bar{V}| = V$ and $|\bar{v}| = v$, then

$$MV = mv.$$

Kinetic energy generated. The explosion generates a total kinetic energy

$$\tfrac{1}{2}mv^2 + \tfrac{1}{2}MV^2,$$

where $|\bar{v}| = v$, $|\bar{V}| = V$. This is the work done by the internal explosive pressure impulsively.

EXAMPLES

Example 1. A gun is rigidly mounted on a carriage on a smooth horizontal plane. The total mass of the carriage and the gun is M. If the gun is elevated at an angle α to the horizon, show that, when a shot of mass m is fired, it leaves the gun in a direction at an angle θ to the horizontal given by

$$\tan\theta = \frac{M+m}{M}\tan\alpha. \qquad \textbf{(M.U., Bn.U.)}$$

Let AB be the carriage, BC, the barrel and O, the initial position of A. Let $\bar{i}, \bar{j}$ be the unit vectors in the horizontal and upward vertical directions.

At time t after the explosion, let

P : Position of the shot

N : Foot of the perpendicular (from P)

$\bar{r}$: P.V. of P w.r.t. O

$\bar{R}$: P.V. of A w.r.t. O

OA : x, $BP = r$

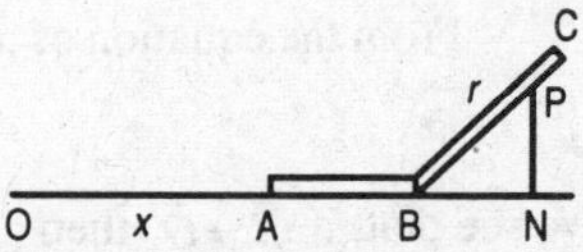

Velocity of the shot at time *t*. The P.V. of the shot at time t is

$$\bar{r} = \overline{OA} + \overline{AB} + \overline{BN} + \overline{NP} = x\,\bar{i} + AB\,\bar{i} + (r\cos\alpha\,\bar{i} + r\sin\alpha\,\bar{j})$$

$$\dot{\bar{r}} = \dot{x}\,\bar{i} + \dot{r}\cos\alpha\,\bar{i} + \dot{r}\sin\alpha\,\bar{j}$$

$$= (\dot{x} + \dot{r}\cos\alpha)\bar{i} + \dot{r}\sin\alpha\,\bar{j}. \qquad ...(1)$$

Velocity of the shot at the time of leaving the barrel. Let the shot leave the barrel at a time T after the explosion and let, at that moment,

$$\dot{x} = V, \qquad \dot{r} = v.$$

Then, at $t = T$, the velocity of the shot, from (1), is

$$(V + v\cos\alpha)\bar{i} + v\sin\alpha\,\bar{j}.$$

$$\therefore \qquad \tan\theta = \frac{j \text{ Comp.}}{i \text{ Comp.}} = \frac{v\sin\alpha}{V + v\cos\alpha}. \qquad ...(2)$$

Momentum of the system. Initially the momentum is $\bar{0}$. The normal reaction is the only external force on the carriage during the explosion which is vertically upward. So there is no external force in the $\bar{i}$ direction. Therefore the momentum in the $\bar{i}$ direction when the shot leaves the barrel is the same as it was initially. So it is zero. But the momentum of the carriage and the shot at time t is

$$M\dot{\bar{R}} + m\dot{\bar{r}} \quad \text{or} \quad M\dot{x}\bar{i} + m\left[(\dot{x} + \dot{r}\cos\alpha)\bar{i} + \dot{r}\sin\alpha\,\bar{j}\right]$$

and at the time $t = T$ it is

$$MV\bar{i} + m\left[(V + v\cos\alpha)\bar{i} + v\sin\alpha\,\bar{j}\right].$$

Since its $\bar{i}$ component is zero,

$$MV + m\ (V + v\cos\alpha) = 0 \quad \text{or} \quad V = -\frac{m\,v\cos\alpha}{M + m}. \qquad ...(3)$$

Substituting this in (2), we get

$$\tan\theta = \frac{v\sin\alpha}{-\dfrac{m\,v\cos\alpha}{M+m} + v\cos\alpha} = \frac{M+m}{M}\tan\alpha.$$

Remark. From (3) it may be noticed that V is negative, that is, the carriage develops a velocity in the negative direction of $\bar{i}$.

Example 2. A shell of mass m is moving with velocity v. An internal explosion generates an energy E and breaks the shell into two portions whose masses are in the ratio $a : b$. They continue to move in the original line of motion. Show that their velocities after explosion are

$$v + \sqrt{\frac{2bE}{am}}, \qquad v - \sqrt{\frac{2aE}{bm}}. \qquad \textbf{(M.U)}$$

Now the masses of the two fragments are

$$\frac{a}{a+b}m, \qquad \frac{b}{a+b}m.$$

Let the velocities of these masses after explosion be

$$v + v_1, \qquad v - v_2$$

in the direction of v. Since the momentum after explosion equals momentum before explosion,

$$\frac{am}{a+b}(v + v_1) + \frac{bm}{a+b}(v - v_2) = mv.$$

In this the v-terms get cancelled giving the result

$$av_1 = bv_2. \qquad ...(1)$$

Since the increase in energy is E,

$$\left[\frac{1}{2}\frac{am}{a+b}(v+v_1)^2+\frac{1}{2}\frac{bm}{a+b}(v-v_2)^2\right]-\frac{1}{2}m\,v^2=E.$$

In this the v^2-terms get cancelled themselves and the v term vanish by (1), giving the result,

$$\frac{1}{2}\frac{am}{a+b}v_1^{\,2}+\frac{1}{2}\frac{bm}{a+b}v_2^{\,2}=E. \qquad ...(2)$$

Solving (1) and (2) for v_1 and v_2, we get

$$v_1^{\,2}=\frac{2bE}{am},\quad v_2^{\,2}=\frac{2aE}{bm}.$$

Thus the velocities $v+v_1$, $v-v_2$ of the fragments are

$$v+\sqrt{\frac{2bE}{am}},\quad v-\sqrt{\frac{2aE}{bm}}.$$

Example 3. A shell of mass m_1+m_2 is fired with a given velocity in a given direction. At the highest point of its path, the shell explodes into two fragments of mass m_1 and m_2. The explosion produces an additional kinetic energy E and the fragments separate in a horizontal direction. Show that, if the fragments strike the ground at A_1 and A_2, then

$$A_1A_2=\frac{V}{g}\sqrt{2E\left(\frac{1}{m_1}+\frac{1}{m_2}\right)}, \qquad \textbf{(M.U.)}$$

where V is the vertical component of the velocity of projection.

Let us make the following assumptions (see figure):

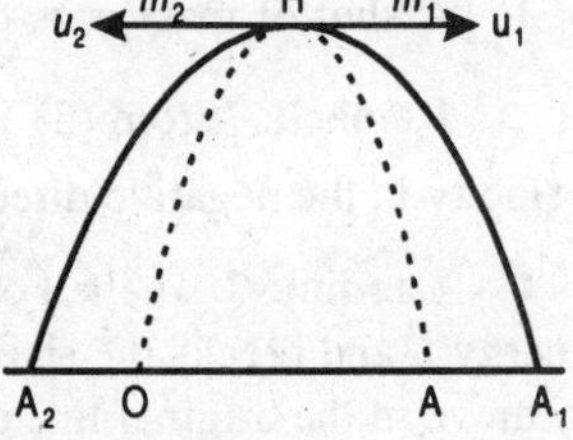

O : Point from which the shell is fired.

H : Highest point at which explosion takes place.

U : Horizontal component of the initial velocity of m_1+m_2

T : Time taken by m_1+m_2 to reach H.

u_1, u_2 : Speeds of m_1, m_2 after explosion.

Considering the vertical displacement of m_1+m_2 in the motion from O to H, from "$v=u+at$".

$$0=V+(-g)T \quad \text{or} \quad T=\frac{V}{g}$$

The fragments m_1 and m_2 take the same time T to reach the ground. In this duration the horizontal component of the relative speed of the fragments is u_1+u_2. So.

$$A_1A_2=(u_1+u_2)\,T=(u_1+u_2)\frac{V}{g}. \qquad ...(1)$$

Kinetic energy of m_1+m_2 just before explosion is

$$\tfrac{1}{2}(m_1+m_2)U^2.$$

The generation of K.E. by explosion is E. So immediately after explosion the K.E. is $\frac{1}{2}(m_1+m_2)U^2+E$. Thus

$$\tfrac{1}{2}(m_1+m_2)U^2+E=\tfrac{1}{2}m_1u_1^{\,2}+\tfrac{1}{2}m_2u_2^{\,2}. \qquad ...(2)$$

Lastly, from the principle of conservation of momentum,

$$(m_1 + m_2)U = m_1u_1 - m_2u_2. \qquad ...(3)$$

Eliminating U from (2) and (3) and then using (1) we get

$$2E\,\frac{m_1 + m_2}{m_1\, m_2} = (u_1 + u_2)^2 = \frac{(A_1A_2)^2 g^2}{V^2}$$

$$\therefore \qquad A_1A_2 = \frac{V}{g}\sqrt{2E\left(\frac{1}{m_1} + \frac{1}{m_2}\right)}.$$

EXERCISES

1. A shot of mass m gm. is fired horizontally from a gun of mass M gm. with a velocity v cm/sec. Find the steady pressure which acting on the gun will bring it to rest, when it has recoiled a cm. **(A.U.)**

   [Hint: If V is the velocity of recoil, $VM = mv$ or $V = \frac{mv}{M}$. If the retardation due to pressure is α, then

   $$0 = V^2 - 2\alpha a. \qquad \text{Force} = M\alpha = M\frac{V^2}{2\,a} = \frac{m^2\,v^2}{2aM}]$$

2. A gun is mounted on a gun carriage movable on a smooth horizontal plane and the gun is elevated at an angle α to the horizon. A shot is fired in a direction inclined at an angle θ to the horizon. If the mass of the carriage and gun is n times that of the shot, show that

   $$\tan\theta = 1 + \tfrac{1}{n}\tan\alpha. \qquad \textbf{(M.U.)}$$

3. A shot of mass m is discharged horizontally from a gun of mass M which is free to recoil horizontally. If the velocity of m relative to the gun is v, find the velocities of m and M and show that the total kinetic energy generated is

   $$\frac{1}{2}\,\frac{m\,M\,v^2}{m + M}. \qquad \textbf{(M.U.)}$$

   [Hint: Velocities of m, M : $u\,\bar{i}$, $V(-\bar{i})$. Relative velocity : $(u + V)\bar{i}$. So $u + V = v$. Since momentum is zero, $m\,u\,\bar{i} - MV\,\bar{i} = \bar{0}$ or $m\,u = MV$. Solving for u and V,

   $$u = \frac{Mv}{M + m}, \qquad V = \frac{mv}{M + m}; \qquad \text{K.E} = \frac{1}{2}mu^2 + \frac{1}{2}MV^2.]$$

4. A gun of mass M fires a shell of mass m horizontally and the energy of the explosion is such as would be sufficient to project the shell vertically to a height h. Show that the velocity of the horizontal recoil V of the gun is given by

   $$V^2 = \frac{2\,m^2 gh}{M(M + m)}. \qquad \textbf{(M.U., M.K.U., C.U.)}$$

   [Hint: If u is the initial velocity of a particle to reach a height h, $u^2 = 2gh$. Energy to lift the shell to a height h is $\tfrac{1}{2}mu^2$ or mgh. If v, V are the velocities of the shell and gun after explosion

   $$\tfrac{1}{2}mv^2 + \tfrac{1}{2}MV^2 = mgh, \qquad MV = mv. \text{ Solve for } V]$$

5. A gun of mass M firing a shot of mass m recoils with a velocity V. Show that, if the mass of the shot is increased to $2m$, the K.E. of the explosion remaining the same, the velocity of the recoil becomes

$$V\sqrt{\frac{2(M+m)}{M+2m}}.$$ **(M.U., Bn.U., M.K.U.)**

[Hint: With usual meanings, for the two cases, $MV = mv$, $MV' = 2m\,v'$. Substitute the values of v, v' in

$$\tfrac{1}{2}MV^2 + \tfrac{1}{2}mv^2 = \tfrac{1}{2}MV'^2 + \tfrac{1}{2}(2m)v'^2\ ]$$

6. A shell is at rest. An internal explosion breaks it into two masses m_1 and m_2 which move freely in a straight line. If s is the distance between them after a time t, then show that the work done by the explosion is

$$\frac{1}{2}\frac{m_1 m_2 s^2}{(m_1+m_2)t^2}$$ **(M.U.)**

[Hint: $m_1 v_1 = m_2 v_2$; Distances of $m_1, m_2 : v_1 t,\ v_2 t$. So $s = (v_1 + v_2)t$;

$$v_1 = \frac{m_2 s}{(m_1+m_2)t},\ v_2 = \frac{m_1 s}{(m_1+m_2)t}.\ \text{Find } \frac{1}{2}m_1 v_1^2 + \frac{1}{2}m_2 v_2^2\ ].$$

8. A shell explodes and breaks into two fragments of masses m_1, m_2 which move with velocities u_1 and u_2 in opposite directions. Show that there is a gain in kinetic energy of magnitude

$$\frac{1}{2}\frac{m_1 m_2}{m_1+m_2}(u_1+u_2)^2.$$ **(M.U.)**

9. A body of mass $m_1 + m_2$ is split into two parts of masses m_1 and m_2 by an internal explosion which generates a kinetic energy E. Show that, if after explosion the parts move in the same line as before, their relative speed is

$$\sqrt{\frac{2E(m_1+m_2)}{m_1 m_2}}.$$ **(M.U., M.K.U.)**

[Hint: $\tfrac{1}{2}m_1 v_1^2 + \tfrac{1}{2}m_2 v_2^2 = E$; $m_1 v_1 = m_2 v_2$. So solving for v_1^2 and v_2^2,

$$v_1^2 = \frac{2Em_2}{m_1(m_1+m_2)},\quad v_2^2 = \frac{2Em_1}{m_2(m_1+m_2)}.$$

$$v_1 + v_2 = \sqrt{\frac{2Em_2}{m_1(m_1+m_2)}} + \sqrt{\frac{2Em_1}{m_2(m_1+m_2)}} = \sqrt{\frac{2E}{m_1+m_2}}\left(\sqrt{\frac{m_2}{m_1}} + \sqrt{\frac{m_1}{m_2}}\right)\ ]$$

10. A mass m after falling freely through a distance a begins to raise a mass M ($M > m$) connected to it by means of an inextensible string passing over a fixed pulley. Show that M will have returned to its original position in a time

$$\frac{2m}{M-m}\sqrt{\frac{2a}{g}}.$$ **(C.U.)**

[Hint: The momentum of the particles is the total mass multiplied by the common speed. If the velocity acquired in falling through a distance a is u, then $u = \sqrt{2ag}$. If after the jerk the velocity of m is v, then equating the momentum before and momentum after jerk,

$$mu = (M+m)v \text{ or } v = \frac{mu}{M+m} = \frac{m\sqrt{2ag}}{M+m}.$$

But m has a retardation $\dfrac{M-m}{M+m}g$. So if T is the required time, then, by $s = ut + \frac{1}{2}at^2$,

$$0 = vT - \frac{1}{2}\frac{M-m}{M+m}gT^2 \quad \text{or} \quad T = \frac{2v(M+m)}{(M-m)g}.$$

Substitute the value of v]

11. Two masses weighing 15 lb. and 5 lb. are connected by a string passing over a smooth pulley and the whole system is at rest with the former on the ground. A third mass of 5 lb. falls through a height of 20 feet, strikes the second mass, adheres to it and sets the whole in motion. Prove that the first mass will rise from the ground to a height of 4 feet. **(C.U.)**

[**Hint:** Velocity due to fall $u = \sqrt{40g}$. If the velocity after jerk is v, $25v = 5u$ or $v = \dfrac{u}{5}$.

$v^2 = 2 \times \left(\dfrac{10-5}{25}g\right)s$. So $s = 4$]

12. A mass m after falling freely through a distance a begins to raise a mass M connected to it by means of a string passing over a fixed pulley. Show that the fraction of the kinetic energy of m destroyed at the instant when M is jerked into motion is $\dfrac{M}{m+M}$. **(M.U.)**

[**Hint:** If u, v, are the velocities of m before and after the system begins to move, $mu = (M+m)v$. If the initial K.E. of m is T, $T = \frac{1}{2}mu^2$ and loss in K. E. is $\frac{1}{2}mu^2 - \frac{1}{2}(m+M)v^2$ or $\dfrac{M}{m+M}T$]

14.2 IMPACT OF SPHERES

In this chapter we consider collision of two smooth spheres and that of a smooth sphere on a smooth plane.

14.2.1 Laws of impact

Law 1. As in explosion, the forces exerted in collision of two smooth spheres, are purely internal if the spheres are thought of to form a single unit. Hence by the conservation of momentum we get that

The momentum after collision is the same as the momentum before collision.

Law 2. (Newton's experimental law). When two balls collide, during the time in which the balls are in contact, they become distorted losing their original shapes. Though this distortion is a complicated process, it was observed from experiments by Newton that the relative speed along the line of centres of the balls after collision, bears a constant ratio to the relative speed before collision. This constant which depends chiefly on the materials of which the balls are composed and not on the size, is called the coefficient of restitution and is usually denoted by e. Further, it was observed that $0 < e < 1$. Thus

$$\left\{\begin{matrix}\textit{Component of the relative}\\ \textit{velocity after impact}\end{matrix}\right\} = -e\left\{\begin{matrix}\textit{Component of the relative}\\ \textit{velocity before impact}\end{matrix}\right\}.$$

Ideal cases. In the cases where $e = 0$, and $e = 1$ the balls are said to be inelastic and perfectly elastic. These cases are theoretical cases and do not happen in practice.

14.3 IMPACT OF TWO SMOOTH SPHERES

Suppose two smooth spheres collide with each other. In the infinitesimal interval of time during which the spheres are in contact, each is subject to the action of an impulsive force which is towards its centre. Thus there will be two impulsive forces acting on the spheres. By N. 3, they are equal in magnitude but opposite in direction. So also are the impulses imparted to the spheres.

Direct and oblique impacts. Impact of spheres can be classified into two groups, namely, direct and oblique impacts. If C_1 and C_2 are the positions of the centres of the spheres at the time of

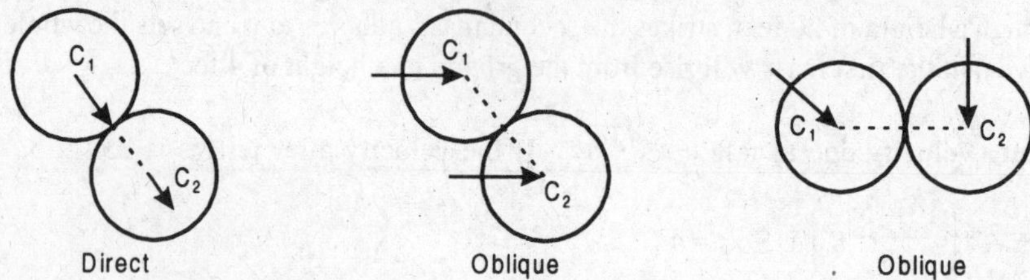

Direct Oblique Oblique

impact and if the centres of the spheres had been moving before the impact along the straight line through C_1 and C_2, then the impact is said to be *direct* ; otherwise , it is said to be *oblique.*

14.3.1 Direct impact of two smooth spheres

In this section, given the motion before impact of two smooth spheres, we obtain

(*i*) The motion after impact

(*ii*) The impulse imparted to each sphere due to impact

(*iii*) The change in K.E. due to impact.

Direction of velocity. In general, we choose the direction from left to right as the positive direction to denote the velocities. If the velocity in this direction is positive, then the sphere moves from left to right and if the velocity in this direction is negative , then the sphere moves from right to left.

Bookwork 14.1. To find the velocities of two smooth spheres after a direct impact between them.

Let us have the following assumptions :

m_1, m_2 : Masses of the spheres.

u_1, u_2 : Velocities of the spheres before impact ($u_1 > u_2$).

e : Coefficient of restitution

v_1, v_2 : Velocities of the spheres after impact.

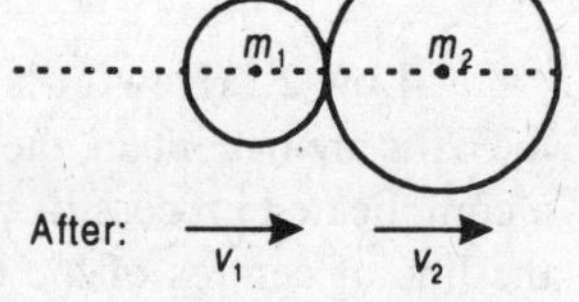

From the principle of conservation of linear momentum, the momentum after impact equals the momentum before impact. So

$$m_1v_1 + m_2v_2 = m_1u_1 + m_2u_2, \qquad ...(1)$$

and , from the Newton's experimental law, we have

$$v_1 - v_2 = -e\,(u_1 - u_2) \qquad ...(2)$$

(1) + $m_2 \times$ (2) and (1) – $m_1 \times$ (2) respectively give

$$(m_1 + m_2)v_1 = m_1u_1 + m_2u_2 + em_2(u_2 - u_1),$$

$$(m_1 + m_2)v_2 = m_1u_1 + m_2u_2 + em_1(u_1 - u_2)$$

and consequently, the velocities v_1 and v_2 after impact.

Bookwork 14.2. To show that, when two spheres of equal masses m collide directly, the velocities of the spheres are interchanged if $e = 1$.

With the notations as in the previous bookwork,

$$mv_1 + mv_2 = mu_1 + mu_2 \quad \text{or} \quad v_1 + v_2 = u_1 + u_2. \qquad ...(1)$$

$$v_1 - v_2 = -1(u_1 - u_2) \quad \text{or} \quad v_1 - v_2 = -u_1 + u_2. \qquad ...(2)$$

Solving (1) and (2), we get $v_1 = u_2, \quad v_2 = u_1$.

Bookwork 14.3. When two smooth spheres collide directly, to find the impulse imparted to each sphere and the change in the total kinetic energy of the spheres.

Let us make the same assumptions as in Bookwork 14.1. Furthermore let C_1 and C_2 be the centres of the spheres at the time of impact and $\overline{i}$, the unit vector in the direction of $\overline{C_1 C_2}$. Then, if I is the magnitude of the impulse imparted to each of the spheres, then the impulse imparted to the spheres C_2, is

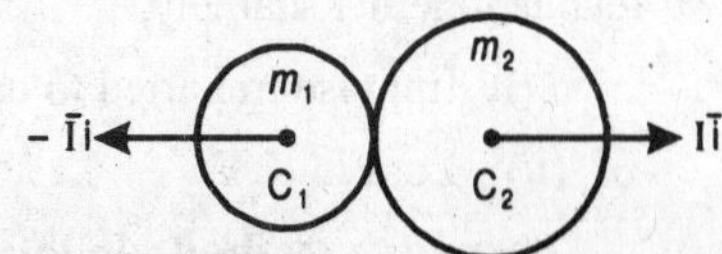

$$I\,\overline{i} = m_2v_2\,\overline{i} - m_2u_2\,\overline{i}$$

since the impulse imparted is the change in momentum. The impulse imparted to the sphere C_1 is

$$I\,(-\overline{i}) = m_1v_1\,\overline{i} - m_1u_1\,\overline{i}.$$

Thus we get the scalar relations

$$I = m_2(v_2 - u_2), \quad -I = m_1(v_1 - u_1). \qquad ...(1)$$

Dividing them respectively by m_2 and m_1 and subtracting, we get

$$I\left(\frac{1}{m_1} + \frac{1}{m_2}\right) = (v_2 - u_2) - (v_1 - u_1)$$

$$= -(v_1 - v_2) + (u_1 - u_2)$$

$$= e(u_1 - u_2) + (u_1 - u_2) \text{ by experimental law}$$

$$= (1+e)\,(u_1 - u_2).$$

$$\therefore \quad I = \frac{m_1m_2}{m_1 + m_2}(1+e)(u_1 - u_2). \qquad ...(2)$$

The total kinetic energies of the spheres after and before impact are

$$\tfrac{1}{2}m_1v_1^2 + \tfrac{1}{2}m_2v_2^2, \quad \tfrac{1}{2}m_1u_1^2 + \tfrac{1}{2}m_2u_2^2.$$

The increase in the kinetic energy due to impact is

$$\tfrac{1}{2}\{(m_1v_1^2 + m_2v_2^2) - (m_1u_1^2 + m_2u_2^2)\} = \tfrac{1}{2}\{(m_1(v_1^2 - u_1^2) + m_2(v_2^2 - u_2^2)\}$$

$$= \tfrac{1}{2}\{m_1(v_1 - u_1)(v_1 + u_1) + m_2(v_2 - u_2)(v_2 + u_2)\}$$

$$= \tfrac{1}{2}\{(-I)(v_1 + u_1) + (I)(v_2 + u_2)\} \text{ by (1)}$$

$$= -\tfrac{1}{2} I\{(v_1 + u_1) - (v_2 + u_2)\}.$$

$$= -\tfrac{1}{2} I\{(v_1 - v_2) + (u_1 - u_2)\}$$

$$= -\tfrac{1}{2} I\{-e\,(u_1 - u_2) + (u_1 - u_2)\} \text{ by experimental law}$$

$$= -\tfrac{1}{2} I(1-e)\,(u_1 - u_2)$$

$$= -\tfrac{1}{2}\frac{m_1\,m_2}{m_1 + m_2}(1+e)\,(1-e)\,(u_1 - u_2)^2 \quad \text{by} \quad (2)$$

$$= -\tfrac{1}{2}\frac{m_1\,m_2}{m_1 + m_2}(1-e^2)\,(u_1 - u_2)^2 \qquad \text{...(3)}$$

Since it is a negative quantity, there is actually a decrease in kinetic energy, that is, a loss in kinetic energy due to impact.

There is an alternative method to find the loss in K.E. However, in the first method we obtain two results together, namely,

(*i*) Impulse imparted to each sphere.

(*ii*) Loss in K.E.

Alternative method. In this method we use the identity

$$(m_1 + m_2)(m_1 v_1^2 + m_2 v_2^2) = (m_1 v_1 + m_2 v_2)^2 + m_1 m_2\,(v_1 - v_2)^2.$$

i.e., $$m_1 v_1^2 + m_2 v_2^2 = \frac{1}{m_1 + m_2}[(m_1 v_1 + m_2 v_2)^2 + m_1 m_2 (v_1 - v_2)^2]$$

i.e., $$\frac{1}{2} m_1 v_1^2 + \frac{1}{2} m_2 v_2^2 = \frac{1}{2}\frac{1}{m_1 + m_2}[(m_1 v_1 + m_2 v_2)^2 + m_1 m_2 (v_1 - v_2)^2]$$

Similarly we have

$$\frac{1}{2} m_1 u_1^2 + \frac{1}{2} m_2 u_2^2 = \frac{1}{2}\frac{1}{m_1 + m_2}[(m_1 u_1 + m_2 u_2)^2 + m_1 m_2\,(u_1 - u_2)^2].$$

By subtraction we get the change in kinetic energy as

$$\frac{1}{2}\frac{1}{m_1 + m_2}\{m_1 m_2 (v_1 - v_2)^2 - m_1 m_2\,(u_1 - u_2)^2\}$$

since $m_1 v_1 + m_2 v_2 = m_1 u_1 + m_2 u_2$

$$= \frac{1}{2}\frac{1}{m_1 + m_2}\{m_1\,m_2 e^2 (u_1 - u_2)^2 - m_1\,m_2\,(u_1 - u_2)^2\} \text{ by Newton's experimental law}$$

$$= -\frac{1}{2}\frac{m_1\,m_2}{m_1 + m_2}(1-e^2)\,(u_1 - u_2)^2.$$

Remark. Only in the ideal case where $e = 1$, the loss in kinetic energy is zero.

EXAMPLES

Example 1. The masses of three spheres A, B, C, are $7m, 7m, m$, their coefficient of restitution is unity. Their centres are in a straight line and C lies between A and B. Initially A and B are at rest and C is given a velocity in the line of centres in the direction of A. Show that it strikes A twice and B once, and that the final velocities of A, B, C are 21: 12 : 1. **(M.U.)**

For each impact we write down two equations which respectively arise out of the principle of conservation of linear momentum and the Newton's experimental law. We choose the left-to-right direction as the positive direction to denote the velocities.

Impact No. 1. This takes place between C and A. Let u be the initial velocity of C and v_1, v_2 the velocities of C, A after impact . Then

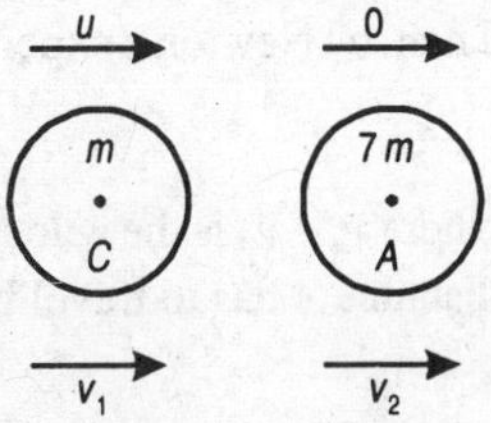

$$mv_1 + 7mv_2 = mu + 0$$

$$v_1 - v_2 = -1(u - 0).$$

$$\therefore \qquad v_1 = -\frac{3u}{4}, \quad v_2 = \frac{u}{4}.$$

Impact No.2. This takes place between B and C. Let w_1, w_2 be the velocities of B, C after impact. Then, omitting m,

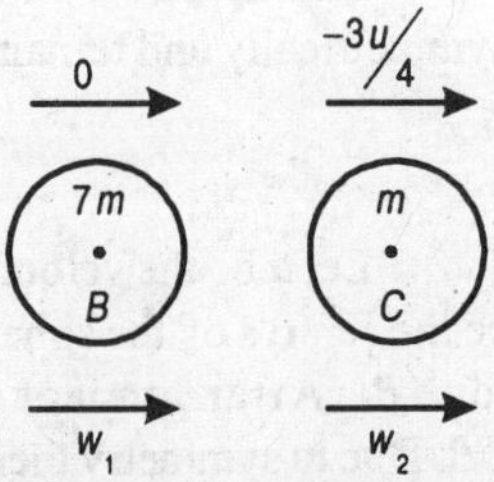

$$7w_1 + w_2 = 0 - \frac{3u}{4},$$

$$w_1 - w_2 = -(0 + \frac{3u}{4}).$$

$$\therefore \qquad w_1 = -\frac{3u}{16}, \quad w_2 = \frac{9u}{16}.$$

Impact No.3. This takes place between C and A. Let x_1, x_2 be the velocities of C, A after impact. Then omitting m,

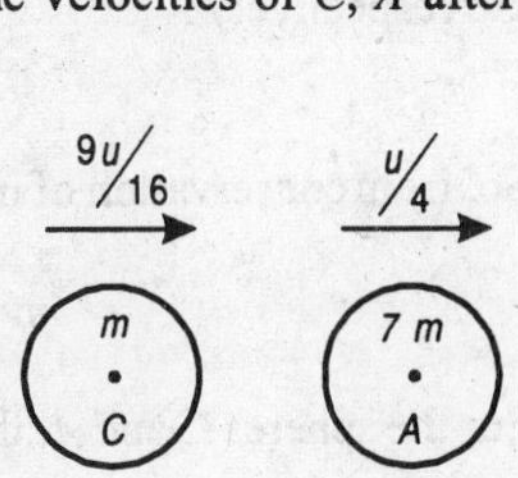

$$x_1 + 7x_2 = \frac{9u}{16} + \frac{7u}{4}$$

$$x_1 - x_2 = -\left(\frac{9u}{16} - \frac{u}{4}\right).$$

$$\therefore \qquad x_1 = \frac{u}{64}, \quad x_2 = \frac{21u}{64}.$$

Therefore the velocities of B, C, A after the third impact are

$$-\frac{3u}{16}, \frac{u}{64}, \frac{21u}{64}.$$

This shows that B moves to the left and C, A move to the right, where the velocity of C is less than that of A. So there is no further impact. The ratio of the final speeds of A, B, C is 21 : 12 : 1.

Example 2. Two spheres A and B of same size lie on a smooth, horizontal circular groove at opposite ends of a diameter. A is projected along the groove and after a time t it impinges upon B. Show that, if e is the coefficient of restitution, it then the second impact will occur after a time

$$\frac{2t}{e}.$$ **(Bn.U., M.U., C.U.)**

Let the velocity of projection of A be u. Then A has to travel a distance equal to half the perimeter to hit B. So

$$\pi a = u\,t.$$

Now the velocities of A, B before impact are

$$u,\ 0$$

and, after impact, let them be

$$v_1,\ v_2$$

Then, by Newton's experimental law,

$$v_1 - v_2 = -e\,(u - 0),$$

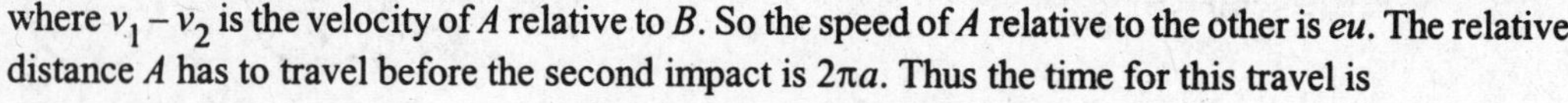

where $v_1 - v_2$ is the velocity of A relative to B. So the speed of A relative to the other is eu. The relative distance A has to travel before the second impact is $2\pi a$. Thus the time for this travel is

$$\frac{\text{Distance}}{\text{Speed}} = \frac{2\pi a}{eu} = \frac{2(ut)}{eu} = \frac{2t}{e}.$$

Example 3. Two equal balls of mass m are in contact on a table. A third equal ball strikes both symmetrically and remains at rest after impact. Show that

$$e = \frac{2}{3}.$$ **(M.U.)**

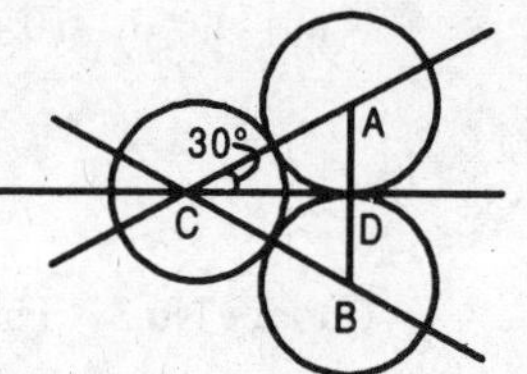

Let u be the velocity of the third sphere before impact. Let A, B, C be the centres of the spheres at the time of impact and CD, perpendicular to AB. After impact the first two spheres move along CA, CB. Due to symmetry their speeds are equal. Let them be v. The momenta of the spheres A, B, C before impact and after impact in the direction CD are respectively

$$0,\ 0,\ mu\ ; \quad mv\cos 30^\circ,\ mv\cos 30^\circ,\ 0.$$

So, from conservation of momentum,

$$mv\cos 30^\circ + mv\cos 30^\circ + 0 = 0 + 0 + mu \quad \text{or} \quad v = \frac{1}{\sqrt{3}}u. \qquad \text{...(1)}$$

For the spheres C and A, the experimental law is

$$0 - v = -e\,(u\cos 30^\circ - 0) \quad \text{or} \quad v = eu\frac{\sqrt{3}}{2}. \qquad \text{...(2)}$$

From (1) and (2), we get $e = 2/3$.

EXERCISES

1. A ball of mass 8 gm. moving with a velocity of 10 cm./sec. impinges directly on another of mass 24 gm., moving at 2 cm./sec. in the same direction. If $e = 1/2$, find the velocities after impact. Also calculate the loss in kinetic energy. **(C.U.)**

   [Hint: $8v_1 + 24v_2 = 8(10) + 24(2)$, $\ v_1 - v_2 = -\tfrac{1}{2}(10 - 2)$. So $v_1 = 1$, $v_2 = 5$, Loss in K.E. = 144]

2. A ball of mass m impinges on another of mass $2m$ which is moving in the same direction as the first but with one-seventh of its velocity. If $e = 3/4$, show that the first ball is reduced to rest after impact. **(M.U., Bn.U.)**

[**Hint:** $mv_1 + 2mv_2 = mu + 2m\frac{u}{7}, \quad v_1 - v_2 = -\frac{3}{4}\left(u - \frac{u}{7}\right)$.]

3. A ball A impinges directly on an exactly equal and similar ball B lying on a horizontal plane. If the coefficient of restitution is e, prove that after impact, the velocity of B will be to that of A is as

$$1 + e : 1 - e.$$ **(M.U., M.K.U.)**

[**Hint:** $mv_1 + mv_2 = mu + 0; \quad v_1 - v_2 = -e(u - 0)$. Find $v_2 : v_1$]

4. Two perfectly elastic smooth spheres of masses m and $3m$ are moving with equal momentum in the same straight line and in the same direction. Show that the smaller sphere is reduced to rest after it strikes the other. **(M.U.)**

[**Hint:** Masses m, $3m$; $e = 1$, $u_1 = u$, $u_2 = u/3$; $mv_1 + 3mv_2 = mu + 3m(u/3)$; $v_1 - v_2 = -(u - u/3)$. Solving $v_1 = 0$]

5. A ball impinges directly on another ball, m times its mass, which is moving with $1/n$ times its velocity in the same direction. If the impact reduces the first ball to rest, prove that

(*i*) $e = \dfrac{m + n}{m(n-1)}$. **(M.U., M.K.U., K.U.)**

(*ii*) m must be greater than $\dfrac{n}{n-2}$. **(M.U., Bn.U.)**

[**Hint:** Masses : M, mM; Velocities (before and after) : u, u/n ; $0, v; 0 + mMv = Mu + mM(u/n)$;

$0 - v = -e(u - u/n)$; Divide one by the other. $m > \dfrac{n}{n-2}$ follows from $e < 1$]

6. A ball of mass $2m$ impinges directly on a ball of mass m which is at rest. If the velocity after impact of the latter ball is equal to that of the former before impact, show that the coefficient of restitution is $\frac{1}{2}$. **(M.U., Bn.U.)**

7. Two balls impinge directly and interchange their velocities after impact. Prove that they are perfectly elastic and are of equal masses. **(M.U., M.K.U.)**

[**Hint:** If the velocities before impact are u_1, u_2, then the velocities after impact are u_2, u_1.
(*i*) $m_1u_2 + m_2u_1 = m_1u_1 + m_2u_2$ or $(m_1 - m_2)(u_1 - u_2) = 0$ or $m_1 = m_2$.
(*ii*) $(u_2 - u_1) = -e(u_1 - u_2)$ or $(u_1 - u_2)(1 - e) = 0$ or $e = 1$]

8. A body of mass 3 gm. moving with a velocity of 15 cm./sec. collides with a body of mass 2 gm. moving in the same direction with a velocity of 5 cm./sec. If they coalesce into one body, find the velocity of the coalesced body. **(M.U.)**

[**Hint:** If v is the common velocity after coalescence, by " Momentum (after) = momentum (before)", $(3 + 2)v = 3 \times 15 + 2 \times 5$ or $v = 11$]

9. Two spheres of equal mass moving in the same straight line with velocities u, u' collide and rebound, the coefficient of restitution being $1/2$. Prove that exactly half the energy is lost in collision if

$$(1-\sqrt{2})\,u = (1+\sqrt{2})\,u'. \qquad \textbf{(M.U.)}$$

[Hint: $\frac{1}{2}\frac{m_1\,m_2}{m_1+m_2}(1-e^2)(u_1-u_2)^2 = \frac{1}{2}\left(\frac{1}{2}m_1\,u_1^{\ 2} + \frac{1}{2}m_2\,u_2^{\ 2}\right)$, where $m_1 = m_2 = m,\ u_1 = u,\ u_2 = u',\ e = \frac{1}{2}$. Get $u = -(3+2\sqrt{2})\,u'$ **]**

10. *A, B, C* are three smooth spheres of same size and of masses *m*, 2*m*, and *m* respectively lying in a straight line on a smooth horizontal table. *A* is projected along the line *ABC* with a velocity *u*. If the coefficient of restitution is 0·5, show that after *B* strikes *C*, the velocities of *A, B, C* are in the ratio 0 : 1 : 2 and that there are no further impacts. **(M.U.)**

11. Three equal spheres are in a straight line on a table and one of them moves towards the other two which are at rest and not in contact. If $e = \frac{1}{2}$, show that there will be three impacts and that the ultimate speeds of the spheres are in the ratio 13 : 15 : 36. **(M.U.)**

12. Three balls of masses m_1, m_2 and m_3 of same size for which *e* is the same, are lying in a straight line. m_1 is projected with a given velocity so as to impinge on m_2 which in its turn impinges on m_3. If each impinging ball after impact is reduced to rest, prove that $m_2^{\ 2} = m_1\,m_3$ and find the velocity of the third ball after impact with the second.

[Hint: If the velocity of the first ball is *u* and if it is reduced to rest by the impact, then, by experimental law, the velocity of the second ball is *ue* and similarly the final velocity of the third ball is (*ue*) *e* or ue^2. The conservation of momentum gives $m_1 u = m_2 ue$, $m_2\,eu = m_3 ue^2$ which give $m_2^{\ 2} = m_1 m_3$ **]**

13. Three perfectly elastic smooth spheres whose masses are as 1 : 3 : 6 move with equal momentum in a straight line. Show that each of the two smaller spheres will be reduced to rest when it impinges the sphere in front of it. **(M.U.)**

14. Three spherical balls of masses m_1, *m*, m_2 are placed with their centres in a line. m_1 is projected with a velocity *v* towards *m* which in turn strikes m_2. If *v*, m_1, m_2 are given, show that the value of *m* for which the velocity communicated to m_2 is a maximum is the geometric mean of m_1 and m_2. **(M.U.)**

[Hint: Velocity V of $m_2 = (1+e)^2\ vm_1\ \frac{m}{(m+m_1)\,(m+m_2)}$; $\frac{dV}{dm} = 0$ gives $m = \sqrt{m_1 m_2}$ **]**

14.4 IMPACT OF A SMOOTH SPHERE ON A PLANE

In this section we consider a smooth sphere impinging on a fixed plane.

Direct and oblique impacts. If a sphere collides with a plane with its centre moving along a normal to the plane, then the collision is said to be direct; otherwise, it is said to be oblique.

14.4.1 Direct impact of a smooth sphere on a plane.

Bookwork 14.4. A smooth sphere impinges directly on a fixed plane with a velocity *u*. To find its velocity of rebound and the loss in its kinetic energy due to impact and the impulse imparted to the sphere.

Velocity of rebound. Let *v* be the velocity of rebound and *e*, the coefficient of restitution. Then we can get *v* using only Newton's experimental law. Since the plane is fixed, its velocity before and after impact are zero and so the relative velocity of the sphere before and after impact are

$$u-0,\ -v-0.$$

$$\therefore \quad (-v-0) = -\,e(u-0) \quad \text{or} \quad v = eu.$$

That is, the velocity of rebound is a reduced velocity eu because $e < 1$.

Loss in K. E. If m is the mass of the sphere, then the increase in K.E. due to impact is

$$\tfrac{1}{2}mv^2 - \tfrac{1}{2}mu^2 = \tfrac{1}{2}me^2u^2 - \tfrac{1}{2}mu^2$$

$$= -\tfrac{1}{2}mu^2(1-e^2)$$

Since $e^2 < 1$, there is actually a loss in K.E. which is $\tfrac{1}{2}mu^2(1-e^2)$.

Impulse imparted to the sphere. At the time of collision, the sphere is subject to the action of an impulsive force by the plane in the direction of the sphere. In this direction the change in momentum of the sphere is

$$mv - (-mu) \quad \text{or} \quad mu(1+e)$$

which is the impulse imparted to the sphere.

14.4.2 Oblique impact of a smooth sphere on a plane

Bookwork 14.5. A smooth sphere of mass m collides obliquely with a fixed smooth plane with a velocity u inclined to the normal to the plane at an angle α. To find its velocity of rebound, the loss in its kinetic energy and the impulse imparted to it.

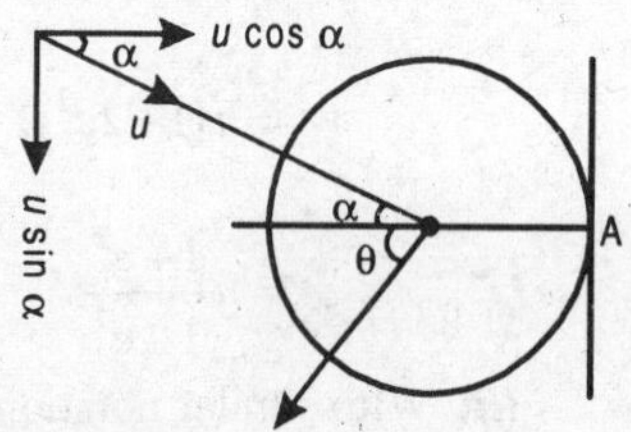

Before impact, the components of the velocity of the sphere in the directions normal to and parallel to the plane are

$$u\cos\alpha,\ u\sin\alpha.$$

Since the sphere is smooth, the velocity component parallel to the plane is unaltered by impact and so, after impact, it is

$$u\sin\alpha$$

itself. But the impact reduces the normal component of velocity $u\cos\alpha$ (before impact) to

$$eu\cos\alpha.$$

Therefore the velocity of rebound is

$$\sqrt{(u\sin\alpha)^2 + (eu\cos\alpha)^2} \quad \text{or} \quad u\sqrt{\sin^2\alpha + e^2\cos^2\alpha}$$

in the direction inclined to the normal to the plane at an angle θ given by

$$\tan\theta = \frac{u\sin\alpha}{eu\cos\alpha} = \frac{\tan\alpha}{e}. \qquad \text{...(1)}$$

Note. Since $e < 1$, $\theta > \alpha$.

Loss in K.E. If m is the mass of the sphere, then the increase in K. E. is

$$\tfrac{1}{2}mu^2(\sin^2\alpha + e^2\cos^2\alpha) - \tfrac{1}{2}mu^2 = \tfrac{1}{2}mu^2(1-\cos^2\alpha + e^2\cos^2\alpha - 1)$$

$$= -\tfrac{1}{2}mu^2(1-e^2)\cos^2\alpha.$$

Thus the loss in K.E. is $\tfrac{1}{2}mu^2(1-e^2)\cos^2\alpha$.

Impulse imparted to the sphere. At the time of collision, the sphere is subject to the action of an impulsive force by the plane in the direction opposite to the direction of the sphere. In this direction the change in momentum of the sphere is

$$m(eu\cos\alpha) - m(-u\cos\alpha) = m(1+e)u\cos\alpha.$$

EXAMPLES

Example 1. A ball dropped from a height h on a horizontal plane bounces up and down. If the coefficient of restitution is e, prove that

(*i*) The whole distance H covered before it comes to rest is $h\dfrac{1+e^2}{1-e^2}$ **(M.U.,M.K.U.)**

(*ii*) The total time T taken is $\dfrac{1+e}{1-e}\sqrt{\dfrac{2h}{g}}$. **(M.U., C.U.)**

(*i*) If v is the velocity at the end of the first fall, $v^2 = 2gh$. The velocity of the succeeding rebounds are

$$ev,\ e^2v,\ e^3v,........$$

and the respective maximum heights, namely, $h_1,\ h_2,\ h_3,......$, are given by

$$(ev)^2 = 2gh_1,\quad (e^2v)^2 = 2gh_2,\quad (e^3v)^2 = 2gh_3,.......$$

$$\therefore \quad H = h + 2h_1 + 2h_2 + ... = \frac{v^2}{2g}[1 + 2e^2 + 2e^4 + ...]$$

$$= h\,[1+2e^2(1+e^2+e^4+.....)] = h\left[1+\frac{2e^2}{1-e^2}\right]$$

$$= h\frac{1+e^2}{1-e^2}.$$

(*ii*) With similar notations, if v is the velocity acquired in falling during a time t, then $v = gt$. Thus

$$T = t + 2t_1 + 2t_2 + ... = \frac{v}{g} + 2\frac{ev}{g} + 2\frac{e^2v}{g} + ...$$

$$= \frac{v}{g}[1+2e+2e^2+.....] = \frac{\sqrt{2gh}}{g}[1+2e(1+e+e^2+.....)]$$

$$= \sqrt{\frac{2h}{g}}\left(1+\frac{2e}{1-e}\right) = \sqrt{\frac{2h}{g}}\,\frac{1+e}{1-e}.$$

Example 2. A small ball A impinges directly upon an equal ball B. Then B strikes a cushion which is at right angles to the direction of motion of B and, after rebounding, meets A at a point exactly halfway between the cushion and its own initial position. If the coefficient of restitution between the balls is e and that between the ball and the cushion is e', then show that

$$e' = \frac{1-e}{3e-1}. \qquad \textbf{(A.U.)}$$

If the initial velocity of A is u, and the velocities of A, B after impact are v_1, v_2 then, omitting m's,

$$v_1 + v_2 = u,$$
$$v_1 - v_2 = -eu.$$

$$\therefore \quad v_1 = \tfrac{1}{2}(1-e)u,$$
$$v_2 = \tfrac{1}{2}(1+e)u,$$

u d
A B

If the distance between B and the cushion is d, then the distances travelled by B, with different velocities, before colliding with A again, are d, $d/2$ and the distance travelled by A is $d/2$. Since the velocity of rebound of B from the cushion is

$$e'[\tfrac{1}{2}(1+e)u],$$

The respective three times of travels of B, A are

$$t_1 = \frac{d}{\frac{1}{2}(1+e)u},\quad t_2 = \frac{d/2}{e'[\frac{1}{2}(1+e)u]},\quad t_1+t_2 = \frac{d/2}{\frac{1}{2}(1-e)u}.$$

$$\therefore\quad \frac{2}{1+e} + \frac{1}{e'(1+e)} = \frac{1}{1-e} \quad \text{or} \quad e' = \frac{1-e}{3e-1}.$$

Example 3. A smooth circular table is surrounded by a smooth rim whose interior surface is vertical. Show that a ball projected along the table from a point A on the rim in a direction making an angle α with the radius through A will return to the point of projection after two impacts if

$$\tan\alpha = \frac{e^{3/2}}{\sqrt{1+e+e^2}}.$$ **(M.U., M.K.U.)**

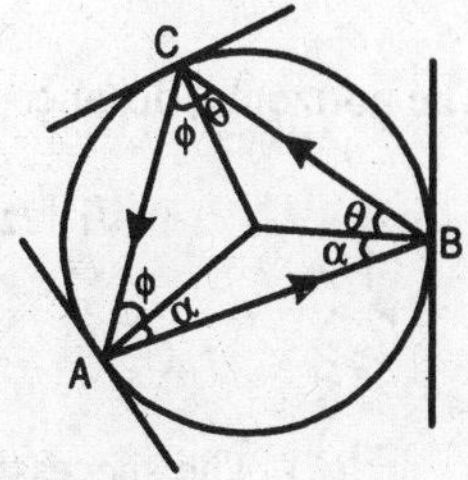

Let the ball impinge the rim at B and C and then return to A. Immediately after the projection, the path of the ball is inclined to the normal at A at an angle α. So also, before the impact at B, the path is inclined to the normal at B at an angle α. Let the path make an angle θ with the normal at B after impact at B. Then, by (1) of bookwork, 14.5,

$$\tan\theta = \frac{\tan\alpha}{e}.$$

Similarly, if the path is inclined to the normal at C at an angle ϕ, after impact at C,

$$\tan\phi = \frac{\tan\theta}{e} \quad \text{or} \quad \tan\phi = \frac{\tan\alpha}{e^2}.$$

Now $2\alpha + 2\theta + 2\phi = 180°$. So $\alpha = 90° - (\theta+\phi)$ and

$$\tan\alpha = \tan[90° - (\theta+\phi)] = \cot(\theta+\phi) = \frac{1}{\tan(\theta+\phi)}$$

$$= \frac{1-\tan\theta\tan\phi}{\tan\theta+\tan\phi} = \frac{1-\dfrac{\tan\alpha}{e}\cdot\dfrac{\tan\alpha}{e^2}}{\dfrac{\tan\alpha}{e}+\dfrac{\tan\alpha}{e^2}}$$

or $$\tan^2\alpha\left(\frac{1}{e}+\frac{1}{e^2}\right) = 1 - \frac{1}{e^3}\tan^2\alpha$$

from which the result follows as stated.

Example 4. **(*i*)** A particle is projected from a point in a smooth fixed horizontal plane with velocity u at an elevation α. Show that the particle ceases to rebound from the plane at the end of time

$\dfrac{2u\sin\alpha}{g(1-e)}$ and that the total horizontal distance described in this period is $\dfrac{u^2\sin 2\alpha}{g(1-e)}$, where e is the coefficient of restitution. **(M.U., M.K.U.)**

(*ii*) Show that the spans of successive rebounds a decreasing G.P as well as the maximum heights of the particle. **(A.U.)**

Let O be the point of projection. Let A_1, A_2, A_3,......... be the points at which the ball impinges the plane, and t_1, t_2, t_3,........ the times of flight from O to A_1, from A_1 to A_2, etc. The vertical and horizontal components of the initial velocity of projection are

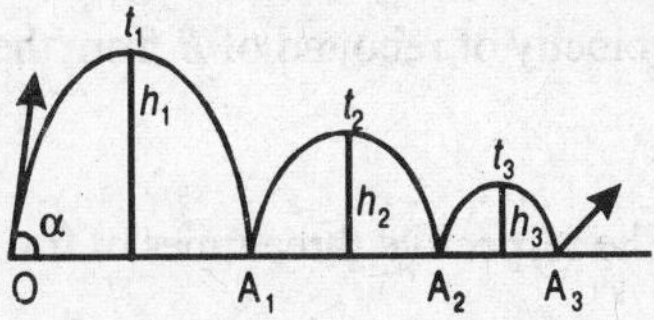

$$u \sin\alpha,\ u \cos\alpha.$$

So the vertical component of the velocity of hit at A_1 is u sin α and the vertical components of the velocities of rebounds at A_1, A_2, A_3,....... are

$$e\,(u \sin\alpha),\ e^2(u \sin\alpha),\ e^3(u \sin\alpha), \qquad ...(1)$$

$$\therefore \quad t_1 = \frac{2u\sin\alpha}{g},\ t_2 = \frac{2(eu)\sin\alpha}{g},\ t_3 = \frac{2(e^2u)\sin\alpha}{g},...... \qquad ...(2)$$

$$\therefore \quad t_1 + t_2 + t_3 + ... = \frac{2u \sin\alpha}{g}(1 + e + e^2 + ...)$$

$$= \frac{2u \sin\alpha}{g}\frac{1}{1-e}.$$

The horizontal distance travelled in this time is

$$(t_1 + t_2 + t_3 + ...)\,(u \cos\alpha) = \frac{2u \sin\alpha}{g}\frac{1}{1-e}u \cos\alpha$$

$$= \frac{u^2 \sin 2\alpha}{g}\frac{1}{1-e}.$$

(*ii*) The successive spans are the ranges which are

$$t_1\, u \cos\alpha,\ t_2\, u \cos\alpha,\ t_3\, u \cos\alpha,.....$$

i.e., by (2), they are

$$R,\ Re,\ Re^2,.....,\text{where } R = \frac{u^2 \sin 2\alpha}{g},$$

which are in G.P with the common ratio e.

If v is the vertical component of the velocity of rebound, then the maximum height h attained is given by

$$v^2 = 2gh \quad \text{as} \quad h = \frac{v^2}{2g}.$$

Therefore, from (1), the maximum heights attained by the particle are

$$\frac{1}{2g}(u \sin\alpha)^2,\ \frac{1}{2g}(eu \sin\alpha)^2,\ \frac{1}{2g}(e^2u \sin\alpha)^2,.......$$

which are in a G.P. with the common ratio e^2.

Example 5. A particle is projected from a point on an inclined plane and at the rth impact it strikes the plane perpendicularly and at the nth impact is at the point of projection. Show that

$$e^n - 2e^r + 1 = 0. \qquad \textbf{(M.U.)}$$

Let t_1, t_2, t_3..... be the times of flights for the first, second , third,.... spans. First we shall consider the motion in the direction normal to the plane, in the upward sense. In each span the initial and final velocities in this direction are equal but opposite in direction because the acceleration in this direction is a constant, namely, $-g \cos \beta$. Also the normal rebound velocity equals e times the normal velocity of hit. Therefore, in this direction, the initial velocities for the spans are

$$v \text{ (say)}, \; ev, \; e^2v, \ldots\ldots$$

Thus, by $s = ut + \frac{1}{2} at^2$, we have for the first span

$$0 = vt_1 - \tfrac{1}{2} g \cos \beta \;\; t_1^2 \quad \text{or} \quad t_1 = \frac{2v}{g \cos \beta}.$$

Similarly, for the other spans,

$$t_2 = \frac{2ev}{g \cos \beta}, \; t_3 = \frac{2e^2 v}{g \cos \beta}, \ldots\ldots$$

If the total time for r spans is T_r, then

$$T_r = t_1 + t_2 + t_3 + \ldots\ldots + t_r$$

$$= \frac{2v}{g \cos \beta}(1 + e + e^2 + \ldots\ldots + e^{r-1}) = \frac{2v}{g \cos \beta} \frac{1-e^r}{1-e}.$$

In the rth span, the final velocity of the ball is perpendicular to the plane. That is, at $t = T_r$, the velocity along the plane is zero and thereafter the downward motion follows. The return motion upto the point of projection takes the same time T_r since the velocity along the plane is unaffected by impacts and the acceleration is a constant, namely, $-g \sin \beta$.

$$\therefore \quad T_n = T_r + T_r \quad \text{or} \quad T_n = 2T_r.$$

$$\therefore \quad \frac{2v}{g \cos \beta} \frac{1-e^n}{1-e} = 2 \frac{2v}{g \cos \beta} \frac{1-e^r}{1-e}.$$

$$\therefore \quad 1 - e^n = 2(1 - e^r) \quad \text{or} \quad e^n - 2e^r + 1 = 0.$$

Example 6. *(i)* An elastic ball falls through a height h and impinges at A on a smooth plane inclined at an angle β to the horizontal. Show that, if the ball impinges on the inclined plane again at B and if e is the coefficient of restitution, then

$$AB = 4he(e+1) \sin \beta. \qquad \textbf{(M.U., C.U., M.K.U.)}$$

(ii) If the ball falls through a height 20 m. and if the plane is inclined at 30° to the horizontal and if the ball descends to the bottom B in 3 jumps which is 12 m. below the point of hitting, along the plane, show that

$$e(1+e)(1+e^2)(1+e+e^2) = 0{\cdot}3 \qquad \textbf{(M.U., M.K.U.)}$$

(*i*) If the ball hits the plane with a velocity v, then

$$v^2 = 2gh. \qquad \ldots(1)$$

The component of v normal to the plane is

$$v \cos \beta$$

and the component of the velocity of rebound normal to the plane is

$$ev \cos \beta.$$

In this direction the acceleration of the ball is

$$-g \cos \beta$$

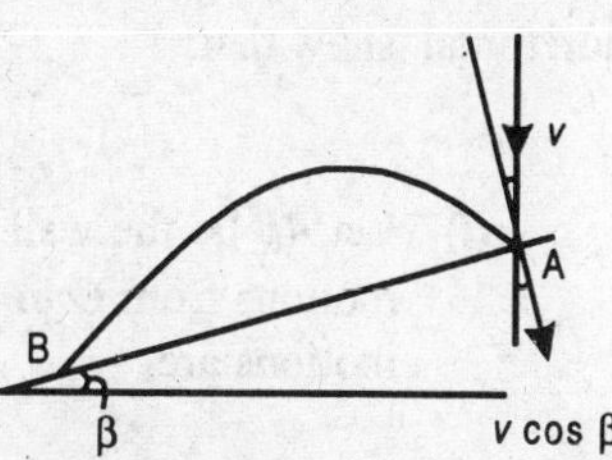

and the distance of the ball from the plane is zero when the ball hits the plane again. Then, for the corresponding time interval t_1, from $s = ut + \frac{1}{2}at^2$, we have

$$0 = ev\cos\beta\, t_1 - \tfrac{1}{2} g\cos\beta\, t_1^2 \text{ or } t_1 = \frac{2ev}{g}. \qquad \text{...(2)}$$

But, for the displacement AB down the plane, we have

Initial velocity : $v\sin\beta$

Acceleration : $g\sin\beta$

Time : t_1

$$\therefore \quad AB = v\sin\beta\, t_1 + \tfrac{1}{2} g\sin\beta\, t_1^2$$

$$= 4he(e+1)\sin\beta \text{ by (1), (2).} \qquad \text{...(3)}$$

(*ii*) If the time interval for the second and the third jumps are t_2, t_3, then, as in (2), we get

$$t_2 = \frac{2e^2v}{g}, \qquad t_3 = \frac{2e^3v}{g}$$

and thus the total time T for the 3 jumps is

$$T = \frac{2v}{g}e(1+e+e^2).$$

Now, as in (3), we have

$$AB = v\sin\beta\, T + \tfrac{1}{2} g\sin\beta\, T^2$$

$$= v\sin\beta\,\frac{2v}{g}e(1+e+e^2) + \tfrac{1}{2} g\sin\beta\left[\frac{2v}{g}e(1+e+e^2)\right]^2$$

$$= e(1+e+e^2)\left[\frac{2v^2}{g}\sin\beta + \frac{2v^2}{g}\sin\beta\, e(1+e+e^2)\right]$$

Substituting $v^2 = 2g(20)$, $\beta = 30°$, $AB = 12$, we get

$$e(1+e+e^2)\left[40 + 40e(1+e+e^2)\right] = 12$$

$$\therefore \quad e(1+e+e^2)\left[(1+e)(1+e^2)\right] = 0{\cdot}3.$$

Example 7. (*i*) A sphere projected from a given point O with given velocity u at an inclination α to the horizontal, after hitting a smooth vertical wall at a distance d from O, returns to O. If e is the coefficient of restitution, show that

$$d = \frac{u^2\sin 2\alpha}{g}\cdot\frac{e}{1+e} \qquad \textbf{(M.U., M.K.U.)}$$

(*ii*) If the line joining the point of projection and the point of impact makes an angle θ with the horizontal, show that

$$(1+e)\tan\theta = \tan\alpha. \qquad \textbf{(M.U.)}$$

(*i*) Let AB be the wall and A, the point where the ball hits it. Let t_1, t_2 be the times for the motions from O to A and back to O. The horizontal component of velocity in these two motions are

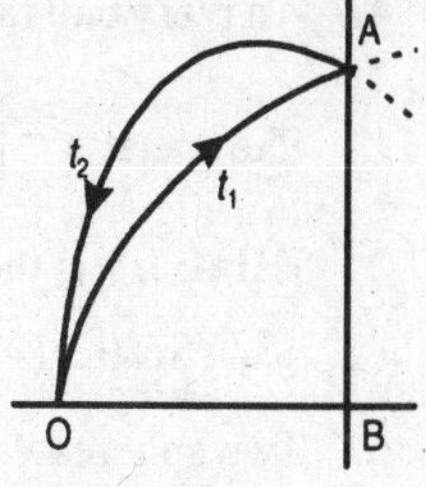

$$u \cos \alpha, \quad eu \cos \alpha.$$

$$\therefore \quad d = u \cos \alpha \, t_1, \quad d = (eu \cos \alpha)\, t_2.$$

Due to the hit the vertical component of the velocity is not altered since the wall is smooth. So, for the vertical displacement in the entire motion from O to A and then back to O, using $s = ut + \frac{1}{2}at^2$,we get

$$0 = u \sin \alpha\,(t_1 + t_2) - \tfrac{1}{2}g(t_1 + t_2)^2 \quad \text{or} \quad t_1 + t_2 = \frac{2u \sin \alpha}{g}.$$

$$\therefore \quad \frac{d}{u \cos \alpha} + \frac{d}{eu \cos \alpha} = \frac{2u \sin \alpha}{g} \quad \text{or} \quad d\left(1 + \frac{1}{e}\right) = \frac{u^2 \sin 2\alpha}{g}.$$

$$\therefore \quad d = \frac{u^2 \sin 2\alpha}{g} \cdot \frac{e}{1+e}. \qquad ...(1)$$

(ii) The point of impact is $(d, d \tan \theta)$ which satisfies the equation of the trajectory

$$y = x \tan \alpha - \frac{gx^2}{2u^2 \cos^2 \alpha}.$$

$$\therefore \quad d \tan \theta = d \tan \alpha - \frac{gd^2}{2u^2 \cos^2 \alpha} \quad \text{or} \quad \tan \theta = \tan \alpha - \frac{gd}{2u^2 \cos^2 \alpha}.$$

Substituting the value of d obtained in (1),

$$\tan \theta = \tan \alpha - \frac{g}{2u^2 \cos^2 \alpha} \cdot \frac{u^2 \sin 2\alpha}{g} \cdot \frac{e}{1+e} = \frac{\tan \alpha}{1+e}.$$

$$\therefore \quad (1+e) \tan \theta = \tan \alpha.$$

EXERCISES

1. A particle falls from a height h in time t upon a fixed horizontal plane. Prove that it rebounds and reaches the maximum height $e^2 h$ in time et and the loss in K.E in the hit is $mgh(1-e^2)$.

(Bn.U., M.K.U., M.U.)

[Hint: Let v be the velocity developed in the fall. Then $v = gt$ and $v^2 = 2gh$. Velocity of rebound is ev. If H is the max. ht. and T, the time, $0^2 = (e\,v)^2 - 2g\,H$, $0 = e\,v - g\,T$. Loss in K.E $= \frac{1}{2}mv^2 - \frac{1}{2}m(ev)^2$]

2. A ball is dropped from the ceiling of a room. After rebounding twice from the floor it reaches a height equal to one half of that of the room. Show that its coefficient of restitution is $(1/2)^{1/4}$.

(M.U., M.K.U.)

[Hint: Ceiling ht : h; If v is the velocity developed in falling through h, $v^2 = 2gh$. Velocity after the second rebound is $e^2 v$. So $0 = (e^2 v)^2 - 2g(h/2)$]

3. A ball falls from a height of 64 cm. on a smooth horizontal plane. If the coefficient of restitution is $1/2$, find the height to which it rises after rebounding four times. (C.U.)

[Hint: If v is the velocity developed in the fall, $v^2 = 2g(64)$. Velocity after fourth rebound is $e^4 v$. So $(e^4 v)^2 = 2gh$ or $h = 1/4$]

4. An ivory ball falling from a height of 100 cm. rises to a height of 46 cm. after rebounding twice.

Show that $e = \left(\frac{23}{50}\right)^{1/4}$ **(M.K.U.)**

[**Hint:** If v is the velocity of the fall, $v^2 = 2g(100)$ and the velocity after the second rebound is $e^2 v$. So $0 = (e^2 v)^2 - 2g\,(46)$]

5. Two spheres A and B of same size and of masses 2 kg. and 30 kg. respectively lie on a smooth floor so that their line of centres is perpendicular to a fixed vertical wall, A being nearer to the wall. A is projected towards B. Show that, if the coefficient of restitution between the two spheres and that between the first sphere and the wall is $3/5$, then A will be reduced to rest after its second impact with B. **(M.U., C.U., K.U., M.K.U.)**

[**Hint:** The velocities of A, B, before and after their successive impacts, in the direction from the wall to the balls, are

(*i*) $u,\ 0$; (*ii*) $-\frac{u}{2},\ \frac{u}{10}$; (*iii*) $\frac{3u}{10},\ \frac{u}{10}$; (*iv*) $0,\ \frac{3u}{25}$]

6. Hailstones are observed to strike the surface of a frozen lake in a direction making an angle of 30° with the vertical and to rebound at an angle of 60°. Assuming the contact to be smooth, find e. **(M.U.)**

[**Hint:** In $\tan\theta = (1/e)\tan\alpha$, set $\alpha = 30^\circ, \theta = 60^\circ$: So $e = 1/3$]

7. A smooth ball impinges on a fixed plane. If its direction is deviated by impact through a right angle show that the coefficient of restitution is $\tan^2\alpha$, where α is the angle made by the direction of the ball before impact with the normal to the plane. **(M.U.)**

[**Hint:** In $\tan\theta = (1/e)\tan\alpha$, $\alpha + \theta = 90^\circ$ or $\theta = 90^\circ - \alpha$]

8. A smooth elliptical tray is surrounded by a smooth vertical rim. Prove that a perfectly elastic ball projected from a focus along the tray in any direction will after two impacts return to the focus. **(M.U.)**

[**Hint:** In an ellipse, the normal PN at any point on it bisects the angle SPS'. Now $e = 1$ and so $\alpha = \theta$. That is, a ball travelling along SP, after the hit, travels along PS'.]

9. A billiard ball of coefficient of elasticity e is projected from the centre O of a billiard table $ABCD$, where $AB = CD = 2a$ and $BC = AD = 2b$ so as to return to O after three impacts, first with AB, then with BC and afterwards with CD. Show that, if α is the angle the direction of projection makes with AB,

$$\tan\alpha = \frac{b\,(1+e)}{ae}.$$ **(M.U.)**

[**Hint:** Let the path be the quadrilateral $OPQR$ and the times to travel along OP, PQ, QR, RO be t_1, t_2, t_3, t_4. If the initial velocity has components u, v parallel to AB, CB, then $\tan\alpha = v/u$.

$$vt_1 = b,\ u(t_1+t_2) = a,\ ev(t_2+t_3) = 2b,\ eu(t_3+t_4) = a,\ e^2vt_4 = b.$$

Substitute in $t_1 - (t_1+t_2) + (t_2+t_3) - (t_3+t_4) + t_4 = 0$.]

10. A ball falls vertically for 2 seconds and hits a plane inclined at 30° to the horizon. If the coefficient of restitution is $3/4$, show that the time that elapses before it again hits the plane is 3 seconds. **(M.U., M.K.U.)**

[**Hint:** The ball falls vertically and hits the plane with a velocity $\frac{1}{2}gt^2$ or $2g$. Its component normal to the plane is $2g\cos 30°$ and the velocity component of rebound normal to the plane is $\frac{3}{4}(2g\cos 30°)$. In this direction acceleration is $-g\cos 30°$ and distance is zero when the ball hits the plane again. Thus $0 = \frac{3}{4}(2g\cos 30°)\,t - \frac{1}{2}(g\cos 30°)\,t^2$]

11. A ball is projected from a point on a smooth horizontal plane with a velocity u at an elevation α and it continues to rebound. Show that, if the coefficient of restitution is e, the range between the nth and $(n+1)^{th}$ impacts is

$$\frac{u^2 e^n \sin 2\alpha}{g}.$$

(M.U.)

[**Hint:** The velocity of nth rebound has a vertical component $e^n(u\sin\alpha)$ and a horizontal component $u\cos\alpha$.]

$$\therefore \text{ Range} = \frac{2\,(\text{vertical component} \times \text{horizontal component})}{g} = \frac{e^n(u^2\sin 2\alpha)}{g}\ ]$$

12. A ball is projected at an angle α and from a point on a smooth horizontal plane. After hitting the plane, the ball rebounds and describes a second trajectory whose range is equal to the greatest height to which the ball rises above the plane. Show that, if e is the coefficient of restitution. $\tan\alpha = 4e$. **(A.U.)**

[**Hint:** Range after the first impact $= \frac{2}{g}(eu\sin\alpha)(u\cos\alpha)$. But the greatest height is in the first range and it is $\frac{u^2\sin^2\alpha}{2g}$]

13. A ball is projected with a velocity of $24\sqrt{3}$ ft./ sec. at an elevation of 45°. It strikes a wall at a distance of 18 ft. and returns to the point of projection. Show that $e = \frac{1}{2}$. **(M.K.U., K.U.)**

[**Hint:** $t_1 = \dfrac{18}{v\cos\alpha}$, $t_2 = \dfrac{18}{ev\cos\alpha}$, $0 = v\sin\alpha - \frac{1}{2}g(t_1+t_2)$,
where $v = 24\sqrt{3}$, $\alpha = 45°$, $g = 32$. Eliminate t_1, t_2]

14. A ball is projected at an elevation α with a velocity v from a point in a horizontal plane and it impinges on a smooth vertical wall at a distance d from the point of projection. If e is the coefficient of restitution and if the ball rebounds to a point on the plane at a distance a from the wall, then

$$a = e\left(\frac{v^2\sin 2\alpha}{g} - d\right).$$

(Bn., U.)

[**Hint:** $v\cos\alpha\, t_1 = d$, $ev\cos\alpha\, t_2 = a$; $0 = v\sin\alpha\,(t_1+t_2) - \frac{1}{2}g(t_1+t_2)^2$. Eliminate t_1, t_2 and find a]

15. A small elastic sphere is projected with a given velocity v from the foot of a vertical wall, in the vertical plane normal to the wall. It strikes a second parallel wall at a distance a and after rebounding, strikes the first wall at P. Show that the greatest height of P above the point of projection is

$$\frac{1}{2g}\left[v^2 - \frac{(1+e)^2 g^2 a^2}{e^2 v^2}\right].$$

(M.U.)

[**Hint:** $t_1 = \dfrac{a}{v\cos\alpha}$, $t_2 = \dfrac{a}{ev\cos\alpha}$; $h = v\sin\alpha\,(t_1+t_2) - \tfrac{1}{2}g\,(t_1+t_2)^2$; Eliminating t_1, t_2, $h = kt - \dfrac{1}{2}\dfrac{gk^2}{v^2}(1+t^2)$, where $k = a\,(1+\frac{1}{e})$, $t = \tan\alpha$. Now $\dfrac{dh}{dt} = 0$ gives $t = \dfrac{v^2}{gk}$]

14.5 OBLIQUE IMPACT OF TWO SMOOTH SPHERES

Bookwork 14.6. Two smooth spheres of masses m_1, m_2 and coefficient of restitution e, collide obliquely with velocities u_1, u_2 whose directions are inclined to the common normal C_1, C_2 at angles α_1, α_2 as shown in the figure. To find the velocities of the spheres after impact.

Let v_1 and v_2 be the velocities of the spheres after impact whose directions make angles θ_1 and θ_2 with C_1C_2 respectively. Since the spheres are smooth, the components of their velocities in the direction of the common tangent are unaffected by impact. So

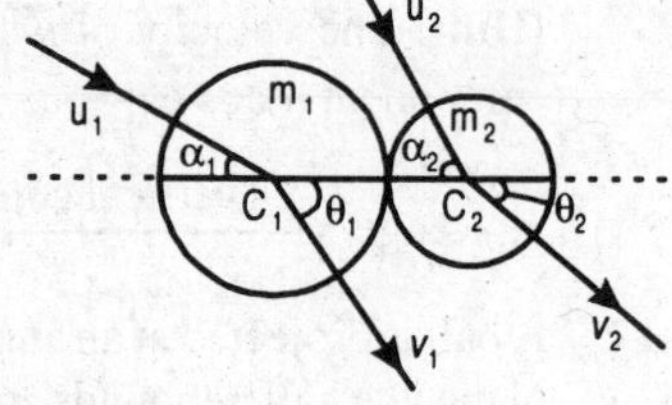

$$v_1 \sin\theta_1 = u_1 \sin\alpha_1, \quad \text{...(1)}$$

$$v_2 \sin\theta_2 = u_2 \sin\alpha_2, \quad \text{...(2)}$$

Also, by the principle of momentum, the total momentum of the spheres along C_1C_2, before and after impact, are equal ; that is ,

$$m_1v_1\cos\theta_1 + m_2v_2\cos\theta_2 = m_1u_1\cos\alpha_1 + m_2u_2\cos\alpha_2 \quad \text{...(3)}$$

and by Newton's experimental law

$$v_1\cos\theta_1 - v_2\cos\theta_2 = -e\,(u_1\cos\alpha_1 - u_2\cos\alpha_2). \quad \text{...(4)}$$

Since $m_1, m_2, u_1, u_2, \alpha_1, \alpha_2$ and e are known, from the above four equations the four unknowns v_1, v_2, θ_1 and θ_2 which specify the motion after impact can be calculated. (3) + (4) × m_2 and (3) – (4) × m_1 give respectively.

$$v_1\cos\theta_1 = \frac{1}{m_1+m_2}[(m_1 - em_2)\,u_1\cos\alpha_1 + m_2(1+e)u_2\cos\alpha_2] \quad \text{...(5)}$$

$$v_2\cos\theta_2 = \frac{1}{m_1+m_2}[m_1(1+e)\,u_1\cos\alpha_1 + (m_2 - em_1)\,u_2\cos\alpha_2] \quad \text{...(6)}$$

$(1)^2 + (5)^2$ and $(2)^2 + (6)^2$ give respectively v_1^2 and v_2^2 and (1) ÷ (5) and (2) ÷ (6) give $\tan\theta_1$ and $\tan\theta_2$. Thus $v_1, v_2, \theta_1, \theta_2$ are known.

Remark 1. If $\bar{i}$ is the unit vector in the direction of $\overline{C_1C_2}$ and $\bar{j}$ the unit vector along the common tangent, the velocities of the sphere C_1 before and after impact are

$$u_1\cos\alpha_1\,\bar{i} + u_1\sin\alpha_1\,\bar{j}, \quad v_1\cos\theta_1\,\bar{i} + v_1\sin\theta_1\,\bar{j}$$

and those of the sphere C_2 are

$$u_2\cos\alpha_2\,\bar{i} + u_2\sin\alpha_2\,\bar{j}, \quad v_2\cos\theta_2\,\bar{i} + v_2\sin\theta_2\,\bar{j}$$

Thus, if I is the magnitude of the impulse imparted to each sphere, then impulse imparted to the sphere C_2 is

$$I\bar{i} = m_2\{(v_2\cos\theta_2\,\bar{i} + v_2\sin\theta_2\,\bar{j}) - (u_2\cos\alpha_2\,\bar{i} + u_2\sin\alpha_2\,\bar{j})$$

$$= m_2(v_2\cos\theta_2 - u_2\cos\alpha_2)\,\bar{i} \quad \text{by (2)}$$

The impulse imparted to the sphere C_1 is

$$I(-\bar{i}) = m_1(v_1 \cos\theta_1 \bar{i} + v_1 \sin\theta_1 \bar{j}) - (u_1 \cos\alpha_1 \bar{i} + u_1 \sin\alpha_1 \bar{j})$$
$$= m_1(v_1 \cos\theta_1 - u_1 \cos\alpha_1)\bar{i} \text{ by (1)}$$

Thus we get the scalar relations

$$I = m_2(v_2 \cos\theta_2 - u_2 \cos\alpha_2), \quad -I = m_1(v_1 \cos\theta_1 - u_1 \cos\alpha_1).$$

Proceeding in the same way as the impulse was obtained for direct impact of the spheres, now we have

$$I = \frac{m_1 m_2}{m_1 + m_2}(1+e)(u_1 \cos\alpha_1 - u_2 \cos\alpha_2).$$

Remark 2. The change in kinetic energy due to impact is

$$\left(\tfrac{1}{2} m_1 v_1^2 + \tfrac{1}{2} m_2 v_2^2\right) - \left(\tfrac{1}{2} m_1 u_1^2 + \tfrac{1}{2} m_2 u_2^2\right)$$
$$= \tfrac{1}{2} m_1 (v_1^2 - u_1^2) + \tfrac{1}{2} m_2 (v_2^2 - u_2^2)$$
$$= \tfrac{1}{2} m_1 (v_1^2 \cos^2\theta_1 + v_1^2 \sin^2\theta_1 - u_1^2 \cos^2\alpha_1 - u_1^2 \sin^2\alpha_1)$$
$$+ \tfrac{1}{2} m_2 (v_2^2 \cos^2\theta_2 + v_2^2 \sin^2\theta_2 - u_2^2 \cos^2\alpha_2 - u_2^2 \sin^2\alpha_2)$$
$$= \tfrac{1}{2} m_1 (v_1^2 \cos^2\theta_1 - u_1^2 \cos^2\alpha_1) + \tfrac{1}{2} m_2 (v_2^2 \cos^2\theta_2 - u_2^2 \cos^2\alpha_2) \text{ by (1), (2)}$$
$$= \tfrac{1}{2} \{m_1 (v_1 \cos\theta_1)^2 + m_2 (v_2 \cos\theta_2)^2 - m_1 (u_1 \cos\alpha_1)^2 - m_2 (u_2 \cos\alpha_2)^2\}.$$

This can be shown to be equal to

$$-\frac{1}{2} \frac{m_1 m_2}{m_1 + m_2}(1 - e^2)(u_1 \cos\alpha_1 - u_2 \cos\alpha_2)^2$$

proceeding in the same way as in the case of the direct impact.

EXAMPLES

Example 1. ***(i)*** A smooth sphere of mass m_1 impinges obliquely on a smooth sphere of mass m_2 at rest. If the directions after the impact are at right angles, show that

$$m_1 = m_2 e. \qquad \textbf{(M.U., A.U.)}$$

(ii) and that, if the spheres are perfectly elastic, show that the massses are equal. **(M.U.)**

Let the velocity of the sphere m_1 before impact be u_1 making an angle α with C_1C_2, where C_1, C_2 are the centres of the sphere. The components in the direction perpendicular to C_1C_2 are unaffected by impact. The component of the sphere of mass m_2, before impact is zero. So the component after the impact also is zero . It means that this sphere after impact has a velocity say v_2 , in the direction C_1C_2. But the velocities of the spheres after impact are perpendicular. So the velocity of the sphere of mass m_1 after impact is perpendicular to C_1C_2. Let it be v_1. Then, from the conservation of momentum corresponding to the direction C_1C_2 and from the experimental law,

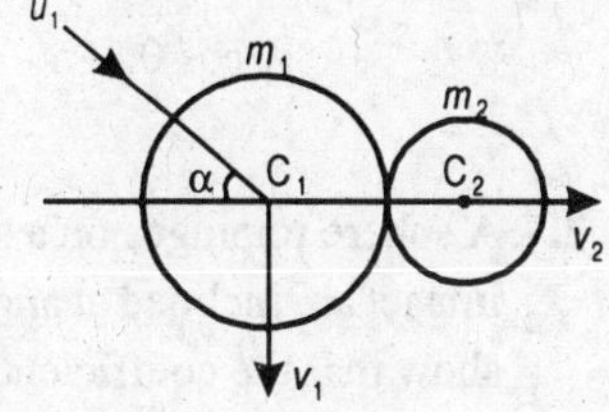

$$m_1(0) + m_2 v_2 = m_1 u_1 \cos\alpha + m_2(0), \quad 0 - v_2 = -e(u_1 \cos\alpha - 0)$$

which reduce to

$$m_2 v_2 = m_1 u_1 \cos\alpha, \quad v_2 = e u_1 \cos\alpha.$$

These equations give the relation $m_1 = m_2 e$. ...(1)

(*ii*) Now $e = 1$, then (1) becomes $m_1 = m_2$.

Remark. It should be remembered that if a sphere C_1 collides on a sphere C_2 at rest, then the sphere C_2 moves along the line C_1C_2 whatever the direction of C_1 be.

Example 2. Two equal and perfectly elastic spheres *A* and *B* move with equal speeds in mutually perpendicular directions. Just when the direction of motion of *B* is perpendicular to the line of centres *AB*, they collide. Show that the direction of motion of *B* is turned through 45° due to collision. **(M.U., M.K.U., Bn.U.)**

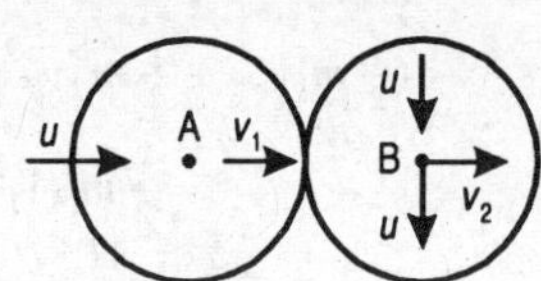

Now the velocity of *A* before impact, along *AB* and perpendicular to *AB*, are *u* (say),0. Then the velocity of *B* before impact in these directions are 0, *u*. By impact the velocities perpendicular to *AB* are unaltered. So, after impact, velocities of *A*, along and perpendicular to *AB*, are v_1 (say), 0 and those of *B* are v_2 (say), *u*.

Considering the momenta after and before impact along *AB*,

$$mv_1 + mv_2 = mu \quad \text{or} \quad v_1 + v_2 = u. \qquad ...(1)$$

By Newton's experimental law,

$$v_1 - v_2 = -1(u - 0). \qquad ...(2)$$

$$\therefore \qquad v_2 = u.$$

Therefore the velocity components of *B*, along and perpendicular to *AB*, are *u*, *u*. So the angle between the velocity of *B* and the perpendicular to *AB* is $45°$.

Alternative method. With usual notations, we should write down the four equations wherein $m_1 = m_2 = m$; $u_1 = u_2 = u$; $\alpha_1 = 0, \alpha_2 = 90°$; $e = 1$. Get $\theta_2 = 45°$.

EXERCISES

1. *A* and *B* are two perfectly elastic equal balls. *B* is at rest and is struck obliquely by *A*. Show that, after impact their directions are at right angles. **(M.U., M.K.U., Bn.U)**

   [Hint: Since *B* is at rest before impact, it moves along the line of centres after impact, say with velocity v_2. Then, from the motion along *AB*, omitting *m's*,

   $$v_1 \cos\theta_1 + v_2 = u_1 \cos\alpha_1 + 0, \quad v_1 \cos\theta_1 - v_2 = -1(u_1 \cos\alpha_1 - 0).$$

   $$\therefore \qquad \cos\theta_1 = 0 \quad \text{or} \quad \theta_1 = 90°\,]$$

2. A sphere impinges on a sphere of equal mass which is at rest. If the directions of motion after impact are inclined at angles of $30°$ to the original direction of motion of the impinging sphere, show that the coefficient of restitution is $\frac{1}{3}$. **(M.U., M.K.U.)**

   [Hint: The ball at rest moves along the line of centres, say with velocity v_2. Eliminate u_1, v_1, v_2 from $v_1 \cos\theta_1 + v_2 = u_1 \cos\alpha_1 + 0$, $v_1 \cos\theta_1 - v_2 = -e(u_1 \cos\alpha_1 - 0)$, $v_1 \sin\theta_1 = u_1 \sin\alpha_1$, where $\alpha_1 = 30°, \theta_1 = 60°$]

3. A smooth ball impinges on another smooth equal ball at rest in a direction making an angle α with the line of centres at the instant of impact. If the impinging ball is deviated through an angle α, show that the coefficient of restitution is equal to $\tan^2\alpha$. **(M.U.)**

[**Hint:** See the previous sum, Now $\alpha_1 = \alpha, \theta_1 = 2\alpha$]

4. A body of mass m rests on a smooth table. Another mass M moving with velocity u collides with it. Both are perfectly elastic and smooth. The body m is driven in a direction at an angle α to the previous line of motion of the body M. Show that the velocity of m is

$$\frac{2M}{M+m}u\cos\alpha. \qquad \textbf{(M.U.)}$$

[**Hint:** $Mv_1\cos\theta_1 + mv_2 = Mu_1\cos\alpha_1$, $v_1\cos\theta_1 - v_2 = -e(u_1\cos\alpha_1)$, where $\alpha_1 = \alpha$, $u_1 = u$, $e = 1$]

5. If two equal, perfectly elastic, smooth spheres impinge at right angles, then show that their directions after impact will still be at right angles. **(M.U.)**

[**Hint:** In the Bookwork 14.6, in (1), (2), (3), (4), set $e = 1$, $m_1 = m_2$, $\alpha_2 = 90° + \alpha_1$ and show that $\theta_1 = 90° + \theta_2$. The first two equations are $v_1\sin\theta_1 = u_1\sin\alpha_1$, $v_2\sin\theta_2 = u_2\cos\alpha_1$ and the addition and subtraction of the third and fourth equations gives respectively

$$v_1\cos\theta_1 = -u_2\sin\alpha_1,\ v_2\cos\theta_2 = u_1\cos\alpha_1.$$

Thus $\tan\theta_1 = -\dfrac{u_1}{u_2}$ and $\tan\theta_2 = -\dfrac{u_2}{u_1}$ and so $\tan\theta_1\tan\theta_2 = -1$]

CIRCULAR MOTION

15.1 CIRCULAR MOTION

In this chapter we study the motion of a particle constrained to move along a circle. To obtain the circular motion we recall the components of velocity and acceleration in the tangential direction in the sense in which θ increases and in the inward-drawn normal direction, which are as follows :

$$\text{Velocity} \quad : a\dot{\theta}, \ 0$$
$$\text{Acceleration} : a\ddot{\theta}, \ a\dot{\theta}^2.$$

In some cases we will have to use the components in the tangential direction in the sense in which s increases and in the inward-drawn normal direction, which are as follows :

$$\text{Velocity} : \dot{s} \ , \ 0$$

$$\text{Acceleration} : \ddot{s}, \quad \frac{\dot{s}^2}{P}$$

15.2 CONICAL PENDULUM

A simple case of a circular motion is the motion of a conical pendulum.

Conical pendulum. A conical pendulum is a simple arrangement in which a heavy particle, attached by a light inelastic string (or a light rod) to a fixed point, describes a horizontal circle with a constant angular velocity.

Bookwork 15.1. To discuss the motion of a conical pendulum.

Let O be the fixed point, P the position of the particle and C the centre of the path . Let us make the following assumptions:

l : Length of the string OP.

m : Mass of the particle

ω : The constant angular velocity $d\theta/dt$.

We shall calculate now

(*i*) Tension T in the string

(*ii*) Angle $COP = \alpha$,

(*iii*) Radius of the circular path a.

The forces acting on the particle are

(i) Tension T (having components $T \cos \alpha$ vertically upwards and $T \sin \alpha$ along the inward drawn normal)

(ii) Weight mg vertically downward.

So the equations of motions corresponding to the inward drawn normal and corresponding to the upward vertical are

$$ma\,\dot{\theta}^2 = T \sin \alpha, \qquad ...(1)$$
$$0 = T \cos \alpha - mg \qquad ...(2)$$

Tension and angle α. Since $a = l \sin \alpha$, the first equation gives

$$ml \sin \alpha\, \omega^2 = T \sin \alpha.$$

$$\therefore \qquad T = ml\omega^2.$$

Substitution of this value in (2) leads to

$$0 = ml\omega^2 \cos \alpha - mg \quad \text{or} \quad \cos \alpha = \frac{g}{l\omega^2}.$$

Thus α is known; So also a, since $a = l \sin \alpha$.

Limit for ω. ω should be fairly large so that $g/l\omega^2$ is less than 1 such that $\cos \alpha < 1$. In other words, it becomes possible for the particle to describe uniformly a horizontal circle only if

$$\omega > \sqrt{\frac{g}{l}}.$$

Independence of h from l. For a given ω, the depth OC of the particle below O is

$$h = l \cos \alpha = l\, \frac{g}{l\omega^2} = \frac{g}{\omega^2}.$$

This quantity is independent of l. That is, whatever be the length of the string, the particle is below O at a vertical distance g/ω^2.

Period of one revolution. The period of one revolution is

$$\frac{\text{Angle}}{\text{Angular speed}} = \frac{2\pi}{\omega}.$$

This quantity in terms of h is

$$\frac{2\pi}{\omega} = \frac{2\pi}{\sqrt{g/h}} = 2\pi\sqrt{\frac{h}{g}}.$$

Number of revolutions in a second. If n is the number of revolutions of the particle in 1 second, then

$$n = \frac{\omega}{2\pi} = \frac{1}{2\pi}\sqrt{\frac{T}{ml}}.$$

Expressing T in n, $T = 4\, mln^2 \pi^2$.

Remark. From $\cos \alpha = \dfrac{g}{l\omega^2}$, it is evident that $\alpha = 90°$ only when ω is infinite.

Steam governor. The fact that, as the angular velocity of a conical pendulum increases, α also increases, is made use of in governors in steam engines for regulating the flow of steam. The governor consists of two conical pendulums OA, OB hinged to a fixed point O on a shaft OC. OA and OB are connected to a collar which slides along OC. When the train moves at a normal speed the governor revolves with a required angular speed, resulting the flow of the steam at a normal rate. When the speed of the train increases, the speed of rotation of the shaft also increases and consequently α increases. This reduces the supply of steam so that the speed of the engine is decreased to its normal value.

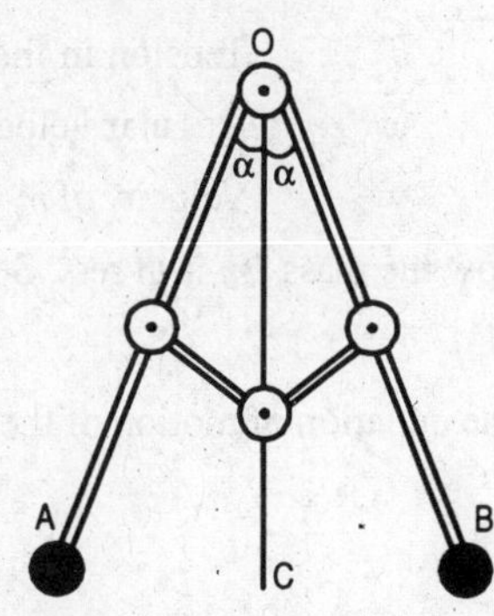

EXAMPLES

Example 1. A particle P of mass m, tied to the end of a light inelastic string of length l, is made describe a circle with a constant angular speed ω on a smooth horizontal table, the other end of the string being fixed at a point O in the table. Show that the tension in the string is

$$ml\omega^2. \qquad \textbf{(M.U.)}$$

If the string is elastic, its natural length being a and the coefficient of elasticity being λ, find the tension and the length of the string when the particle is in motion. **(M.U., A.U.)**

The forces acting on the particle are the reaction R and the weight mg, in the vertically upward and downward directions, and the tension T along the inward drawn normal. The equation of motion corresponding to the normal direction is

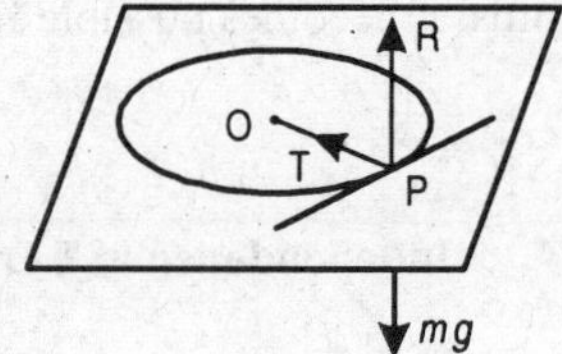

$$ml\dot{\theta}^2 = T.$$

But $\dot{\theta} = \omega$. So $T = ml\,\omega^2$.

If the string is elastic and if l is the length of the string when the particle is in motion with an angular velocity ω,

$$T = ml\,\omega^2. \qquad \text{...(1)}$$

But , by Hooke's law, we have

$$T = \lambda\frac{l-a}{a}. \qquad \text{...(2)}$$

Eliminating l, from (1), (2), we get the tension as

$$T = \frac{am\lambda\omega^2}{\lambda - am\omega^2}.$$

Eliminating T, from (1), (2), we get the length as

$$l = \frac{a\lambda}{\lambda - am\omega^2}.$$

Example 2. A particle of mass m on a smooth horizontal table is fastened to one end of a fine string which passes through a small hole in the table and supports at the other end a particle of mass $2m$, the particle m being held at a distance a from the hole. Find the velocity with which m must be projected horizontally so as to describe a circle of radius a. **(M.U.)**

Let us have the following assumptions :

O : Centre of the circle

T : Tension in the string

ω : Angular velocity of m

v : Velocity of m

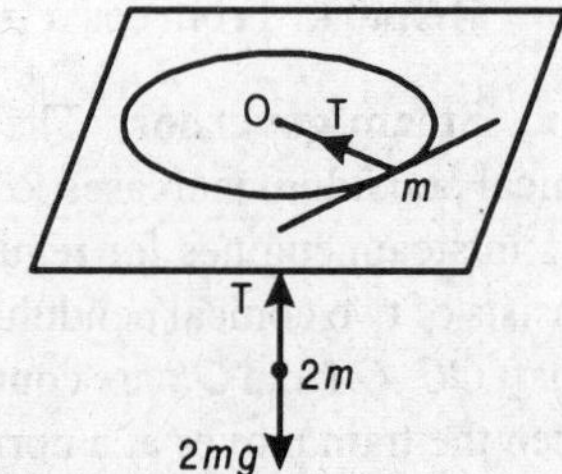

Now the mass $2m$ is at rest. So

$$T - 2mg = 0 \quad \text{or} \quad T = 2mg.$$

The equation of motion of the particle corresponding to the inward drawn normal is

$$ma\dot{\theta}^2 T \quad \text{or} \quad ma\omega^2 = 2mg.$$

$$\therefore \qquad v = a\omega = \sqrt{2ag}\,.$$

Example 3. A particle C of mass m is tied to two elastic strings AC, BC whose ends A, B are fixed such that A is vertically above B. The whole system rotates about AB with angular velocity ω. Show that, in order that both the strings may be stretched, $\omega^2 > \dfrac{g}{b \cos A}$, where b is the stretched length of AC. **(M.U.)**

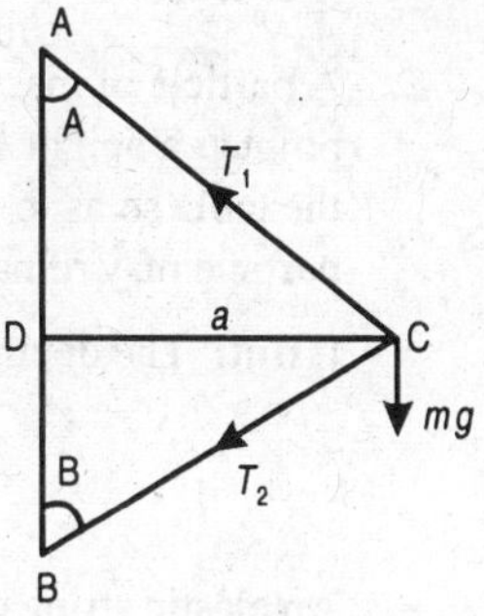

The forces on the particle are the tensions T_1, T_2 and the weight mg. Let CD be the perpendicular from C to AB and $CD = a$. Now there is no vertical motion. So

$$T_1 \cos A = T_2 \cos B + mg.$$

or

$$T_1 \cos A - T_2 \cos B = mg.$$

The motion of the particle in the horizontal plane is a uniform circular motion. So, considering the direction of the inward drawn normal,

$$ma\omega^2 = T_1 \sin A + T_2 \sin B \text{ or } mb \sin A\, \omega^2 = T_1 \sin A + T_2 \sin B.$$

Solving for T_2, we get

$$T^2 = \frac{m \sin A\,(\omega^2\, b \cos A - g)}{\sin (A + B)}.$$

So long T_2 is positive, the lower string is stretched. That is, the lower string also is stretched if

$$\omega^2\, b \cos A - g > 0 \text{ or } \omega^2 > \frac{g}{b \cos A}.$$

Example 4. A heavy particle P of mass M is attached to the middle point of a string of length $2l$, one end of which is fastened to a fixed point O and the other end is tied to a ring of mass m which slides on a vertical rod through O. Show that, if the particle moves in a horizontal plane with uniform angular velocity ω about the rod, the inclination α of both the portions of the string to the vertical is given by

$$\cos \alpha = \frac{M + 2m}{Ml\omega^2}\, g. \qquad \textbf{(M.U.)}$$

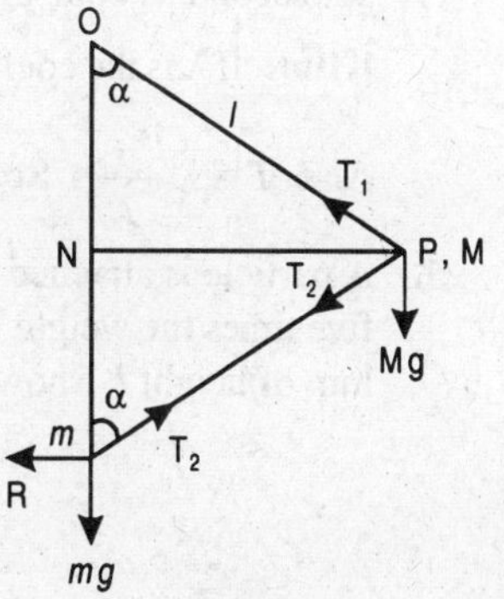

The forces on M and m are as shown in the figure. Since m is at rest, resolving T_2 vertically,

$$T_2 \cos \alpha - mg = 0. \qquad \text{...(1)}$$

M describes a circle of radius PN. The equation of its motion corresponding to the direction of PN.

$$M \cdot PN \cdot \dot{\theta}^2 = T_1 \sin \alpha + T_2 \sin \alpha, \qquad \text{...(2)}$$

where $PN = l \sin \alpha$, $\dot{\theta} = \omega$. Since M does not move vertically,

$$M\,(0) = T_1 \cos \alpha - T_2 \cos \alpha - Mg. \qquad \text{...(3)}$$

Elimination of T_1, T_2 from these three equations gives α as stated.

EXERCISES

1. If the velocity of the bob of a conical pendulum is v and its length is l, prove that the inclination of the string to the vertical is given by

$$\frac{\sin^2\theta}{\cos\theta} = \frac{v^2}{gl}.$$ **(M.K.U.)**

[**Hint:** $\cos\theta = \dfrac{g}{l\omega^2}$, where $v = a\omega$, $\sin\theta = \dfrac{a}{l}$.]

2. A particle of mass m is attached to one end of a string of length l whose other end is fixed to a point at a height h above a smooth horizontal table. The particle is made revolve in a circle on the table so as to make n revolutions per second. Find the greatest value of n in order that the particle may remain in contact with the table. **(M.U.)**

[**Hint:** The depth below O is g/ω^2. If $g/\omega^2 \geq h$, the particle is on the table. But $n = \omega/2\pi$. So

$$\frac{g}{(2\pi n)^2} \geq h \quad \text{or} \quad n \leq \frac{1}{2\pi}\sqrt{\frac{g}{h}}\ \text{S}]$$

3. An elastic string of natural length l attached to a fixed point P. When it supports a given mass at rest, its length is twice its natural length. Its length is three times its natural length when the system is rotating in a horizontal circle below P with a uniform angular velocity ω. Prove that

$$\omega^2 = \frac{2g}{3l}.$$ **(M.U.)**

[**Hint:** When the mass is supported, $\lambda\dfrac{l}{l} = mg$; Now $T = ml'\omega^2$, where $l' = 3l$. Also $T = \lambda\dfrac{2l}{l}$]

4. An elastic string has a natural length l and can be extended by an amount a by a mass of m suspended from it. Find the length of the string when, with the weight, it makes n revolutions per second as conical pendulum. **(M.U.)**

[**Hint:** If λ is the coefficient of elasticity $\lambda\,(a/l) = mg$. If l' is the required length, $T = 4ml'n^2\pi^2$.

Also $T = \lambda\dfrac{l'-l}{l}$. So $l' = \dfrac{lg}{g - 4\pi^2 n^2 a}$]

5. A particle is attached to an elastic string of natural length l and modulus of elasticity equal to five times the weight of the particle. The particle is whirled so as to move in a conical pendulum of height l. Show that when the motion is steady, the velocity of the particle is

$$\frac{3}{4}\sqrt{gl}.$$ **(M.K.U.)**

[**Hint:** Radius: a; Length: l'; Angle: α; Tension: T; $\dfrac{mv^2}{a} = T\sin\alpha$, $mg = T\cos\alpha$.

$$\therefore \quad \frac{v^2}{ag} = \tan\alpha = \frac{a}{l} \quad \text{or} \quad a^2 = \frac{v^2 l}{g}.$$

Now $T = ml'\omega^2 \Rightarrow 5mg\dfrac{l'-l}{l} = ml'\dfrac{v^2}{a^2}$ or $l'\left(\dfrac{5g}{l} - \dfrac{v^2}{a^2}\right) = 5g.$

But $l' = \sqrt{a^2 + l^2}$ and substitute $a^2 = \dfrac{v^2 l}{g}$]

6. A particle moves along a circular path of radius a with a uniform acceleration α. Show that its acceleration towards the centre when it has completed n revolutions from rest is $4\pi n\alpha$. **(M.U.)**

[Hint: $a\ddot{\theta}=\alpha$. So $\theta=\dfrac{\alpha t^2}{2a}+At+B$ or $\theta=\dfrac{\alpha t^2}{2a}$ since, when $t=0, \theta=0, \dot{\theta}=0$. If the time for n revolutions is T, then

$$(2\pi)n=\frac{\alpha}{2a}T^2 \quad \text{or } T=\sqrt{\frac{4\pi a n}{\alpha}}.$$

But $\dot{\theta}=\dfrac{\alpha t}{a}$. At $t=T$, $a\dot{\theta}^2=a\left(\dfrac{\alpha T}{a}\right)^2=4\pi n\alpha$]

7. A steam governor of which the arms are 10 cm. long, rotates at a speed of 7 revolutions per second. Find the angle of inclination of the arms.

[Hint: In $\cos\alpha=\dfrac{g}{l\omega^2}$, $g=9{\cdot}8$, $l=\dfrac{10}{100}$, $\omega=2\pi n=(2\pi)7$. So $\cos\alpha=\dfrac{1}{2\pi^2}$]

8. A conical pendulum of length l makes n revolutions per second. If the length is diminished by a small length x and if the tension remains to be the same, show that the increase in the number of revolutions per second is nearly $\dfrac{nx}{2l}$. **(M.U.)**

[Hint: $T=ml(2\pi n)^2$. The logarithmic differentiation gives $0=\dfrac{\Delta l}{l}+2\dfrac{\Delta n}{n}$, where $\Delta l=-x$]

15.3 MOTION OF A CYCLIST ON A CIRCULAR PATH

If a cyclist is to move along a circle, then there should be an applied force towards the centre of the circle, that is, along the inward drawn normal. This is provided by his weight and the friction when he leans towards the centre as will be seen in the following bookwork.

Bookwork 15.2. To find a uniform motion of a cyclist on a rough circular path.

We shall consider the cycle and cyclist as a single unit. Let us have the following assumptions:

AB	:	Cyclist
r	:	Radius of path
G	:	Mass centre ($AG=h$)
mg	:	Weight
R	:	Normal reaction
F	:	Frictional force
θ	:	Angle GAR
v	:	Velocity
ω	:	Angular velocity

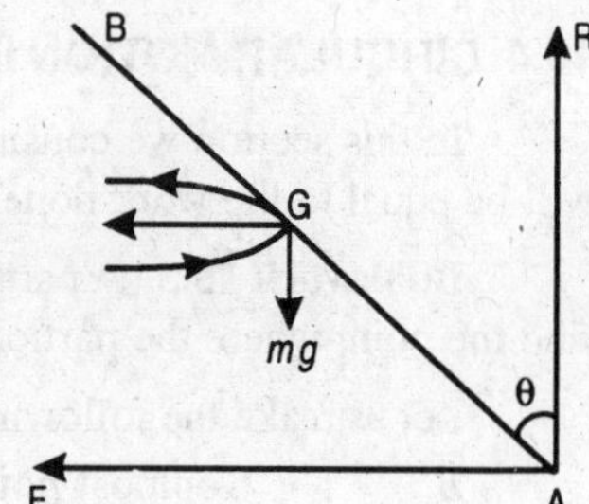

We shall consider the motion of G. The equation corresponding to the inward drawn normal is

$$mr\,\dot{\theta}^2=F \quad \text{or} \quad m\frac{v^2}{r}=F. \qquad ...(1)$$

The equation corresponding to the vertical direction is

$$0=R-mg \quad \text{or} \quad R=mg. \qquad ...(2)$$

Taking moments about G,

$$(h\sin\theta)R-(h\cos\theta)F=0.$$

$$\therefore \qquad \tan\theta = \frac{F}{R} = \frac{mv^2}{r} \cdot \frac{1}{mg} = \frac{v^2}{rg}.$$

This prescribes the inclination of the cyclist to the vertical for a possible circular motion.

Slipping of the cycle. Since $F = m\dfrac{v^2}{r}$, as the velocity increases, the frictional force F called into play increases. If the coefficient of friction is μ, then the maximum friction that can be called into play is

$$F_{max} = \mu R = \mu mg.$$

If $F > F_{max}$, then slipping takes place, that is, if

$$\frac{mv^2}{r} > \mu mg \quad \text{or} \quad v > \sqrt{\mu rg},$$

slipping takes place.

EXERCISES

1. A cyclist riding at 21 km.p.h. wants to take a turn describing a circular path. What is the least radius of the path so that the cycle does not slip if the coefficient of friction between the tyres and the road is $^{25}/_{36}$? **(C.U.)**

   [Hint: $v < \sqrt{\mu rg}$ or $r > \dfrac{v^2}{\mu g}$; $v = \dfrac{21 \times 1000}{60 \times 60}$ and $g = 9{\cdot}8$ give $r = 5$]

2. A cyclist travels on a level circular track of radius 4 m. If the coefficient of friction between the tyres and the ground is $^5/_9$, show that the greatest speed at which he can travel without slipping is 16·8 km.p.h. **(Br.U.)**

   [Hint: $v^2 = \mu rg$ or $v^2 = (^5/_9) \times 4 \times 9{\cdot}8$ m./sec.]

15.4 CIRCULAR MOTION IN A VERTICAL PLANE

In this section we consider frictionless systems so that the increase in the K.E. in an interval will be equal to the work done in the same interval by gravity.

Bookwork 15.3. A particle slides on a smooth sphere starting from rest at the highest point. To find the point where the particle leaves the sphere.

Let us make the following assumptions :

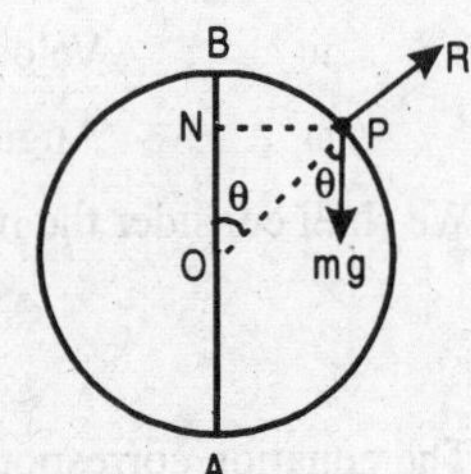

B	:	Topmost point
AB	:	A diameter
O	:	Centre
a	:	Radius
P	:	Position at time t
θ	:	Angle BOP
R	:	Reaction along the outward normal
mg	:	Earth's gravity vertically downwards.

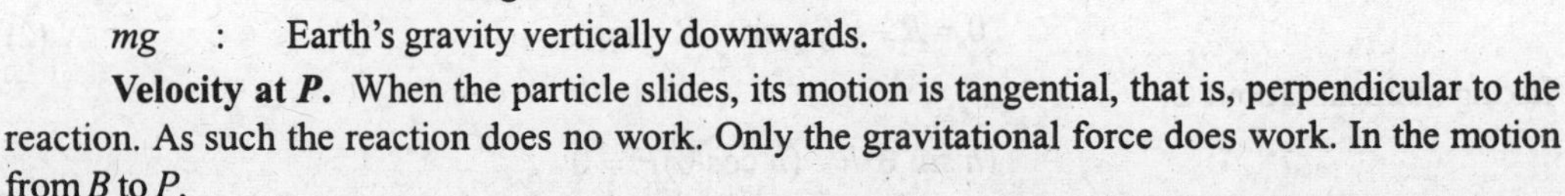

Velocity at *P*. When the particle slides, its motion is tangential, that is, perpendicular to the reaction. As such the reaction does no work. Only the gravitational force does work. In the motion from B to P,

$$\text{Workdone by gravity} = \text{Increase in K.E.}$$

If BN is the height descended in this motion,

$$mg(BN) = \tfrac{1}{2}mv^2 - \tfrac{1}{2}m0^2.$$

But $BN = a\,(1 - \cos\theta)$. Therefore

$$mga(1 - \cos\theta) = \tfrac{1}{2}mv^2$$

$$\therefore \qquad v^2 = 2ag\,(1 - \cos\theta).$$

Reaction at *P*. The equation of motion corresponding to the inward drawn normal at P is

$$ma\dot{\theta}^2 = mg\cos\theta - R \quad \text{or} \quad m\frac{v^2}{a} = mg\cos\theta - R.$$

Substituting the value of v^2,

$$R = mg\cos\theta - 2mg(1 - \cos\theta)$$
$$= mg(3\cos\theta - 2).$$

$\cos\theta$ is a decreasing function of θ. So the reaction decreases as θ increases and the particle loses contact with the sphere when $R = 0$. But $R = 0$, when

$$3\cos\theta - 2 = 0 \quad \text{or} \quad \theta = \cos^{-1}\tfrac{2}{3}.$$

Height descended when the particle leaves the sphere. The height H descended is

$$H = BN \text{ where } \theta = \cos^{-1}\tfrac{2}{3}.$$
$$= a\,(1 - \cos\theta), \text{ where } \cos\theta = \tfrac{2}{3}$$
$$= a\,(1 - \tfrac{2}{3}) = \tfrac{a}{3}.$$

Velocity of leaving. When $\theta = \cos^{-1}\tfrac{2}{3}$

$$\text{Velocity} = \sqrt{2ag\,(1 - \cos\theta)}, \quad \text{where } \cos\theta = \tfrac{2}{3}$$
$$= \sqrt{2ag\,(1 - \tfrac{2}{3})} = \sqrt{\tfrac{2}{3}ag}.$$

Bookwork 15.4. To find the motion of a particle which slides on the interior surface of a smooth sphere being projected from the lowest point with a speed u.

Let us make the following assumptions :

A	:	Lowest point
AB	:	A diameter
O	:	Centre
a	:	Radius
P	:	Position at time t
θ	:	Angle AOP
R	:	Reaction along the inward normal
mg	:	Earth's gravity vertically downwards

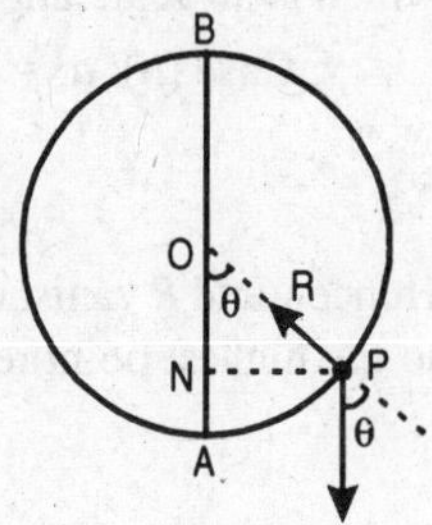

Velocity at *P*. When the particle slides, its motion is tangential, that is, perpendicular to the reaction. As such the reaction does no work. Only the gravitational force does work. In the motion from A to P,

Work done by gravity = Increase in K.E.

If AN is the height ascended in this motion

$$(-mg)\ AN = \tfrac{1}{2} mv^2 - \tfrac{1}{2} mu^2.$$

But $AN = a\,(1-\cos\theta)$. Therefore

$$-mg\ a(1-\cos\theta) = \tfrac{1}{2} mv^2 - \tfrac{1}{2} mu^2.$$

$$\therefore \qquad v^2 = \left(u^2 - 2ag\right) + 2ag\cos\theta. \qquad ...(1)$$

Reaction. The equation of motion corresponding to the inward drawn normal direction is

$$ma\,\dot{\theta}^2 = R - mg\cos\theta.$$

Using $v = a\,\dot{\theta}$ and substituting the value of v^2, we get

$$R = ma\,\dot{\theta}^2 + mg\cos\theta = \frac{m}{a}v^2 + mg\cos\theta$$

$$= \frac{m}{a}\left\{(u^2 - 2ag) + 2ag\cos\theta\right\} + mg\cos\theta$$

$$= \frac{m}{a}\left\{(u^2 - 2ag) + 3ag\cos\theta\right\} \qquad ...(2)$$

Expressing R in v, we get from (1) and (2),

$$R = \frac{m}{2a}\left\{3v^2 + (2ag - u^2)\right\} \qquad ...(3)$$

We know that $\cos\theta$ decreases as θ increases. So, from (1), we see that v decreases as θ increases. Also we see, from (2), that R decreases as θ increases. But (3) helps us find which of R and v becomes zero first.

Case (*i*) $u^2 < 2ag$: In this case $2ag - u^2$ is positive and, by (3)

$$R > \frac{m}{2a}(3v^2).$$

Hence v vanishes first. At the moment of v vanishing $R \neq 0$ and so the particle does not leave the surface but begins to retrace its path. The θ corresponding to this highest point reached by the particle is obtained from

$$0^2 = (u^2 - 2ag) + 2ag\cos\theta$$

as

$$\theta = \cos^{-1}\left(1 - \frac{u^2}{2ag}\right)$$

which is an acute angle.

Case (*ii*) $u^2 = 2ag$: In this case

$$R = \frac{m}{2a}(3v^2).$$

Hence v and R vanishes simultaneously. Thereafter the particle retraces its path. The θ corresponding to the highest point reached by the particle is obtained from

$$0^2 = (0) + 2ag\cos\theta \text{ as } \theta = 90^\circ.$$

That is, the particle oscillates along a vertical semicircle.

Case (*iii*) $u^2 > 2ag$: In this case

$$R < \frac{m}{2a}(3v^2).$$

Hence R vanishes first. At the moment of R vanishing $v \neq 0$ and so the particle leaves the surface and begins to describe a parabolic path under gravity.

Case (*iv*) If the particle is to make complete revolutions, then R should either be zero or a non-zero quantity when $\theta = 180°$. Then corresponding values of u is given by (2) as

$$(u^2 - 2ag) + 3ag\cos 180° \geq 0$$

i.e., $$u^2 - 2ag - 3ag \geq 0 \text{ or } u^2 \geq 5ag.$$

Summarising these results as four different cases

(*i*) if $u < \sqrt{2ag}$, the particle oscillates along a vertical circular arc in the lower half of the sphere,

(*ii*) if $u = \sqrt{2ag}$, the particle oscillates along a verticle semicircle in the lower half of the sphere.

(*iii*) if $\sqrt{2ag} < u < \sqrt{5ag}$, the particle leaves the circular path at a point above the centre

(*iv*) if $u \geq \sqrt{5ag}$, the particle describes complete circles.

Bookwork 15.5. A particle hangs, being attached to a fixed point O by an inextensible string of length a. If it is projected horizontally with a velocity u, to find its motion.

The motion is the same as in the previous bookwork 15.4, the only difference being that the force along PO is the tension T instead of the reaction R.

Bookwork 15.6. A small ring, threaded to a smooth vertical circular wire, is projected from the lowest point. To find its motion.

We shall have the same assumptions as in the bookwork 15.4. Then

$$v^2 = (u^2 - 2ag) + 2ag\cos\theta.$$

Case (*i*) $u^2 < 2ag$: In this case v becomes zero when

$$\theta = \cos^{-1}\left(1 - \frac{u^2}{2ag}\right) \quad ...(1)$$

and the ring oscillates in the lower half of the wire through the angle (1) on either of the vertical.

Case (*ii*) $u^2 = 2ag$: In this case, $v = 0$ when $\theta = 90°$ and the ring oscillates along a vertical semicircle in the lower half of the wire.

Case (*iii*) $2ag < u^2 < 4ag$: The velocity vanishes at the highest point if

$$(u^2 - 2ag) + 2ag\cos 180° = 0 \text{ or } u^2 = 4ag.$$

Hence, if $\sqrt{2ag} < u < \sqrt{4ag}$, the ring oscillates with its velocity vanishing at points higher than the centre.

Case (*iv*) $u^2 \geq 4ag$: The ring makes complete revolutions.

EXAMPLES

Example 1. A particle slides outside a fixed smooth circle in a vertical plane, starting from rest at the top, and another is projected from the lowest point inside the circle with a velocity which is just sufficient to carry it to the top. Prove that both leave the circle at the same point and proceed to describe parts of the same parabola. **(M.U.)**

Let B be the topmost point and P be the positions of the particles and angle BOP be θ (O : centre). In the first case, if the velocity and reaction at P are v, R, then, from Bookwork 15.3,

$$v^2 = 2ag(1 - \cos\theta), \qquad \text{...(1)}$$

$$R = mg(3\cos\theta - 2). \qquad \text{...(2)}$$

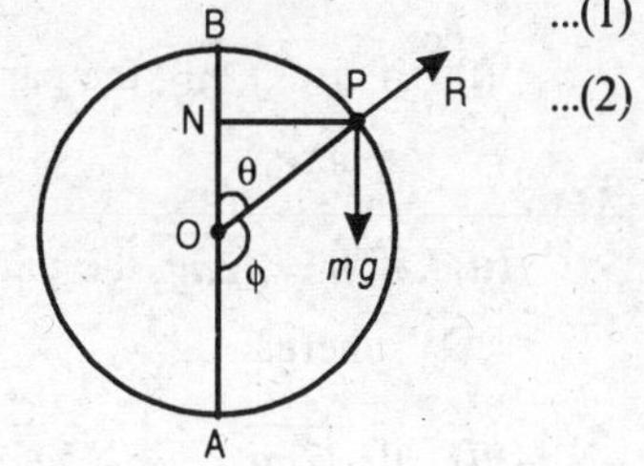

In the second case, from Bookwork 15.4, they are

$$v^2 = (u^2 - 2ag) + 2ag\cos\phi,$$

$$R = \frac{m}{a}\left[(u^2 - 2ag) + 3ag\cos\phi\right],$$

where $\phi = \underline{|AOP} = 180° - \theta$ and $u^2 = 2(g)(2a)$ so that

$$v^2 = 2ag(1 - \cos\theta), \qquad \text{...(3)}$$

$$R = mg(2 - 3\cos\theta) \qquad \text{...(4)}$$

because the velocity of projection to take the particle from the lowest point just to B is $\sqrt{2(g)(2a)}$. In both the cases R vanishes when

$$\cos\theta = 2/3$$

that is, the particle leaves the sphere at the same point in the directions tangential to the sphere. Of course, the particles move in the downward and upward senses respectively. Their respective velocities are equal in magnitude by (1) and (3). Thus the particles move along the same line in opposite directions with same speeds. Therefore their trajectories are the same parabola.

Example 2. A particle is projected from the lowest point A of a smooth sphere along its inside with a velocity $\sqrt{7ag/2}$, a being the radius of the sphere. Show that the particle leaves the sphere after reaching a height $\frac{3a}{2}$ and then returns to the point of projection A.

The velocity of projection u is such that

$$\sqrt{2ag} < u < \sqrt{5ag}.$$

So the particle leaves the sphere at some point, say P, above the centre O and describes a parabola under gravity. Let A, B be the lowest and highest points of the sphere and

$$\underline{|AOP} = \theta, \ \underline{|BOP} = \alpha$$

so that

$$\theta = 180° - \alpha.$$

Now the reaction at "θ" is

$$R = \frac{m}{a}\left\{(u^2 - 2ag) + 3ag\cos\theta\right\}$$

$$= 3mg\left[\frac{1}{2} + \cos\theta\right] \quad \text{since } u^2 = \frac{7ag}{2}.$$

At P, $R = 0$ and so, at P,

$$\cos\theta = -\tfrac{1}{2} \quad \text{or} \quad \theta = 120^\circ,$$

$$\alpha = 180^\circ - \theta = 60^\circ .$$

If PN is the perpendicular from P to AB, then

$$AN = AO + ON = a + a\cos 60^\circ = \frac{3a}{2}.$$

If V is the velocity at P, then it is along the tangent to the circle, that is, it is inclined to the horizontal PN at an angle 60° and

$$V^2 = \left[(u^2 - 2ag) + 2ag\cos\theta\right]^{\theta=120^\circ}$$

$$= \left(\frac{7ag}{2} - 2ag\right) + 2ag\left(-\frac{1}{2}\right) = \frac{ag}{2}.$$

Choose PN as the x axis and the vertical through P as the y axis.Then the equation of the trajectory of the particle is

$$y = x\tan\alpha - \frac{gx^2}{2V^2\cos^2\alpha}, \quad \alpha = 60^\circ, \; V^2 = \frac{ag}{2}$$

or $$y = x\sqrt{3} - \frac{4x^2}{a}. \qquad \text{...(1)}$$

But A is $(PN, -AN)$ or $\left(\frac{\sqrt{3}}{2}a, -\frac{3a}{2}\right)$. This satisfies (1) showing that the particle passes through A.

Example 3. A heavy bead slides on a smooth vertical circular wire of radius a. If it is projected from the lowest point with velocity just sufficient to carry it to the highest point, show that at time t, the radius to the bead is inclined to the vertical at an angle

$$2\tan^{-1}\left[\sinh\sqrt{\frac{g}{a}}\,t\right]. \qquad \textbf{(M.U.)}$$

We know that the initial velocity of projection

$$u = \sqrt{4ag}$$

takes the bead just to the topmost point B. Let A be the lowest point and P, the position of the particle at time t and $\angle AOP = \theta$.

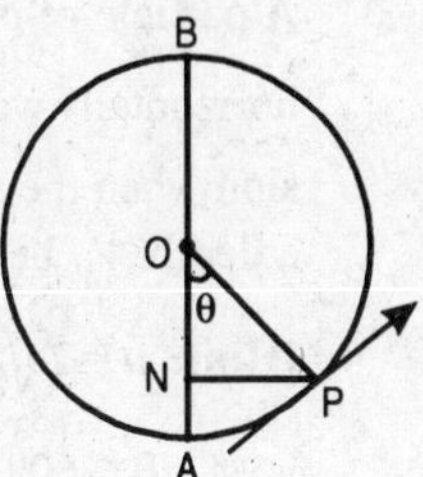

$$\left.\begin{array}{l}\text{Work done in}\\ \text{travelling from } A \text{ to } P\end{array}\right\} = -mg\,AN$$

$$= -mg(a - a\cos\theta)$$

$$\text{Increase in K.E.} \quad = \tfrac{1}{2}m(a\dot{\theta})^2 - \tfrac{1}{2}mu^2$$

$$= \tfrac{1}{2}ma^2\dot{\theta}^2 - 2amg$$

So, by the principle of energy,

$$\tfrac{1}{2}a^2\dot{\theta}^2 - 2ag = -g(a - a\cos\theta)$$

or $$\tfrac{1}{2}a^2\dot{\theta}^2 = ag(1 + \cos\theta) = 2ag\cos^2\theta/2.$$

$$\dot{\theta} = \sqrt{\frac{4g}{a}} \cos\frac{\theta}{2} \quad \text{or} \quad \sec\frac{\theta}{2}\, d\theta = 2\sqrt{\frac{g}{a}}\, dt.$$

Therefore, integrating, we get

$$\frac{\log(\sec \theta/2 + \tan \theta/2)}{1/2} = 2\sqrt{\frac{g}{a}}\, t + C.$$

But, when $t = 0, \theta = 0$. So $C = 0$. Thus, if $\lambda = \sqrt{\frac{g}{a}}$, then

$$e^{\lambda t} = \sec \theta/2 + \tan \theta/2.$$

$$\therefore \quad e^{-\lambda t} = \frac{1}{\sec \theta/2 + \tan \theta/2} = \sec \theta/2 - \tan \theta/2.$$

Subtracting and dividing by 2,

$$\sinh \lambda t = \tan\frac{\theta}{2} \quad \text{or} \quad \frac{\theta}{2} = \tan^{-1}\left[\sinh \sqrt{\frac{g}{a}}\, t\right].$$

EXERCISES

1. A particle moves on the inside of a smooth vertical circle on being projected from the lowest point and just reaches the horizontal diameter. Show that the reaction at any point varies as its depth below the horizontal diameter. **(C.U.)**

[Hint: $v^2 = (u^2 - 2ag) + 2ag\cos\theta$ gives $u^2 = 2ag$ if $v = 0$ at $\theta = 90°$;

$R = (m/a)\{(u^2 - 2ag) + 3ag\cos\theta\} = 3mg\cos\theta$ which is proportional to $a\cos\theta$ **]**

2. A heavy particle hanging by a light string of length l from a fixed point is projected horizontally from its lowest point with a velocity $\sqrt{\frac{7gl}{2}}$. Prove that the string slackens after swinging through $120°$. Show that it is then at a height $3l/2$ above the starting point and find its velocity then. **(M.K.U., M.U.)**

[Hint: $u^2 = 7/2\, gl$; Tension $T = m/l\,\{(u^2 - 2lg) + 3lg\cos\theta\} = 0$ gives $\theta = 120°$. Htight is $l + l$ sin $30°$ and $v^2 = 3/2\, gl + 2lg\cos 120°$ **]**

3. A particle of mass m is suspended from a fixed point by a string of length a. It is projected horizontally with a velocity of $2\sqrt{ag}$. Find the height of the particle above the point of suspension when the string becomes slack. Find also the tension in the string when the particle is at a depth $a/2$ below the point of suspension. **(M.U.)**

[Hint: $u = 2\sqrt{ag}$; $T = 0$ gives $\cos\theta = -\,2/3$; *Hight* is $a\cos(180° - \theta)$ or $2a/3$. When the depth is $a/2$, $\theta = 60°$, $T = 7/2\, mg$ **]**

4. A particle is projected along the inner surface of a smooth vertical circle of radius a its velocity at the lowest point being $1/5\sqrt{95ga}$. . Show that it will leave the circle at an angular distance $\cos^{-1} 3/5$ from the highest point and that its velocity then is $1/5\sqrt{15ga}$. **(M.U., S.V.U.)**

[Hint: A, B : lowest and topmost points; P : Particle ; Angles AOP, BOP : θ, ϕ ; when $R = 0$, $\cos\theta = -\,^3\!/_5$; $\cos\phi = \cos(180° - \theta) = -\,^3\!/_5$]

5. A particle slides from rest, at a depth $^r\!/_2$ below the highest point, down the outside of a smooth sphere of radius r. Prove that it leaves the sphere at a height $^r\!/_3$ above the centre. **(M.U.)**

[Hint: Increase in K.E.=W.D. So $\frac{1}{2} m(v^2 - 0^2) = mg\,(^r\!/_2 - r\cos\theta)$ .But $m\,^{v^2}\!/_r = mg\cos\theta - R$. When $R = 0$, $\cos\theta = \frac{1}{3}$]

6. A heavy particle P of weight w is tied to one end of a string the other end of which is fastened to a fixed point O. Initially OP is horizontal with the string taut and the particle is let go. When the string becomes vertical, it strikes against a peg at C which isvertically below O such that $OC = \frac{1}{2}\,OP$. Find the height to which P subsequently rises above its lowest position and the change in the tension of the string at the moment of striking C. **(M.U.)**

[Hint: See case (ii) in Bookwork 15.4, where $u^2 = 2ag$. From (2),

$$T = \frac{m}{a}\left[(u^2 - 2ag) + 3ag\cos\theta\right]_{\theta=0} = 3mg.$$

After striking the peg, the length is $^a\!/_2$. If T' is the tension immediately after striking,

$$T' = \frac{m}{(^a\!/_2)}\left[(u^2 - 2\cdot\tfrac{a}{2}\cdot g + 3\cdot\tfrac{a}{2}\cdot g\cos\theta\right]_{\theta=0} = 5mg\ ;\ T' - T = 2mg.$$

After striking the radius is $^a\!/_2$ and if V is the velocity, by conservation of angular momentum,

$$^a\!/_2\,(mV) = a\,(mu) \quad \text{or} \quad V = 2u = \sqrt{8ag}$$

and m makes complete revolutions about the peg]

7. A particle is projected horizontally with speed $\sqrt{^{ag}\!/_2}$ from the highest point of the outside of a fixed smooth sphere of radius a. Show that it will leave the sphere at the point whose vertical distance below the point of projection is $^a\!/_6$. Find also the magnitude of the velocity of the particle when it strikes the plane upon which the sphere stands. **(M.U.)**

[Hint: By energy principle and motion in the normal direction,

$$\frac{1}{2}mv^2 - \frac{1}{2}m\left(\frac{ag}{2}\right) = mg\,a\,(1 - \cos\theta), \quad m\frac{v^2}{a} = mg\cos\theta - R.$$

So $R = \dfrac{mg}{2}(6\cos\theta - 5)$ and $R = 0$ when $\cos\theta = \dfrac{5}{6}$. If the velocity of hit is V, from the full motion, $\dfrac{1}{2}mV^2 - \dfrac{1}{2}m\dfrac{ag}{2} = 2a\,mg$]

8. If a particle is projected from the lowest point of a smooth vertical circular hoop with a speed $u = \left(\dfrac{ag}{2}\right)^{1/2}(\sqrt{4 + 3\sqrt{3}})$, find where it leaves the circle and show that it strikes the hoop again at an end of the horizontal diameter. **(M.U.)**

[Hint: See Bookwork 15.4. $R = \dfrac{m}{a}\left[(u^2 - 2ag) + 3ag\cos\theta\right]$; when $R = 0, \theta = 150°$ and $V^2 = (\text{velocity } V)^2 = \dfrac{ag\sqrt{3}}{2}$. For the trajectory

$$y = x \tan \alpha - \frac{gx^2}{2V^2 \cos^2 \alpha}, \quad \alpha = 30°.$$

The end of the diameter is $\left(\frac{3a}{2}, -\frac{\sqrt{3}a}{2}\right)$]

9. A particle is projected along the inner side of a smooth vertical circle of radius a, the velocity at the lowest point being u. Show that, if $2ga < u^2 < 5ga$ the particle will leave the circle before reaching the highest point and will describe a parabola whose latus rectum is

$$\frac{2(u^2 - 2ga)^3}{27g^3a^2}.$$ **(S.V.U.)**

[**Hint:** See Bookwork 15.4. When $R = 0$, if V is the velocity,

$$u^2 - 2ag + 3ag \cos \theta = 0, \; V^2 = \frac{u^2 - 2ag}{3}.$$

If α is the angle of projection, when $R = 0, 180° - \theta = \alpha$ .The latus rectum $= \frac{2V^2 \cos^2 \alpha}{g}$. Substitute for V and $\cos \alpha$]

15.5 RELATIVE REST IN A REVOLVING CONE

Bookwork 15.7. Suppose a smooth cone with semivertical angle α revolves with constant angular velocity ω about its axis which is vertical. If the vertex is downwards, to find where a particle can be placed on the inner surface of the cone so as to be at relative rest.

Let O be the centre of the circular path, a the radius and P the position of the particle at time t. Now the forces on the particle are

(*i*) Weight mg

(*ii*) Reaction of surface R.

The equations of motion corresponding to the inward drawn normal to the circle and vertical direction are

$$ma\,\omega^2 = R \cos \alpha,$$
$$mg = R \sin \alpha.$$

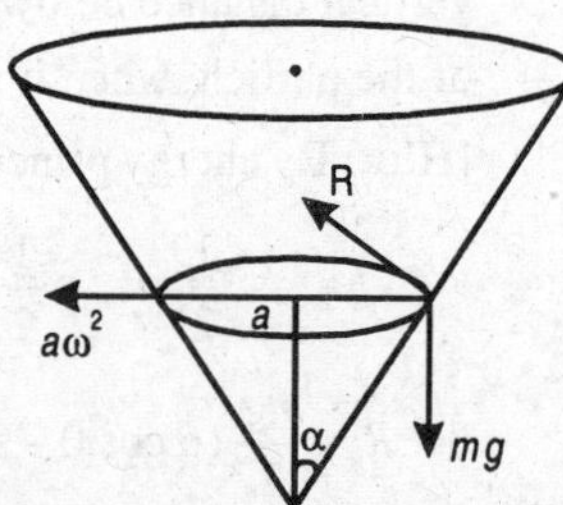

Thus dividing one by the other, we get

$$\frac{a\omega^2}{g} = \frac{1}{\tan \alpha} \quad \text{or} \quad a = \frac{g}{\omega^2 \tan \alpha}.$$

That is, the particle should be placed on the inner surface of the cone whose distance from axis is

$$\frac{g}{\omega^2 \tan \alpha}.$$

EXERCISES

1. A smooth cone with semivertical angle $30°$ revolves with constant angular velocity ω about its axis which is vertical. If the vertex is downwards, show that the particle can be placed on the inner surface of the cone so as to be at relative rest if the distance of the particle from the axis is $\frac{g\sqrt{3}}{\omega^2}$. **(M.U.)**

[**Hint:** See Bookwork 15.7. Here $\alpha = 30°$].

2. A heavy particle of mass m rests on a smooth inclined plane, being attached to a fixed point O on the plane by a string of length l lying along the line of greatest slope when the plane rotates about a vertical axis through O with uniform angular velocity ω. If the plane is inclined at an angle α to the horizontal, show that the tension in the string is equal to $m(g \sin \alpha + \omega^2 l \cos^2 \alpha)$.

(M.U.)

[**Hint:** If a is the radius of the circular path which is horizontal, then $a = l \cos \alpha$ and the equations of motion corresponding to the inward drawn normal and vertical directions are

$$ma\omega^2 = T \cos \alpha - R \sin \alpha, \quad mg = T \sin \alpha + R \cos \alpha.$$

Eliminate R and find T.]

15.6 SIMPLE PENDULUM

In the circular motion we next study the small oscillation of a simple pendulum.

Definition. A *simple pendulum* is an arrangement in which a heavy particle swings in a vertical circle about a fixed point to which it is attached by a light inextensible string (or a light rod). The particle is called the *bob* of the pendulum and the length of the string is called the *length of the pendulum*.

Bookwork 15.8. To find the period of a small oscillation of a simple pendulum.

Let us make the following assumptions :

O : Point of suspension

l : Length of the pendulum

m : Mass of the particle (bob)

OA : Downward vertical through O

P : Position of the bob at time t

θ : Angle AOP.

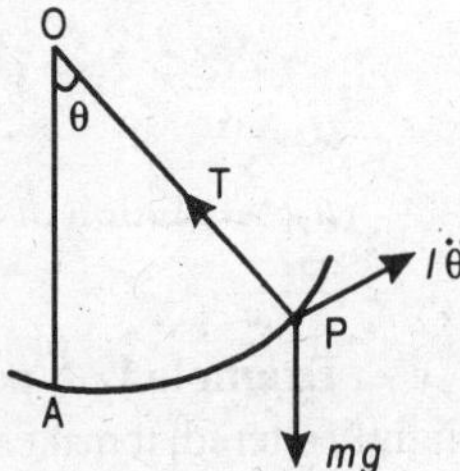

The forces on the bob are

(*i*) Earth's gravitation mg

(*ii*) Tension T.

Now we shall consider the equation of motion corresponding to the tangential direction in the sense in which θ increases. In this direction the component of the acceleration is $l\ddot{\theta}$ and the component of the applied forces is $-mg \sin \theta$. So the equation of motion is

$$m(l\ddot{\theta}) = -mg \sin \theta \quad \text{or} \quad l\ddot{\theta} = -g \sin \theta.$$

Let the pendulum swing on either side through a small angle. Then

$$\sin \theta = \theta$$

approximately so that the equation of motion becomes

$$l\ddot{\theta} = -g\theta \quad \text{or} \quad \ddot{\theta} = -\frac{g}{l}\theta.$$

So the motion is harmonic.

Period. We assumed that the oscillation is small. The period of this small oscillation is

$$\frac{2\pi}{\sqrt{g/l}} \quad \text{or} \quad 2\pi\sqrt{\frac{l}{g}}.$$

15.6.1 Seconds pendulum

Definition. A pendulum whose period of oscillation is two seconds is called a *seconds pendulum*. In other words, the pendulum whose time of one vibration, which is otherwise known as a *beat*, is a second, is called a seconds pendulum.

Length of a seconds pendulum. Since the period of the seconds pendulum is 2 seconds,

$$2\pi\sqrt{\frac{l}{g}} = 2.$$

$$\therefore \quad l = \frac{g}{\pi^2} = \frac{9{\cdot}8}{(3{\cdot}1416)^2} = 0{\cdot}99 \text{ m.}$$

Thus the length of a seconds pendulum is nearly a metre.

Number of oscillations in a day. The period T of a pendulum is

$$T = 2\pi\sqrt{\frac{l}{g}} \text{ seconds}.$$

So the number of oscillations m in a day is

$$m = \frac{24\times 60\times 60}{T} = \frac{24\times 60\times 60}{2\pi}\sqrt{\frac{g}{l}}.$$

In the case of a seconds pendulum,

$$m = \frac{24\times 60\times 60}{2} = 43200.$$

EXAMPLES

Example 1. A pendulum whose length is l makes m oscillations in 24 hours. When its length is slightly altered, it makes $m + n$ oscillations in 24 hours. Show that the diminution of the length is nearly

$$\frac{2nl}{m}.$$

(M.U.)

The period T of a pendulum of length l is

$$2\pi\sqrt{\frac{l}{g}}.$$

It is assumed that g is a constant. Now m is the number of oscillations in 24 hours. Therefore

$$m = \frac{24\times 60\times 60}{T} = \frac{24\times 60\times 60}{2\pi}\sqrt{\frac{g}{l}}.$$

Logarithmic differentiation of this gives

$$\frac{\delta m}{m} = -\frac{1}{2}\frac{\delta l}{l}.$$

Now δm is the small change in m which is given to be n. So

$$\frac{n}{m} = -\frac{1}{2}\frac{\delta l}{l} \quad \text{or} \quad \delta l = -\frac{2nl}{m}.$$

Example 2. A clock with a seconds pendulum loses 40 seconds per day at a place where the acceleration due to gravity is 981cm./sec^2. Find what change in the length is necessary to make it accurate. **(M.U.)**

The period T of a pendulum of length l is

$$2\pi\sqrt{\frac{l}{g}}. \qquad ...(1)$$

If m is the number of oscillations in 24 hours, then

$$m = \frac{24\times 60\times 60}{T} = \frac{24\times 60\times 60}{2\pi}\sqrt{\frac{g}{l}} = \frac{43200}{\pi}\sqrt{\frac{g}{l}}. \qquad ...(2)$$

Since g is a constant, by logarithmic differentiation,

$$\frac{\delta m}{m} = -\frac{1}{2}\frac{\delta l}{l} \text{ or } \delta l = -\frac{2l}{m}\delta m.$$

Now $\delta m = -20$ (oscillations). Thus, using (2),

$$\delta l = -\frac{2l\times\pi}{43200}\sqrt{\frac{l}{g}}(-20).$$

But, from (1), $2\pi\sqrt{\frac{l}{g}} \simeq 2$ or $\pi\sqrt{\frac{l}{g}} \simeq 1$. So

$$\delta l = \frac{2l}{43200}\times 20 = \frac{l}{1080} = \frac{1}{1080}\frac{g}{\pi^2} = \frac{981}{1080\pi^2} = 0{\cdot}092 \text{ cm.}$$

Which is in excess over the length of a true pendulum.

Example 3. If l_1 is the length of an imperfectly adjusted seconds pendulum which loses n seconds in one hour and l_2, the length of one which gains n seconds in one hour, at the same place, show that the true length of the seconds pendulum is

$$\frac{4\,l_1\,l_2}{l_1 + l_2 + 2\sqrt{l_1 l_2}}. \qquad \textbf{(M.U., A.U.)}$$

Let l be the true length of the seconds pendulum. Let m be the number of oscillations of this pendulum in 1 hour. Then

$$m = \frac{60\times 60}{T} = \frac{60\times 60}{2\pi}\sqrt{\frac{g}{l}}. \qquad ...(1)$$

In the first and second cases, the lengths are l_1, l_2 and the numbers of oscillations are

$$m - (n/2), \quad m + (n/2).$$

Therefore, from (1), we have

$$\therefore \quad m - \frac{n}{2} = \frac{60\times 60}{2\pi}\sqrt{\frac{g}{l_1}} \qquad ...(2)$$

$$m + \frac{n}{2} = \frac{60\times 60}{2\pi}\sqrt{\frac{g}{l_2}} \qquad ...(3)$$

Adding (2) and (3) and using (1),

$$2\sqrt{\frac{g}{l}} = \sqrt{\frac{g}{l_1}} + \sqrt{\frac{g}{l_2}} \quad \text{or} \quad 2 = \sqrt{l}\,\frac{\sqrt{l_1}+\sqrt{l_2}}{\sqrt{l_1 l_2}}.$$

$$\therefore \quad 4 = l\,\frac{l_1 + l_2 + 2\sqrt{l_1 l_2}}{l_1 l_2} \quad \text{or} \quad l = \frac{4\,l_1 l_2}{l_1 + l_2 + 2\sqrt{l_1 l_2}}.$$

Example 4. A pendulum which beats seconds at the surface of the earth loses 10 seconds in 24 hours when taken to the summit of a hill. Find the height of the hill, taking the radius of the earth to be 6400 km. **(M.K.U.)**

If g and g' are the accelerations due to gravity on the plain and on the hill, then by Newton's inverse square law of gravitation

$$g = \frac{\mu}{6400^2}, \quad g' = \frac{\mu}{(6400+h)^2}, \qquad \text{...(1)}$$

where h km. is the height of the hill. If the number of oscillations in the plain is m, then

$$m = \frac{24\times 60\times 60}{T} = \frac{24\times 60\times 60}{2\pi}\sqrt{\frac{g}{l}} \qquad \text{...(2)}$$

Number of oscillations lost on the hill is 5. Therefore,

$$m - 5 = \frac{24\times 60\times 60}{2\pi}\sqrt{\frac{g'}{l}}. \qquad \text{...(3)}$$

Dividing (2) by (3) and using (1),

$$\left(\frac{m}{m-5}\right)^2 = \frac{g}{g'} = \frac{(6400+h)^2}{6400^2}$$

or

$$\frac{m}{m-5} = \frac{6400+h}{6400}.$$

Since, in the plain, the period is 2 seconds,

$$m = \frac{24\times 60\times 60}{2} = 43200.$$

$$\therefore \quad \frac{43200}{43200-5} = 1 + \frac{h}{6400} \quad \text{or} \quad 1 + \frac{5}{43195} = 1 + \frac{h}{6400}$$

$$\therefore \quad h = \frac{5\times 6400}{43195} = 0\cdot 7408 \text{ km.} = 740\cdot 8 \text{ m.}$$

EXERCISES

1. Show that an incorrect seconds pendulum of a clock which loses x seconds a day must be shortened by $\frac{x}{432}$ percent of its length in order to keep correct time. **(M.K.U.)**

[Hint: If m is the number of oscillations in a day,

$$m = \frac{24 \times 60 \times 60}{2\pi}\sqrt{\frac{g}{l}}\text{. So } \frac{\delta m}{m} = -\frac{1}{2}\frac{\delta l}{l},$$

where $\delta m = \dfrac{x}{2}$ and $m = \dfrac{24 \times 60 \times 60}{2}$. Find $\dfrac{\delta l}{l}100$]

2. A seconds pendulum gains n seconds a day in one place and loses n seconds a day in another. If N is the number of seconds in a day and n is very small compared with N, show that the values of g at the two places are approximately in the ratio

$$\frac{N+3n}{N-n}.$$

(M.U., A.U)

[Hint: $24 \times 60 \times 60 = \dfrac{N+n}{2} 2\pi\sqrt{\dfrac{l}{g_1}}$; $24 \times 60 \times 60 = \dfrac{N-n}{2} 2\pi\sqrt{\dfrac{l}{g_2}}$. Put $\dfrac{n}{N} = x$. Then

$$\frac{g_1}{g_2} = \frac{(N+n)^2}{(N-n)^2} = (1+x)^2(1-x)^{-2} \simeq (1+2x)(1+2x) \simeq 1+4x.$$

Also $\dfrac{N+3n}{N-n} = (1+3x)(1-x)^{-1} \simeq (1+3x)(1+x) \simeq 1+4x$]

3. A seconds pendulum which gains 10 seconds per day at one place loses 10 seconds per day at another. Compare the acceleration due to gravity at the two places. **(M.U.)**

[Hint: $\dfrac{g_1}{g_2} = \left(\dfrac{43200+10}{43200-10}\right)^2 = \dfrac{4321^2}{4319^2}$]

CENTRAL ORBITS

16.1 GENERAL ORBITS

In this section we get the orbits of particles when their velocity components or their acceleration components are given. Central orbit is an orbit under a central force.

Central force. When a particle is subject to the action of a force which is always either towards or away from a fixed point, the particle is said to be under the action of a central force.

The velocity and acceleration components in the radial and transverse directions are as follows.

Velocity components : $\dot{r},\ r\,\dot{\theta}$

Acceleration components : $\ddot{r} - r\,\dot{\theta}^2,\quad \dfrac{1}{r}\dfrac{d}{dt}(r^2\,\dot{\theta})$

Conic. Now it is necessary to remember that the polar equation of a conic is

$$\frac{l}{r} = 1 + e\cos\theta,$$

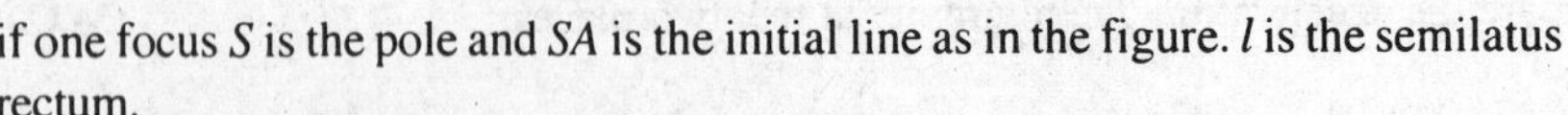

if one focus S is the pole and SA is the initial line as in the figure. l is the semilatus rectum.

Equiangular spiral. Equiangular spiral is a curve which is such that the angle between the radius vector and the respective tangent is a constant, say α. Its polar equation is

$$r = Ae^{(\cot\alpha)\theta},$$

where A is a constant.

EXAMPLES

Example 1. The velocities of a particle along and perpendicular to the radius vector are λr and $\mu\theta$. Find the path and show that the acceleration components along and perpendicular to the radius vector are

$$\lambda^2 r - \frac{\mu^2\theta^2}{r},\quad \mu\theta\left(\lambda + \frac{\mu}{r}\right).$$ **(M.U., K.U., Bn.U., C.U.)**

It is given that

$$\dot{r} = \lambda r \text{ or } \frac{dr}{dt} = \lambda r, \qquad \text{...(1)}$$

$$r\theta = \mu\theta \text{ or } r\frac{d\theta}{dt} = \mu\theta. \qquad \text{...(2)}$$

Dividing (1) by (2), we get

$$\frac{1}{r}\frac{dr}{d\theta} = \frac{\lambda r}{\mu\theta} \text{ or } \frac{1}{r^2}dr = \frac{\lambda}{\mu}\frac{1}{\theta}\,d\theta.$$

On integration, we get the equation of the path as

$$-\frac{1}{r}=\frac{\lambda}{\mu}\log\theta+A.$$

The acceleration along the radius vector is

$$\ddot{r}-r\dot{\theta}^2=\frac{d\dot{r}}{dt}-r\dot{\theta}^2=\frac{d(\lambda r)}{dt}-r\left(\frac{\mu\theta}{r}\right)^2 \quad \text{by (1), (2)}$$

$$=\lambda\frac{dr}{dt}-\frac{\mu^2\theta^2}{r}=\lambda\,(\lambda r)-\frac{\mu^2\theta^2}{r}$$

$$=\lambda^2 r-\frac{\mu^2\theta^2}{r}.$$

The acceleration perpendicular to the radius vector is

$$\frac{1}{r}\frac{d}{dt}(r^2\dot{\theta})=\frac{1}{r}\frac{d}{dt}\left(r^2\frac{\mu\theta}{r}\right) \quad \text{by (2)}$$

$$=\frac{\mu}{r}[\dot{r}\theta+r\dot{\theta}]=\frac{\mu}{r}[\lambda r\theta+\mu\theta]$$

$$=\mu\theta\left[\lambda+\frac{\mu}{r}\right].$$

Example 2. The velocities of a particle along and perpendicular to the radius vector from a fixed origin are a and b. Find the path and the accelerations along and perpendicular to the radius vector. **(M.U.)**

It is given that $\dot{r}=a,\ \ r\dot{\theta}=b$. Dividing the first by the second,

$$\frac{\dot{r}}{r\dot{\theta}}=\frac{a}{b}. \text{ So } \frac{1}{r}\frac{dr}{d\theta}=\frac{a}{b}.$$

$$\therefore \qquad \frac{1}{r}dr=\frac{a}{b}d\theta.$$

Integration gives the equation of the path as

$$\log r=\frac{a}{b}\theta+\log C \text{ or } \frac{r}{C}=e^{a/b\,\theta} \text{ or } r=Ce^{a/b\,\theta}$$

which is the equation of an equiangular spiral. Also $\ddot{r}=0$ and $\dot{\theta}=b/r$. So the acceleration components are

$$(i)\quad \ddot{r}-r\dot{\theta}^2=0-r\frac{b^2}{r^2}=-\frac{b^2}{r}$$

$$(ii)\quad \frac{1}{r}\frac{d}{dt}(r^2\dot{\theta})=\frac{1}{r}\frac{d}{dt}(br)=\frac{b\dot{r}}{r}=\frac{ab}{r}.$$

Example 3. Show that the path of a point P whose velocity is such that its components in a fixed direction and in the direction perpendicular to the line joining P to a fixed point O are respectively the constants u and v, is a conic with a focus at O and eccentricity u/v. **(M.U.,M.K.U.)**

Let O be the pole and OA, the given fixed direction, the initial line. Then the components of the velocity u in the radial and transverse directions are

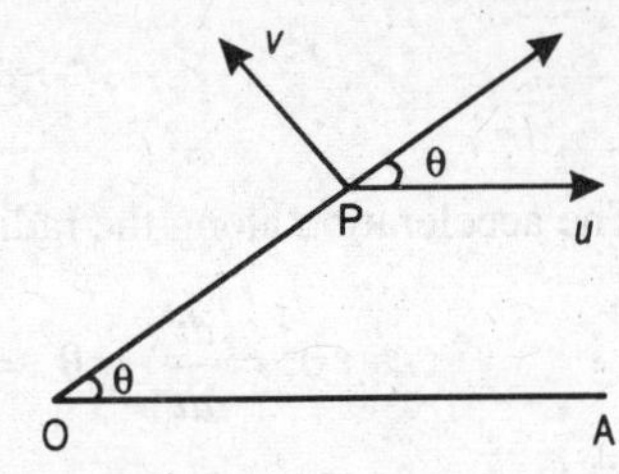

$$u\cos\theta,\ -u\sin\theta.$$

$$\therefore \qquad \dot{r} = u\cos\theta,\ r\dot{\theta} = v - u\sin\theta.$$

Dividing $\dot{r}$ by $r\dot{\theta}$, we get

$$\frac{1}{r}\frac{dr}{d\theta} = \frac{u\cos\theta}{v - u\sin\theta}.$$

Integration gives

$$\log r = -\log(v - u\sin\theta) + \log C$$

i.e., $$r = \frac{C}{v - u\sin\theta} \quad \text{or} \quad \frac{C}{r} = v - u\sin\theta$$

i.e., $$\frac{C/v}{r} = 1 - \frac{u}{v}\sin\theta.$$

So the path is a conic with its focus at O and eccentricity is u/v.

Example 4. A point P describes an equiangular spiral with a constant angular velocity about the pole O. Show that its acceleration varies as OP and is in a direction making with the tangent at P the same constant angle that OP makes. **(M.U., M.K.U.)**

The equation of an equiangular spiral is $r = a\,e^{\theta\cot\alpha}$, where a, α are constants. α is the angle between the tangent at any point and the radius vector to that point. Let the constant angular velocity be ω. Now

$$\dot{r} = a\,e^{\theta\cot\alpha}\cot\alpha\,\dot{\theta} = \omega\cot\alpha\, r,$$

$$\ddot{r} = \omega\cot\alpha\,\dot{r} = \omega^2\cot^2\alpha\, r.$$

Then the radial and the transverse components of acceleration are

$$\ddot{r} - r\dot{\theta}^2 = \omega^2\cot^2\alpha\, r - r\omega^2 = \omega^2 r(\cot^2\alpha - 1)$$

$$\frac{1}{r}\frac{d}{dt}(r^2\dot{\theta}) = \frac{\omega}{r}(2r\,\dot{r}) = \frac{\omega}{r}(2r\,\omega\cot\alpha\, r) = 2\omega^2 r\cot\alpha.$$

$$\therefore \quad \text{Acceleration} = \sqrt{\omega^4 r^2(\cot^2\alpha - 1)^2 + 4\omega^4 r^2\cot^2\alpha}$$

$$= \sqrt{\omega^4 r^2(1 + \cot^2\alpha)^2} = \omega^2 r\,\mathrm{cosec}^2\alpha$$

which is proportional to r.

If β is the angle between the radial direction and the direction of the acceleration, then

$$\tan\beta = \frac{\text{Transverse component}}{\text{Radial component}} = \frac{2\omega^2 r\cot\alpha}{\omega^2 r(\cot^2\alpha - 1)}$$

$$= \frac{2\tan\alpha}{1 - \tan^2\alpha} = \tan 2\alpha.$$

So $\beta = 2\alpha$. But the angle between the radial direction and the tangent is α. So the angle between the tangent and the acceleration is α.

EXERCISES

1. **If the angular velocity of a point moving on a plane curve is constant about a fixed origin, show that its transverse acceleration is proportional to its radial velocity.** **(M.U.)**

[Hint: $\dot{\theta} = \omega$, say. Now the radial velocity is $\dot{r}$. But

$$\left.\begin{array}{l}\text{Transverse}\\ \text{acceleration}\end{array}\right\} = \frac{1}{r}\frac{d}{dt}(r^2\omega) = \frac{1}{r}\omega\,(2r\,\dot{r}) = 2\omega\dot{r}\ ]$$

2. **If a point moves so that its radial velocity is k times its transverse velocity, show that its path is an equiangular spiral.** **(M.K.U.)**

[Hint: $\dot{r} = k(r\dot{\theta})$. So $\frac{dr}{dt} = kr\frac{d\theta}{dt}$ or $\frac{1}{r}dr = k\,d\theta$]

3. **A particle moves in a plane. Its velocity parallel to the y axis is constant and its velocity parallel to the x axis is proportional to ordinate. Show that its path is a parabola.**

[Hint: $\dot{y} = c, \dot{x} = y$. On division $\frac{dy}{dx} = \frac{c}{y}$ or $\frac{y^2}{2} = cx + A$]

4. **The velocities of a particle along and perpendicular to the radius vector are λr^2 and $\mu\theta^2$ where μ and λ are constants. Show that the equation to the path of the particle is**

$$\frac{\lambda}{\theta} + C = \frac{\mu}{2r^2}.$$

where C is a constant. **(M.U.,M.K.U.)**

[Hint: $\dot{r} = \lambda r^2,\quad r\dot{\theta} = \mu\theta^2$. So $\frac{1}{r}\frac{dr}{d\theta} = \frac{\lambda r^2}{\mu\theta^2}$ or $\frac{1}{r^3}dr = \frac{\lambda}{\mu}\frac{1}{\theta^2}d\theta$]

5. **A particle describes the equiangular spiral $r = a\,e^{\theta\cot\alpha}$ whose pole is O. If its radial velocity at distance r from O is k/r (k: constant), prove that the acceleration of the particle towards O is**

$$\frac{k^2\sec^2\alpha}{r^3}.$$ **(M.U.)**

[Hint: Given $\dot{r} = \frac{k}{r}$...(1). From $r = a\,e^{(\cot\alpha)\theta}$, $\dot{r} = r\cot\alpha\,\dot{\theta}$...(2). From (1) and (2), $\dot{\theta} = \frac{k\tan\alpha}{r^2}$.

Also $\ddot{r} = -\frac{k}{r^2}\dot{r} = -\frac{k^2}{r^3}$. Find $\ddot{r} - r\dot{\theta}^2$]

6. **A particle moves in the path given by the equation $r = a\,e^{\theta}$ with no force in the line joining the particle to the pole. Show that**

(*i*) **The angular velocity of the pole is constant** **(M.K.U.)**

(*ii*) **The speed varies as its distance from the pole** **(M.K.U.)**

(*iii*) **The acceleration is directly proportional to r in magnitude.** **(M.K.U.)**

[Hint: Given $r = a\,e^{\theta}$. So $\dot{r} = a\,e^{\theta}\,\dot{\theta} = r\dot{\theta}$; $\ddot{r} = \dot{r}\dot{\theta} + r\ddot{\theta}$ or $\ddot{r} - [r\dot{\theta}]\dot{\theta} = r\ddot{\theta}$ or $\ddot{r} - r\dot{\theta}^2 = r\ddot{\theta}$. But $\ddot{r} - r\dot{\theta}^2 = 0$. So $\ddot{\theta} = 0$;

(*i*) $\dot{\theta} = k$.

(*ii*) $v^2 = \dot{r} + (r\dot{\theta})^2 = \dot{r}^2 + \dot{r}^2 = 2\dot{r}^2 = 2(rk)^2$;

(*iii*) $\frac{1}{r}\frac{d}{dt}(r^2\,\dot{\theta}) = \frac{1}{r}k\,(2r\,\dot{r}) = \frac{2k}{r}(r\,r\dot{\theta}) = 2k^2 r$]

7. A particle of mass m moves along the curve $r = 1 + \cos\theta$ under the action of a force P towards the pole and a force Q in the positive direction of the initial line. If the angular velocity of the particle about the pole is constant and equal to ω, find the values of P and Q and show that the kinetic energy of the particle is $\dfrac{2P+3Q}{8}$ at any point of its path. **(M.U.)**

[Hint: Since $\dot{\theta} = \omega$, from $r = 1 + \cos\theta$, $\dot{r} = -\omega\sin\theta$, $\ddot{r} = -\omega^2\cos\theta$. Set in the equations of motion

$$m(\ddot{r} - r\dot{\theta}^2) = -P + Q\cos\theta, \quad m\frac{1}{r}\frac{d}{dt}(r^2\dot{\theta}) = -Q\sin\theta.$$

Solving, $P = m\omega^2(1 + 4\cos\theta)$, $Q = 2m\omega^2$; K.E $= \frac{1}{2}m(\dot{r}^2 + r^2\dot{\theta}^2)$]

8. A particle moves with a uniform speed v along a cardioid $r = a(1 + \cos\theta)$. Show that its angular velocity about the pole and the radial acceleration component are

$$\frac{v}{2a}\sec\frac{\theta}{2}, \; -\frac{3v^2}{4a}.$$ **(M.U.)**

[Hint: $r = a(1 + \cos\theta)$, $\dot{r} = -a\sin\theta\,\dot{\theta}$; $v = \sqrt{\dot{r}^2 + (r\dot{\theta})^2} = 2a\dot{\theta}\cos\theta/2$. So $\dot{\theta} = \dfrac{v}{2a}\sec\dfrac{\theta}{2}$ and

$\dot{r} = -a\sin\theta.\dfrac{v}{2a}.\sec\dfrac{\theta}{2} = -v\sin\dfrac{\theta}{2}$. $\ddot{r} = -\dfrac{v^2}{4a}$; $\ddot{r} - r\dot{\theta}^2 = -\dfrac{3v^2}{4a}$]

9. A particle is at rest on a smooth horizontal plane which commences to turn about a straight line lying in itself with constant angular velocity ω downwards, if a be the distance of the particle from the axis of rotation at zero time, show that the body will leave the plane at time t given by the equation

$$a\sinh\omega t + \frac{g}{2\omega^2}\cosh\omega t = \frac{g}{\omega^2}\cos\omega t.$$ **(C.U.)**

[Hint: If θ is the angle through which the plane rotates in time t, then $\dot{\theta} = \omega$ and $\theta = \omega t$. The equations corresponding to the radial and transverse directions are

$$\ddot{r} - r\omega^2 = g\sin\omega t. \quad \text{...(1)}$$

$$\frac{1}{r}\frac{d(r^2\omega)}{dt} = g\cos\omega t - \frac{R}{m} \text{ or } \frac{R}{m} = g\cos\omega t - 2\omega\dot{r} \quad \text{...(2)}$$

The solution of (1) and $\dot{r}$ are

$$r = A\cosh\omega t + B\sinh\omega t - \frac{g}{2\omega^2}\sin\omega t.$$

$$\therefore \dot{r} = A\omega\sinh\omega t + B\omega\cosh\omega t - \frac{g}{2\omega}\cos\omega t.$$

But, when $t = 0$, $r = a$ and $\dot{r} = 0$. So $A = a$, $B = \dfrac{g}{2\omega^2}$. From (2), when $R = 0$, $\dot{r} = \dfrac{g\cos\omega t}{2\omega}$]

16.2 CENTRAL ORBIT

In this chapter we study the motion of a particle subject to the action of a central force.

Central force. When a particle is subject to the action of a force which is always either towards or away from a fixed point, the particle is said to be under the action of a central force. That is, a central force is a force whose line of action always passes through a fixed point.

Centre of force. A central force is a force whose line of action always passes through a fixed point. The fixed point is called the centre of force.

Polar coordinates. To study the central motion of a particle we use polar coordinates r, θ, choosing the centre of force as the pole and a fixed line through it as the initial line.

Notation. We shall denote the central force per unit mass by

$$\phi(r)\,\hat{r},$$

where $\hat{r}$ is the unit vector in the radial direction in the sense in which r increases and $\phi(r)$ is a function of distance r of the particle from the centre of force.

Central orbit. The path described by a particle under a central force is called a central orbit.

Bookwork 16.1. To show that a central orbit is a plane curve.

Let us make the following assumptions:

O : Centre of force

P : Position of the particle at time t

$\bar{r}$: $\overline{OP}$ $(r = OP)$

$\hat{r}$: Unit vector along OP

m : Mass of the particle

$\phi(r)\,\hat{r}$: Central force per unit mass

Then the equation of motion of the particle is

$$m\ddot{\bar{r}} = m\,\phi(r)\,\hat{r} \quad \text{or} \quad \ddot{\bar{r}} = \phi(r)\,\hat{r}. \qquad ...(1)$$

Let us consider, in particular,

$$\frac{d}{dt}(\bar{r}\times\dot{\bar{r}}) = \dot{\bar{r}}\times\dot{\bar{r}} + \bar{r}\times\ddot{\bar{r}}$$

$$= \bar{0} + \bar{r}\times\phi(r)\,\hat{r} = \bar{0} + \bar{0} = \bar{0}.$$

This implies that $\bar{r}\times\dot{\bar{r}}$ is a constant vector, say $\bar{c}$. Then $\bar{r}$ or $\overline{OP}$ is always perpendicular to $\bar{c}$. So P is always in the plane through O and perpendicular to $\bar{c}$. Hence the motion of P is coplanar and the orbit is a plane curve.

16.2.1 Differential equation of a central orbit.

We now obtain the equation of a central orbit in polar coordinates.

Bookwork 16.2. To obtain the differential equation of a central orbit in polar coordinates.

Let us make the following assumptions:

O : Centre of force

O : Pole

OA : Initial line

$P(r, \theta)$: Position of the particle at time t

$\phi(r)$: Central force per unit mass in the direction OP

m : Mass of the particle

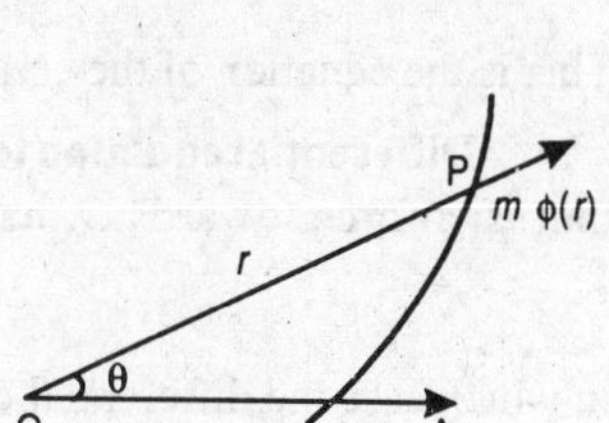

The motion is a coplanar motion. We shall consider the equations of motion corresponding to the radial and transverse directions. We know that, in these directions, the acceleration components are

$$\ddot{r} - r\dot{\theta}^2, \ \frac{1}{r}\frac{d}{dt}(r^2\dot{\theta}).$$

The force components in these directions are

$$m\phi(r), 0.$$

Therefore the respective equations of motions are

$$m(\ddot{r} - r\dot{\theta}^2) = m\phi(r) \text{ or } \ddot{r} - r\dot{\theta}^2 = \phi(r), \quad ...(1)$$

$$m\frac{1}{r}\frac{d}{dt}(r^2\dot{\theta}) = 0 \text{ or } \frac{1}{r}\frac{d}{dt}(r^2\dot{\theta}) = 0. \quad ...(2)$$

Of these, the second implies that $r^2\dot{\theta}$ is a constant, say h. If $1/r$ is denoted by u, then

$$\dot{\theta} = \frac{h}{r^2} = hu^2. \quad ...(3)$$

Differentiation of $r = \frac{1}{u}$ with respect to t gives

$$\frac{dr}{dt} = -\frac{1}{u^2}\frac{du}{dt} = -\frac{1}{u^2}\frac{du}{d\theta}\frac{d\theta}{dt}$$

$$= -\frac{1}{u^2}\frac{du}{d\theta}(hu^2) = -h\frac{du}{d\theta} \text{ by (3)}. \quad ...(4)$$

$$\therefore \quad \frac{d^2r}{dt^2} = -h\frac{d}{dt}\left(\frac{du}{d\theta}\right) = -h\frac{d}{d\theta}\left(\frac{du}{d\theta}\right)\frac{d\theta}{dt}$$

$$= -h\frac{d^2u}{d\theta^2}(hu^2) = -h^2u^2\frac{d^2u}{d\theta^2} \text{ by (3)}. \quad ...(5)$$

Substituting these values of $\ddot{r}$ and $\dot{\theta}$ in (1),

$$-h^2u^2\frac{d^2u}{d\theta^2} - r(hu^2)^2 = \phi(r)$$

Since $r = 1/u$, this can be written as

$$\frac{d^2u}{d\theta^2} + u = -\frac{\phi(r)}{h^2u^2}.$$

This is the equation of the central orbit in polar coordinates.

Differential equation for an attractive central force. If the central force is an attractive one, that is, a force towards O, having a magnitude F per unit mass, then

$$\phi(r) = -F$$

in which case the differential equation of the orbit becomes

$$\frac{d^2u}{d\theta^2} + u = \frac{F}{h^2u^2}.$$

Apse. If O is the pole and P is a point on a curve such that OP is perpendicular to the tangent at P, then P is an apse. If P is an apse OP is a maximum or minimum of r. For example, in an ellipse, if S is the pole, then the ends of the major axes are apses.

Maximum and minimum angular velocity. Since $r^2\dot{\theta}$ is a constant in a central orbit, the angular velocity of the particle about O is a maximum or minimum according as the radius vector r is a minimum or maximum. So, at an apse, the angular velocity of the particle is either a maximum or minimum. The apses are given by $du/d\theta = 0$.

Force per unit mass. The force per unit mass is

$$\phi(r)\,\hat{r} = -h^2u^2\left(\frac{d^2u}{d\theta^2}+u\right)\hat{r}. \qquad \text{...(6)}$$

Velocity v at P. We know that in a coplanar motion the velocity components along the radial and transverse directions are

$$\dot{r},\ r\dot{\theta}.$$

$$\therefore \qquad v^2 = (\dot{r})^2+(r\dot{\theta})^2 = h^2\left(\frac{du}{d\theta}\right)^2+\frac{1}{u^2}(hu^2)^2 \text{ by (4), (3)}$$

$$= h^2\left(\frac{du}{d\theta}\right)^2+h^2u^2 = h^2\left[\left(\frac{du}{d\theta}\right)^2+u^2\right]. \qquad \text{...(7)}$$

Areal velocity. Let the initial position of the particle be Q and the position at time t be $P(r,\theta)$. Let the area OQP swept by the radius vector moving from OQ to OP be A. Then

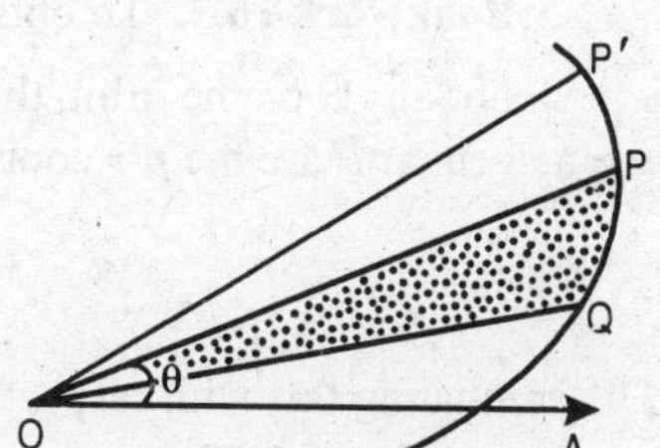

$$\frac{dA}{dt}$$

is called the areal velocity of the particle.

Let P' be the position of the particle at time $t+\Delta t$, then

$$\Delta A = \text{Area } POP' = \tfrac{1}{2}\,OP.OP'.\sin\Delta\theta$$

$$= \tfrac{1}{2}r(r+\Delta r)\,\Delta\theta \text{ since } \Delta\theta \text{ is small.}$$

$$\therefore \qquad \frac{\Delta A}{\Delta t} = \frac{1}{2}r(r+\Delta r)\frac{\Delta\theta}{\Delta t}.$$

So the areal velocity of P is

$$\lim_{\Delta t\to 0}\frac{\Delta A}{\Delta t} = \frac{dA}{dt} = \frac{1}{2}r^2\dot{\theta}.$$

Constancy of the areal velocity in central orbit. In a central orbit $r^2\dot{\theta}$ is a constant which we have denoted by h. So in a central orbit the areal velocity

$$\frac{1}{2}r^2\dot{\theta}$$

is a constant $h/2$.

Alternative form for areal velocity. If $ON (= p)$ is the perpendicular drawn from O to the chord PP' and the length of the arc PP' is Δs, then

$$\Delta A = \tfrac{1}{2}\, PP' \times ON \simeq \tfrac{1}{2}\, \Delta s \times ON$$

$$\therefore \quad \frac{\Delta A}{\Delta t} = \frac{1}{2}\frac{\Delta s}{\Delta t} \times ON$$

$$\therefore \quad \frac{dA}{dt} = \frac{1}{2}\frac{ds}{dt}\, p = \frac{1}{2} vp = \frac{1}{2} pv,$$

where v is the velocity of the particle at P.

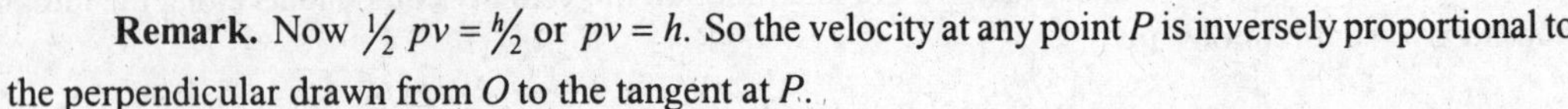

Remark. Now $\tfrac{1}{2} pv = \tfrac{h}{2}$ or $pv = h$. So the velocity at any point P is inversely proportional to the perpendicular drawn from O to the tangent at P.

Constancy of moment of momentum. The momentum of the particle is mv which is along the tangent. Its moment about O is

$$ON \times (mv) = m\,(pv) = mh.$$

Thus the moment of momentum about O, otherwise known as angular momentum about O, is the constant mh.

Bookwork 16.3. To obtain the differential equation of a central orbit in p-r coordinates.

For any P on the orbit, the radius vector $r\ (= OP)$ and the perpendicular distance p of O from the tangent at P are the p-r coordinates of P. From Differential Geometry, we know that

$$\frac{1}{p^2} = u^2 + \left(\frac{du}{d\theta}\right)^2.$$

Differentiating this with respect to θ,

$$-\frac{2}{p^3}\frac{dp}{d\theta} = 2u\frac{du}{d\theta} + 2\frac{du}{d\theta}\frac{d^2u}{d\theta^2} = 2\frac{du}{d\theta}\left[u + \frac{d^2u}{d\theta^2}\right].$$

If the central force (per unit mass) in the radial direction is $\phi(r)$, then

$$\frac{d^2u}{d\theta^2} + u = -\frac{\phi(r)}{h^2u^2}.$$

$$\therefore \quad -\frac{2}{p^3}\frac{dp}{d\theta} = 2\frac{du}{d\theta}\left[-\frac{\phi(r)}{h^2u^2}\right] \quad \text{or} \quad \frac{1}{p^3}\frac{dp}{d\theta} = \frac{\phi(r)}{h^2u^2}\frac{du}{d\theta}.$$

$$\therefore \quad \frac{1}{p^3}\frac{dp}{dr}\cdot\frac{dr}{d\theta} = \frac{\phi(r)}{h^2u^2}\frac{d\,(1/r)}{d\theta} \quad \text{since } u = \frac{1}{r}.$$

$$= \frac{\phi(r)}{h^2u^2}\left(-\frac{1}{r^2}\frac{dr}{d\theta}\right) = -\frac{\phi(r)}{h^2}\frac{dr}{d\theta}.$$

$$\therefore \quad \frac{h^2}{p^3}\frac{dp}{dr} = -\phi(r).$$

This equation is in terms of p and r. This is the p-r equation of the orbit. This is also called pedal equation of the orbit.

Equation for an attractive central force. If the central force is an attractive one of magnitude F per unit mass, then $\phi(r) = -F$ and the p-r equation of the orbit is

$$\frac{h^2}{p^3}\frac{dp}{dr} = F.$$

16.2.2 Law of a central force

When the equation of a central orbit is given, to obtain the force per unit mass and the speed of the particle at a distance r from the centre of force, we have to calculate

$$-h^2u^2\left(\frac{d^2u}{d\theta^2}+u\right)\hat{r},\quad h\sqrt{\left(\frac{du}{d\theta}\right)^2+u^2}.$$

16.2.3 Method to find the central orbit

If F is the central acceleration towards the centre of force, then to obtain the equation of the respective orbit, we have to solve the differential equation

$$\frac{d^2u}{d\theta^2}+u = \frac{F}{h^2u^2}. \qquad ...(1)$$

Here h may be found by using $h = pv$ from the given condition.

One method of solving the differential equation is by multiplying both sides of it by $2\frac{du}{d\theta}$ and then integrating w. r. t. θ. Then we get

$$\left(\frac{du}{d\theta}\right)^2 + u^2 = 2\int\frac{F}{h^2u^2}\frac{du}{d\theta}\,d\theta$$

$$= 2\int\frac{F}{h^2u^2}\,du$$

because

$$\frac{d}{d\theta}\left[\left(\frac{du}{d\theta}\right)^2+u^2\right] = 2\left(\frac{d^2u}{d\theta^2}+u\right)\frac{du}{d\theta}.$$

Thus we get a first order differential equation

$$\frac{du}{d\theta} = \text{(A function of } u\text{)}$$

which can be solved as such or after replacing u by $1/r$.

Bookwork 16.4. To find the orbit of a particle moving under an attractive central force varying inversely as the square of the distance.

Let the pole be the centre of force. Let the force per unit mass be $\frac{\mu}{r^2}$. Then the differential equation of the orbit is

$$\frac{d^2u}{d\theta^2}+u = \frac{1}{h^2u^2}\frac{\mu}{r^2} \quad\text{or}\quad \frac{d^2u}{d\theta^2}+u = \frac{\mu}{h^2}. \qquad ...(1)$$

Using the operator $\frac{d}{d\theta} = D$, we have

$$(D^2+1)u = \frac{\mu}{h^2}.$$

$$\text{C. F.} = A\cos(\theta+B); \quad \text{P. I.} = \frac{1}{D^2+1}\left(\frac{\mu}{h^2}\right) = \frac{\mu}{h^2}.$$

So the general solution is

$$u = A\cos(\theta+B) + \frac{\mu}{h^2} \qquad \text{...(2)}$$

i.e., $\frac{h^2 u}{\mu} = 1 + \frac{h^2 A}{\mu}\cos(\theta+B)$

i.e.,

$$\frac{(h^2/\mu)}{r} = 1 + \frac{h^2 A}{\mu}\cos(\theta+B).$$

It represents a conic whose semilatus rectum and eccentricity are

$$l = \frac{h^2}{\mu}, \quad e = \frac{h^2 A}{\mu}. \qquad \text{...(3)}$$

Nature of the orbit. Multiplying both sides of (1) by $2\frac{du}{d\theta}$ and integrating w. r. t. θ, we get

$$\left(\frac{du}{d\theta}\right)^2 + u^2 = 2\int\frac{\mu}{h^2}\,du \quad \text{or} \quad \left(\frac{du}{d\theta}\right)^2 + u^2 = 2\frac{\mu u}{h^2} + C$$

$$\therefore \quad h^2\left[\left(\frac{du}{d\theta}\right)^2 + u^2\right] = 2\,\mu u + C. \qquad \text{...(4)}$$

In this LHS is the square of the velocity. Therefore

$$v^2 = 2\mu u + C. \qquad \text{...(5)}$$

Substituting in (4) the value of u obtained from (2),

$$h^2\left[A^2\sin^2(\theta+B) + \frac{\mu^2}{h^4} + 2.\frac{\mu}{h^2}.A\cos(\theta+B) + A^2\cos^2(\theta+B)\right] = 2\mu u + C$$

or $$h^2\left[A^2 + \frac{\mu^2}{h^4} + \frac{2\mu A}{h^2}\cos(\theta+B)\right] = 2\mu u + C$$

or $$h^2A^2 + \frac{\mu^2}{h^2} + 2\mu\left[u - \frac{\mu}{h^2}\right] = 2\mu u + C \text{ by (2)}$$

or $$h^2A^2 - \frac{\mu^2}{h^2} = C \text{ or } h^2A^2 = \frac{\mu^2}{h^2} + C.$$

$$\therefore \quad \frac{h^4A^2}{\mu^2} = 1 + \frac{Ch^2}{\mu^2} \quad \text{or} \quad e^2 = 1 + \frac{Ch^2}{\mu^2} \text{ by (3).}$$

Thus the orbit is an ellipse or parabola or hyperbola according as

	Ellipse	*Parabola*	*Hyperbola*
	$e<1$	$e=1$	$e>1$
or	$C<0$	$C=0$	$C>0$
From (5)	$v^2-2\mu u<0$	$v^2-2\mu u=0$	$v^2-2\mu u>0$
or	$v^2-\frac{2\mu}{r}<0$	$v^2-\frac{2\mu}{r}=0$	$v^2-\frac{2\mu}{r}>0$
or	$v^2<\frac{2\mu}{r}$	$v^2=\frac{2\mu}{r}$	$v^2>\frac{2\mu}{r}$
or	$v<\sqrt{\frac{2\mu}{r}}$	$v=\sqrt{\frac{2\mu}{r}}$	$v>\sqrt{\frac{2\mu}{r}}$

Therefore the nature of the orbit depends on the velocity with which the particle is projected from the point whose distance from the centre of force is r.

Critical velocity. The quantity $\sqrt{\frac{2\mu}{r}}$ is called the critical velocity at the distance r. So the nature of the orbit depends on the critical velocity.

The critical velocity can be seen to be the velocity that would be acquired by a particle, in the same force field, in reaching the point in question, starting from rest at the point at infinity. The equation for the motion from ∞ towards the pole is

$$\ddot{r}=-\frac{\mu}{r^2}.$$

Multiplying both sides by $2\dot{r}$ and then integrating w. r. t. t, we get

$$2\int \dot{r}\,\ddot{r}dt=-2\mu\int\frac{1}{r^2}dr \quad\text{or}\quad \dot{r}^2=2\mu\frac{1}{r}+C.$$

$$\therefore\quad \left[\dot{r}^2\right]_0^v=2\mu\left[\frac{1}{r}\right]_\infty^r \quad\text{or}\quad v^2=\frac{2\mu}{r}.$$

Alternative method. The orbit and its nature can also be obtained from the differential equation

$$\frac{h^2}{p^3}\frac{dp}{dr}=F$$

which is in p-r coordinates. Now it is

$$\frac{h^2}{p^3}\frac{dp}{dr}=\frac{\mu}{r^2} \quad\text{or}\quad h^2\int\frac{dp}{p^3}=\mu\int\frac{dr}{r^2}$$

$$\frac{h^2}{-2p^2}=\frac{\mu}{-r}+A \quad\text{or}\quad \frac{h^2}{p^2}=\frac{2\mu}{r}+D \qquad ...(6)$$

But we know that the p-r equations of an ellipse, a parabola, the nearer branch of a hyperbola are

$$\frac{b^2}{p^2}=\frac{2a}{r}-1,\qquad p^2=ar,\qquad \frac{b^2}{p^2}=\frac{2a}{r}+1.$$

So the orbit is an ellipse or a parabola or a hyperbola according as

$$D<0, \quad D=0, \quad D>0. \qquad ...(7)$$

Also we know that $pv = h$. Hence (6) becomes

$$v^2 = \frac{2\mu}{r} + D \quad \text{or} \quad D = v^2 - \frac{2\mu}{r}.$$

Thus the conditions (7) become that the orbit is an ellipse, a parabola, a hyperbola if

$$v < \sqrt{2\mu/r}, \quad v = \sqrt{2\mu/r}, \quad v > \sqrt{2\mu/r}.$$

Bookwork 16.5. To find the orbit of a particle moving under an attractive force varying as the distance.

Let the P.V. of the particle of mass m, at time t, be $\overline{r}$. If $n^2 r$ is the force per unit mass, then the equation of motion is

$$m\ddot{\overline{r}} = -mn^2 r\,\hat{r} \quad \text{or} \quad \ddot{\overline{r}} = -n^2\overline{r}.$$

If $\overline{r} = x\overline{i} + y\overline{j}$, then we get

$$\ddot{x} = -n^2 x, \quad \ddot{y} = -n^2 y.$$

The general solutions of these differential equations are

$$x = A\cos nt + B\sin nt,$$
$$y = C\cos nt + D\sin nt,$$

where the constants A, B, C, D depend upon the initial conditions. Solving these two equations for $\cos nt$, $\sin nt$,

$$\frac{\cos nt}{\begin{vmatrix} B & -x \\ D & -y \end{vmatrix}} = \frac{-\sin nt}{\begin{vmatrix} A & x \\ C & y \end{vmatrix}} = \frac{1}{\begin{vmatrix} A & B \\ C & D \end{vmatrix}}$$

$$\therefore \quad \cos nt = \frac{-By + Dx}{AD - BC}, \quad \sin nt = \frac{-Ay + Cx}{AD - BC}.$$

Squaring and adding, we get the equation of the path as

$$(Cx - Ay)^2 + (Dx - By)^2 = (AD - BC)^2$$

which being a second degree equation represents a conic. Further it satisfies "$h^2 - ab < 0$". Hence it represents an ellipse. Since $(-x, -y)$ satisfies the equation, the ellipse is symmetrical about the origin. So the centre of force is at the centre of the ellipse.

EXAMPLES

Example 1. Show that the force towards the pole under which a particle describes the curve $r^n = a^n \cos n\theta$ varies inversely as the $(2n+3)^{th}$ power of the distance of the particle from the pole.

(M.U., C.U., M.K.U.)

Expressing the equation in terms of u,

$$\frac{1}{u^n} = a^n \cos n\theta.$$

Taking logarithm and differentiating w. r. θ,

$$-\frac{n}{u}\frac{du}{d\theta} = -\frac{1}{\cos n\theta}(n \sin n\theta) \quad \text{or} \quad \frac{du}{d\theta} = u \tan n\theta.$$

$$\therefore \quad \frac{d^2u}{d\theta^2} = \frac{du}{d\theta}\tan n\theta + u\,(n \sec^2 n\theta)$$

$$= u \tan^2 n\theta + un \sec^2 n\theta = u\,(\tan^2 n\theta + n \sec^2 n\theta)$$

$$\therefore \quad h^2u^2\left(\frac{d^2u}{d\theta^2} + u\right) = h^2u^3(\tan^2 n\theta + n \sec^2 n\theta + 1)$$

$$= h^2u^3\,(n+1)\sec^2 n\theta = h^2 . \frac{1}{r^3} . (n+1)\frac{a^{2n}}{r^{2n}}$$

$$= \frac{h^2\,(n+1)\,a^{2n}}{r^{2n+3}},$$

This is the central attractive force which varies inversely as r^{2n+3}

Example 2. A particle moves with a central acceleration μr^{-7} and starts from an apse at a distance a with a velocity equal to the velocity which would be acquired by the particle travelling from rest at infinity to the apse. Show that the equation of its orbit is

$$r^2 = a^2 \cos 2\theta. \qquad \textbf{(M.K.U.)}$$

For the motion along the radius vector, from ∞ to any point $P\,(r, \theta)$ on the orbit, we have

$$\ddot{r} = -\frac{\mu}{r^7}. \qquad ...(1)$$

Let v be the velocity attained by the particle, travelling from rest at ∞ to P. Then multiplying both sides of (1) by $2\dot{r}$ and integrating w. r. t,

$$[\dot{r}^2]_0^v = -\int_{\infty}^{r}\frac{\mu}{r^7}\left(2\frac{dr}{dt}\right)dt = -2\mu\int_{\infty}^{r}\frac{1}{r^7}dr$$

i.e.,
$$v^2 = \frac{\mu}{3r^6}.$$

So the square of velocity v^2 of projection at the apse $r = a$ is

$$v^2 = \frac{\mu}{3a^6}.$$

Next we shall find the value of the constant h^2. Initially at the apse $r = p = a$ and, from $h = pv$,

$$h^2 = p^2v^2 = a^2\left(\frac{\mu}{3a^6}\right) = \frac{\mu}{3a^4}. \qquad ...(2)$$

Now the differential equation of the orbit is

$$\frac{d^2u}{d\theta^2} + u = \frac{\mu}{h^2u^2r^7}.$$

Eliminating h^2 by (2) and simplifying,

$$\frac{d^2u}{d\theta^2}+u=3a^4u^5.$$

Multiplying both sides by $2\frac{du}{d\theta}$ and integrating w. r. t. θ, we get

$$\left(\frac{du}{d\theta}\right)^2+u^2=\int 2\,(3a^4u^5)\,du$$

or
$$\left(\frac{du}{d\theta}\right)^2+u^2=a^4u^6+C.$$

But, initially $\frac{du}{d\theta}=0,\ u=\frac{1}{a}$. Therefore $C=0$ and

$$\left(\frac{du}{d\theta}\right)^2=a^4u^6-u^2.$$

Since $u=\frac{1}{r},\ \frac{du}{d\theta}=-\frac{1}{r^2}\frac{dr}{d\theta}$. Therefore

$$\frac{1}{r^4}\left(\frac{dr}{d\theta}\right)^2=\frac{a^4}{r^6}-\frac{1}{r^2}\quad\text{or}\quad\frac{dr}{d\theta}=\frac{\sqrt{a^4-r^4}}{r}.$$

$\therefore$
$$\frac{r}{\sqrt{a^4-r^4}}\,dr=d\theta.$$

Setting $r^2=y$ and integrating,

$$\frac{1}{2}\frac{1}{\sqrt{a^4-y^2}}\,dy=d\theta,\qquad \sin^{-1}\frac{y}{a^2}=2\theta+C.$$

$\therefore$
$$\sin^{-1}\frac{r^2}{a^2}=2\theta+C.$$

If the initial line is chosen through the apse so that the apse is $(a, 0)$, then, when $r=a,\ \theta=0$. This gives $C=\pi/2$.

$\therefore$
$$\frac{r^2}{a^2}=\sin\left(2\theta+\frac{\pi}{2}\right)\quad\text{or}\quad r^2=a^2\cos 2\theta.$$

EXERCISES

1. The position vector of a particle at time t is $\overline{r}=\overline{a}\cos nt+\overline{b}\sin nt$, where $\overline{a}$ and $\overline{b}$ are constant vectors and n, a constant. Show that the particle is moving under a central attractive force varying as the distance.
   [Hint: Force $\overline{F}=m\ddot{\overline{r}}$ or $\overline{F}=-mn^2\,\overline{r}=-mn^2\,r\,\hat{r}$]

2. A particle moves along the path $r=e^{\theta}$ under a central force. Show that the force is $\frac{2mh^2}{r^3}$ and speed of the particle is $\frac{h}{r}\sqrt{2}$. **(M.U., Bn.U.)**

[Hint: $u = e^{-\theta}, \ \dfrac{du}{d\theta} = -e^{-\theta} = -u, \ \dfrac{d^2u}{d\theta^2} = u.$ Force towards O is

$$mh^2u^2\left(\frac{d^2u}{d\theta^2}+u\right) = mh^2u^2\ (u+u) = \frac{2mh^2}{r^3}.$$

$$v^2 = h^2\left[\left(\frac{du}{d\theta}\right)^2 + u^2\right] = h^2\ [2u^2];\ v = \frac{\sqrt{2}\,h}{r}\ ]$$

3. In an orbit described under a force to a centre, the velocity at any point is inversely proportional to the distance of the point from the centre of force. Show that the path is an equiangular spiral. **(Bn.U.)**

[Hint: $v = \dfrac{k}{r}$. But $v^2 = h^2\left[\left(\dfrac{du}{d\theta}\right)^2 + u^2\right]$. So $\left(\dfrac{du}{d\theta}\right)^2 = \lambda^2u^2$, where $\lambda^2 = \dfrac{k^2}{h^2} - 1$. So

$\dfrac{1}{u}\,du = \lambda\,d\theta;\ r = Ae^{-\lambda\theta}$

4. A particle describes a circular orbit under an attractive central force directed towards a point on the circle. Show that the force varies as the inverse fifth power of the distance. **(M.U., A.U.)**

[Hint: The polar equation of the circle is $r = 2a\cos\theta$. So

$$u = \frac{\sec\theta}{2a},\ \frac{du}{d\theta} = \frac{\sec\theta\tan\theta}{2a},\ \frac{d^2u}{d\theta^2} = \frac{\sec^3\theta + \sec\theta\tan^2\theta}{2a}.$$

$$\text{So } h^2u^2\left(\frac{d^2u}{d\theta^2}+u\right) = h^2u^2\sec\theta\,\frac{\sec^2\theta\ \tan^2\theta+1}{2a} = 8a^2h^2u^5.]$$

5. A particle moves with a central acceleration $\mu[3au^4 - 2(a^2-b^2)u^5]$ being projected from an apse at a distance $a+b$ with a velocity $\dfrac{\sqrt{\mu}}{a+b}$. Show that the equation of its orbit is

$$r = a + b\cos\theta.$$ **(M.U., C.U., A.U.)**

[Hint: $h^2 = p^2v^2 = (a+b)^2\,\dfrac{\mu}{(a+b)^2} = \mu.$ D.E. of the orbit is

$$\frac{d^2u}{d\theta^2} + u = \frac{\mu\,[3au^4 - 2(a^2-b^2)u^5]}{h^2u^2} = 3au^2 - 2(a^2-b^2)u^3.$$

$$\therefore \quad \left(\frac{du}{d\theta}\right)^2 + u^2 = 2\left[au^3 - (a^2-b^2)\frac{u^4}{2}\right] + C,\ C = 0.$$

Using $\dfrac{du}{d\theta} = -\dfrac{1}{r^2}\dfrac{dr}{d\theta}$, $\dfrac{dr}{\sqrt{b^2-(r-a)^2}} = d\theta$ or $\sin^{-1}\dfrac{r-a}{b} = \theta + A$. Choose the initial line through the apse so that the apse is $(a+b, 0)$. $A = \pi/2$]

6. A particle acted on by a central attractive force μu^3 is projected with a velocity $\frac{1}{a}\sqrt{\mu}$ at an angle of $\pi/4$ with its initial distance a from the centre of force. Show that the path is the equiangular spiral $r = ae^{-\theta}$. **(M.U.)**

[**Hint:** Initially $p = a\cos 45° = \frac{a}{\sqrt{2}}$. So $h^2 = p^2v^2 = \frac{a^2}{2}\frac{\mu}{a^2} = \frac{\mu}{2}$.

$$\text{D.E.}: \frac{d^2u}{d\theta^2} + u = \frac{\mu u^3}{h^2u^2} \text{ or } \frac{d^2u}{d\theta^2} = u.$$

Multiplying both sides by $2\frac{du}{d\theta}$ and integrating w.r.t. θ, $\left(\frac{du}{d\theta}\right)^2 = u^2$ or $\frac{du}{d\theta} = u$ or

$\frac{1}{u}\,du = d\theta$. Choose the initial line through the apse so that the apse is $(a,0)$]

16.3 CONIC AS A CENTRAL ORBIT

Bookwork 16.6. When a central orbit is a conic with the centre of the force at one focus, to find the law of force and the speed of the particle.

Force. Choosing the focus S as the pole we get the polar equation of the conic as

$$\frac{l}{r} = 1 + e\cos\theta \quad \text{or} \quad u = \frac{1}{l} + \frac{e}{l}\cos\theta,$$

where l is the semilatus rectum. Therefore

$$\frac{du}{d\theta} = -\frac{e}{l}\sin\theta, \quad \frac{d^2u}{d\theta^2} = -\frac{e}{l}\cos\theta.$$

$$\therefore \quad h^2u^2\left(\frac{d^2u}{d\theta^2} + u\right) = h^2u^2\left[-\frac{e}{l}\cos\theta + \frac{1}{l} + \frac{e}{l}\cos\theta\right]$$

$$= h^2u^2\frac{1}{l} = \frac{h^2}{l}\cdot\frac{1}{r^2}.$$

Thus the force per unit mass in the radial direction but towards the pole is

$$\frac{h^2}{l}\cdot\frac{1}{r^2}. \qquad ...(1)$$

which is inversely proportional to the square of the distance from the pole. It is an attractive central force,

Inverse square law. In the above book work the force (1) is

$$\frac{h^2}{l}\cdot\frac{1}{r^2},$$

which is inversely proportional to the square of the distance. This rule of force is called inverse square law.

Velocity. The square of the speed of the particle at a distance r is

$$v^2 = h^2\left[\left(\frac{du}{d\theta}\right)^2 + u^2\right]$$

$$= h^2\left[\left(-\frac{e}{l}\sin\theta\right)^2 + \left(\frac{1}{l}+\frac{e}{l}\cos\theta\right)^2\right]$$

$$= \frac{h^2}{l^2}\left(e^2\sin^2\theta + 1 + 2e\cos\theta + e^2\cos^2\theta\right)$$

$$= \frac{h^2}{l^2}\left(e^2 + 1 + 2e\cos\theta\right) = \frac{h^2}{l^2}\left[e^2 + 1 + 2\left(\frac{l}{r}-1\right)\right]$$

$$= \frac{h^2}{l^2}\left(e^2 + 1 + 2\frac{l}{r} - 2\right) = \frac{h^2}{l^2}\left(e^2 - 1 + \frac{2l}{r}\right)$$

$$= \frac{h^2}{l}\left[\frac{e^2-1}{l} + \frac{2}{r}\right] = \mu\left[\frac{2}{r} + \frac{e^2-1}{l}\right],$$

where $\mu = \dfrac{h^2}{l}$.

Parabola. When the path is a parabola, $e = 1$ and therefore

$$v^2 = \mu\frac{2}{r}.$$

Ellipse. When the path is an ellipse,

$$v^2 = \mu\left[\frac{2}{r} + \frac{e^2-1}{l}\right] = \mu\left[\frac{2}{r} + \frac{e^2-1}{b^2/a}\right]$$

$$= \mu\left[\frac{2}{r} + \frac{a\,(e^2-1)}{b^2}\right] = \mu\left[\frac{2}{r} + \frac{a^2\,(e^2-1)}{ab^2}\right]$$

$$= \mu\left[\frac{2}{r} - \frac{b^2}{ab^2}\right] \text{ since } b^2 = a^2\,(1-e^2)$$

$$= \mu\left[\frac{2}{r} - \frac{1}{a}\right].$$

Maximum and minimum velocities. If A, A' are the ends of the major axis such that A is closer to S (the pole) than A', r is a minimum at A and maximum at A'. But the velocity is a maximum when r is a minimum. Thus the velocity is a maximum at A and a minimum at A'.

Periodic time. When the orbit is an ellipse the periodic time of the particle is the total area divided by the constant areal velocity. So it is

$$\frac{\pi ab}{h/2} = \frac{\pi ab}{\frac{1}{2}\sqrt{\mu l}} = \frac{2\pi ab\sqrt{a}}{\sqrt{\mu}\,b} = \frac{2\pi}{\sqrt{\mu}}\,a^{3/2}.$$

Hyperbola. When the path is the branch of the hyperbola nearer to the centre of force,

$$b^2 = a^2\,(e^2-1) \text{ or } e^2 - 1 = \frac{b^2}{a^2}$$

and consequently

$$v^2 = \mu\left(\frac{2}{r} + \frac{1}{a}\right).$$

Remark. It is important to note that when the path is the branch of the hyperbola not nearer to the centre of force, its equation is

$$\frac{l}{r} = -1 + e\cos\theta.$$

In this case the force per unit mass is

$$\frac{h^2}{l}\frac{1}{r^2}\hat{r}$$

It is a repulsive force as we have in the case of like charges.

16.3.1 Kepler's laws of planetary motion

Before the development of mathematical theory of planetary motion by Newton, with the assumption that any two particles attract each other with a force $\gamma m_1 m_2 / r^2$, where γ is a universal constant, m_1 and m_2 are the masses of the particles and r is the distance between them, Kepler propounded the following three laws on the basis of astronomical observations :

K. 1. : The planets describe ellipses about the sun as focus.

K. 2. : The radius vector drawn from the sun to a planet sweeps out equal areas in equal times.

K. 3. : The squares of the periodic times of the planets are proportional to the cubes of the semimajor axis of their respective orbits.

It is obvious that K.2 implies that for each planet the areal velocity $\frac{1}{2}r^2\dot{\theta}$ is a constant and the transverse component of the force acting on the planet is zero. So the force acting on the planet is along the radius vector and thus it is a central force, the sun being the centre of force. K. 1 implies that the force of attraction on the planet is inversely proportional to the square of its distance from the sun. So Newton's work is the assumption of inverse square law establishing the truth of Kepler's statement mathematically.

EXAMPLES

Example 1. A particle describes an elliptic orbit under a central force towards one focus S. If v_1 is the speed at the end B of the minor axis and v_2, v_3 the speeds at the ends A, A' of the major axis, show that $v_1^2 = v_2 v_3$. **(M.U., M.K.U., C.U.)**

In the present case the velocity formula is

$$v^2 = \mu\left(\frac{2}{r} - \frac{1}{a}\right).$$

Now the distances r of the points A, A', B from S are

$$SA = CA - CS = a - ae = a(1-e).$$

$$SA' = SC + CA' = ae + a = a(1+e).$$

$$SB = \sqrt{(ae)^2 + b^2} = a.$$

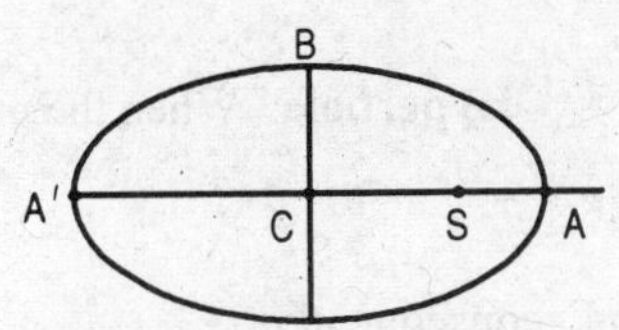

$$\therefore \quad v_1^2 = \mu\left(\frac{2}{a} - \frac{1}{a}\right) = \frac{\mu}{a},$$

$$v_2^2 = \mu\left\{\frac{2}{a(1-e)} - \frac{1}{a}\right\} = \frac{\mu}{a}\frac{2-1+e}{1-e} = \frac{\mu}{a}\frac{1+e}{1-e},$$

$$v_3^2 = \mu\left\{\frac{2}{a(1+e)} - \frac{1}{a}\right\} = \frac{\mu}{a}\frac{2-1-e}{1+e} = \frac{\mu}{a}\frac{1-e}{1+e}.$$

$$\therefore \qquad v_2^2\, v_3^2 = \frac{\mu^2}{a^2} = v_1^4 \quad \text{or} \quad v_2 v_3 = v_1^2.$$

Example 2. Show that the velocity of a particle moving in an ellipse about the centre of force at a focus is compounded of two constant velocities, namely,

(*i*) $\frac{\mu}{h}$ perpendicular to the radius vector.

(*ii*) $\frac{e\mu}{h}$ perpendicular to the major axis. **(M.U., A.U.)**

If the equation of the ellipse is

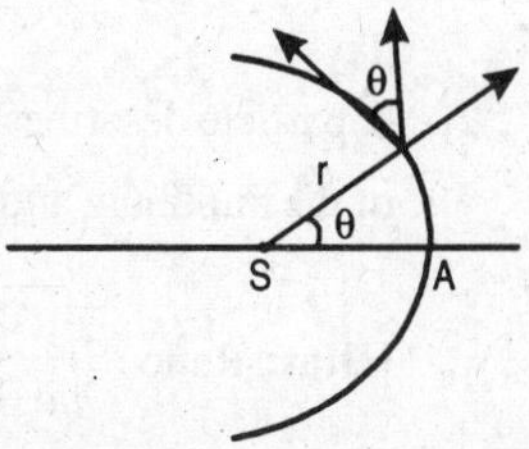

$$\frac{l}{r} = 1 + e\cos\theta, \qquad \text{...(1)}$$

then we know that

$$\mu = \frac{h^2}{l} \quad \text{or} \quad l = \frac{h^2}{\mu}. \qquad \text{...(2)}$$

Also we have

$$r^2\dot{\theta} = h. \qquad \text{...(3)}$$

The velocity components in the radial and transverse directions are

$$\dot{r},\ r\dot{\theta}.$$

Differentiating the equation (1) w. r. t. t,

$$-\frac{l}{r^2}\dot{r} = -e\sin\theta\,\dot{\theta}.$$

by (3)

$$\therefore \qquad \dot{r} = \frac{e\sin\theta}{l}(r^2\dot{\theta}) = \frac{eh}{l}\sin\theta \text{ by (3)}$$

$$= \frac{e\mu}{h}\sin\theta \text{ by (2)}. \qquad \text{...(4)}$$

$$r\dot{\theta} = \frac{r^2\dot{\theta}}{r} = \frac{h}{r} \text{ by (3)}$$

$$= h\,\frac{1+e\cos\theta}{l} = \frac{\mu}{h}(1+e\cos\theta) \text{ by (2)}$$

$$= \frac{\mu}{h} + \frac{e\mu}{h}\cos\theta. \qquad \text{...(5)}$$

From (4) and (5), we can say that the velocity of the particle is composed of three velocities, namely,

$$\frac{e\mu}{h}\sin\theta \text{ in the radial direction,} \qquad \text{...(6)}$$

$$\frac{e\mu}{h}\cos\theta \text{ in the transverse direction,} \qquad \text{...(7)}$$

$$\frac{\mu}{h} \text{ in the transverse direction.} \qquad ...(8)$$

From the figure it is clear that the radial and transverse directions are inclined to the perpendicular to the major axis at an angle θ and $90° - \theta$. So the resultant of (6) and (7) is the velocity

$$\frac{e\mu}{h} \text{ perpendicular to the major axis.} \qquad ...(9)$$

Now (8) and (9) constitute the required result.

EXERCISES

1. The eccentricity of the earth's orbit round the sun is $1/60$. Show that the earth's distance from the sun exceeds the length of the semimajor axis of the orbit during about 2 days more than half the year.

[Hint: Area of $\Delta SBB' = \frac{1}{2}(2b)\,ae$. But the area πab corresponds to 365 days. So abe, to 1·94 days]

2. A particle describes an elliptic orbit under a central force towards one focus. Show that the ratio of the minimum and maximum speeds of the particle is $1-e:1+e$, where e is the eccentricity.

[Hint: Ratio : $\sqrt{\dfrac{\mu}{a}\dfrac{1-e}{1+e}} : \sqrt{\dfrac{\mu}{a}\dfrac{1+e}{1-e}}$ or $\sqrt{(1-e)^2} : \sqrt{(1+e)^2}$]

3. A particle describes an ellipse under a force $\dfrac{\mu}{(\text{distance})^2}$ towards the focus; if it was projected with a velocity V from a point distant r from the centre of force, show that the periodic time is

$$\frac{2\pi}{\sqrt{\mu}}\left[\frac{2}{r} - \frac{V^2}{\mu}\right]^{-3/2}$$

(M.K.U.)

[Hint: $V^2 = \mu\left(\dfrac{2}{r} - \dfrac{1}{a}\right)$ or $a = \left(\dfrac{2}{r} - \dfrac{V^2}{\mu}\right)^{-1}$. But $T = \dfrac{2\pi}{\sqrt{\mu}} a^{3/2}$]

4. A planet is describing an ellipse about the sun as focus. Show that its velocity away from the sun is greatest when the radius vector to the planet is at right angles to the major axis of the path, and that it is $\dfrac{2\pi ae}{T\sqrt{1-e^2}}$ where $2a$ is the major axis, e the eccentricity and T the periodic time. **(Bn.U.)**

[Hint: Find max $\dot{r}$; $\dfrac{l}{r} = 1 + e\cos\theta$, $-\dfrac{l}{r^2}\dot{r} = -e\sin\theta\,\dot{\theta}$. So

$$\dot{r} = \frac{e}{l}(r^2\dot{\theta})\sin\theta = \frac{e}{l}h\sin\theta;\ \text{Max } \dot{r} = \frac{eh}{l}.$$

Eliminate h, μ, l using $\dfrac{h^2}{l} = \mu$, $T = \dfrac{2\pi}{\sqrt{\mu}} a^{3/2}$, $l = \dfrac{b^2}{a}$]

MOMENT OF INERTIA

17.1 MOMENT OF INERTIA

Moment of inertia of a particle of mass m about a straight line is defined to be mr^2, where r is the perpendicular distance of the particle from the straight line. The moment of inertia of a system of particles of masses $m_1, m_2, \ldots, m_n$ at distances $r_1, r_2, \ldots, r_n$ from the straight line is

$$m_1 r_1^2 + m_2 r_2^2 + \ldots = \Sigma m_i r_i^2.$$

The M.I. of a continuous distribution of mass may be calculated by integration. We shall now obtain the M.I.'s in the following cases of uniform bodies of mass M about a line l.

Body	*Line l*	*M.I.*	*Figure*
1. Thin circular ring of radius a	Line through the centre of the circle and perpendicular to the plane of the circle	Ma^2	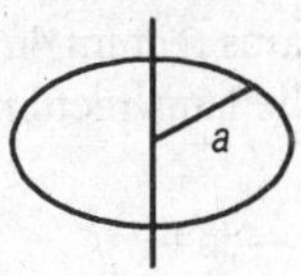
2. Hollow right circular cylinder of base radius a	Axis of the cylinder	Ma^2	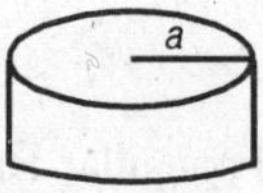
3. Circular lamina of radius a	Line as in case 1 (Also see case 17)	$\frac{1}{2}Ma^2$	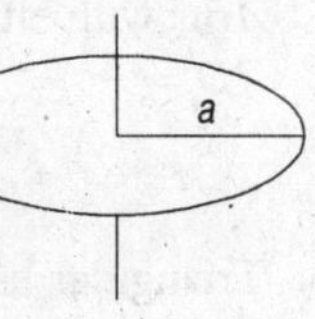
4. Solid right circular cylinder of base radius a	Axis of the cylinder (Also see case 21)	$\frac{1}{2}Ma^2$	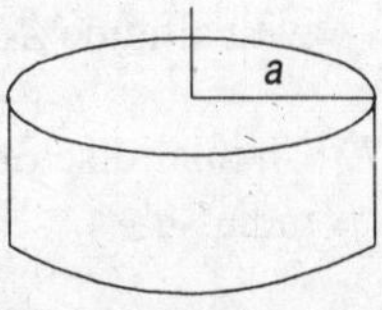
5. Solid sphere of radius a	A diameter	$\frac{2}{5}Ma^2$	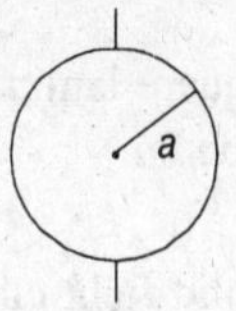
6. Solid right circular cone of base radius a.	Axis of the cone	$\frac{3}{10}Ma^2$	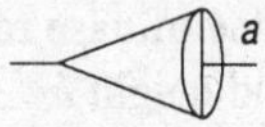
7. Spherical shell of radius a	A diameter	$\frac{2}{3}Ma^2$	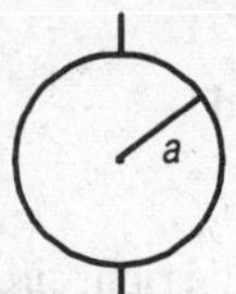
8. Thin rod of length $2a$	Line through one end and perpendicular to the rod	$\frac{4}{3}Ma^2$	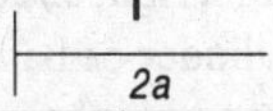

Body	Line *l*	M.I.	Figure
9. Thin rod of length $2a$	Line through the mid-point and perpendicular to the rod	$\frac{1}{3}Ma^2$	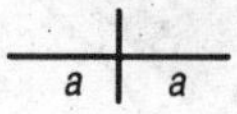 a a
10. Rectangular lamina of sides $2a$, $2b$	Line through the side of length $2a$	$\frac{4}{3}Mb^2$	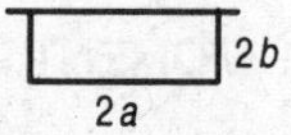 2b 2a
11. — do —	Line through the centre and parallel to the side of length $2a$	$\frac{1}{3}Mb^2$	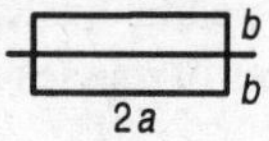 b b 2a
12. Elliptic lamina of axes $2a$, $2b$	Major axis	$\frac{1}{4}Mb^2$	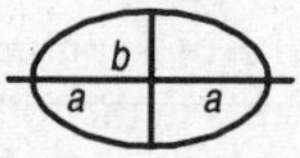 b a a
13. Parabolic lamina of latus rectum $4a$ cut off by the latus rectum	Axis of the parabola	$\frac{4}{5}Ma^2$	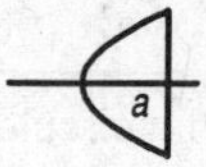 a
14. —do—	Tangent at the vertex	$\frac{3}{7}Ma^2$	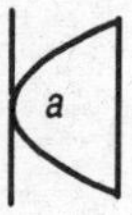 a
15. Triangular lamina ABC with altitude $AD = p$	Line through A and parallel to BC	$\frac{1}{2}Mp^2$	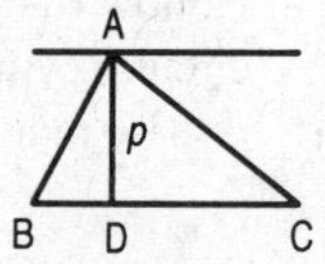 A p B D C
16. Triangular lamina ABC with altitude $AD = p$	Side BC	$\frac{1}{6}Mp^2$	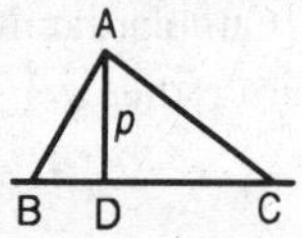 A p B D C
17. Circular disc of radius a	A diameter	$\frac{1}{4}Ma^2$	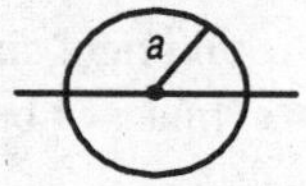 a
18. Square lamina of side $2a$	A diagonal	$\frac{1}{3}Ma^2$	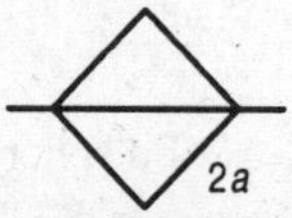 2a
19. Solid right circular cone of base radius a and height h	Line through the vertex and perpendicular to the axis	$\frac{3M(a^2+4h^2)}{20}$	 a h
20. —do—	A base diameter	$\frac{3M(3a^2+2h^2)}{20}$	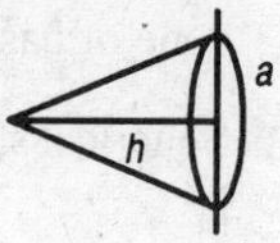 a h
21. Solid right circular cylinder of base radius a and height h	A base diameter	$\frac{M(3a^2+4h^2)}{12}$	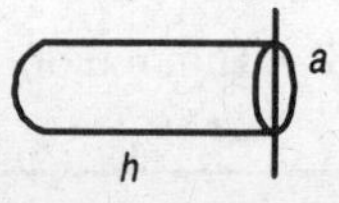 a h

DERIVATION

Case 1. Circular ring. Let the ring be divided into particles of masses $m_1, m_2, m_3, \ldots$. Then their M.I.'s about l are

$$m_1a^2,\ m_2a^2,\ m_3a^2, \ldots$$

So the M.I. of the ring about l is

$$m_1a^2 + m_2a^2 + \ldots = (m_1 + m_2 + \ldots)\,a^2 = Ma^2.$$

Case 2. Right circular hollow cylinder. Divide the cylinder into thin circular rings whose planes are perpendicular to l. If their masses are $m_1, m_2, m_3, \ldots$ then, from case 1, the M.I. of the cylinder about l is

$$m_1a^2 + m_2a^2 + \ldots = (m_1 + m_2 + \ldots)a^2 = Ma^2.$$

Case 3. Circular lamina. Divide the circular lamina into thin concentric circular rings. Consider the ring whose inner and outer radii are

$$x,\ x + \Delta x.$$

For this ring we have the following :

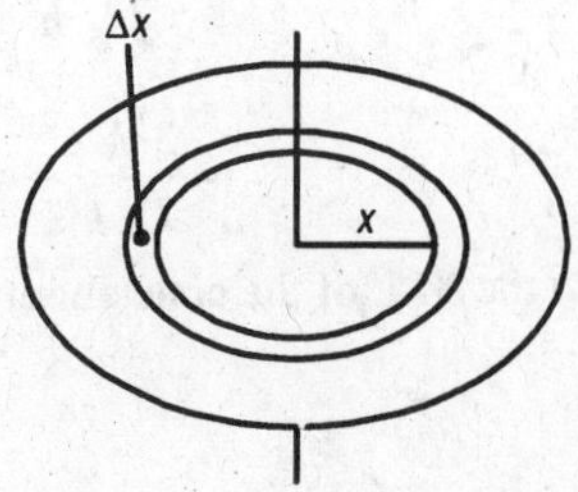

Area: $2\pi x\,\Delta x$

(From $A = \pi x^2$, $dA = 2\pi x\,\Delta x$)

Mass $= (2\pi x\,\Delta x) \times$ (Mass per unit area)

$$= (2\pi x\,\Delta x)\frac{M}{\pi a^2} = \frac{2M}{a^2}\,x\,\Delta x$$

M.I. about l: $\left(\frac{2M}{a^2}\,x\,\Delta x\right)x^2 = \frac{2M}{a^2}\,x^3\,\Delta x$ from case 1

M.I. of the lamina about $l = \frac{2M}{a^2}\int_0^a x^3\,dx = \frac{1}{2}Ma^2.$

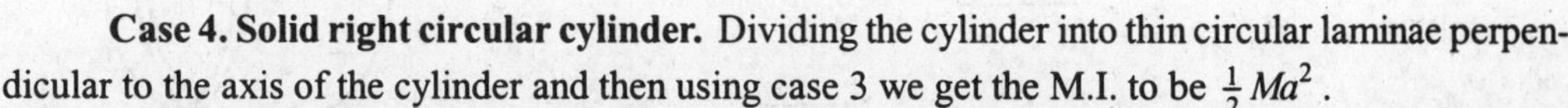

Case 4. Solid right circular cylinder. Dividing the cylinder into thin circular laminae perpendicular to the axis of the cylinder and then using case 3 we get the M.I. to be $\frac{1}{2}Ma^2$.

Case 5. Solid sphere. Divide the sphere into thin circular laminae perpendicular to the diameter l. Consider the lamina whose distance from the centre of the sphere is x and thickness is Δx. For this lamina, we have the following:

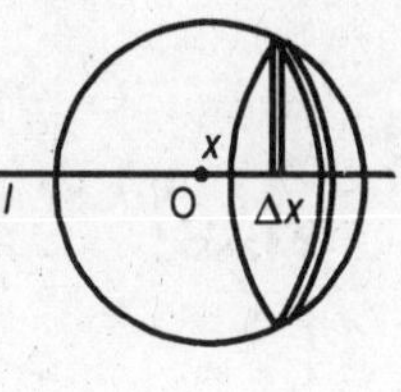

Radius : $\sqrt{a^2 - x^2}$

Volume : $\pi(a^2 - x^2)\,\Delta x$

Mass $= \pi\,(a^2 - x^2)\,\Delta x \times$ (Mass per unit volume)

$$= \pi(a^2 - x^2)\,\Delta x \cdot \frac{M}{\frac{4}{3}\pi a^3} = \frac{3M}{4a^3}(a^2 - x^2)\,\Delta x$$

M.I. about $l = \frac{1}{2}\left[\frac{3M}{4a^3}(a^2 - x^2)\,\Delta x\right]\left[\sqrt{a^2 - x^2}\right]^2$ by case 3.

So M.I. of the whole sphere about l is

$$2\int_0^a \frac{3M}{8a^3}(a^2-x^2)^2\,dx = \frac{2}{5}Ma^2.$$

Case 6. Solid right circular cone. Divide the cone into thin circular laminae perpendicular to its axis. Consider the lamina whose distance from the vertex is x and thickness is Δx. For this lamina we have the following:

Radius : $\frac{ax}{h}$, (By similar triangles)

Volume : $\pi\left(\frac{ax}{h}\right)^2 \Delta x$

Mass : $\frac{\pi a^2x^2}{h^2}\Delta x\left(\frac{M}{\frac{1}{3}\pi a^2 h}\right) = \frac{3M}{h^3}x^2\,\Delta x$

M.I. about l $=\frac{1}{2}\left(\frac{3M}{h^3}x^2\,\Delta x\right)\left(\frac{ax}{h}\right)^2$ by case 3

$$=\frac{3}{2}\frac{Ma^2}{h^5}x^4\,\Delta x.$$

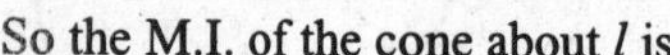

So the M.I. of the cone about l is

$$\frac{3}{2}\frac{Ma^2}{h^5}\int_0^h x^4\,dx = \frac{3}{10}Ma^2.$$

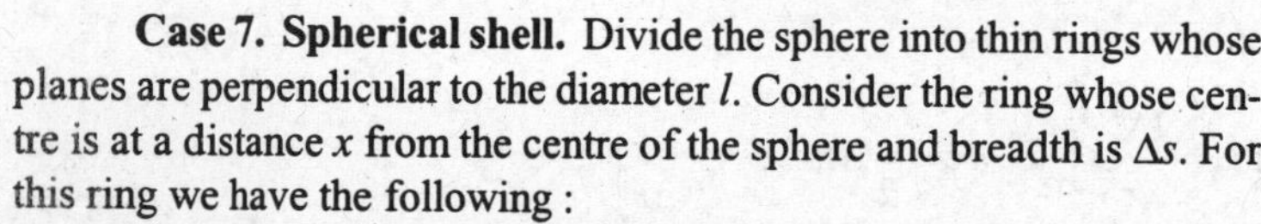

Case 7. Spherical shell. Divide the sphere into thin rings whose planes are perpendicular to the diameter l. Consider the ring whose centre is at a distance x from the centre of the sphere and breadth is Δs. For this ring we have the following :

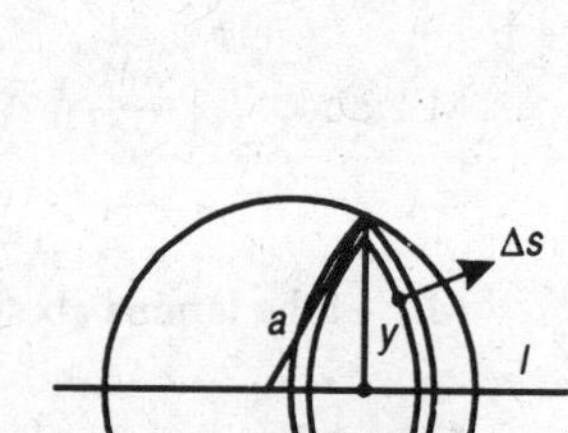

Radius : $y=\sqrt{a^2-x^2}$

Surface area : $(2\pi y)\,\Delta s = (2\pi y)\sqrt{1+{y_1}^2}\,\Delta s$

$$=2\pi y\sqrt{1+(-x/y)^2}\,\Delta x = 2\pi y\sqrt{\frac{y^2+x^2}{y^2}}\,\Delta x$$

$$=2\pi y\sqrt{\frac{a^2}{y^2}}\,\Delta x = 2\pi a\,\Delta x.$$

Mass : $(2\pi a\,\Delta x)\frac{M}{4\pi a^2} = \frac{M}{2a}\Delta x$

M.I. about l $=\left(\frac{M}{2a}\Delta x\right)y^2$ by case 1

$$=\frac{M}{2a}(a^2-x^2)\,\Delta x.$$

So M.I. of the spherical shell about l is

$$2\int_0^a \frac{M}{2a}(a^2 - x^2)\,dx = \frac{2}{3}Ma^2.$$

Case 8. Rod. Consider an elementary length of the rod at a distance x from l. Let its length be Δx. For the elementary length we have the following:

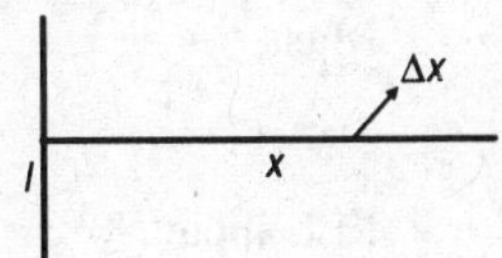

Mass : $\Delta x \dfrac{M}{2a}$

M.I. about l : $\left(\dfrac{M}{2a}\Delta x\right)x^2$.

So M.I. of the rod about l is

$$\frac{M}{2a}\int_0^{2a} x^2\,dx = \frac{4}{3}Ma^2.$$

Case 9. Rod. It is evident in this case that the M.I. is

$$2\left[\frac{M}{2a}\int_0^a x^2\,dx\right] = \frac{1}{3}Ma^2.$$

Cases 10.11. Rectangular lamina. Dividing the lamina into thin parallel strips and using the results of cases 8 and 9 we get the M.I's as stated.

Case 12. Elliptic lamina. Divide the lamina into thin straight strips perpendicular to the major axis. Consider a typical strip of length $2y$ and of breadth Δx, at a distance x from the centre of the ellipse. For this strip we have the following:

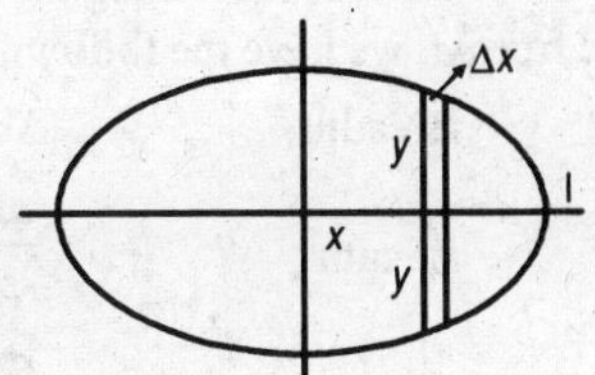

Area : $2y\,\Delta x$

Mass : $(2y\,\Delta x)\dfrac{M}{\pi ab} = \dfrac{2M}{\pi ab}y\,\Delta x$

M.I. about l : $\dfrac{1}{3}\left(\dfrac{2M}{\pi ab}y\,\Delta x\right)y^2$ by case 9.

So the moment of inertia I of the lamina about l is

$$I = 2\int_0^a \frac{1}{3}\cdot\frac{2M}{\pi ab}y^3\,dx = \frac{4M}{3\pi\,ab}\int_0^a y^3\,dx.$$

If we put $x = a$, $\cos\theta$, $y = b\sin\theta$, then, when $x = 0$, $\theta = \pi/2$ and when $x = a$, $\theta = 0$ and

$$I = \frac{4M}{3\pi\,ab}\int_{\pi/2}^{0}(b\sin\theta)^3(-a\sin\theta\,d\theta)$$

$$= \frac{4\,Mb^2}{3\pi}\int_0^{\pi/2}\sin^4\theta\,d\theta = \frac{4\,Mb^2}{3\pi}\left(\frac{3}{4}\cdot\frac{1}{2}\cdot\frac{\pi}{2}\right) = \frac{1}{4}Mb^2$$

Case 13. Parabolic lamina. Dividing the lamina into thin parallel strips perpendicular to the axis of the parabola, for a typical strip, we have the following:

Area : $2y\,\Delta x$

Mass : $(2y\,\Delta x)\dfrac{M}{A}=\dfrac{3M}{4a^2}\,y\,\Delta x$, since $A=2\displaystyle\int_0^a y\,dx=\dfrac{8}{3}a^2$

M.I. about l : $\dfrac{1}{3}\left(\dfrac{3M}{4a^2}\,y\,\Delta x\right)y^2=\dfrac{M}{4a^2}\,y^3\,\Delta x$.

So the moment of inertia of the parabolic lamina about l is

$$\left(\frac{M}{4a^2}\right)\int_0^a y^3\,dx=\frac{M}{4a^2}\int_0^a (4\,ax)^{3/2}\,dx$$

$$=\frac{M}{4a^2}\left(\frac{16a^4}{5}\right)=\frac{4}{5}Ma^2.$$

Case 14. Moment of inertia of the parabolic lamina about l, the tangent at the vertex, is

$$\left(\frac{3M}{4a^2}\right)\int_0^a (y\,dx)\,x^2=\frac{3M}{4a^2}\int_0^a 2\,a^{1/2}\,x^{5/2}\,dx$$

$$=\frac{3M}{4a^2}(2a^{1/2})\,a^{7/2}\cdot\frac{2}{7}=\frac{3}{7}Ma^2.$$

Case 15. Dividing the lamina into strips parallel to the base BC, for a typical strip at a distance x from A, we have the following:

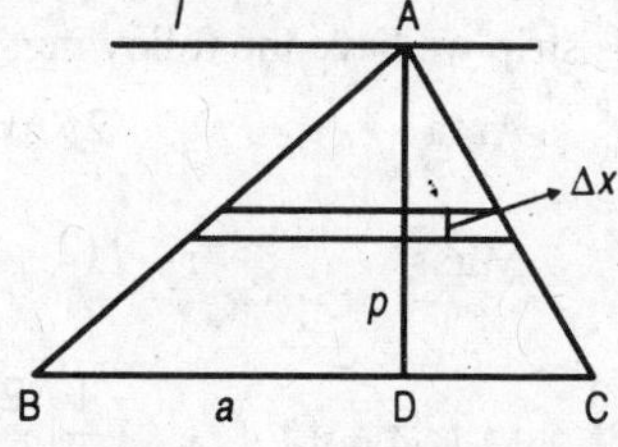

Breadth : Δx

Length : $\dfrac{ax}{p}$ by similar triangles

Area : $\dfrac{ax}{p}\Delta x$

Mass $=\left(\dfrac{ax}{p}\Delta x\right)\dfrac{M}{\frac{1}{2}ap}$

$=\dfrac{2M}{p^2}\,x\,\Delta x$

M.I. about l : $\left(\dfrac{2M}{p^2}\,x\,\Delta x\right)x^2$.

Thus the M.I. of the lamina about l is

$$\frac{2M}{p^2}\int_0^p x^3\,dx=\frac{2M}{p^2}\cdot\frac{p^4}{4}=\frac{1}{2}Mp^2.$$

Case 16. The strip is at a distance $p-x$ from BC. So its moment of inertia about BC is

$$\frac{2M}{p^2}\int_0^p (x)\,(p-x)^2\,dx=\frac{2M}{p^2}\left(\frac{p^4}{4}-\frac{2p^4}{3}+\frac{p^4}{2}\right)=\frac{1}{6}Mp^2.$$

Case 17 to 21. These cases are dealt with in the next section.

Radius of gyration. If the M.I. of a system of mass M about a straight line is written as Mk^2, then k is called the *radius of gyration* of the system about the straight line. For example, the radius of gyration of the cases 1 to 5 are respectively

$$a,\ a,\ \frac{a}{\sqrt{2}},\ \frac{a}{\sqrt{2}},\ a\sqrt{\frac{2}{5}}.$$

EXERCISES

1. Find the M.I. of a lamina in the form of a quadrant of an ellipse, about the major axis.

[**Hint:** M.I. $= \int_0^a \frac{1}{3}(y\,dx\,\sigma)\,y^2$ where $\sigma = \frac{M}{\frac{1}{4}\pi ab}$. Set $x = a\cos\theta$, $y = b\sin\theta$. M.I. $= \frac{Mb^2}{4}$]

17.1.1 Perpendicular and parallel axes theorems

The two important theorems connected with the M.I., are

(*i*) Perpendicular axis theorem,

(*ii*) Parallel axis theorem.

They are dealt with in Bookworks 17.1 and 17.2.

Bookwork 17.1. Perpendicular axis theorem. The M.I. of a lamina about a line l perpendicular to the plane of the lamina is equal to the sum of the M.I's of the lamina about two mutually perpendicular lines in the plane of the lamina, both passing through the point of intersection of the lamina and the line.

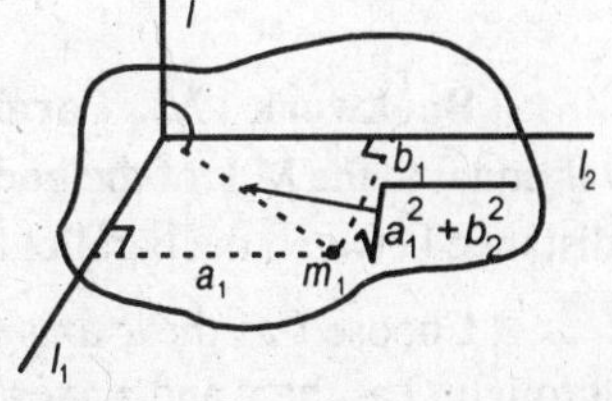

Let l_1, l_2 be the perpendicular lines in the plane of the lamina. Let the lamina be constituted by particles of masses $m_1, m_2, \ldots$ Let their distances from l_1 and l_2 be respectively,

$$a_1, a_2, a_3, \ldots\ldots;\ b_1, b_2, b_3, \ldots\ldots$$

Then the M.I.'s I_1 and I_2 of the lamina about l_1 and l_2 are

$$I_1 = m_1a_1^2 + m_2a_2^2 + \ldots\ldots,\quad I_2 = m_1b_1^2 + m_2b_2^2 + \ldots\ldots$$

But the distance of $m_1, m_2\ldots\ldots$ from the perpendicular line l are

$$\sqrt{a_1^2+b_1^2},\ \sqrt{a_2^2+b_2^2},\ \ldots\ldots$$

So the moment of inertia I of the lamina about l is

$$I = m_1\left[\sqrt{a_1^2+b_1^2}\right]^2 + m_2\left[\sqrt{a_2^2+b_2^2}\right]^2 + \ldots\ldots$$

$$= m_1(a_1^2+b_1^2) + m_2(a_2^2+b_2^2) + \ldots.$$

$$= (m_1a_1^2 + m_2a_2^2 + \ldots\ldots) + (m_1b_1^2 + m_2b_2^2 + \ldots.)$$

$$= I_1 + I_2.$$

Case 17. As an illustration of the perpendicular axis theorem we now obtain the moment of inertia of a circular lamina about a diameter. By symmetry, the M.I. about any diameter is a constant, say I. Then the M.I.'s about two perpendicular diameters are I, I. But the M.I. about the line through the centre and perpendicular to the plane of the lamina is

$$\tfrac{1}{2} Ma^2 .$$

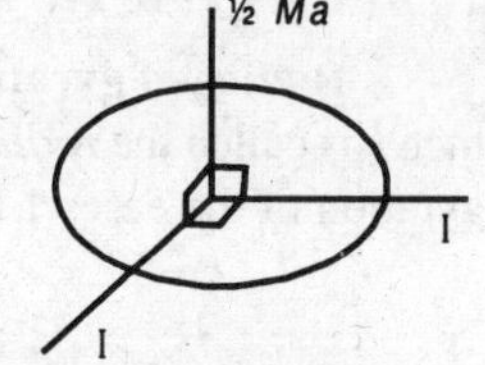

So, by perpendicular axis theorem,

$$\tfrac{1}{2} Ma^2 = I + I$$

or

$$I = \tfrac{1}{4} Ma^2 .$$

Case 18. Another illustration is to obtain the moment of inertia of a square lamina of side $2a$ about a diagonal. From the figure we see that the M.I.'s of the lamina about the perpendicular lines AB and CD are the same quantity due to symmetry, namely

$$\frac{Ma^2}{3} .$$

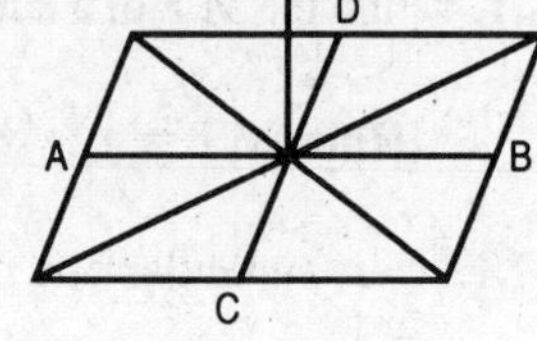

So, if the M.I. about the perpendicular line through the centre is I, then

$$I = \frac{Ma^2}{3} + \frac{Ma^2}{3}$$

or

$$I = \frac{2\,Ma^2}{3} .$$

Now the diagonals also are perpendicular and the M.I's about them are equal, say I', I'. Then

$$I = I' + I' \text{ or } \frac{2Ma^2}{3} = I' + I' \text{ or } I' = \frac{Ma^2}{3} .$$

Bookwork 17.2. Parallel axis theorem. The M.I, say I, of any body of mass M about a line l is equal to the M.I. of the body about a line l_G through G and parallel to l plus Md^2, where d is the distance between the parallel lines.

Choose l as the x axis and any point O on it as the origin. Choose two perpendicular lines through O as the y and z axes. With respect to the frame $(Oxyz)$, let the coordinates of a particle of mass m be (x, y, z) and those of G be (x_1, y_1, z_1). Then the distances of m and G from l, the x axis, are

$$\sqrt{y^2 + z^2} , \; \sqrt{y_1^2 + z_1^2} .$$

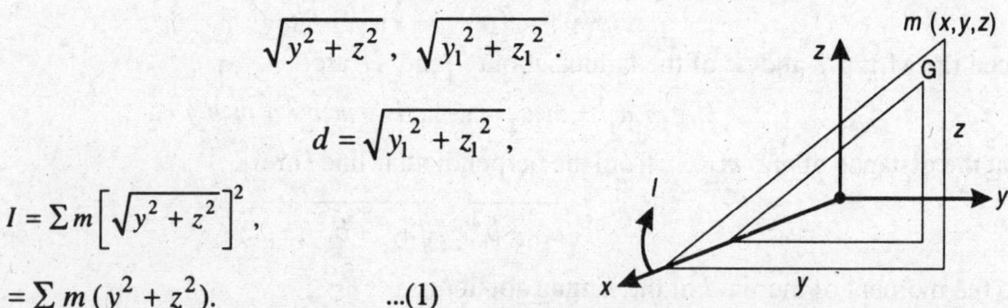

$$\therefore \qquad d = \sqrt{y_1^2 + z_1^2} ,$$

$$I = \Sigma m \left[\sqrt{y^2 + z^2} \right]^2 ,$$

$$= \Sigma m (y^2 + z^2). \qquad ...(1)$$

Let $(Gx' \, y' \, z')$ be the frame whose axes are parallel to the axes of $(Oxyz)$. Then Gx' is l_G. Let the coordinates of m with respect to $(Gx' \, y' \, z')$ be (x', y', z') and I_G, the M.I. of the body about l_G. Then

$$x = x_1 + x' , \; y = y_1 + y' , \; z = z_1 + z' .$$

$$\therefore \qquad I = \Sigma m \left[(y_1 + y')^2 + (z_1 + z')^2 \right]$$

$$= \Sigma m \left[(y_1^2 + z_1^2) + (y'^2 + z'^2) + 2\, y_1 y' + 2\, z_1 z' \right]$$

$$= (y_1^2 + z_1^2)(\Sigma m) + \Sigma m (y'^2 + z'^2) + 2 y_1 \, \Sigma my' + 2\, z_1 \, \Sigma mz'$$

$$= d^2 M + I_G + 2\, y_1\,(0) + 2\, z_1\,(0)$$

$$= Md^2 + I_G,$$

since $\Sigma\, my'$ and $\Sigma\, mz'$ vanish, being the y and z coordinates of the mass centre G with reference to the frame $(Gx'\, y'\, z')$.

Remark. It is noteworthy that the proof of parallel axis theorem involves the three dimensional frame and it is true for any type of objects while the perpendicular axis theorem is true only for a mass distribution in a plane.

Case 19. Solid right circular cone. Here l is a line through the vertex and perpendicular to the axis. Consider the typical disc as in case 6. From case 17 the M.I. of the disc about any of its diameter is

$$\frac{1}{4}\left(\frac{3M}{h^3}\, x^2\, \Delta x\right)\left(\frac{ax}{h}\right)^2.$$

So, by parallel axis theorem, its M.I. about l is

$$\frac{1}{4}\left(\frac{3M}{h^3}\, x^2\, \Delta x\right)\left(\frac{ax}{h}\right)^2 + \left(\frac{3M}{h^3}\, x^2\, \Delta x\right) x^2.$$

Thus the M.I. of the cone about l is

$$\int_0^h \left(\frac{3\, Ma^2}{4h^5}\, x^4 + \frac{3M}{h^3}\, x^4\right) dx = \frac{3M}{20}\,(a^2 + 4h^2).$$

Case 20. Let l_V, l_G, l_B be three parallel lines, perpendicular to the axis, where l_V passes through the vertex V, l_G passes through the mass centre G and l_B is a base diameter. Let I_V, I_G, I_B be the M.I'.s of the cone about these lines. Then, by parallel axis theorem,

$$I_V = I_G + M(\tfrac{3}{4}\, h)^2,$$

$$I_B = I_G + M(\tfrac{1}{4}\, h)^2,$$

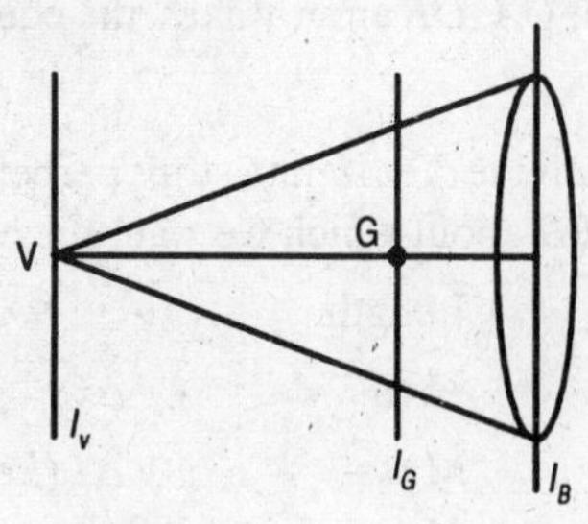

since $VG = \tfrac{3}{4}\, h$. Subtraction leads to

$$I_B = I_V + M(\tfrac{1}{4}\, h)^2 - M(\tfrac{3}{4}\, h)^2,$$

$$= \frac{3M}{20}\,(a^2 + 4h^2) + \frac{Mh^2}{16} - \frac{9\, Mh^2}{16}$$

$$= \frac{M}{20}\,(3a^2 + 2h^2).$$

Case 21. Working for this case is similar to that of case 19. This is left to the reader as an exercise.

EXAMPLES

Example 1. Show that the M.I. of a rectangular lamina of mass M and sides $2a$ and $2b$ about a diagonal is

$$M\,\frac{2\, a^2 b^2}{3\,(a^2 + b^2)}.$$ **(M.U.)**

Let $ABCD$ be the rectangle, $AB = 2a$, $BC = 2b$. Let BN be the perpendicular from B to AC and $BN = p$. If $\angle BAN = \theta$, then

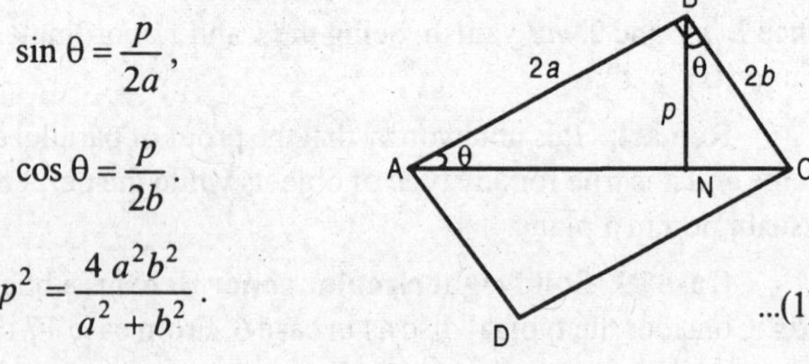

$$\sin\theta = \frac{p}{2a},$$

$$\cos\theta = \frac{p}{2b}.$$

So $$p^2 = \frac{4a^2b^2}{a^2+b^2}. \quad ...(1)$$

Now $M/2$, $M/2$ are the masses of ΔABC, ΔADC. So

M.I. of ΔABC about $AC = \frac{1}{6}\frac{M}{2}p^2$ (case 16)

M.I. of ΔADC about $AC = \frac{1}{6}\frac{M}{2}p^2$.

$\therefore$ M.I. of $ABCD = \frac{1}{6}\frac{M}{2}p^2 + \frac{1}{6}\frac{M}{2}p^2 = \frac{M}{6}p^2$

$$= \frac{M}{6}\frac{4a^2b^2}{a^2+b^2} = \frac{2Ma^2b^2}{3(a^2+b^2)}.$$

Example 2. Find the M.I. of a square lamina of side l about one of its diagonals, the density at any point varying as the square of its distance from this diagonal. **(M.U.)**

Let $ABCD$ be the square with centre O. Consider ΔOAB.

$$OA = \frac{l}{\sqrt{2}} = \lambda, \text{ say}. \quad ...(1)$$

If OA, OB are x, y axes, the equation of AB is

$$x + y = \lambda.$$

Divide ΔOAB into strips perpendicular to OA. Consider a typical strip at a distance x from the diagonal BD about which we want the M.I. Its density is kx^2. For this strip, we have

Length : y

Area : $y\,\Delta x$

Mass : $y\,\Delta x\,(kx^2)$

M.I. : $[y\,\Delta x\,(kx^2)]\,x^2$.

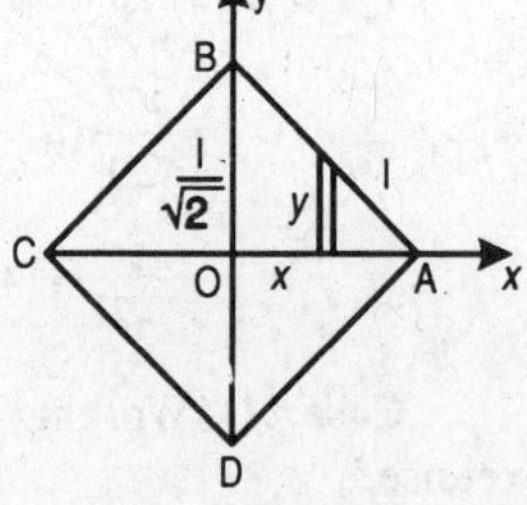

M.I. of $\Delta OAB = k\int_0^{OA} yx^4\,dx = k\int_0^{\lambda}(\lambda - x)\,x^4\,dx = \frac{k\lambda^6}{30}$.

$\therefore$ M.I. of the square $ABCD = 4.\frac{k\lambda^6}{30} = \frac{2}{15}k\lambda^6$. ...(2)

Mass of $\Delta OAB = \int_0^{OA} y(kx^2)\,dx = k\int_0^{\lambda}(\lambda - x)\,x^2\,dx = \frac{k\lambda^4}{12}$.

$\therefore$ Mass M of the square $ABCD = 4\cdot\frac{k\lambda^4}{12} = \frac{1}{3}k\lambda^4$. ...(3)

Dividing (2) by (3), we get

$$\text{M.I.} = M \cdot \frac{2}{15} k \lambda^6 \cdot \frac{3}{k \lambda^4} = \frac{2 M \lambda^2}{5} = \frac{2M}{5} \frac{l^2}{2} \text{ by (1)}$$

$$= \frac{Ml^2}{5}.$$

EXERCISES

1. Find the M.I. of a square about its diagonal of length l. **(M.U.)**

   [Hint: If $2a$ is the side, M.I. about the diagonal $= \frac{Ma^2}{3}$. (case 18.). Now

   $$(2a)^2 + (2a)^2 = l^2 \text{ or } a = \frac{l}{\sqrt{8}}. \text{ So M.I.} = \frac{Ml^2}{24}]$$

2. Show that the M.I. of an isosceles right angled triangle about its hypotenuse whose length is a is $\frac{Ma^2}{24}$. **(M.U.)**

   [Hint: If a is the length of the hypotenuse, the altitude to it is $p = \frac{a}{2}$. So M.I.$= \frac{M\,(a/2)^2}{6} = \frac{Ma^2}{24}$]

3. Show that the M.I. of a triangular lamina ABC of mass M about any line through the vertex A is $\frac{1}{6} M (q^2 + qr + r^2)$, where q and r are the distances of B and C from the line. **(M.U.)**

   [Hint: Let the line meet BC produced at O. Then

   $$\Delta\, ACO = \tfrac{1}{2}\, AO \,.\, r\,,\ \Delta\, ABO = \tfrac{1}{2}\, AO \,.\, q\,;\ \Delta\, ABC = \tfrac{1}{2}\, AO\,(q - r).$$

   If σ is the mass per unit area, from case 16, for ΔABC, $M = \frac{1}{2} AO\,(r - q)\,\sigma$,

   $$\text{M.I.} = \frac{1}{6}\left(\frac{1}{2} AO \,.\, r\,\sigma\right) r^2 - \frac{1}{6}\left(\frac{1}{2} AO \,.\, q\,\sigma\right) q^2.$$

   Eliminate σ and find M.I.]

4. Find the M.I. of a uniform elliptic lamina about
   (*i*) the line through the centre of the lamina and perpendicular to the plane
   (*ii*) the tangent at the extremity of the major axis. **(M.U.)**

   [Hint: (*i*) By perpendicular axis Theorem, M.I. $= \frac{1}{4} Ma^2 + \frac{1}{4} Mb^2$

   (*ii*) By parallel axis Theorem, M.I. $= \frac{1}{4} Ma^2 + Ma^2$]

5. Obtain the M.I. of a uniform circular plate about a line perpendicular to the plane of the lamina and at a distance c from the centre. **(M.U.)**

   [Hint: By parallel axis Theorem, $I = I_G + Md^2 = \frac{Ma^2}{2} + Mc^2$]

6. If M is the mass of a right circular cone whose base radius is r and height is h, show that

   (*i*) Its M.I. about the line through the vertex, perpendicular to the axis is

   $$\frac{3M}{20}(r^2 + 4h^2).$$ **(M.U.)**

(*ii*) Its M.I. about the line through the centre of gravity perpendicular to its axis is

$$\frac{3M}{80}(h^2+4r^2).$$ **(M.U.)**

[Hint: (*i*) See case 19. (*ii*) $I_V = I_G + M\left(\frac{3h}{4}\right)^2$. Find I_G **]**

7. Show that the M.I. of a hollow sphere whose external and internal radii are a and b about a diameter is

$$\frac{2M}{5}\left(\frac{a^5-b^5}{a^3-b^3}\right).$$

Deduce the M.I. of a hollow sphere of radius a. **(Bn.U.)**

[Hint: If ρ is the density and I_a, I_b are the M.I's of solid spheres of radii a, b, then

$$I_a = \frac{2}{5}\left(\frac{4}{3}\pi a^3 \rho\right)a^2,\ I_b = \frac{2}{5}\left(\frac{4}{3}\pi b^3\rho\right)b^2,\ M = \frac{4}{3}\pi(a^3-b^3)\rho.$$

Find $I = I_a - I_b$ eliminating ρ. The M.I. of the hollow sphere is

$$\lim_{b\to a}\frac{2M}{5}\frac{a^5-b^5}{a^3-b^3} = \lim_{b\to a}\frac{2M}{5}\frac{a^4+a^3b+a^2b^2+ab^3+b^4}{a^2+ab+b^2} = \frac{2}{3}Ma^2$$ **]**

8. M_1, M_2 are two masses whose C. G's G_1, G_2 are at a distant d apart and their moments of inertia are I_1, I_2 respectively about parallel lines through G_1, G_2. Show that the moment of inertia of the system about a parallel line through G, the C.G. of the system, is

$$I_1 + I_2 + \frac{M_1M_2d^2}{M_1+M_2}.$$ **(A.U.)**

[Hint: G divides G_1G_2 in the ratio $M_2 : M_1$ and if $d_1 = G_1G$, $d_2 = G_2G$, then

$$d_1 = \frac{M_2}{M_1+M_2}d,\ d_2 = \frac{M_1}{M_1+M_2}d \text{ and } M.I. = I_1 + M_1d_1^2 + I_2 + M_2d_2^2$$ **]**

9. A square lamina of side a has a circular hole of radius b cut out from it, the centre of the hole being at the centre of the square. If the mass of the remainder is M, show that the M.I. of it about a diagonal of the square is

$$\frac{a^4-3\pi b^4}{12}\cdot\frac{M}{a^2-\pi b^2}.$$ **(M.U.)**

[Hint: If I_S, I_C, I_R are M.I's of the square area, circular area and remainder and σ is the mass per unit area,

$$I_S = (a^2\sigma)\frac{a^2}{12},\ I_C = (\pi b^2\sigma)\frac{b^2}{4},\ M = (a^2-\pi b^2)\sigma$$

where M is the mass of the remainder. Find $I_R = I_S - I_C$, eliminating σ **]**

10. From a circular disc of radius r, a circular portion whose diameter is a radius of the disc is removed. Show that the radius of gyration of the remainder about the common tangent is $^{5r}/_4$.

(A.U.)

[Hint: If M is the mass of the full circle of radius r, then $\frac{3}{4}Mk^2 = \frac{Mr^2}{4} + Mr^2 - \left(\frac{Mr^2}{64}+\frac{Mr^2}{16}\right)$ **]**

11. Show that the M.I. of a paraboloidal solid of revolution of mass M and base radius r about its axis (the solid being generated by revolving a parabolic segment about its axis) is $\frac{Mr^2}{3}$. **(M.U.)**

[Hint: Let ρ be the density and $y^2 = ax$ be the parabola. If x varies from O to h, then $r^2 = ah$ or $h = r^2/a$. As in case 5,

$$\text{M.I} = \frac{1}{2}\rho\pi \int_0^h a^2x^2\, dx\,;\; M = \pi\rho \int_0^h ax\, dx\,]$$

TWO DIMENSIONAL MOTION OF A RIGID BODY

18.1 TWO DIMENSIONAL MOTION OF A RIGID BODY

In section 4.2.1. we obtained the equations of the general motion of a rigid body. Now we consider a particular case, namely, a two dimensional motion whose definition is as follows:

Two dimensional motion. If the velocities of the particles of a system of particles are always perpendicular to a fixed direction, then the motion is said to be two dimensional.

Remark. In two dimensional motion the particles in any plane perpendicular to the fixed direction will always remain in that plane.

Example 1. Motions of a circular disc, a circular hoop and a sphere rolling down an inclined plane are simple cases of two dimensional motions. In these cases the velocities of the particles are perpendicular to the horizontal base line of the inclined plane.

Example 2. Motion of a rigid body rotating about a fixed axis, is two dimensional. In this case the velocities of the particles are perpendicular to the fixed axis.

18.1.1 Motion of a rigid body rotating about a fixed axis

When a rigid body rotates about a fixed axis, the particles constituting the rigid body describe circles, their centres lying on the axis of rotation. At any particular moment all the particles possess the same angular velocity about the fixed axis.

Bookwork 18.1. A rigid body revolves about a fixed axis. To find its

(*i*) K.E.,

(*ii*) Moment of momentum (otherwise known as angular momentum) about the fixed axis,

(*iii*) Moment of the effective forces about the fixed axis.

(*i*) Let the rigid body be constituted by particles of masses $m_1, m_2, m_3,$......... at distances $r_1,\ r_2,$ $r_3,$.......... from the fixed axis OA.

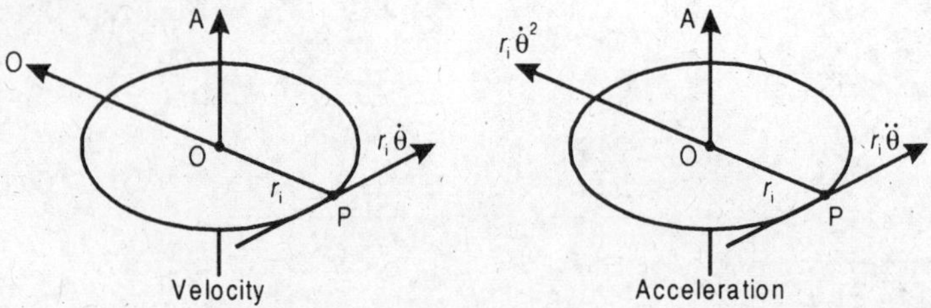

Let us consider a typical particle P of mass m_i and let O be the centre of its circular path. The velocity of this particle is $r_i\dot{\theta}$ along the tangent. So its K.E. is $\frac{1}{2} m_i\ (r_i\dot{\theta})^2$. Thus K.E.of the body is

$$\Sigma \tfrac{1}{2}\, m_i\, r_i^{\,2}\, \dot{\theta}^2 = \tfrac{1}{2}\left(\Sigma m_i\,.\,r_i^{\,2}\right)\dot{\theta}^2 = \tfrac{1}{2} I\,\dot{\theta}^2,$$

where I is the M.I. of the body about the fixed axis.

(ii) The momentum of the typical particle is $m_i(r_i\,\dot{\theta})$. So its moment of momentum about the fixed axis is $r_i(m_i\,r_i\,\dot{\theta})$. Thus the moment of momentum of the body about the fixed axis is

$$\Sigma\, m_i r_i^2\,\dot{\theta} = (\Sigma\, m_i\, r_i^2)\dot{\theta} = I\,\dot{\theta}.$$

(iii) The effective force (*i.e.*, mass × acceleration) of the typical particle has components

$$m_i\,r_i\,\ddot{\theta},\;\; m_i\,r_i\,\dot{\theta}^2$$

in the tangential and the inward drawn normal directions. So the moment of these components about the fixed axis are

$$r_i\,(m_i\,r_i\,\ddot{\theta}),\, 0.$$

Hence the sum of the moments of the effective forces of the body about the fixed axis is

$$\Sigma\, m_i r_i^2\,\ddot{\theta} = (\Sigma\, m_i\, r_i^2)\ddot{\theta} = I\,\ddot{\theta}.$$

Angular velocity of a revolving body at a moment. Now we consider the rotation of a rigid body of mass M about a fixed axis under gravity. Here the reaction of the axis does no work and the gravity only does work. In an interval, if the C. G. of the body descends through a vertical distance h, then the work done by gravity is Mgh. By the principle of energy, in the interval,

Increase in K.E. = Work done.

To find the K.E.we use the formula $\frac{1}{2} I\,\dot{\theta}^2$ where I is the M. I. of the body about the fixed axis. Thus we can obtain the angular velocity of the body at any moment.

EXAMPLES

Example 1. A rod of length $2a$ can turn freely about a fixed end. It is held vertically at rest in the unstable equilibrium position and let go. Show that, when it passes through the lower vertical position, its angular velocity is $\sqrt{\dfrac{3g}{a}}$. **(M.U.)**

Let O be the fixed end , M the mass of the rod and ω, the angular velocity in its lower vertical position.

M.I. about the fixed axis $= \dfrac{4}{3}Ma^2$

K. E. initially $= 0$

K.E. in the lowest position $= \dfrac{1}{2}\left(\dfrac{4}{3}Ma^2\right)\omega^2$

Increase in K.E. $= \dfrac{1}{2}\left(\dfrac{4}{3}Ma^2\right)\omega^2$

Height decended by C.G. $= a + a = 2a$

Work done $= (Mg)\, 2a.$

By principle of energy, we get

$$\frac{2}{3}Ma^2\omega^2 = Mg\,2a \text{ or } \omega = \sqrt{\frac{3g}{a}}.$$

Example 2. A weightless rod ABC of length $2a$ is movable about the end A which is fixed, and carries two particles of same mass, one fastened to the mid point B and the other to the end C of the rod. If the rod is held in the horizontal position and then let go, show that its angular velocity when it is vertical is $\sqrt{\frac{6g}{5a}}$. **(M.U.)**

Let m, m be the masses. They describe circular paths of radii.

$$a, \ 2a.$$

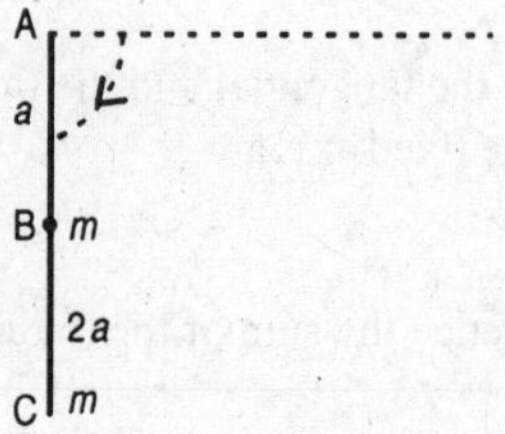

So their velocities in their lowest positions are

$$a\omega, (2a)\omega.$$

Their K.E.'s then are

$$\frac{1}{2} m (a\omega)^2, \ \frac{1}{2} m (2a\omega)^2.$$

$\therefore$ Increase in K.E. $= \frac{5}{2} ma^2\omega^2 - 0$.

The masses have descended through vertical heights

$$a, \ 2a.$$

So work done by gravity is

$$(mg)a + mg\,(2a) = 3mga.$$

So, by the principle of energy,

$$\frac{5}{2} ma^2\omega^2 = 3mga \quad \text{or} \quad \omega = \sqrt{\frac{6g}{5a}}.$$

Example 3. A solid cube of side $2a$ is free to rotate about an edge which is fixed in a horizontal position and is released from rest from the position of unstable equilibrium. Show that the angular velocity ω of the cube when the centre of gravity is in the horizontal plane containing the axis of rotation is given by

$$\omega^2 = \frac{3g\sqrt{2}}{4a}. \qquad \textbf{(M.U.)}$$

M.I. of a square lamina of mass m and side $2a$, about a line through the centre and perpendicular to the plane of the lamina is

$$\frac{2}{3} ma^2.$$

Since the distance between the centre and one corner is $\sqrt{2}a$, the M.I. about a parallel line through the corner is

$$\frac{2}{3} ma^2 + m(\sqrt{2}a)^2 = \frac{8}{3} ma^2.$$

If M is the mass of the solid cube, its moment about the edge is $\frac{8}{3} Ma^2$.

$$\therefore \quad \text{Increase in K.E.} = \frac{1}{2}\left(\frac{8}{3} Ma^2\right)\omega^2 - 0 \qquad ...(1)$$

Now the mass centre decends through a distance $a\sqrt{2}$.

$$\therefore \quad \text{Work done} = Mg\,(a\sqrt{2}). \qquad ...(2)$$

Equating (1) and (2) . we get the result as stated.

Example 4. A cylinder of mass M and radius a can turn round its axis which is horizontal. A fine thread tied to the cylinder and wrapped round it , has a mass m attached to its free end. The system moves from rest. Show that, when m has descended a vertical distance h, the angular velocity of the cylinder is

$$\frac{2}{a}\sqrt{\frac{mgh}{M+2m}}.$$ **(Am.U.)**

From " $\dot{s} = a\,\dot{\theta}$ ", we get that, when the angular velocity of the cylinder is ω, the velocity of m is $a\omega$. So their K.E's are

$$\frac{1}{2}\left(\frac{1}{2}Ma^2\right)\omega^2,\ \frac{1}{2}m\,(a\omega)^2.$$

$$\therefore \qquad \text{Increase in K.E.} = \left(\frac{1}{4}Ma^2 + \frac{1}{2}a^2 m\right)\omega^2. \qquad ...(1)$$

When m descends through a height h,

$$\text{Work done by gravity} = mgh. \qquad ...(2)$$

Therefore , equating (1) and (2) , we get

$$a^2\frac{M+2m}{4}\omega^2 = mgh \ \text{ or } \ \omega = \frac{2}{a}\sqrt{\frac{mgh}{M+2m}}.$$

EXERCISES

1. A circular disc of radius a and mass M is rotating with angular velocity ω about a fixed axis at right angles to its plane at a distance b from its centre. Find its K.E. **(M.U.)**

[Hint: By parallel axis Theorem, $I = \frac{1}{2}Ma^2 + Mb^2$. K.E. $= \frac{1}{2}I\omega^2$]

2. A rod of mass M and length $2a$ can turn freely about a fixed end. Show that the least angular velocity with which it must be started from the lowest position so as to make complete revolutions is $\sqrt{\frac{3g}{a}}$. **(M.U., M.K.U., Bn.U.)**

[Hint: Increase in K.E. $= 0 - \frac{1}{2}\left(\frac{4}{3}Ma^2\right)\omega^2$; W.D $= -2aMg$]

3. A rod of length $2a$ can turn freely about an end. If it falls from a horizontal position, show that its angular velocity when it is vertical is $\sqrt{\frac{3g}{2a}}$. **(M.U., M.K.U., C.U.)**

[Hint: Increase in K.E. $= \frac{1}{2}\left(\frac{4}{3}Ma^2\right)\omega^2 - 0$; W.D $= aMg$]

4. A rod of length $2a$ can turn freely about an end. Show that the angular velocity with which it must be started from its lowest position so that its angular velocity becomes zero when it attains a horizontal position is $\sqrt{\frac{3g}{2a}}$. **(M.U.)**

[Hint: $0 - \frac{1}{2}\left(\frac{4}{3}Ma^2\right)\omega^2 = -mga$]

5. A rod of length $2a$ is free to turn about one end. It is released from rest at its horizontal position. Show that, when it has revolved through an angle α, its angular velocity ω is given by

$$\omega^2 = \frac{3g \sin \alpha}{2a}. \qquad \textbf{(M.U.)}$$

[**Hint:** Height descended by C.G $= a \sin \alpha$. W.D $= Mga \sin \alpha$. Increase in K.E. $= \frac{1}{2}\left(\frac{4}{3} Ma^2\right)\omega^2$]

6. A circular lamina can turn freely about a horizontal axis which passes through a point O on its circumference and perpendicular to its plane. The motion commences when the diameter through O is vertical and above O. Find the angular velocity when the diameter has turned through a right angle. **(M.U.)**

[**Hint:** By parallel axis Theorem, M.I. $= \frac{1}{2} Ma^2 + Ma^2$ (a : radius),

Increase in K.E. $= \frac{1}{2}\left(\frac{3}{2} Ma^2\right)\omega^2$; W.D $= Mga$; $\omega = \sqrt{\frac{4g}{3a}}$.]

7. In the previous sum show that the angular velocity when the centre of gravity of the lamina is vertically below the axis is

$$\sqrt{\frac{8g}{3a}}.$$

8. A rectangular lamina $ABCD$ can move about AB as a horizontal axis and is allowed to fall from rest at a horizontal position. Show that the velocity of a point on CD when the lamina reaches the vertical position is

$$\sqrt{\frac{3g}{BC}} \qquad \textbf{(M.U.)}$$

[**Hint:** Increase in K.E. $= \frac{1}{2}\left[\frac{M(BC)^2}{3}\right]\omega^2$; W.D $= \frac{1}{2} Mg\ BC$]

18.1.2 Compound pendulum

Earlier we studied the small oscillation of a simple pendulum, consisting of heavy particle attached to a fixed point by a light string. We now proceed to study the small oscillation of a compound pendulum.

Definition of compound pendulum. A compound pendulum is a rigid body free to oscillate under gravity about a smooth fixed horizontal axis.

Centre of suspension. Let the plane of the paper denote the plane through the mass centre G of the compound pendulum and perpendicular to the fixed axis. If the fixed axis intersects this page at O, then O is called the *centre of suspension* of the compound pendulum.

Bookwork 18.2. To find the period of small oscillation of a compound pendulum.

Let us have the following assumptions :

O	:	Centre of suspension
G	:	Mass centre
OG	:	h
M	:	Mass

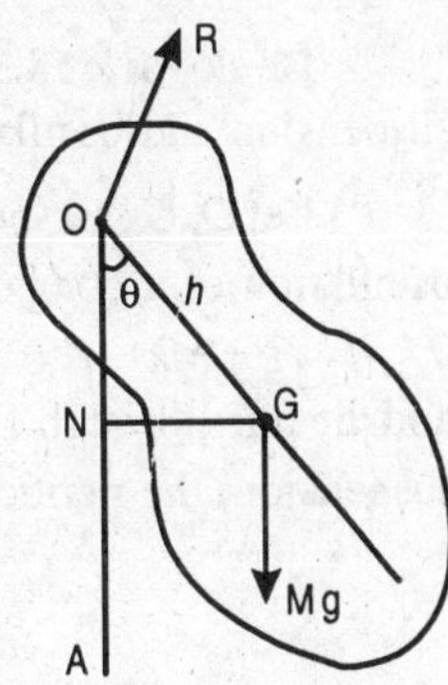

k : Radius of gyration

I : M.I. $(= Mk^2)$

OA : Downward vertical

OG : Position at time t

θ : Angle AOG.

The forces acting on the compound pendulum are

(*i*) Its weight Mg vertically downwards through G,

(*ii*) The reaction R of the axis meeting the axis at O.

Now we use the result

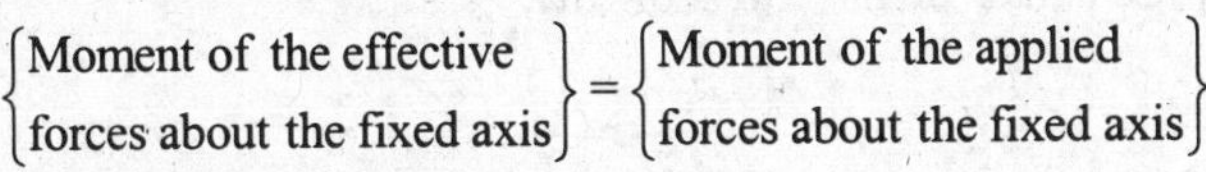

$$\begin{Bmatrix}\text{Moment of the effective} \\ \text{forces about the fixed axis}\end{Bmatrix} = \begin{Bmatrix}\text{Moment of the applied} \\ \text{forces about the fixed axis}\end{Bmatrix}$$

If N is the perpendicular from G to OA, then

$$GN = h \sin\theta.$$

Taking moments about O, we have

$$\therefore \qquad \text{Mt. of } Mg = -Mgh\sin\theta, \ \text{Mt. of } R = 0.$$

$$\therefore \qquad I\ddot{\theta} = -Mgh\sin\theta, \ \text{ or } \ Mk^2\ddot{\theta} = -Mgh\sin\theta.$$

For small oscillations, $\sin\theta = \theta$ nearly and therefore

$$\ddot{\theta} = -\frac{gh}{k^2}\theta \quad \text{or} \quad \ddot{\theta} = -n^2\theta, \text{ where } n^2 = \frac{gh}{k^2}.$$

So the motion is harmonic with a period

$$\frac{2\pi}{n} \quad \text{or} \quad 2\pi\sqrt{\frac{1}{g}\frac{k^2}{h}}. \qquad ...(1)$$

This period is said to be period of small oscillation.

Simple equivalent pendulum. We know that the period of a simple pendulum of length l is

$$2\pi\sqrt{\frac{l}{g}}. \qquad ...(2)$$

From (1) and (2) we see that the periods of the compound pendulum and the simple pendulum are equal if

$$l = \frac{k^2}{h}.$$

In such a case the simple pendulum is called the simple equivalent pendulum of the compound pendulum.

Simple equivalent pendulum. The simple pendulum whose period is equal to a given compound pendulum is called the simple equivalent pendulum of the compound pendulum.

Centre of oscillation. The point O', on OG such that

$$OO' = \frac{k^2}{h},$$

as shown in the figure, is called the centre of oscillation of the compound pendulum.

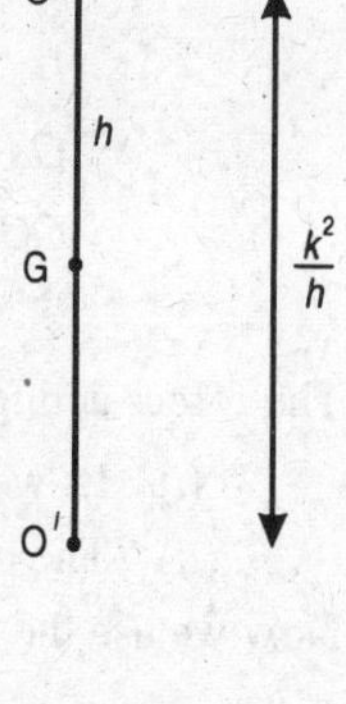

Bookwork 18.3. To show that the period is unaltered when the centres of suspension and oscillation are interchanged.

Let O, G, O' be the centre of suspension, the mass centre and the centre of oscillation of a compound pendulum of mass M. Let $OG = h,\ O'G = h'$. Let I, I_G, I' $(I = Mk^2, I' = Mk'^2)$ be the M. I's of the pendulum about the fixed axis and the lines through G, O' and parallel to the axis. When O, O' are the centres of suspension, the periods are

$$2\pi\sqrt{\frac{1}{g}.\frac{k^2}{h}},\quad 2\pi\sqrt{\frac{1}{g}.\frac{k'^2}{h'}}.$$

So, to show that they are equal, we have to show that

$$\frac{k'^2}{h'} = \frac{k^2}{h}.$$

But, by parallel axis theorem,

$$I' = I_G + Mh'^2,\quad I = I_G + Mh^2.$$

$$\therefore \qquad I' - I = Mh'^2 - Mh^2 \text{ or } Mk'^2 - Mk^2 = Mh'^2 - Mh^2.$$

$$\therefore \qquad k'^2 - k^2 = h'^2 - h^2 = (h' - h)(h' + h)$$

$$= (h' - h)\,OO' = (h' - h)\frac{k^2}{h}.$$

$$= \frac{k^2}{h}h' - k^2$$

$$\therefore \qquad \frac{k'^2}{h'} = \frac{k^2}{h}.$$

Hence the result.

Minimum period. Given the fixed axis l of a compound pendulum, we shall find the minimum of the periods of the compound pendulum oscillating about axes parallel to l.

Let l' be a parallel axis, O' the point of suspension, $GO' = x$ and T the period of oscillation about l'. Then, with usual notations,

$$T = 2\pi\sqrt{\frac{1}{g}\frac{k'^2}{x}}$$

$$= 2\pi\sqrt{\frac{1}{g}\cdot\frac{k_G^2 + x^2}{x}}$$

$$= \frac{2\pi}{\sqrt{g}}\sqrt{\frac{k_G^2}{x} + x}$$

$$= \frac{2\pi}{\sqrt{g}}\sqrt{L}, \text{ say.}$$

Now T is a minimum, when L is a minimum. But

$$\frac{dL}{dx} = -\frac{k_G^2}{x^2} + 1 = 0$$

gives that, L is a minimum when $x = k_G$ and correspondingly T is a minimum. That is, when the axis about which the compound pendulum oscillates is at a distance k_G from G, T is a minimum. All the corresponding points of suspension lie on a vertical circle whose centre is G and radius is k_G.

EXAMPLES

Example 1. A rod of length $2a$ and mass m has a particle of mass m_1 fixed at one end. The whole oscillates as a compound pendulum about the other end of the rod. Show that the period of small oscillation is

$$4\pi\sqrt{\frac{(m+3m_1)a}{3(m+2m_1)g}}.$$ **(M.U.,M.K.U.)**

See the figure. About the axis,

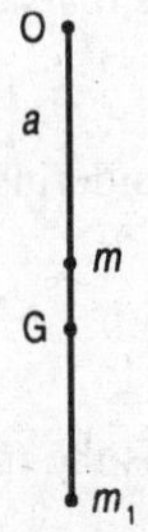

$$\text{M.I. of } m = m\frac{4a^2}{3},$$

$$\text{M.I. of } m_1 = m_1(2a)^2.$$

If k is the radius of gyration about the axis,

$$(m+m_1)\,k^2 = \tfrac{4}{3}\,ma^2 + m_1(2a)^2.$$

If $OG = h$, taking moments of the masses about O,

$$h\,(m+m_1) = am + 2am_1.$$

$$\therefore \quad \frac{k^2}{h} = \frac{\tfrac{4}{3}\,ma^2 + m_1\,(2a)^2}{am + 2am_1} = \frac{4(m+3m_1)a}{3(m+2m_1)}.$$

Therefore the period T of small oscillation is

$$T = 2\pi\sqrt{\frac{1}{g}\cdot\frac{k^2}{h}} = 4\pi\sqrt{\frac{(m+3m_1)a}{3(m+2m_1)g}}.$$

Example 2. (*i*) A solid cone of height h and vertical angle 2α oscillates about a horizontal axis through its vertex. Show that the length of the S.E.P. is

$$\frac{h}{5}\left(4+\tan^2\alpha\right).$$ **(M.U., M.K.U.)**

(*ii*) If the vertical angle is $90°$, then show that the length of the S.E.P. is h. **(M.U.)**

(*i*) If a is the base radius, M, the mass and k, the radius of gyration about the axis, then

$$Mk^2 = \frac{3M}{20}(a^2+4h^2) = \frac{3Mh^2}{20}\left(\frac{a^2}{h^2}+4\right)$$

$$= \frac{3Mh^2}{20}\left(\tan^2\alpha+4\right) \text{ since } \frac{a}{h} = \tan\alpha.$$

$$\therefore \quad k^2 = \frac{3h^2}{20}\left(\tan^2\alpha+4\right).$$

But the distance of C.G. from the axis, is $3h/4$.

$$\therefore \quad \text{Length of S.E.P.} = \frac{k^2}{3h/4} = \frac{h}{5}\left(\tan^2\alpha + 4\right).$$

(*ii*) Here $\alpha = 45°$. So the length is h.

Example 3. A thin circular wire of radius a oscillates about an axis through its middle point perpendicular to its plane. Show that, whatever be the length of the arc, the length of the S.E.P is $2a$. **(M.U.)**

Let A be the midpoint of the wire, G the mass centre, C the centre of the circle and $AG = h$. Let the M. I's of the wire about the axes through A, G, C perpendicular to the plane of the wire be I_A, I_G, I_C. Then, by parallel axis theorem,

$$I_A = I_G + Mh^2.$$

$$I_C = I_G + M(a-h)^2.$$

Thus, by subtraction,

$$I_A - I_C = M[2ah - a^2].$$

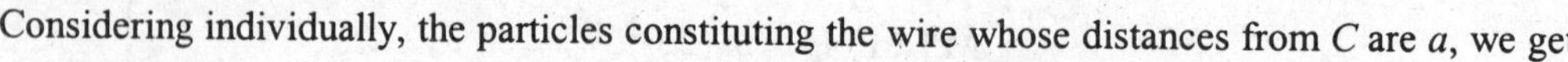

Considering individually, the particles constituting the wire whose distances from C are a, we get

$$I_C = m_1a^2 + m_2a^2 + \ldots\ldots = Ma^2.$$

$$\therefore \quad I_A - Ma^2 = M[2ah - a^2] \text{ or } I_A = M2ah.$$

If k is the radius of gyration about the axis, then

$$I_A = Mk^2. \text{ So } Mk^2 = M2ah \text{ or } k^2 = 2ah.$$

$$\therefore \quad \text{Length of S.E.P} = \frac{k^2}{h} = \frac{2ah}{h} = 2a.$$

EXERCISES

1. A weightless rod ABC of length $2a$ is capable of free rotation about a horizontal axis through A. A particle of mass m is attached to B, the midpoint of the rod, and another of mass m at C. Show that the length of the S.E.P. is $\frac{5a}{3}$. **(M.U.)**

   [Hint: $h = \frac{3a}{2}$; $(m+m)k^2 = ma^2 + m(2a)^2$. Find $\frac{k^2}{h}$]

2. Three equal particles are attached to a weightless rod at equal distances a apart. The system is suspended and is free to move about a point of the rod distant x from the middle particle. Find the period of small oscillation and show that it is least when $x = 0{\cdot}82a$ nearly. **(M.U.)**

   [Hint: $(m+m+m)k^2 = m(x-a)^2 + mx^2 + m(x+a)^2$; $h = x$. So

   $$T = 2\pi\sqrt{\frac{1}{g}\frac{k^2}{h}} = 2\pi\sqrt{\frac{1}{g}\left(x + \frac{2a^2}{3x}\right)}$$

   which is a minimum when $x + \frac{2a^2}{3x}$ is a minimum or when $x = \sqrt{\frac{2}{3}}\,a$]

3. A circular disc oscillates about a horizontal axis in its own plane. Show that the distance of the axis from the centre is one half its radius when the time of oscillation is a minimum. **(M.U.)**

[Hint: If k_G is the radius of gyration about an axis through the centre G, $Mk_G^2 = \frac{1}{4} Ma^2$ or $k_G = a/2$. So for a minimum period, the distance of the axis from G is $a/2$]

4. Show that the minimum period of oscillation of a solid sphere of radius R vibrating as a compound pendulum occurs when the axis is at a distance $0{\cdot}632R$ nearly, from the centre of the sphere. **(A.U.)**

[Hint: As in the above sum $Mk_G^2 = \frac{2}{5}MR^2$ or $k_G = R\sqrt{\frac{2}{5}} \approx 0{\cdot}632R$]

5. A heavy particle of mass λm is rigidly attached to the midpoint of a uniform rod of mass m and length $2a$. Show that for any $\lambda > \frac{1}{3}$, there are two points on each side of the midpoint of the rod, such that, when each of them is the point of suspension, the period of small oscillation of the resulting compound pendulum is $2\pi\sqrt{\frac{a}{g}}$. **(M.U.,M.K.U.)**

[Hint: G : Midpoint; O : Point of suspension; $GO = x$. Then

$$h = x;\ (m+\lambda m)k^2 = \left(\frac{ma^2}{3} + mx^2\right) + \lambda mx^2$$

$$\therefore \quad 2\pi\sqrt{\frac{1}{g}\frac{k^2}{h}} = 2\pi\sqrt{\frac{a}{g}} \text{ gives } (x - \tfrac{a}{2})^2 = a^2\,\frac{3\lambda - 1}{12(1+\lambda)}.$$

So x has two positive values that correspond to the same side of G]

6. A solid cone of height h and semivertical angle 60° oscillates about a line perpendicular to its axis through the vertex. Find the time of small oscillation. **(M.U.)**

[Hint: $Mk^2 = \frac{3M}{20}(a^2 + 4h^2),\ OG = \frac{3h}{4};\ \frac{a}{h} = \tan 60^\circ;\ T = 2\pi\sqrt{\frac{7h}{5g}}$]

7. A solid cone of height h and semivertical angle α oscillates about a diameter of its base. Show that the length of the simple equivalent pendulum is

$$\frac{h}{5}(2 + 3\tan^2\alpha).$$ **(M.U.)**

[Hint: $Mk^2 = \frac{M}{20}(3a^2 + 2h^2),\ OG = \frac{h}{4};\ \frac{a}{h} = \tan\alpha$. Find $\frac{k^2}{OG}$]

8. A uniform circular disc of radius a has a particle of mass equal to that of the disc fixed to a point of its circumference. The disc can turn freely about a fixed horizontal axis through its centre at right angles to its plane. Show that the length of the S.E.P. is $\frac{3a}{2}$. **(M.U.)**

[Hint: $(m+m)k^2 = m.\frac{a^2}{2} + ma^2,\ h = \frac{a}{2}$. Find $\frac{k^2}{h}$]

9. A triangular lamina swings about one of its sides placed horizontally. Prove that the length of the S.E.P. is equal to half the altitude of the triangle perpendicular to the horizontal side. Hence deduce that a triangular lamina will swing most rapidly about the greatest side in the horizontal position. **(M.U.)**

[Hint: $Mk^2 = M\frac{p^2}{6}, h = \frac{p}{3}$. So $\frac{k^2}{h} = \frac{p}{2}$. The perpendicular to the biggest side is the smallest]

10. An elliptic lamina oscillates about one latus rectum as a horizontal axis and it is found that the centre of oscillation lies on the other latus rectum. Prove that the eccentricity of the ellipse is $1/2$. **(M.U.)**

[Hint : $Mk^2 = M\frac{a^2}{4} + M(ae)^2,\ h = ae;$ Given $\frac{k^2}{h} = SS' = 2ae$]

11. An elliptic lamina swings about a horizontal axis at right angles to its plane and passing through one focus. If the centre of oscillation is at the other focus, show that the eccentricity of the ellipse is $\sqrt{\frac{2}{5}}$. **(M.U.)**

[Hint: $Mk^2 = M\frac{a^2 + b^2}{4} + M(ae)^2,\ h = ae;$ Given that $\frac{k^2}{h} = SS' = 2ae$. Use $b^2 = a^2(1 - e^2)$]

12. A square lamina of side $2a$ oscillates about a horizontal axis through one of its corners which is perpendicular to the plane of the lamina. Show that the length of the S.E.P. is $\frac{8a}{3\sqrt{2}}$. **(M.U.)**

[Hint: Half of the diagonal $= a\sqrt{2};\ Mk^2 = M\frac{2a^2}{3} + M(a\sqrt{2})^2,\ h = a\sqrt{2}$; Find $\frac{k^2}{h}$]

13. A square lamina of side $2a$ is free to rotate in a vertical plane about a horizontal axis passing through a vertex and perpendicular to the plane of the lamina and a weight equal to that of the lamina is placed at the opposite vertex. Find the length of the S.E.P. **(M.U.)**

[Hint: Half of the diagonal $= a\sqrt{2}$. $Mk^2 = M\frac{2a^2}{3} + M(a\sqrt{2})^2 + M(2\sqrt{2}\,a)^2,$

$$h = a\sqrt{2}, \frac{k^2}{h} = \frac{16a\sqrt{2}}{3}\ ]$$

14. Find the time of small oscillation of a compound pendulum consisting of a rod of mass M and length a carrying at one end a solid sphere of mass m and diameter $2b$, the other end of the rod being fixed. **(M.U.)**

[Hint: Find $2\pi\sqrt{\frac{1}{g}\cdot\frac{k^2}{h}}$ from $(M + m)h = m\frac{a}{2} + m(a + b)$ and

$(M + m)k^2 = M\frac{a^2}{3} + \left[\frac{2}{5}mb^2 + m(a + b)^2\right]$]

15. A pendulum is constructed of a solid sphere of mass M and radius a, which is attached to the end of a rod of mass $\frac{M}{6}$ and length $24a$. Find the length of the S.E.P and the period of the given pendulum. **(M.U.)**

[Hint: $\frac{7}{6}h = 27a,\ \frac{7}{6}k^2 = \frac{3287}{5}a^2$. Length of S. E. P $= \frac{3287}{135}a$]

16. A pair of equal rods AB, BC of length a are rigidly connected at B so that $\angle ABC$ is a right angle. It oscillates in a vertical plane about a fixed horizontal axis through B. Show that the length of the equivalent pendulum is $\frac{2a\sqrt{2}}{3}$. **(M.K.U.)**

[Hint: $h = \frac{a}{2}\cos 45^\circ = \frac{a}{2\sqrt{2}};\ (m + m)k^2 = \frac{ma^2}{3} + \frac{ma^2}{3}$. Find $\frac{k^2}{h}$]

17. A bent lever whose arms are of length a and b, the angle between them being α, makes small oscillations in its own plane about the fulcrum. Prove that the length of the simple equivalent pendulum is

$$\frac{2}{3}\frac{a^3+b^3}{(a^4+2a^2b^2\cos\alpha+b^4)^{1/2}}. \quad \textbf{(M.U.)}$$

[**Hint:** $h=\frac{1}{2}\frac{(a^4+2a^2b^2\cos\alpha+b^4)^{1/2}}{a+b}$ from example sum in Section 6.2.1;

$Mk^2=\frac{1}{3}(a\lambda)a^2+\frac{1}{3}(b\lambda)b^2$, where $\lambda=\frac{M}{a+b}$.]

18. A thin rod AB of mass m and length $2a$ can turn about the end A which is fixed, and a circular disc of mass $12m$ and radius $\frac{a}{3}$ can be clamped to the rod so that its centre C is on the rod. Show that, for oscillations in which the plane of the disc remains vertical, the length of the S.E.P. lies between $\frac{2a}{3}$ and $2a$. **(A.U.)**

[**Hint:** Let $AC=x$. Get $\frac{k^2}{h}=\frac{2(a^2+6x^2)}{a+12x}$ from $(m+12m)h=am+x(12m)$ and $(m+12m)k^2=\frac{4}{3}ma^2+12m\left[\left(\frac{1}{2}\right)\left(\frac{a}{3}\right)^2+x^2\right]$. If $\frac{k^2}{h}=y$, $\frac{dy}{dx}=0$ gives $(2x+a)(3x-a)=0$. So y attains its extreme value at $x=-a/2, x=a/3$. But $0\le x\le 2a$. The values of y at $x=0$, $x=a/3$, $x=2a$ are $2a$, $2a/3$, $2a$. Thus y is a minimum at $x=a/3$ and y varies from $2a/3$ to $2a$]

18.1.3 Reaction of the axis on a rigid body revolving about it

We consider, in the following bookwork, a simple case where a rigid body revolves about a horizontal fixed axis and the rigid body is symmetrical about the plane π through G and perpendicular to the axis so that the reaction reduces to a single force in π.

Bookwork 18.4. A rigid body revolves about a fixed horizontal axis under gravity. To find the resultant reaction of the axis on the rigid body.

Let us make the following assumptions :

M	:	Mass of the body
G	:	Mass Centre
O	:	Meet of the axis with the vertical plane through G
OG	:	a
OA	:	Downward vertical
θ	:	Angle AOG

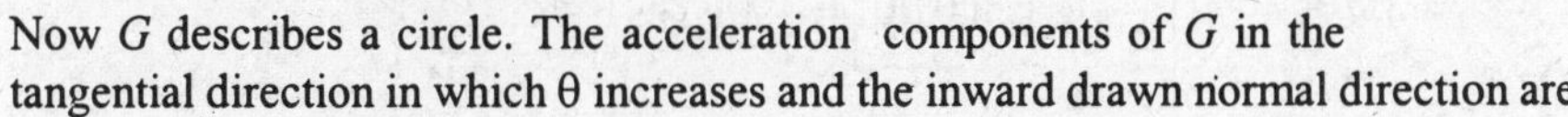
Now G describes a circle. The acceleration components of G in the tangential direction in which θ increases and the inward drawn normal direction are

$$a\ddot{\theta},\, a\dot{\theta}^2.$$

But the forces on the rigid body are

(*i*) The weight Mg at G

(*ii*) Reaction R of the axis at O.

Now their components in the tangential and inward-drawn normal directions are

(*i*) $-Mg\sin\theta,\ -Mg\cos\theta$

(*ii*) $P,\ Q$ say.

Therefore the respective equations of motion are

$$Ma\ddot{\theta} = -Mg\sin\theta + P, \qquad ...(1)$$

$$Ma\dot{\theta}^2 = -Mg\cos\theta + Q. \qquad ...(2)$$

Taking moments about the fixed axis,

$$I\ddot{\theta} = -Mga\sin\theta, \qquad ...(3)$$

where I is the M.I. of the body about the fixed axis. Eliminating $\ddot{\theta}$ from (1) and (3) we get P. Also, integrating the third equation and obtaining $\dot{\theta}$, we get Q from (2). Thus the reaction $\sqrt{P^2+Q^2}$ is known.

EXAMPLES

Example 1. A rod of mass M free to turn about a fixed smooth pivot at one end O is held horizontally and released. Prove that, when the rod makes an angle θ with the vertical, the pressure on the pivot is

$$\frac{Mg}{4}\left(1+99\cos^2\theta\right)^{1/2}. \qquad \textbf{(M.U., K.U.)}$$

Let the length of the rod be $2a$. Then M.I. about the fixed axis is

$$I = \frac{4M}{3}a^2.$$

As in the bookwork 18.4, the equations of motion are

$$Ma\ddot{\theta} = -Mg\sin\theta + P, \qquad ...(1)$$

$$Ma\dot{\theta}^2 = -Mg\cos\theta + Q, \qquad ...(2)$$

$$I\ddot{\theta} = -Mga\sin\theta \quad \text{or} \quad Ma\ddot{\theta} = -\frac{3}{4}Mg\sin\theta. \qquad ...(3)$$

Eliminating $\ddot{\theta}$ from (1) and (3), we get

$$P = Mg\sin\theta - \frac{3}{4}Mg\sin\theta = \frac{1}{4}Mg\sin\theta.$$

Multiplying (3) by $2\dfrac{d\theta}{dt}$ and integrating w.r.t. t,

$$Ma\dot{\theta}^2 = -2\left[\frac{3}{4}Mg\int\sin\theta\,d\theta\right] = \frac{3}{2}Mg\cos\theta + C.$$

Initially $\theta = 90^\circ, \dot{\theta} = 0$. Therefore $C = 0$.

$$\therefore \quad Ma\dot{\theta}^2 = \frac{3}{2}Mg\cos\theta. \qquad ...(4)$$

Thus, from (2) and (4), we get

$$Q = \frac{5}{2} Mg \cos \theta.$$

$\therefore$ $$\text{Reaction} = \sqrt{P^2 + Q^2} = \frac{1}{4} Mg\,(1 + 99 \cos^2 \theta)^{1/2}.$$

EXERCISES

1. A rod of length $2a$ and mass M, oscillates about a horizontal axis through one end. If the rod travels through 60° on each side of the vertical, show that the thrust on the axis when the rod is vertical is $\frac{7}{4} Mg$. **(M.U.)**

   [Hint: See Example 1. $P = \frac{1}{4} Mg \sin \theta$. Since $\dot{\theta} = 0$ when $\theta = 60°$, we get

   $Q = \frac{5}{2} Mg \cos \theta - \frac{3}{4} Mg$. When $\theta = 0$, $P_0 = 0$, $Q_0 = \frac{7}{4} Mg$.]

2. A rod of length $2a$ and mass M can turn freely about one end O which is fixed, and is released from rest at an inclination α to the vertical. Find the reaction at O when the rod makes an angle θ to the vertical. **(M.U.)**

   [Hint: See Example 1. $P = \frac{1}{4} Mg \sin \theta$, Since $\dot{\theta} = 0$ when $\theta = \alpha$, we get

   $$Q = \frac{5}{2} Mg \cos \theta - \frac{3}{2} Mg \cos \alpha. \text{ Find } \sqrt{P^2 + Q^2}\ ]$$

3. A circular lamina of mass M can turn freely about a horizontal axis perpendicular to its plane which passes through a point O on its circumference. It starts from rest with the diameter through O vertically above O. Show that, when the diameter is horizontal, the pressure on this axis is $\frac{\sqrt{17}}{3} Mg$. **(M.U.)**

   [Hint: See Example 1. Now $I = \frac{Ma^2}{2} + Ma^2 = \frac{3Ma^2}{2}$. Choosing θ as the same angle AOG, $P = \frac{1}{3} Mg \sin \theta$. Since $\dot{\theta} = 0$, when $\theta = 180°$, we get $Q = \frac{7}{3} Mg \cos \theta + \frac{4}{3} Mg$; when $\theta = 90°$, $P = \frac{1}{3} Mg$, $Q = \frac{4}{3} Mg$]

18.2 EQUATIONS OF MOTION FOR TWO DIMENSIONAL MOTION

We know that the general motion of a rigid is a composition of

(*i*) Motion of the mass centre G,

(*ii*) Motion about the mass centre G.

In cartesian coordinates, if (x, y) is the position of G at time t and F_x, F_y are the x, y, components of the forces in x, y directions, then the equations

$$M\ddot{x} = F_x,\quad M\ddot{y} = F_y$$

give the motion of G. The motion about G is obtained from the equation

$$I\ddot{\theta} = G,$$

where

(*i*) $I\ddot{\theta}$ is the moment of the effective forces relative to G about the line l through G and perpendicular to the xy plane.

(*ii*) G is the moment of the applied forces about l.

18.2.1 Motion of a uniform circular disc rolling down an inclined plane

Bookwork 18.5. A circular disc rolls down a rough inclined plane from rest . To find its acceleration and the distance travelled in time t.

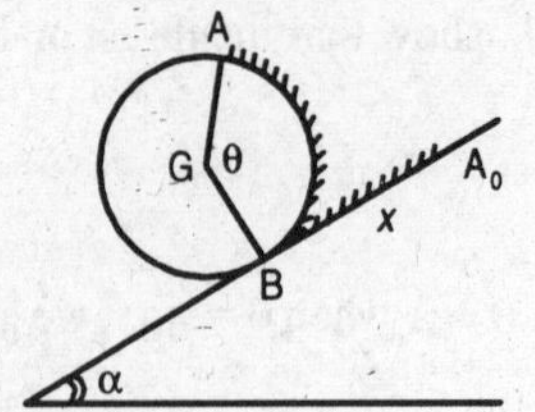

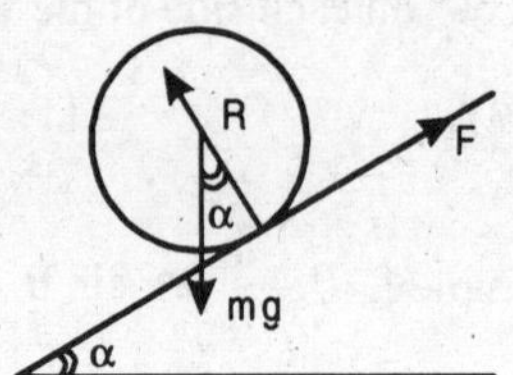

Let us make the following assumptions :

α	:	Angle of inclination of the plane
M, a, G	:	Mass, radius and mass centre of the disc
A_0	:	Point of contact on the plane initially
A	:	Point on the rim which was in coincidence with A_0 initially
B	:	Point of contact at time t
θ	:	Angle BGA; $x = A_0B$

Rolling condition. The disc rolls down without slipping. So the length of the arc BA equals the distance BA_0. Therefore

$$x = a\theta, \quad \ddot{x} = a\ddot{\theta}. \qquad \text{...(1)}$$

Motion of *G*. The acceleration of G down the plane is $\ddot{x}$. The forces on M are

(*i*) Weight Mg vertically downward.

(*ii*) Normal reaction R of the plane in the upward sense.

(*iii*) Friction F up the plane.

The components of these along the plane in the downward sense and normal to the plane in the upward sense are

$$Mg \sin\alpha - F, \quad R - Mg\cos\alpha.$$

So the equations of motion corresponding to these directions are

$$M\ddot{x} = Mg\sin\alpha - F, \qquad \text{...(2)}$$

$$0 = R - Mg\cos\alpha. \qquad \text{...(3)}$$

Motion about *G*. The moment of the effective forces about the horizontal line through G and perpendicular to the disc is

$$I\ddot{\theta} \quad \text{or} \quad \left(M\frac{a^2}{2}\right)\ddot{\theta},$$

where I is the M.I. of the disc about the line. The moment of the applied forces about the same line is

$$aF$$

because the weight and reaction pass through G and hence their moments are zero.

$$\therefore \qquad M\frac{a^2}{2}\ddot{\theta} = aF \text{ or } \frac{M}{2}a\ddot{\theta} = F. \qquad \text{...(4)}$$

Acceleration of *G*. By (1), the result (4) becomes

$$\frac{M}{2}\ddot{x} = F. \qquad \text{...(5)}$$

Eliminating F from this and (2), we get

$$M\ddot{x} = Mg\sin\alpha - \frac{M}{2}\ddot{x} \quad \text{or} \quad \ddot{x} = \frac{2}{3}g\sin\alpha$$

which is a constant.

Reaction and friction. It is evident, from (3) and (5), that

$$R = Mg\cos\alpha, \quad F = \tfrac{1}{3}Mg\sin\alpha.$$

Velocity of *G* at time *t* and the distance travelled by it. Now the acceleration $\ddot{x}$ is a constant. Since the disc rolls down from rest the velocity of G down the plane at time t is, by $v = u + at$,

$$\dot{x} = \left(\frac{2}{3}g\sin\alpha\right)t$$

and the distance travelled is, by $s = ut + \tfrac{1}{2}at^2$,

$$x = \frac{1}{2}\left(\frac{2}{3}g\sin\alpha\right)t^2.$$

Other rolling bodies. In the above bookwork, if the body which rolls down the inclined plane is one of

(*i*) a circular hoop (*ii*) a solid sphere

(*iii*) a hollow sphere (*iv*) a circular wheel,

the equations (1), (2), (3) remain to be the same, while the equation (4) alone varies with I. The values of the acceleration $\ddot{x}$ and the friction F are tabulated below along with I.

Body	I	$\ddot{x}$	F
Circular hoop	Ma^2	$\frac{1}{2}g\sin\alpha$	$\frac{1}{2}Mg\sin\alpha$
Solid sphere	$\frac{2}{5}Ma^2$	$\frac{5}{7}g\sin\alpha$	$\frac{2}{7}Mg\sin\alpha$
Hollow sphere	$\frac{2}{3}Ma^2$	$\frac{3}{5}g\sin\alpha$	$\frac{2}{5}Mg\sin\alpha$
Circular wheel (M.I. $= Mk^2$)	Mk^2	$\frac{a^2 g\sin\alpha}{a^2+k^2}$	$\frac{k^2 Mg\sin\alpha}{a^2+k^2}$

Condition for rolling without sliding. The friction F cannot exeed the limiting friction μR. If k is the radius of gyration of the rolling body, then

$$F = \frac{Mk^2}{a^2 + k^2} g \sin\alpha.$$

But the maximum friction that can be called into play is

$$\mu R = \mu\, Mg \cos\alpha.$$

So the body rolls without sliding if

$$\frac{Mk^2}{a^2 + k^2} g \sin\alpha < \mu\, Mg \cos\alpha.$$

or
$$\tan\alpha < \frac{a^2 + k^2}{k^2} \mu.$$

EXERCISES

1. A solid sphere of mass M rolls down a rough plane inclined to the horizontal at an angle α. Find its acceleration. **(M.U.)**

   [Ans. $\frac{5}{7} g \sin\alpha$ **]**

2. A uniform solid cylinder is placed with its axis horizontal on a plane whose inclination to the horizon is α. Show that the least coefficient of friction between it and the plane, so that it may roll and not slide, is $\frac{1}{3}\tan\alpha$.

   [Hint: Least value of μ is $\frac{k^2}{a^2 + k^2}\tan\alpha$. Now $k^2 = \frac{a^2}{2}$]

18.2.2 Motion of a system having a heavy pulley.

In the motions of the connected particles we assumed the involved pulleys to be of negligible weights. Now we consider such a case but the pulley being heavy.

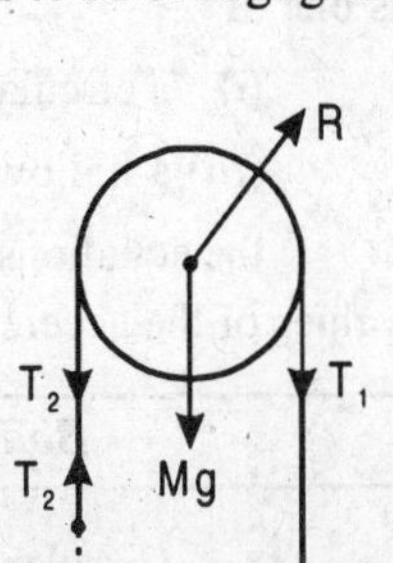

Bookwork 18.6. A fine string has two masses m_1 and m_2 $(m_1 > m_2)$ tied to its ends and passes over a rough pulley rough enough to prevent slipping. The mass of the pulley is M. If there is no frictional force between the fixed axis and the pulley, show that the acceleration of masses m_1 and m_2 are

$$\frac{m_1 - m_2}{m_1 + m_2 + (I/a^2)} g,$$

where a is the radius and I, the M.I. of the pulley about the axis.

We shall measure the distance of m_1 vertically downward and the distance of m_2 vertically upward. These distances x, x are equal at any time t, so the accelerations of m_1, m_2 in their respective directions are $\ddot{x}$ and $\ddot{x}$. With the forces as shown in the figure, their equations of motion are

$$m_1\ddot{x} = m_1 g - T_1, \quad ...(1)$$

$$m_2\ddot{x} = T_2 - m_2 g. \quad ...(2)$$

The equation of motion for the rotation of M is

$$I\ddot{\theta} = aT_1 - aT_2, \qquad ...(3)$$

since the moments of the weight Mg and the reaction R are zero because they pass through the axis. When the pulley rotates, the string does not slip. So the respective rolling condition is

$$x = a\theta \quad \text{or} \quad \ddot{x} = a\ddot{\theta}. \qquad ...(4)$$

Eliminating $T_1, T_2, \ddot{\theta}$ from (1), (2), (3), (4) we get $\ddot{x}$ as stated.

EXAMPLES

Example 1. The end of a thread wound round a reel of mass M and radius a is held fixed and the reel is allowed to fall so that the thread is unwound. Find the acceleration of the reel, assuming its axis to remain horizontal. **(M.U.)**

Let the centre G of the reel move vertically through a distance x in time t and the reel turns through an angle θ. Then

$$x = a\theta, \quad \ddot{x} = a\ddot{\theta}.$$

The forces on the reel are the tension and the weight

$$T, \ Mg$$

as in the figure. The equation of motion of G is

$$M\ddot{x} = Mg - T. \qquad ...(1)$$

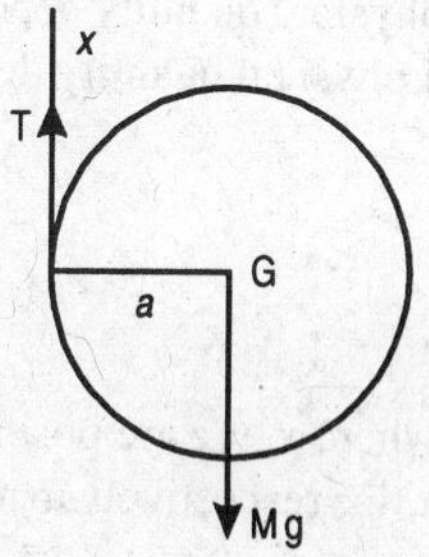

Taking moments about G,

$$I\ddot{\theta} = aT.$$

Since $\ddot{x} = a\ddot{\theta}$, this becomes

$$\frac{I}{a^2}\ddot{x} = T \qquad ...(2)$$

From (1) and (2), we get the acceleration as

$$\ddot{x} = \frac{a^2}{Ma^2 + I} Mg.$$

EXERCISES

1. A bucket of mass m is fastened to one end of a light rope ; the rope is coiled round a pulley in the form of a circular cylinder (radius a) which is left free to rotate about its axis. Show that the bucket descends with an acceleration

$$\frac{g}{1+\left(I/ma^2 \right)},$$

where I is the moment of inertia of the cylinder about its axis.

[Hint: Equations of motion of the bucket and the pulley are $m\ddot{x} = mg - T, \ I\ddot{\theta} = aT \ ; \ x = a\theta.$**]**

THEORY OF DIMENSIONS

19.1 DEFINITION OF DIMENSIONS

In the beginning chapters we studied units of fundamental physical quantities, namely,

Mass, Length, Time

and the units of quantities derived from them. Once a unit for a physical quantity is defined, any quantity of its kind can be denoted by its measure and the unit. For example, when we speak of a length of $\frac{1}{2}$ kilometre, we mean that its measure is 500 when the unit is a metre, and that its measure is 50,000 when the unit is a centimetre. So the measure is a pure number.

In a specified system of units of the fundamental physical quantities, the measure of any physical quantity depends upon the measures of the fundamental quantities. Thus, if the measure of a physical quantity depends on the measures of the fundamental quantities in the manner,

$$\begin{bmatrix}\text{Measure}\\ \text{of physical}\\ \text{quantity}\end{bmatrix} = \begin{bmatrix}\text{Measure}\\ \text{of}\\ \text{mass}\end{bmatrix}^x \begin{bmatrix}\text{Measure}\\ \text{of}\\ \text{length}\end{bmatrix}^y \begin{bmatrix}\text{Measure}\\ \text{of}\\ \text{time}\end{bmatrix}^z$$

where x, y, z are positive or negative numbers, then the physical quantity is said to be of dimensions x, y, z respectively in mass, length, time. Symbolically, the dimensions of this physical quantity may be written as $M^x L^y T^z$.

For example, since "Area = Length × Width", the dimensions of area are

$$M^0 L^2 T^0 \quad \text{or} \quad L^2.$$

Since the measure of velocity is measured as the measure of length divided by the measure of time, the dimensions of velocity are

$$LT^{-1}$$

Similarly, from the general form of the results,

$$\text{Acceleration} = \frac{\text{Velocity}}{\text{Time}},$$

$$\text{Force} = \text{Mass} \times \text{Acceleration},$$

$$\text{Work} = \text{Force} \times \text{Displacement},$$

the dimensions of acceleration, force and work are

$$LT^{-2},\ MLT^{-2},\ ML^2T^{-2}.$$

Since an angle is measured as the quotient of the arcual length by the radius, its dimensions are L/L, that is, an angle is a pure number. The following table of dimensions of the other physical quantities will be useful for reference:

Energy	ML^2T^{-2}
Power	ML^2T^{-3}
Impulse	MLT^{-1}

Moment of force	ML^2T^{-2}
Momentum (linear)	MLT^{-1}
Angular momentum	ML^2T^{-1}
Angular velocity	T^{-1}
Moment of inertia	ML^2
Modulus of elasticity	$ML\ T^{-2}$

19.1.1 Uses of dimensional theory

Only the physical quantities of same kind can be compared with one another regarding their magnitude. So equations in which the separate terms have different dimensions cannot be valid. In other words, it is necessary that all equations in mechanics must be dimensionally homogeneous. For example, the dimensions of all the terms of the equation

$$v^2 = u^2 + 2as \text{ are } L^2T^{-2}.$$

We shall now proceed to find the period of oscillation of a simple pendulum by using the theory of dimensions. The period t depends on the mass m and length l of the pendulum, the angle through which the pendulum swings and the gravitational acceleration g. Since an angle is a dimensionless quantity, suppose $t = k\, m^a\, l^b\, g^c$, where k is a pure number without dimensions. The dimensions of t and $k\, m^a\, l^b\, g^c$ should be the same. The dimensions of t are T^1 and those of $km^a l^b g^c$ are

$$M^a L^b (LT^{-2})^c \text{ or } M^a\, L^{b+c}\, T^{-2c}.$$

$$\therefore \quad a = 0,\ b = \tfrac{1}{2},\ c = -\tfrac{1}{2}. \quad \therefore\ t = kl^{\frac{1}{2}}\, g^{-\frac{1}{2}} = k\sqrt{\frac{l}{g}}.$$

The constant k may be obtained from experimental observations.

Similarly, in the case of a point describing a circle with a uniform speed, the acceleration towards the centre of the circle depends upon the radius a and speed v. Let this acceleration be

$$ka^p\, v^q.$$

Its dimensions are

$$L^p\, (LT^{-1})^q \text{ or } L^{p+q}\, T^{-q}.$$

But the dimensions of an acceleration are

$$LT^{-2}.$$

$$\therefore \quad p+q=1, -q=-2 \text{ or } p=-1, q=2.$$

So the required acceleration is $k\dfrac{v^2}{a}$.

We shall conclude our discussion of dimensions with one more example which shows how the theory of dimensions is used to convert one set of units to another. From the definition of the dimensions we see that a newton can be denoted by the symbol

$$(1\ \text{kg.})^1\ (1\ \text{m.})^1\ (1\ \text{sec.})^{-2}$$

and a poundal by

$$(1\ \text{lb.})^1\ (1\ \text{ft.})^1\ (1\ \text{sec.})^{-2}.$$

We shall express a newton by poundals. Since 1 kg.=2·2046 1b. and 1 m.=3·2808 ft.,

$$1\ \text{newton} = 1 \times (1\ \text{kg.})^1\ (1\ \text{m.})^1\ (1\ \text{sec.})^{-2}$$

$= 1 \times (2 \cdot 2046 \text{ lb.})^1 (3 \cdot 2808 \text{ ft})^1 (1 \text{ sec.})^{-2}$

$= 2 \cdot 2046 \times 3 \cdot 2808 \times (1 \text{ lb.})^1 (1 \text{ ft.})^1 (1 \text{ sec.})^{-2}$

$= 2 \cdot 2046 \times 3 \cdot 2803$ poundals

$= 7 \cdot 233$ poundals nearly.

EXERCISES

1. Two masses m and m' at a distance d apart attract each other with a force $\lambda \dfrac{mm'}{d^2}$. Find the dimensions of λ. **(M.U.)**

[**Hint:** Dimensions of force and $\dfrac{mm'}{d^2}$ are MLT^{-2}, M^2L^{-2}. So the dimensions of λ are $M^{-1}L^3T^{-2}$]

2. The kinetic energy of a rigid body rotating about a fixed axis depends upon the moment of inertia and the angular velocity. Obtain the form of this relationship.

[**Hint:** Dimensions of K.E, M.I., say I and angular velocity ω are

$$ML^2T^{-2},\ ML^2,\ T^{-1}.$$

If K.E. $= kI^a \omega^b$, then $ML^2T^{-2} = (ML^2)^a (T^{-1})^b$. So $a = 1$ and $b = 2$. Thus K. E. $= kI\omega^2$]